VOLUME 2

Recovery from Severe Mental Illnesses:
Research Evidence and Implications for Practice

VOLUME 2

Recovery from Severe Mental Illnesses:
Research Evidence and Implications for Practice

Edited by Larry Davidson, Courtenay Harding, and LeRoy Spaniol

Center for Psychiatric Rehabilitation
Sargent College of Health and Rehabilitation Sciences
Boston University

Published by:

Center for Psychiatric Rehabilitation
Sargent College of Health and Rehabilitation Sciences
Boston University
940 Commonwealth Avenue West
Boston, MA 02215
http://www.bu.edu/cpr/

The Center for Psychiatric Rehabilitation is partially funded by the National Institute on Disability and Rehabilitation Research and the Center for Mental Health Services, Substance Abuse and Mental Health Services Administration.

Printed in the United States of America

Cover photo illustration, cover design, and text design by Linda Getgen

Library of Congress Control Number: 2005928298
ISBN–13: 978-1-878512-17-8
ISBN–10: 1-878512-17-x

The publication of this book was supported in part by The Elizabeth Whitney Post Fund, Sargent College of Health and Rehabilitation Sciences, Boston University.

All proceeds from the sale of this book are used to further the work of the Center for Psychiatric Rehabilitation. No royalties are paid to the editors.

Contents for Preceding Volume 1

VOLUME 2

2 VOLUME

Foreword

Until the 1980s, and officially until the appearance of *DSM-III-R,* (American Psychiatric Association, 1987), the understanding in our field was that a severe mental illness, particularly schizophrenia, almost universally followed a deteriorative course. With this understanding mental health researchers, not surprisingly, have tended to focus on psychopathology and symptoms, rather than on processes and interventions that promote role functioning and coping with mental illnesses. This lack of understanding of recovery no doubt inhibited the study of the positive outcomes of schizophrenia and other severe mental illnesses by focusing on maintenance and stabilization, rather than on growth-promoting interventions. More recently, however, research has begun to focus on recovering instrumental roles and quality of life in the community.

In the last several decades, several sources of data have converged to demonstrate that people with severe mental illnesses are achieving higher levels of role functioning, subjective well-being, and adjustment than had previously been considered, and that severe mental illnesses are not universally deteriorative. One source of information has been the writing of people with severe mental illnesses. Another source of knowledge is the synthesis and dissemination of long-term outcome studies, which suggested that a significant percentage of people with severe mental illnesses were dramatically improving over time. Currently, according to Harding, there are 10 national and international longitudinal studies of 22 to 37 years duration investigating the recovery and community integration of people with schizophrenia and other severe mental illnesses. A final source of data is the research evidence suggesting that substantial improvements for individuals with severe mental illnesses can be effected through mental health interventions. All of these different types of evidence are covered in this groundbreaking text.

A review of systems-level literature and mental health policy is also included in this text. Even though there is as of yet no explicit consensus about the meaning of the term *recovery,* our current understanding of recovery is now guiding policies and practice in many state mental health systems as well as in entire countries like New Zealand.

Despite increasing and widespread use in mental health systems' practice, planning, and funding, the concept of recovery until recently has been poorly understood, poorly operationalized, and frequently used in policy/political statements rather than as an empirically-based, operationally defined term. More recently, however, as shown by the readings in this text, there has been a convergence of thinking about the meaning of the term recovery and its definition. Taken together, these sources of information suggest that the recovery process is a long-term, multidimensional process with both objective and subjective dimensions that should be viewed along a continuum (rather than dichotomous as recovered vs. not recovered). Also, recovery outcomes involve interdependent domains of functioning (including social, vocational, emotional, cognitive, and spiritual). Additionally, the literature indicates that recovery involves psychosocial adjustment to the disability itself; achievement of subjective well-being; some degree of remission of the signs and symptoms of the illness; and improvement in instrumental role functioning and community integration.

One definition of recovery outcomes (as opposed to recovery processes) focuses on the psychological dimensions of recovery by suggesting that it involves the development of new meaning and purpose in life as a person grows beyond the effects of mental illness. Other authors have developed criterion-based definitions that emphasize instrumental role functioning across domains such as work, social functioning, and living independence as well as reduced symptomatology. There remains disagreement about the extent to which being symptom free is a requisite for recovery or whether the need for treatment, medications, or hospitalizations should factor into the definition. For example, in one of the Vermont follow-up study reports by Harding and Zahniser (1995), the authors used the following definition of recovery from schizophrenia: "no signs or symptoms of mental illness, no current medications, work, relating well to family and friends, integrated into the community...." A further complication of the use of the term recovery is that some researchers and authors refer to recovery as an outcome while others refer to recovery as a process.

In essence, the term recovery is increasingly being used to denote a severely mentally ill person's potential for growth, healing, and community integration. The literature focused on in this text encompasses this broader understanding of recovery. This conception was largely absent from the last century's diagnostic schemes, maintenance-type interventions, and mental health research. Furthermore, for most of the previous century, throughout North America and Europe, people with severe mental illnesses were not expected to recover, and were also dehumanized and devalued by both society and sometimes inadvertently by treatment professionals. The view that people with mental illnesses lacked potential for growth and change, and responded only to interventions designed to prevent deterioration has gradually dissipated. This change in practice and attitudes essentially views people with psychiatric disabilities as "people first." This text represents the first attempt at presenting the research that has led to this paradigm shift.

The advent of the awareness of recovery has started to change the field of mental health significantly; we are now just beginning that transformation process (President's New Freedom Commission on Mental Health, 2003). This second of two volumes is a beginning effort to overview the key litera- ture that empirically supports this new understanding of recovery. Also addressed are the key roles that the person, peers, family members, practi- tioners, and researchers can play in recovery policy and practice.

WILLIAM A. ANTHONY, PHD

American Psychiatric Association. (1987). *Diagnostic and statistical manual of mental disorders, 3rd ed, revised.* Washington, DC: Author.

Harding, C. M. & Zahniser, J. (1995). Empirical correction of seven myths about schizophrenia. *Acta Psychiatrica Scandinavica, 90* (suppl. 384), 140–146.

President's New Freedom Commission on Mental Health. (2003). *Achieving the promise: Transforming mental health care in America, final report* (No. Pub. No. SMA-03-3832.). Rockville, MD: U.S. Department of Health and Human Services.

Preface

Research efforts to document the fact that not all people with schizophrenia manifest the progressive deteriorating course proposed by Kraepelin to distinguish this condition from other psychiatric conditions with less virulent courses was published by many investigators in the 1960s and 1970s. That was over 45 years ago. Even given the 25-year span it typically takes for scientific breakthroughs to make their way into routine clinical practice (IOM, 2002), it is surprising, and troubling, how much of the mental health field remains ignorant of these findings, thereby perpetuating, albeit unwittingly, the Kraepelinian legacy of hopelessness, helplessness, and despair. Even as these volumes are going to press, the American Psychiatric Association is considering adoption of a new diagnostic category for the next version of the *DSM*, which they have labeled "schizophrenia in remission." Even this step, which is limited to relief of symptoms and still is not without its own controversy, falls well short of recognizing the broad heterogeneity consistently found in the outcome of schizophrenia in many studies conducted in multiple countries over the last 45 years. While others may speculate about the reasons why it has taken psychiatry so long to acknowledge and incorporate this body of knowledge, or what function perpetuating Kraepelin's legacy may serve for the field, we offer these volumes as corrective measures to counteract the prevailing ignorance.

In our opinion, our timing could not be better. The last 5 years in the history of mental health policy in the United States in particular have led to broad adoption of the term *recovery* in relation to serious mental illnesses. Beginning with the landmark 1999 *Mental Health: A Report of the Surgeon General* (DHHS, 1999), and culminating (thus far) in the 2003 Final Report of the President's New Freedom Commission on Mental Health, entitled *Achieving the Promise: Transforming Mental Health Care in America* (DHHS, 2003), a notion of recovery that had resided largely on the margins of psychiatry has been unceremoniously dumped into the mainstream of clinical practice. This is not to say that "recovery" did not already have its advocates within the field. The Community Support Movement as a whole, and the discipline of Psychiatric Rehabilitation more specifically, embraced early notions of recovery as well as the eloquent spokespersons of recovery who were themselves ex-patients, survivors, or consumers. What began to change with the Surgeon General's Report was that this notion which had been held dear by an energetic and idealistic minority was now being proposed as the overarching aim and principle for the field as a whole. As the vision statement of the New Freedom Commission Report explicitly and adamantly announces: "We envision a future when everyone with a mental illness will recover" (DHHS, 2003).

Reactions to this forceful statement have been mixed. Mental health advocates and psychiatric rehabilitation practitioners have rejoiced, of course, but with the nagging suspicion that all of their hard work is about to be co-opted by the very field they have been fighting against for the last 30 years. Many providers, family members, and people with psychiatric disabilities welcome the introduction of a positive and hope-filled message, feeling that it is long overdue. Among those professionals who are more skeptical, some dismiss what they view as recovery "rhetoric" as simply the latest fad in a field that has been slow to embrace the importance of evidence. Others view the introduction of recovery as a short-sighted political gesture that is at least ill-advised, if not altogether irresponsible, claiming that notions such as self-care, self-determination, and client choice are code words used by an uncaring populace to disguise the real agenda of cutting services, and thereby costs. The various forms of skepticism that have surfaced share a common perception that there is no evidence justifying use of the term recovery in relation to serious mental illnesses, dismissing arguments to the contrary as, in the words of one reviewer, "unsubstantiated rubbish."

It is to these skeptics, as well as to the hundreds of thousands of people with psychiatric disabilities, their loved ones, and the compassionate professionals who devote their careers to caring for and supporting them, that these volumes are addressed. We have identified and collected representative publications from the last 30 years of research and clinical and rehabilitative practice that present the evidence supporting use of the term recovery in relation to serious mental illnesses. This literature addresses both the natural history of the illness as well as the effectiveness of various interventions addressing different domains of functioning, such as vocational, emotional, social, physical, cognitive, and spiritual. Overall, it offers a highly variegated picture of a complex, dynamic, and ever evolving condition that, on the one hand, may become lethal when left untreated, but which, on the other hand, also can be contained, managed, and/or overcome over time by the majority of people who experience it. In addition, despite the long-standing belief that psychiatry is a "soft" science in which pretty much anything can masquerade as treatment (from psychoanalysis to lobotomy), the evidence suggests that psychiatric interventions are at least as effective, and in many cases more effective, than their established medical counterparts (DHHS, 1999). Indeed, to the degree that we can emerge out from under the long shadow cast by stigma, discrimination, and societal insensitivity to the needs and dignity of people with serious mental illnesses, we all have much to be hopeful about.

We close this preface with one cautionary note, however. In spite of its broad adoption by policy makers, politicians, and professionals across the globe, the term "recovery" has many different meanings when used in relation to serious mental illnesses. We explore several of these meanings in our first chapter. Throughout the entirety of these volumes, it will be important for the reader to keep in mind that there are dramatically different uses of the same term by different investigators for different purposes. When evaluating or applying the findings of any of the publications reprinted here, it would be wise for the reader to ask him or herself: What definition or sense of the term recovery is being used here, in relation to what population of persons, from which perspective, and to what ends? We offer only two of the possible uses of the term to illustrate this point.

In the early days of research, many investigators utilized a conventional medical sense of the term recovery, restricted to the absence of any symptoms, signs, or other sequelae of the illness. Many people were found to recover from serious mental illnesses in this sense in a way similar to how people recover from other medical conditions such as the flu, an infection, or (in the case of a longer-term course of illness) asthma. Some within the field, including some advocates, insist that this is the only viable or accurate use of the term recovery and suggest that any other use serves solely to obfuscate the issue.

Increasingly common, however, is a use of the term recovery which resembles more a disability paradigm than a purely medical one. In this sense of the term, recovery refers to a person's right and ability to live a safe, dignified, and meaningful life in the community of his or her choice despite continuing disability associated with the illness. Borrowed initially from the addiction self-help community, this sense of recovery refers instead to learning how to live fully in the presence of a disabling condition. As a result, this sense of recovery makes no sense for people who recover fully from their illness in the biomedical sense of the term used above. In other words, this sense of recovery is most relevant for those people whose illness does not simply "go away." Why, then, use the term recovery to refer to this process of learning how to manage and minimize the destructive impact of one's illness on one's life? Doesn't this just confuse things unnecessarily? From our perspective, it is important to include this sense of recovery in the following text because this is the term, and the sense of recovery, that has been chosen and promoted by people living with mental illnesses. For many of them, the term recovery represents first and foremost a crucial civil rights issue that they face as a consequence of several thousand years of discrimination. In the words of Patricia Deegan, one of the most eloquent spokespersons for this sense of the term: "The concept of recovery is rooted in the simple yet profound realization that people who have been diagnosed with a mental illness are human beings" (1992, p. 12).

We understand the ambiguity and confusion that is introduced into a field when one term is used by so many different people to mean such very different things. We agree that this is not an ideal situation, nor does it represent an optimal strategy for promoting the health and well-being of people with psychiatric disabilities. It is, nonetheless, the situation in which we find ourselves. We offer one other recommendation in this regard in addition to encouraging the reader to be as clear as possible about which sense of recovery is being used when and by whom. This recommendation is that we all agree to accept the basic civil rights claims made by people with psychiatric disabilities as our point of departure. This means that we accept the premise that people with psychiatric disabilities are, and remain, people just like everyone else—i.e., just like people who do not have psychiatric disabilities—until we discover otherwise, and then only in the specific ways for which we have accumulated persuasive evidence. Why is this important?

The longitudinal research vividly described in Volume 1 not only discovered a broad heterogeneity in outcome for schizophrenia across people, but also found heterogeneity in functioning across various domains, such as vocational, emotional, social, physical, cognitive, and spiritual, within any given individual over time. Some people may experience florid positive symptoms of hallucinations and delusions while having no cognitive deficits, while others may suffer from profound negative symptoms and cognitive impairments while having few observable positive symptoms. And these profiles can change, even within the same individual, over time. Psychosis does not take over the entirety of the person, as Kraepelin had suggested, but exerts various degrees of impact on various domains of functioning. It leaves some domains of functioning intact, so that people retain areas of health and competence that co-exist alongside of symptoms and dysfunction. As a result, the person is very much still there and should be accorded all of the rights and responsibilities that accrue to this status unless and until he or she offers persuasive evidence to the contrary.

Until we fully accept this premise, we will continue in our research and our practice to stumble across findings that reflect the fact that people with mental illnesses are in fact just like people in general. Several of the contributions to these volumes, including some of our own, conclude with such insights. While still useful to the field, for example, the findings of our early supported socialization studies have been considered somewhat anti-climactic in their suggestion that friendship is important for people with psychiatric disabilities (i.e., just like it is for everyone else). Until we can get beyond proving such obvious, if nonetheless overlooked, points, we will make little progress in determining what it is that is unique in the challenges presented by mental illness and what it is that is specific to the illness that people need to learn to manage and recover from. In reviewing the existing research base for where we are as a field currently, we hope not only to silence the skeptics amongst us, but, even more importantly, to provide the foundation for this next generation of even more promising research.

LARRY DAVIDSON, PHD
COURTENAY HARDING, PHD
LEROY SPANIOL, PHD

Deegan, P.E. (1992). The independent living movement and people with psychiatric disabilities: Taking back control over our own lives. *Psychosocial Rehabilitation Journal, 15*(3), 3–19.

Institute of Medicine. (2001). *Crossing the quality chasm: A new health system for the 21st century.* Washington, DC: National Academy Press.

President's New Freedom Commission on Mental Health. (2003). *Achieving the promise: Transforming mental health care in America, final report* (No. Pub. No. SMA-03-3832.). Rockville, MD: U.S. Department of Health and Human Services.

U.S. Department of Health and Human Services. (1999). *Mental health: A report of the Surgeon General.* Rockville, MD: U.S. Department of Health and Human Services, Substance Abuse and Mental Health Services Administration, Center for Mental Health Services, National Institutes of Health, National Institute of Mental Health.

Introduction to Chapter 4

Courtenay M. Harding

In 1961, a small book entitled *The Vermont Story* appeared and reported on an innovative biopsychosocial rehabilitation program at the only state hospital in Vermont (Chittick et al., 1961). This program targeted the most impaired and chronic group of patients. It was the classic custodial era, when the clinical director, George W. Brooks, MD, received one of the first Smith-Kline and French fellowships to study the effects of thorazine in the early 1950s. All the so-called "hopeless patients," languishing in the back wards, were provided with a therapeutic dosage range of this new medication. Suddenly, 178 people became significantly better and were able to be discharged. This response galvanized the staff to want to help the remaining 269 people who had had only a modest response to the new medication. There were no books written on how to treat the "chronic" patient, so Dr. Brooks returned to the back wards and asked the patients: "What do you need to get out of here?" Thus began a collaborative effort between patients and clinical staff that between the years of 1955 and 1965 developed into a pioneer rehabilitation and community mental health program. (For a more detailed description of this effort and the long-term outcome of these people, see Volume 1, Chapter 2).

With the publication of *The Vermont Story* and the awards that followed, the American Psychiatric Association, the American Academy of Neurology, and the U.S. Department of Justice issued a Joint Commission report called *Action for Mental Health* (1961). In it they said: "The fallacies of 'total insanity, hopelessness, and incurability' should be attacked and the prospects of recovery and improvement through modern concepts of treatment and rehabilitation emphasized." From 1961 onward, ten world studies reported more positive outcomes for once very disabled persons, but the dominance of a deficits paradigm that focuses on problems, disability, deficits, and damage (e.g., Weick, Rapp, Sullivan, & Kisthardt, 1989) persisted over the last century. This volume presents a small sampling of the investigators, persons with psychiatric disabilities, and family members who continue onward and challenge this persistent pessimism within the professions (see Harding, Zubin, & Strauss, 1987, 1992; see also Thomas Kuhn, 1996).

Chapter 4 examines how treatment, case management,* and advocacy helps people to improve. It starts with a strategy proposed by Harding that

---

* The editors of this volume and the authors Rapp and Goscha, acknowledge that many people with psychiatric disabilities take issue with the use of the term *case management*, arguing that they are not "cases" who need to be "managed." The intent within is a reference to the services and/or resources that are managed in order to help people reach their goals.

presents several critical biopsychosocial questions to ask when a person appears to be stopped on the road to recovery. This is followed by a discussion from Rapp and Goscha outlining ten principles for the provision of effective case management based on a review of 22 studies. They contrast the research on Assertive Community Treatment (ACT) approaches to those emphasizing strengths-based work and present findings that indicate that ACT tends to target reducing hospitalizations and strength-based work focuses on non-hospital outcomes.

These articles are followed by a focus on integrated treatment for persons suffering from both mental illness and substance abuse by the Dartmouth group of Mueser, Drake, and Noordsy. Their work, along with that of others, has established some of the six accepted evidence-based practices crucial for this population.

An early article by Malamud and McCrory presents a specific approach to get people back to work by setting up transitional employment (TEP) opportunities with employers to help patients become workers and become adapted to the workplace. TEP often has been dismissed as a program from which patients never graduate and are kept from the "real" world of competitive employment. However, this approach still works for many people emerging into the world of work. A new paper has shown that the approach can be effective and provide competitive employment (Schonebaum, Boyd, & Dudek, in press).

Wayne Fenton, former research director of the well-known Chestnut Lodge, discusses empirical testing of targeted and phase-specific individual psychotherapies including Personal Therapy as proposed by G. Hogarty and associates from Pittsburgh (2002); "flexible psychotherapy" that provides a wide variety of interventions depending on the current needs of the client (e.g., Need-Adapted Treatment by Alanen, [1997]); and the British version of Cognitive Behavioral Therapy for psychoses. This treatment is described at length in an additional paper included here by Garety, Fowler, and Kuipers with many other authors in agreement such as Max Birchwood (1996). Fenton also suggests that the successful practices use evaluation, continuous re-evaluation, timing, titration, and integration with psychopharmacology. The immediate challenge is to transfer what has been learned in the laboratory to general practice.

In addition to all of these strategies, persons with psychiatric disabilities and their families weigh in on what works and does not work for them in working with professionals. Mestemaker not only writes about the obstacles presented by the clinicians, but also speaks about those erected by families and consumers. Chamberlin has been fighting for consumer rights and social justice since the 1970s. Her paper describes the "fundamental expectations that governs the relationship between individuals and societies." An eloquent spokesperson for the rights and needs of family members, Harriet Lefley is also a psychologist and a professor of psychiatry and thus bridges many worlds. Her paper provides an overview of the national efforts for advocacy, a summary of actual organizations with their primary goals and functions and their impact on national health care reform. In his vivid first-hand description of life stresses, drugs, mental illness, and immigration, Patrick Brown writes about taking control in self-management and partnering with professionals in seeking recovery as a process and how he reacquired hopefulness about his future.

In the end, after perusing all of these papers, the reader might be tempted to agree with Falloon and associates (1998) who have decided that "optimal treatment strategies to enhance recovery from schizophrenia" includes "psychoeducation, medication strategies, career-based stress management training, community-based intensive treatment, living skills training, specific drug and cognitive-behavioral strategies for residual symptoms." It seems to take a village to help reclaim lives.

REFERENCES

Alanen, Y. O. (1997). *Schizophrenia: Its origins and need-adapted treatment.* London, Karnac Books.

Birchwood,M. (1996). Early interventions in psychotic relapse: Cognitive approaches to detection and management. In G. Haddock and P. Slade (Eds.) *Cognitive-behavioral interventions with psychotic disorders.* London, England, Routledge, Chap. 10.

Chittick, R. A., Brooks, G. W., Irons, F. S., & Deane, W.N. (1961). *The Vermont story.* Burlington, VT., Queen City Printers.

Falloon, R. H., Held, T., Roncone, R., et al. (1998). Optimal treatment strategies to enhance recovery from schizophrenia. *Australian and New Zealand Journal of Psychiatry, 32*(1), 43–47.

Harding, C. M., Zubin, J., & Strauss, J. S. (1992). Chronicity in schizophrenia: Revisited. *British Journal of Psychiatry,* 161 (Suppl 18), 27–37.

Harding, C. M., Zubin, J., Strauss, J. S. (1987). Chronicity in schizophrenia: Fact, partial fact, or artifact? *Hospital and Community Psychiatry, 38*(5), 477–486.

Hogarty, G. (2002). *Personal Therapy for schizophrenia and related disorders. A guide to individualized treatment.* New York, Guilford Press.

Joint Commission on Mental Illness and Health. (1961). *Action for mental health final report.* New York, Basic Books.

Kuhn, T. (1996). *The structure of scientific revolutions, 3rd ed.* Chicago, University of Chicago Press.

Shonebaum, A. D., Boyd, J. K., & Dudek, K. J. (in press). A comparison of competitive employment outcomes for the Clubhouse and PACT Models. *Psychiatric Services.*

Weick, A., Rapp, C. A., Sullivan,W. P., & Kisthardt,W. (1989) A strengths perspective for social work practice. *Social Work, 89,* 350–352.

Reassessing a Person with Schizophrenia and Developing a New Treatment Plan

Courtenay M. Harding

Courtenay M. Harding, PhD, is at the Institute for the Study of Human Resilience and the Center for Psychiatric Rehabilitation at Boston University.

This article was published previously in J. W. Barron (Ed.), *Making Diagnosis Meaningful: Enhancing Evaluation and Treatment of Psychological Disorders*, 1998, Washington, DC: APA Press, 319–338, and is reprinted with permission.

Nurcombe and Fitzhenry-Coor (1987) suggested that:

> Clinicians are too readily beguiled by exotica, ignorant of base-rates, prone to rely on diagnostic tests of dubious validity, reluctant to correct misconceptions in light of new evidence, overimpressed by confirmatory data, likely to ignore negative evidence, unlikely, without deliberate care, to discount placebo effects, and liable to balance the social utility of outcome against its value. (p. 477)

In this article, I offer 16 crucial questions to assist the clinician and investigator in the systematic collection of evidence for multiaxial diagnoses. These strategies also are designed to aid in the redesign of a more relevant treatment plan than that which existed before the assessment. By following a collaborative comprehensive and systematic biopsychosocial approach, the clinician/investigator can obtain higher validity and reliability in the process. Furthermore, such an approach has been found to help establish the beginnings of a therapeutic relationship between the clinician/investigator and the client. Topics range from evaluation of social supports and cultural and sex differences to medical comorbidity, substance use, and the patient's place in the illness course trajectory. These actors, and many others, are discussed as they have relevance to the diagnostic and treatment process. The questions include the following:

- Have other possible causes of symptoms and behaviors been eliminated?

- Is there an additional neurological impairment?

- Does the person have other medical problems about which to worry?

- Who is this person under a coat of illness?

- What helps or hinders progress?

- What are the specific cognitive deficits being coped with by this patient?

- Are the medications really worth the trade-off?

- Why is the person taking street drugs?

- What are the relevant sex differences?

- Where is the person in the course of illness?

- What myths and misinformation are stressing the patient?

- Who depends on the consumer for help?

- Is there any cohesion in the system of care?

- What is the person's worldview?

- What is missing in the person's repertoire for living?

- Where do the client and clinician start building the recovery process?

I hope that the suggested questions, used consistently to augment the usual cookbook approach in everyday clinical practice with schizophrenia, will improve the "hit rate," eliminate more false positives, and increase opportunities for appropriate treatment.

REASSESSMENT OF DIAGNOSIS

Have Other Possible Causes of Symptoms and Behaviors Been Eliminated?

Early in this century, Eugene Bleuler (1908) renamed dementia praecox "a group of schizophrenias." More recently, this underlying heterogeneity in diagnosis has been subsumed under one umbrella term labeled simply *schizophrenia* (American Psychiatric Association [APA], 1994). No one yet knows whether the heterogeneity in schizophrenia is caused by a variety of etiologies leading to a final common pathway, whether the wide variation in clinical expression is the result of different environmental influences on the genotype, or whether it is an interaction of such factors. The most helpful suggestions to date have come from Kendler and Eaves (1986), who proposed many different models or gene–environment interaction with different weights given to these factors. Furthermore, Strauss, Rakfeldt, Harding, and Lieberman (1989), among others (e.g., M. Bleuler, 1978; Ciompi, 1980), would agree that the person–illness–environment interaction completes the equation. The fact remains that the schizophrenias are extraordinarily complex and difficult to diagnose correctly as well as to treat effectively.

Because there are not yet any known biological markers for schizophrenia, the disorder is diagnosed through a process of "exclusion" that requires careful, systematic, and thorough investigation (Andreasen & Black, 1995; Grebb & Cancro, 1989; Kirch, 1989). There are at least 26 medical, neurological, and other psychiatric disorders whose symptoms often masquerade with a "schizophrenia-like" presentation. These disorders include autism (particularly Asperger's syndrome); temporal lobe epilepsy; tumor, stroke, or brain trauma; endocrine and metabolic disorders (e.g., acute intermittent porphyria [liver enzyme], homocystinuria [a disorder of amino acid metabolism], vitamin deficiency [e.g., B12]; central nervous system infectious processes (e.g., AIDS, neurosyphilis, or heroes encephalitis); autoimmune disorders (e.g., systemic lupus erthymatosa); and heavy metal toxicity (e.g., Wilson's disease with too much copper). Individuals in some drug-induced states (e.g., caused by drugs such as amphetamines, barbiturate withdrawal, cocaine, digitalis, disulfram) may also appear to be schizophrenia-like. Finally, the presenting symptoms of other psychiatric illnesses (e.g., mood disorder, schizoaffective disorder, personality disorder [especially schizotypal, schizoid, borderline, paranoid], brief reactive psychosis, obsessive–compulsive disorder) can appear to be schizophrenia (Andreasen & Black, 1995, p. 220; APA, 1987; Grebb & Cancro, 1989, p. 776; Ryan, 1992). Working within an integrated primary and mental health care system with a skilled internist or with a family or general practitioner can promote more accurate diagnosis.

All diagnoses represent cross-sectional working hypotheses to be repeatedly reassessed and challenged. The unfortunate fact is that most diagnoses, however, become permanently embedded in the chart and thus become longitudinal in nature, whether justified or not. I have reviewed more than 2,000 case records across both the public and private sectors. I rarely found enough evidence "to convict the patient of his or her diagnosis." Few clinicians appear to document the presenting symptoms or the ones that were looked for and are absent. Instead, what is written down are often process notes without hints about how the clinician arrived at the final diagnosis.

Furthermore, as noted in the quote at the beginning of this chapter, many clinicians spend too little time before placing the patient into a diagnostic category. Interviewing then becomes an unconscious effort to prove oneself correct by not asking challenging questions. The use of a standardized clinical interview (e.g., the Structured Clinical Interview for the DSM-III-R [SCID]; Spitzer, Williams, Gibbon, & First, 1990) forces clinicians to consider a broader range of possible diagnoses before coming to a hasty conclusion. Obtaining triangulated information from other individuals in the client's environment is crucial because the client's self-presentation of actual levels of functioning may differ in either direction. Clients can be functioning well in the community but have been trained to tell clinicians about psychopathology. Other clients are functioning poorly but pull themselves together for the interview.

Finally, diagnoses can and do change over time. Therefore, even though a patient may have fulfilled all the criteria at one point or have had several episodes, long-term outcome data have clearly shown that many patients lose their diagnosis of schizophrenia over time or have fallen into another category altogether (e.g., Harding, Brooks, Ashikaga, Strauss, & Breier, 1987a, 1987b).

ASSESSMENT OF THE DEFICIT SYNDROME

Is There an Additional Neurological Impairment?

The deficit syndrome is a relatively new concept in schizophrenia research (Kirkpatrick, Buchanan, McKenney, Alphs, & Carpenter, 1990). The articulation of the syndrome has a distinct advantage over simply listing the positive or negative signs and symptoms that ebb and flow in a client's profile over time. The goal of the research team is to pinpoint stable characteristics and a probable subtype. Such a group may have more than one disorder (i.e., schizophrenia and an additional neurological deficit). The syndrome is correlated with neurological impairments (e.g., sensory integration, stereognosis, graphesthesia, right-left confusion, the face-hand test, and audiovisual integration) as well as poorer premorbid social functioning (Buchanan, Kirkpatrick, Heinrichs, & Carpenter, 1990). The criteria specify that the syndrome is primary (i.e., an illness), not secondary (i.e., it is not the result of demoralization or a drug side effect). Items assessed are restricted affect, diminished emotional range, poverty of speech, a curbing of interests, a diminished sense of purpose, and diminished social drive and duration. Two of these symptom criteria must be met for a 12-month period (Kirkpatrick et al., 1990). Patients who appear to qualify for this syndrome also display diminished glucose uptake in the frontal cortex and the parietal and thalamic areas as shown on positron emission tomography (Tamminga et al., 1992). In addition, patients with this syndrome report increased anhedonia and fewer psychotic events (Kirkpatrick et al., 1990).

A possible neurological screening tool such as the Neurological Evaluation Scale (NES) developed by Buchanan and Heinrichs (1989) might be used to help detect the syndrome. Once the criteria for the syndrome are met, the new atypical antipsychotics (e.g., clozapine, olanzapine, risperidone) might be considered in the treatment regimen. Cognitive remediation (Brenner, Kraemer, Hermantz, & Hodel, 1990; Green, 1993, 1996; Spaulding, Garbin, & Dras, 1989) and other aggressive rehabilitation efforts may be indicated to counteract this situation.

ASSESSMENT OF MEDICAL COMORBIDITY

Does the Person Have Other Medical Problems About Which to Worry?

Clinicians should be aware of the epidemiological data that show a substantial amount of medical comorbidity in schizophrenic patients. An estimated 40% to 60% of patients suffer from other illnesses across all psychiatric treatment settings (e.g., Bartsch, Shern, Feinberg, Fuller, & Willett, 1990; Farmer, 1987; Koran et al., 1989; Koranyi, 1979). Many of these problems are neither recognized nor created. Thus, these patients also have much higher mortality rates (e.g., Jeste, Gladsjo, Lindamer, & Lacro, 1996; Tsuang Woolson, 1977). New models of integrated primary care and mental health care are beginning to put aside the entrenched Cartesian model of mind-body duality in an effort to treat the whole person. Setting up linkages with other physicians, dentists, ophthalmologists, and audiologists would enhance coordinated care and significantly reduce costs in the managed care environment (Bartsch et al., 1990).

A study completed in Colorado by Bartsch et al. (1990) described a screening process at intake that included the following ingredients: a physical conducted by a nurse practitioner, a health history questionnaire, and basic laboratory tests. I would suggest that these tests should include BROCHEM 23 augmented by a toxicology screen, a complete blood count (CBC), urinalysis, T4 and TSH (thyroid function tests), B-12, folate, a VDRL (for syphilis), and/or an HIV test and CT/MRI scans if indicated. Bartsch et al. found that those with personality disorders were more likely to have undetected medical illnesses than any other diagnostic group. Similarly, Ryan and Sunada (1997) studied a large population of developmentally disabled or mentally ill clients and found that greater than 70% of the patients had medical problems that affected their psychological functioning. Ten percent of those patients had three or more such illnesses.

Paying attention to comorbidity helps to avoid confounding diagnoses (as described in the previous paragraphs) and contraindicated medications, as well as reduce the unnecessarily high mortality rates suffered by such clients.

ASSESSMENT OF ADULT DEVELOPMENT

Who Is This Person Under a Coat of Illness?

Schizophrenia significantly disrupts one's life and retards the progression of adult developmental tasks. Grieving for the loss of opportunities is a necessary step that individuals with schizophrenia must take before they can go forward. Clients often press forward to accomplish a postponed task as soon as they have become stabilized. Just as often, their well-meaning clinicians often inadvertently impede the process by saying, "Oh please do not do that activity yet, we just got you stabilized. Wait a while, before you move out of the house, or get another job, or go back to school." McCrory et al. (1982) called this situation a "rehabilitation crisis" and suggested a simple statement that there are ways to reduce the stress and to attempt the desired task. He also proposed role-playing and other stress inoculation strategies to support attempts of the individual to pursue developmental goals that have already been delayed.

Assessment of premorbid levels of functioning (e.g., peer relations, school performance, and dating) with instruments such as the St. Elizabeth's Premorbid Adjustment Scale (PAS) developed by Cannon-Spoor, Potkin, and Wyatt (1982) might help all parties begin to understand where the process was stymied and what has yet to be accomplished.

ASSESSMENT OF THE PERSONALITY

What Helps or Hinders Progress?

Many factors can stand in the way of the recovery process. These factors include socialization into a patient role, limited economic opportunities, medication side effects, lack of rehabilitation, extreme virulence of the illness, lack of staff expectations, and loss of hope (Harding, Zubin, & Strauss, 1992).

The investigators in the Vermont Longitudinal Study (Harding et al., 1987a) were convinced that many individuals with a diagnosis of schizophrenia who did not significantly improve their lives did so because their characterological traits got in the way of the recovery process. Furthermore, Zubin, Steinhauer, Day, and van Kammen (1985) felt that an individual's return to his or her premorbid personality after an episode of schizophrenia was often delayed by the clinician's assumption that the consumer still suffered from schizophrenia.

Characterological traits also can aid progress. A problem-solving style of crisis response, a sense of humor, a philosophical approach to life, flexibility, optimism, and persistence all appear to play a role in the survival and recovery from many kinds of severe and debilitating illnesses (Cousins, 1979, Omish, 1990; Siegel, 1986). These same characteristics also help clinicians survive and flourish (Neligh & Kinzie, 1983).

Therefore, measurement and understanding of the person underneath the disorder is crucial to the development of relevant treatment strategies. Although this approach has been developed to a high degree by psychologists in the past 50 years (see Butter & Satz, 1989, for a review), the present-day use in the public sector of such a systematic assessment with seriously ill psychiatric patients is practically nil. Clinicians often give the diagnosis of borderline personality disorder when, in reality, the question should be,

"What did this person do to make you so frustrated and angry?" A structured and systematic method of assessment is important and needs to be reinstituted.

ASSESSMENT OF NEUROPSYCHOLOGICAL STATUS

What Are the Specific Cognitive Deficits Being Coped With by This Person?

Patients with schizophrenia suffer from multiple deficits in areas such as attention, vigilance, executive functioning (e.g., reasoning, judgment, problem solving, anticipation, planning, decision making), learning, memory, and ability to read affect correctly on the faces of others. A multimodal approach to assessment is often used to gain a more complete picture of the client. Tests include evaluations of laterality: prefrontal, frontal, temporal, and parietal functioning; and the use of tests of semantic, episodic, and working memory, expressive and receptive language, and constructional skills.

New cognitive retraining efforts have been proposed by Brenner et al. (1990), Green (1993, 1996), and Spaulding et al. (1989), along with video training tapes for facial cue recognition. It is important to identify such deficits so that rehabilitation efforts can be targeted much in the same way treatment is directed at other patients with brain disorders. In fact, Green (1996) suggested that clinicians have acquired the triage capacity to begin to select specific types and intensities of rehabilitation on the basis of the pattern of test scores.

ASSESSMENT OF NEED FOR, RESPONSE TO, AND SIDE EFFECTS FROM MEDICATION

Are the Medications Really Worth the Trade-Off?

A thorough history from all possible sources is essential for adequate decisions. This strategy means taking the trouble to acquire old records and talking with others who know the patient well. Collaboration with the patient is critical. After all, it is his or her own body into which all of these chemicals are being fed.

Another critical source of information comes from listening carefully to the comments patients make about the way certain medications make them feel from the inside out. Clinicians often ignore clients when they are unable to describe clearly the subtle subjective feelings that they are experiencing. For example, the side effect of akathisia (i.e., being compelled to be in motion) is especially puzzling and subjectively urgent to a client. The pacing, rocking, rubbing, and other constant behaviors may be perceived as agitation, elopement, need for seclusion, or "acting out" and left untreated. Akathisia is the main reason many outpatients discontinue their neuroleptics. Other major side effects include dyskinesias, dystonias, and Parkinsonism.

Books of psychopharmacology list 20 to 30 additional side effects for each medication. The newer atypical antipsychotics appear to have much lower side effect profiles, but even these profiles are often dose dependent.

Instruments that systematically assess the wide range of neuroleptic side effects ought to be used at least every 6 months (e.g., the Abnormal Involuntary Movement Scale (AIMS) [U.3 Department of Health, Education and Welfare, 1976]; Barnes's, 1989, Akathisia Scale; Simpson and Angus Extrapyrimidal Side Effects Scale, 1970). Clinicians require training on these scales to use them reliably. Clinicians should educate patients about their medications and train them in self-assessment, including the ability to report changes.

In addition, it is important to recognize that there are many sex differences. Estrogens are low-grade dopamine receptor blockaders, thus, women need lower doses of neuroleptics even though the expression of their positive symptoms may be more flamboyant and noisy (Bennett, Handel, Pearsall, 1988; Lewine, 1981; Seeman & Lang, 1990). Women also have lower gastric motility. Therefore, the drugs pass into the bloodstream more slowly, which reduces the intensity of possible side effects, yet the blood–brain barrier is crossed more quickly with delivery of the drug to the brain. However, when women begin to lose their estrogens during menopause, they are much more prone to tardive dyskinesia, and care must be exercised (Seeman, 1985). Perhaps hormone replacement therapy may become a preventive treatment of choice.

I know of no research evidence that supports the use of a lifetime regimen of neuroleptics for many patients with schizophrenia. In fact, the three-decade study of 269 very chronic and once profoundly ill patients from Vermont State Hospital indicated that only 25% were still regularly taking their prescriptions (Harding & Zahniser, 1994). Some of their clinicians were trying to taper the current dosage range, but many of the clients had been frightened by an earlier clinician who had threatened them with dire consequences to keep them "compliant." The findings from the Vermont Study indicate the necessity of periodic reassessment of the current efficacy and ongoing necessity of medications. Anecdotal evidence suggests that a 5-year stabilization period might be an indicator of a possible slow taper.

Clinicians should remember that when changing or eliminating medications, the half-life of the drug and plasma levels are not the only measures to indicate washout. For example, if a client has been on haloperidol for 20 years, it is highly probable that the neurochemical receptor sites have reconfigured themselves to adapt to the drug and they need time to reorganize themselves. Thus, a much slower process may be indicated.

ASSESSMENT OF SUBSTANCE ABUSE

Why Is the Person Taking Street Drugs in Place of or in Addition to Prescriptions?

Epidemiological studies reveal that at least 47% or more of patients with schizophrenia also carry a comorbid diagnosis of substance use or abuse (Dixon & Ribori, 1995). Many of the clients are young men who do not take their prescribed medications and often end up in the hospital. This subgroup is among the most costly to treat.

In their studies of young people with schizophrenia living in Madison, Wisconsin, Test, Wallish, Allness, and Ripp (1989) also noted that drug use was a way to acquire some social contact and to combat loneliness. Furthermore, Andreasen and Black (1995) suggested that perhaps some clients are "abusing drugs to treat their depression or their medication side effects (e.g. akinesia) or to ameliorate their lack of motivation and pleasure" (p. 210).

These factors make an accurate diagnosis even more difficult but crucial for adequate treatment. There are structured interviews such as the SCID interview on psychoactive substance use disorders (Spitzer et al., 1990) and the Addiction Severity Index (ASI; McLellan et al., 1992). I have noted that the response to street drugs of choice, which may ameliorate or exacerbate symptoms, provides another important source of information and lends credence to the basic psychiatric diagnosis.

Unlike standard models of confrontation, treatment for drug and alcohol abuse with people who also have schizophrenia require programs that take into account problems with information processing, attention, concentration, memory deficits, and susceptibility to stress (Dixon & Ribori, 1995). Furthermore, blended funding streams, which allow for joint treatment strategies, also may help the recovery process and empower the clinician. Such programs have been established in several states, which take the dollars allocated for separate treatment modalities (with separate criteria for entry into such treatment) and allow community mental health centers to use these resources for the same patient instead of such patients falling between the cracks of both systems.

ASSESSMENT OF SEX DIFFERENCES

What Are the Relevant Sex Differences?

The clinician needs to acquire a basic knowledge about sex differences across the life span. For example, in neural developmental growth, brain cells migrate and position themselves into place much earlier in the female fetus than in the male fetus. Therefore, female fetuses are in a much better position to withstand a second-trimester viral infection from the mother, which can interfere with any migrating neural cells heading for the brain (Torrey & Petersen, 1976; however, this hypothesis is under dispute by Lewine & Seeman, 1995), as well as other traumatic or anoxic insults prenatally. In addition, female infants suffer from fewer obstetrical insults such as anoxia. As young children, girls explore their environment less than boys and suffer fewer head injuries (e.g., from falling off jungle gyms). Furthermore, girls have fewer high sustained fevers. All of these factors contribute to less vulnerable or traumatized brain structure and functioning in girls.

Estrogen is also a protective factor, as described earlier in the assessment of medications. It also has been conjectured that the presence of estrogens helps delay the onset of schizophrenia for most women compared with men, whose onset of disorder is most likely to occur in their late teens (Lewine, 1981; Seeman & Lang, 1990). Thus, women often have completed schooling, begun a job history, and had an outside relationship. These experiences create a more substantial base of stronger premorbid levels of functioning before becoming ill. These layers of competence facilitate the recovery process. Indeed, women have a better prognosis than their male counterparts during most of the follow-up period. However, much of this edge may be lost during menopause because of the decreased levels of estrogen, and men appear to become a little stronger over time (Harding, 1995; Harding & Zahniser, 1994).

Clinicians need to be aware of differences between the sexes, not only because of the alternate strategies needed in prescribing practices but also because women and men need different help from treatment centers (e.g., Bachrach & Nadelson, 1988; Seeman, 1985; Test & Berlin, 1981).

ASSESSMENT OF POSITION IN TRAJECTORY

Where Is the Person in the Course of Illness?

Patients progress through phases, not only of recovery from a psychosis but also across their life (Strauss, Hafez, Lieberman, & Harding, 1985). The construction of a "lifeline" (Harding, 1996) or a Life Chart (Harding, McCormick, Strauss, Ashikaga, & Brooks, 1989), with each patient using a mutual participation model, seems to be an important enterprise. The use of these structured probes and protocols allows both the clinician and the client to respond and record the events of a life being lived with episodes of schizophrenia. This process permits longitudinal patterns and trends to emerge across multiple domains of functioning: residence, work history, hospitalizations, relationships with significant others, life events, health, medications, and use of community resources (Harding et al., 1989).

Longitudinal patterns provide significantly different data than do one or more cross-sectional samplings of time. Looking at longitudinal patterns allows for a significantly better appreciation of where in the illness process or course the patient is currently functioning. Is he or she early in a highly virulent phase or later, when the illness is lifting? Are the number and spacing of psychotic episodes farther apart or closer together?

Individuals make differential use of social relationships in phases of illness and recovery (Breier & Strauss, 1984) as well as the use acquisition of self-control mechanisms of psychotic symptomatology (Breier & Strauss, 1983). Using this information permits better triage of treatment and selection of treatment options. Clinicians and clients alike enjoy the process of building an overview of a life together. This strategy builds a relationship quickly and has been found to be highly reliable in research (Harding et al., 1989).

ASSESSMENT OF DEFICITS IN UNDERSTANDING ILLNESS

What Myths and Misinformation Are Stressing the Person?

"Knowledge is power." Collaboration with the patient and his or her family helps the clinician be more effective. Increasing the knowledge base within families often reduces "high expressed emotion" (e.g., critical, hostile, or emotionally overinvolved statements or behaviors; Leff & Vaughn, 1985; Vaughn & Leff, 1976). Helping to change the stressful valence in any environment, whether it be the family, the residential setting, the work setting, the clubhouse, or the drop-in center, can significantly reduce relapse rates (e.g., McCreadie, 1992). Teaching patients and families how to manage symptoms and medications promotes competency, reduces complications and exacerbations, and increases self-esteem (Leff, 1995; Liberman, Massel, & Mosk, 1985). Guiding patients to determine their own individualized prodromal profiles helps them to gain control over their illness and thus their life.

ASSESSMENT OF SOCIAL SUPPORTS

Who Depends on the Client for Help?

There is a strong connection between the amount and kind of social supports in a patient's network and the recovery from and prevention of illnesses of all kinds (Berkman & Syme, 1979; Cobb, 1976; Pilisuk & Froland, 1978). Patients with schizophrenia tend to have only a few people in their support systems who are often of one type (family), and they also tend to have little intimacy within these relationships (Tolsdorf, 1976). The joint assessment of the network configuration by type, amount, degree of interdependence, density, size, and clustering (Hammer, 1981) can help both the clinician and the client devise new interventions to improve the situation and to generate suggestions for discharge planning.

Often treatment center staff forget that the community is full of natural support systems (e.g., bowling and baseball leagues, film and stamp clubs, church choirs, glee clubs) that give clients a real link and reconnection back to the community at large.

What is often neglected in the acquisition of critical information for assessment and treatment planning is that many patients with schizophrenia can and do help other people. It has been noted by Manfred Bleuler (1978) and others (Harding & Keller, 1998) that the responsibility of caring for another human being (or plants or animals) can be therapeutic and can contribute to the healing process. Interdependence in social relationships might be considered a higher level of functioning than independence. Measurement instruments often do nor conceptualize this framework and do not capture relevant behaviors because of the prior assumptions made by researchers and clinicians about the lack of relational capacities in patients.

ASSESSMENT OF LINKAGES WITH INPATIENT AND OUTPATIENT SETTINGS

Is There any Cohesion in the System of Care?

Coordination and linkage between all the players are critical for the continuity of care (Bachrach, 1983). The goal is to set up systems with semi-permeable membranes instead of rigid boxes and boundaries for information sharing, case coordination, flexibility, continuity, and integration. Clear and consistent policies at the top shift down through all layers to affect client outcome opportunities (DeSisto, Harding, McCormick, Ashikaga, & Gautam, 1995a, 1995b).

ASSESSMENT OF CULTURAL AND SOCIOECONOMIC INFLUENCES

What Is the Person's Worldview?

Cultural differences have only recently begun to be appreciated by mental health professionals. Diversity is a hallmark of the United States. A savvy clinician acquires a working knowledge of cultural differences and carries a little black book of a wide range of names of cross-cultural colleagues to consult with or to use as interpreters. The clinician needs to know how to decipher incoming interview data to create a valid perception of wellness or illness. What is the importance of religious content (e.g., seeing Virgin Mary or hearing God's voice)? Is the disorganized speech a linguistic variation? Is the displayed affect (e.g., expression, eye contact, body language) congruent with the culture? Is the sense of time (current focus vs. a longer perspective) embedded in the thinking of the group in which the person was raised? What is the importance of family, church, and community? What is the degree of stigma attached to aberrant behaviors by the local community? What is the clinician's (over) reaction to a client's loud voice, broad movements, large body size? How do these factors influence the clinician's decision to place such patients in settings other than therapeutic ones (e.g., prisons or jails; APA, 1994)?

ASSESSMENT OF SKILL DEFICITS

What Is Missing in the Person's Repertoire for Living?

Many studies or treatment regimens focus only on one or two domains of function or dysfunction (e.g., work, symptoms, social capacity). Each of these domains has its own pattern. Symptoms and hospitalizations do not predict work or social functioning (e.g., Strauss & Carpenter, 1974). Only prior work history predicts future work to some degree. Social functioning predicts future ability to relate and somewhat to future work because so much of work is in social interaction. However, most clinicians do not know whether patients can take a bus, manage a job, do the laundry; pay the bills or whether they have a supportive social environment. Despite the old aphorism that "the sum is greater than its parts," structured assessments and triangulated information lead to more appropriate treatment interventions and discharge planning (Rosen, HadziPavlovic, & Parker, 1989; Sederer & Dickey, 1996).

ASSESSMENT OF STRENGTHS

Where Do the Clinician and Client Begin to Start Building the Recovery Process?

Rehabilitation is accomplished by building on the strengths, not the problems or deficits. The treatment plan should always have a place for strengths listed first and everything else listed after that. All goals and objectives should be built on a patient's particular strengths. The clinician should also assess the strengths of the system of care, the family, the case manager, the clinician himself or herself—all the players. Strengths can include domains not often thought of by clinicians, such as playing a musical instrument, having a sense of humor, acquiring a driver's license, knowing how to work on a computer, taking care of others, watering plants, or even manipulating systems of care. The clinician and client should mutually create and set up objectives with small behaviorally measurable steps. Every gain, no matter how small, should be celebrated. If systems of care are in need of rehabilitation, the clinician should itemize the strengths of the system, devise a rehabilitation plan for it, and commemorate every victory.

CONCLUSION

I selected 16 critical questions out of many possibilities for discussion to counteract some of the trends present today in the care of people with schizophrenia as well as to augment the skills of clinicians caring for such patients and of investigators studying their subjects.

Systematic, structured assessment (and reassessment) of people with schizophrenia will dramatically increase the validity and reliability of the diagnostic and treatment planning process. Furthermore, treatment planning will be enhanced through comprehensive evaluations across multiple levels of function from triangulated sources. The clinician and investigator need to be patient, persistent, curious, collaborative, and respectful. Above all, the clinician, and investigator need to see and work with the "person behind the disorder" (Harding & Zahniser, 1994).

Acknowledgments

The author gratefully acknowledges the support of the Robert Wood Johnson Foundation and the editing of Kay Groeneveld and Lisa Kaley-Isley.

REFERENCES

American Psychiatric Association. (1987). *Diagnostic and statistical manual of mental disorders (3rd ed., Revised)*. Washington, DC: Author.

American Psychiatric Association. (1994). *Diagnostic and statistical manual of mental disorders (4th ed.)*. Washington, DC; Author.

Andreasen, N., & Black, D. (1995). *Introductory textbook in psychiatry (2nd ed.)*. Washington, DC: American Psychiatric Press.

Bachrach, L. L. (1983). Planning services for chronic psychiatric patients: A synthesis. *Bulletin of the Menninger Clinic, 47,* 163–188.

Bachrach, L. L., & Nadelson, C. C. (1988). *Treating chronically mentally ill women*. Washington, DC: American Psychiatric Press.

Barnes, T R. (1989). A rating scale for drug-induced akathisia. *British Journal of Psychiatry, 154,* 672–676.

Bartsch, D., Shem, D., Feinberg, L., Fuller, B., & Willett, B. (1990). Screening CMHC outpatients for physical illness. *Hospital and Community Psychiatry, 41,* 786–790.

Bennett, M. B., Handel, M. H., & Pearsall, D. T. (1988). Treating chronically mentally ill women. In L. L. Bachrach & C. C. Nadelson (Eds.), *Treating chronically mentally ill women,* 29–43. Washington, D.C.: American Psychiatric Press.

Berkman, L. F., & Syme, S. L. (1979). Social networks, host resistance, and mortality: A 9 year follow-up of Alameda County residents. *American Journal of Epidemiology, 109,* 186–204.

Bleuler, E. (1908). Die prognose der Dementia praecox (Schizophrenien Gruppe). *Allg Z. Psychitrie, 65,* 436.

Bleuler, M. (1978). *The schizophrenic disorders: The long-term patient and family studies* (S. M. Clemens, Trans.). New Haven, CT: Yale University Press.

Breier, A., & Strauss, J. S. (1983). Self-control of psychotic disorders. *Archives of General Psychiatry, 40,* 1141–1145.

Breier, A., & Strauss, J. S. (1984). Social relationships in the recovery from psychotic disorder. *American Journal of Psychiatry, 40,* 1141–1145.

Brenner, H. D., Kraemer, S., Hermantz, M., & Hodel, B. (1990). Cognitive treatment in schizophrenia. In E. R. Straube & K. Halweg (Eds.), *Schizophrenia: Concepts, vulnerabilities, and interventions* (pp. 161–192). New York: Springer.

Buchanan, R. W. B., & Heinrichs, D. W. (1989). The Neurological Evaluation Scale (NES): A structured instrument for the assessment of neurological signs in schizophrenia. *Psychiatry Research, 27,* 335–350.

Buchanan, R. W., Kirkpatrick, B., Heinrichs, D. W., & Carpenter, W. T. (1990). Clinical correlates of the deficit syndrome of schizophrenia. *American Journal of Psychiatry, 147,* 290–294.

Butler, R. W., & Satz, P. (1989). Psychological assessment of personality of adults and children. In H. I. Kaplan & B. J. Sadock (Eds.), *Comprehensive textbook of Psychiatry* (pp. 475–496). Baltimore: Williams & Wilkins.

Cannon-Spoor, H. E., Potkin, S. G., & Wyatt, R. J. (1982). Measurement of premorbid adjustment in chronic schizophrenia. *Schizophrenia Bulletin, 8,* 470–484.

Ciompi, L. (1980). Is chronic schizophrenia an artifact? Arguments and counterarguments. *Fortschiite der Neurologie-Psychiarrie, 48,* 237–248.

Cobb, S. (1976). Social support as a moderator of life stress. *Psychosomatic Medicine, 37,* 330–341.

Cousins, N. (1979). *Anatomy of an illness as perceived by the patient: Reflections on healing and regeneration.* New York: Norton.

DeSisto, M. J., Harding, C. M. McCormick, R. V, Ashikaga, T., & Gautam, S. (1995a). The Maine-Vermont three decade studies of serious mental illness: Matched comparison of cross-sectional outcome. *British Journal of Psychiatry, 167,* 331–338.

DeSisto, M. J., Harding, C. M., McCormick, R. V., Ashikaga, T, & Gautam, S. (1995b). The Maine-Vermont three decade studies of serious mental illness: Longitudinal course comparisons. *British Journal of Psychiatry, 167,* 338–342.

Dixon, L, & Ribori, T. A. (1995). Psychosocial treatment of substance abuse in schizophrenia patients. In C. L. Shriqui & H. A. Nasrallah (Eds.), *Contemporary issues in the treatment of schizophrenia* (pp. 749–764). Washington, DC: American Psychiatric Press.

Farmer, S. (1987). Medical problems of chronic patients in a community support program. *Hospital and Community Psychiatry, 38,* 745–749.

Grebb, J. A., &. Cancro, R. (1989). Schizophrenia: Clinical features. In H. I. Kaplan & B. J. Sadock (Eds.), *Comprehensive textbook of psychiatry* (pp. 757–777). Baltimore: Williams & Wilkins.

Green, M. (1993). Cognitive remediation in schizophrenia. Is it time yet? *American Journal of Psychiatry, 150,* 178–187.

Green, M. F (1996). What are the functional consequences of neurocognitive deficits in schizophrenia? *American Journal of Psychiatry, 153,* 321–330.

Hammer, M. (1981). Social supports, social networks, and schizophrenia. *Schizophrenia Bulletin, 7,* 45–57.

Harding, C. M. (1995). The interaction of biopsychosocial factors, time, and the course of schizophrenia. In C. L. Shriqui & H. A. Nasrallah (Eds.), *Contemporary issues in the treatment of schizophrenia* (pp. 653–681). Washington, DC: American Psychiatric Press.

Harding, C. M. (1996). *LIFELINES: Probes and protocols.* Unpublished manuscript, University of Colorado School of Medicine, Denver.

Harding, C. M., Brooks, G. W., Ashikaga, T, Strauss, J. S., & Breier, A. (1987a). The Vermont longitudinal study of persons with severe mental illness: I. Methodology, study sample, and overall status. *American Journal of Psychiatry, 144,* 718-726.

Harding, C. M., Brooks, G. W., Ashikaga, T, Strauss, J. S., & Breier, A. (1987b). The Vermont longitudinal study: 11. Long-term outcome of subjects who retrospectively met DSM-III criteria for schizophrenia. *American Journal of Psychiatry, 144,* 727–735.

Harding, C. M., & Keller, A. B. (1998). Long-term outcome of social functioning in schizophrenia. In K T. Mueser & N. Tarrier (Eds.), *The handbook of social functioning.* Needham, MA: Allyn & Bacon.

Harding, C. M., McCormick, R. V., Strauss, J. S., Ashikaga, T, & Brooks, G. W. (1989). Computerized life chart methods to map domains of function and illustrate patterns of interactions in the long-term course trajectories of patients who once met the criteria for DSM-III schizophrenia. *British Journal of Psychiatry, 155 (Suppl. 5),* 100–106.

Harding, C. M., & Zahniser, J. H. (1994). Empirical correction of seven myths about schizophrenia with implications for treatment. *Acta Psychiatrica Scandinavica, 90 (Suppl. 384),* 140–146.

Harding, C. M., Zubin, J., & Strauss, J. S. (1992). *Chronicity in schizophrenia revisited. British Journal of Psychiatry, 161 (Suppl. 18),* 27–37.

Jeste, D. V., Gladsjo, J. A., Lindamer, L. A., & Lacro, J. P. (1996). Medical comorbidity in schizophrenia. *Schizophrenia Bulletin, 22,* 413–430.

Kendler, K. S., & Eaves, L. J. (1986). Models for the joint effect genotype and environment on liability to psychiatric illness. *American Journal of Psychiatry, 143,* 279–289.

Kirch, D. G. (1989). Medical assessment and laboratory testing in psychiatry. In H. I. Kaplan & B. J. Sadock (Eds.), *Comprehensive textbook of psychiatry* (pp. 525–533). Baltimore: Williams & Wilkins.

Kirkpatrick, B., Buchanan, R. W., McKenney, P D., Alphs, L. D., & Carpenter, W. T, Jr. (1990). The schedule for the deficit syndrome: An instrument for research in schizophrenia. *Psychiatry Research, 30,* 119–123.

Koran, D. M., Sox, H. C., Jr., Marton, K. L., Moltzen, S., Sox, C. H., Kraemer, H. C., Imai, K., Kelsey, T. G., Rose, T G., Levin, L. C., & Chandra, S. (1989). Medical evaluation of psychiatric patients. *Archives of General Psychiatry, 46,* 733–740.

Koranyi, E. (1979). Morbidity and race of undiagnosed physical illnesses in a psychiatric clinic population. *Archives of General Psychiatry, 36,* 414–419.

Leff, J. (1995). Family management of schizophrenia. In C. L. Shriqui & H. A. Nasrallah (Eds.), *Contemporary issues in the treatment of schizophrenia* (pp. 683–702). Washington, DC: American Psychiatric Press.

Leff, J., & Vaughn, C. (1985). *Expressed emotion in families: Its significance for mental illness*. New York. Guilford Press.

Lewine, R. J. (1981), Sex differences in schizophrenia: Timing or subtypes? *Psychological Bulletin, 30,* 432–444.

Lewine, R. Seeman. M. V. (1995). Gender, brain, and schizophrenia. In M. V. Seeman (Ed.), *Gender and schizophrenia* (pp. 131–158). Washington, DC. American Psychiatric Press.

Liberman, R. P, Massel, H. K., & Mosk, M. D. (1985). Social skills training for chronic mental patients. *Hospital and Community Psychiatry, 36,* 396–403.

McCreadie, R. G. (1992). The Nithsdale schizophrenia surveys: An overview. *Social Psychiatry: Psychiatric Epidemiology, 27,* 40–45.

McCrory, D. J., Connolly, F. S., Hanson-Mayer, T. P, Sheridan-Landolfi, J. S., Barone, F C., Blood, A. H., & Gilson, A-M. (1982). The rehabilitation crisis: The impact of growth. *Journal of Applied Rehabilitation Counseling, 11,* 136–139.

McLellan, A. T., Cacciola, J., Kushner, H., Peters, R., Smith, L, & Pettinati, H. (1992). The fifth edition of the Addiction Severity Index: Cautions, additions, and normative data. *Journal of Substance Abuse and Treatment, 9,* 461–480.

Neligh G. L, & Kinzie, J. D. (1983). Therapeutic relationships with the chronic patient. In D. L Curler (Ed.), *Effective aftercare for the 1980's: New directions for mental health services* (pp. 73–83). San Francisco: Jossey-Bass.

Nurcombe, B., Fitzhenry-Coor, I. (1987). Diagnostic reasoning and treatment planning: I. Diagnosis. *Australian and New Zealand Journal of Psychiatry, 21,* 477–483.

Ornish, D. (1990). *Dr. Dean Ornish's program for reversing heart disease.* New York: Random House.

Pilisuk, M., & Froland, C. (1978). Kinship, social networks, social support, and health. *Social Science and Medicine, 12B,* 273–280.

Rosen, A., HadziPavlovic, D., & Parker, G. (1989). The Life Skills Profile: A measure assessing function and disability in Schizophrenia. *Schizophrenia Bulletin, 15,* 323–337.

Ryan, R. M. (1992). "Treatment resistant" chronic mental illness: Is it Asperger's syndrome? *Hospital and Community Psychiatry, 43,* 807–811.

Ryan, R., & Sunada, K. (1997). Medical evaluation of persons with mental retardation referred for psychiatric assessment *General Hospital Psychiatry, 19*(4), 274–280.

Sederer, L I., & Dickey, B. (Eds.). (1996). *Outcomes assessment in clinical practice.* Baltimore: Williams & Wilkins.

Seeman, M. V. (1985). Interaction of sex, age, and neuroleptic dose. *Comprehensive Psychiatry, 24,* 124–128.

Seeman, M. V., & Lang, M. (1990). The role of estrogens in schizophrenia: Gender differences. *Schizophrenia Bulletin, 16,* 185–194.

Siegel, B. (1986). *Love, medicine, and miracles*. New York: Harper & Row.

Simpson, G. M., & Angus, J. W S. (1970). A racing scale for extrapyrimidal side effects. *Acta Psychiatrica Scandinavica, 46,* 11–19.

Spaulding, W., Garbin, C. P, & Dras, S. R. (1989). Cognitive abnormalities in schizophrenic patients and schizotypal college students. *Journal of Nervous and Mental Disease, 177,* 717–7218.

Spitzer, R. L., Williams, J. B. W, Gibbon, M., First, M. B. (1990). *SCID: Structured Clinical Interview for DSM-III-R.* Washington, DC: American Psychiatric Press.

Strauss, J. S., Carpenter, W T, Jr. (1974). The prediction of outcome in schizophrenia: II. Relationships between predictor and outcome variables. *Archives of General Psychiatry, 31,* 37–42.

Strauss, J. S., Hafez, H., Lieberman, P, & Harding, C. M. (1985). The course of psychiatric disorder: III. Longitudinal principles. *American Journal of Psychiatry, 142,* 289–296.

Strauss, J. S., Rakfeldt, J. H., Harding, C. M., & Lieberman, P. D. (1989). Psychological and social aspects of negative symptoms. *British Journal of Psychiatry, 155(Suppl. 5),* 128–132.

Tamminga, C. A., Thaker, G. K., Buchanan, R., Kirkpatrick, B., Alphs, L. D., Chase, T. N., Carpenter, W. 1 (1992). Limbic abnormalities identified in schizophrenia using positron emission tomography with flurodeoxyglucose and neocortical alterations with deficit syndrome. *Archives of General Psychiatry, 49,* 522–530.

Test, M. A., & Berlin, S. B. (1981). Issues of special concern to chronically mentally ill women. *Professional Psychology, 12,* 136–145.

Test, M. A., Wallish, L. S., Allness, D. F, & Ripp, K. (1989). Substance use in young adults with schizophrenic disorders. *Schizophrenic Bulletin, 15,* 465–476.

Tolsdorf, C. (1976). Social networks, support, and coping: An exploratory study. *Family Process, 15,* 407–417.

Torrey, E. F., & Peterson, M. R. (1976). The viral hypothesis of schizophrenia. *Schizophrenia Bulletin, 2,* 136–146.

Tsuang, E. F. & Woolson, R. F (1977). Mortality in patients with schizophrenia mania, depression and surgical conditions. *British Journal of Psychiatry, 130,* 162–166.

U.S. Department of Health, Education and Welfare. (1976). The Abnormal Involuntary Scale (AIMS). In W. Guy (Ed.), *ECDEU assessment manual for psychopharmacology (rev. ed.).* Washington, DC: Author.

Vaughn, C. E., & Leff, J. P. (1976). The influence of family and social factors on the course of psychiatric illness: A comparison of schizophrenic and depressed neurotic patients. *British Journal of Psychiatry, 129,* 125–137.

Zubin, J., Steinhauer, S. R., Day, R., & van Kammen, D. P (1985). Schizophrenia at the crossroads: A blueprint for the 1980's. In M. Alpert (Ed.), *Controversies in schizophrenia: Changes and constancies* (pp. 48–76). New York: Guilford Press.

The Principles of Effective Case Management of Mental Health Services

Charles A. Rapp and Richard J. Goscha

At the time of original publication, the author affiliations were listed as follows: Charles A. Rapp, PhD, is a Professor and Director of the Office of Mental Health Research and Training at the University of Kansas, School of Social Welfare, Lawrence, KS; and Richard J. Goscha, MSW, is Director of Training at the Office of Mental Health Research and Training at The University of Kansas, School of Social Welfare, Lawrence, KS.

This article was published previously in the *Psychiatric Rehabilitation Journal,* 2004, 27 (4) 319–333, and is reprinted with permission.

Abstract: This paper identifies ten principles or active ingredients of case management* that are common to interventions that produced statistically significant positive outcomes for people with serious psychiatric disabilities. Twenty-two studies employing experimental or quasi-experimental designs were selected for inclusion in this review. The use of the principles for systems design is briefly discussed.

INTRODUCTION

The national movement to improve outcomes for persons with psychiatric disabilities through the implementation of evidence-based practices in routine mental health services continues to gain momentum. Evidence-based practices are interventions for which there is consistent scientific evidence showing they improve outcomes. The belief is that persons with psychiatric disabilities "have a right to have access to interventions that are known to be effective and that are delivered in a manner faithful to or consistent with current understandings of the interventions' active ingredients" (Drake, Goldman, et al., 2001).

This paper describes ten principles or active ingredients of effective case management of mental health services. Based on a comprehensive review of the research, the approach was to identify the common denominators of case management interventions that produced statistically significant positive outcomes for people with psychiatric disabilities. The position is that these principles should act as the indispensable core ingredients in the design of this service.

* The term case management is used throughout this article because it is the term that is used in the studies reviewed. We acknowledge that this term is considered pejorative to many people with psychiatric disabilities. People with psychiatric disabilities are not "cases" and they do not need to be "managed." A more accurate reflection of what this service entails is that it is the services or resources that are managed in order to help people reach their goals. Until a more appropriate title becomes globally recognized, the term should be used with sensitivity to the negative connotations it carries.

What Is Case Management?

Case management grew in prominence throughout the last two decades of the last century. At the service level, it became one of the most prevalently offered services. Various models were developed and considerable research attention was devoted to it. The paradox is that as we have become more precise in the elements that comprise this service, we have blurred the definition of it.

Case management has traditionally been viewed as an entity (usually a person) that coordinates, integrates, and allocates care within limited resources (Thornicroft, 1991). The primary functions have been seen as assessment, planning, referral, and monitoring (Intagliata, 1982; Levine & Fleming, 1985). The notion is that there is a single point of contact responsible for helping people with psychiatric disabilities receive the services they need from a fragmented system of care. The assumption is that if people receive these benefits and services, they will be able to live more independently in the community and quality of life will improve. While the Broker model is the only model that has stayed true to this definition, other models have emerged transcending these definitions.

The 1980s witnessed the development of enhanced models of "case management": Assertive Community Treatment (ACT), Rehabilitation, Clinical, and Strengths. Driven in part by early research evidence (Franklin, Solovitz, Mason, Clemons, & Miller, 1987) and anecdotal accounts suggesting that "case management" was not producing the outcomes desired, the newer models incorporated dramatically different practices and structures. Examples include small caseloads, team structure, and increased provision of direct service rather than making referrals.

The most dramatic differences between models are ACT and traditional case management. While ACT teams do arrange for benefits and make referrals when necessary, they also directly provide services to help people with everyday problems in living, skill development, housing, medication management, socialization, crisis-intervention, and some teams address employment and substance abuse. ACT resembles a Community Support Service (CSS) program more than a single case management service within a CSS program. Similarly, the Strengths model explicitly requires that segregated mental health and other formal services be the last resort rather than the first choice as in traditional case management referral. In many ways, ACT and Strengths models are not models of case management, but rather, alternatives to it.

Scope of the Review

There have been several reviews of the effectiveness of various case management approaches over the past 15 years. Several of these studies have reviewed the more prominent models comparing their outcomes against traditional or standard service approaches (Holloway, Oliver, Collins, & Carson, 1995; Rapp, 1995; Solomon, 1992; Ziguras & Stuart, 2000). Others have focused specifically on the effectiveness of the ACT model (Bond, Drake, Mueser, & Latimer, 2001; Bond, McGrew, & Fekete, 1995; Burns & Santos, 1995; Scott & Dixon, 1995).

In the most comprehensive review to date, Mueser, Bond, Drake, and Resnick (1998) reviewed the results of 75 studies, which included multiple models (ACT, Intensive Case Management, Strengths, Rehabilitation and Brokerage) as well as multiple designs (random assignment, quasi-experimental, and pre-post designs).

In this project, all the research on case management was reviewed, but much of it was discarded for use in defining the active ingredients. First, only studies that implemented a random assignment or quasi-experimental research design were included. Changes found in pre-post test design studies are more open to being attributed to external factors other than the intervention. Also, only studies conducted in the United States were included. There are four models that have been subject to experimental or quasi-experimental testing in the United States: ACT, Strengths, Intensive Case Management, and the Broker model.

Second, Broker model studies were excluded because only two out of nine studies found any positive findings. The Broker model studies were therefore not able to contribute to identifying "practices that work" and were excluded except as they helped draw contrasts with effective interventions. There are nine studies of the Brokerage model (Bigelow & Young, 1991; Curtis, Millman, Struening, & D'Ercole, 1992; Edwards, Nikkel & Coiner, 1991; Franklin et al., 1987; Hornstra, Bruce-Wolfw, Sagduyu, & Riffle, 1993; Jerrell & Ridgely, 1995; Lehman, Postrado, McNary, & Goldman, 1994; Muller, 1981; Rossler, Loffler, Fatkenheuer, & Riecher-Rossler, 1992). The distinguishing characteristic of the Broker model is that its central purpose and method is to link people with formal mental health services and entitlements (Curtis et al., 1992). Rather than provide help directly to the person, they seek to enroll people in the formal services where the help will be provided. The results include increased use of psychiatric hospitalization (Curtis et al., 1992; Franklin et al., 1987) and no differences in quality of life (Curtis et al., 1992; Lehman et al., 1994). In the nine studies, statistically significant results favoring the brokerage model intervention were found for 6 variables (26% of all variables). However, four of the positive results derived from one study (Bigelow & Young, 1991). The results in this study may be due to differences between groups (the experimental group had significantly fewer people diagnosed with schizophrenia than the control group) and measures were taken after only 3 months of service. If this study is excluded, only 2 positive findings were found for 8 studies.

Intensive Case Management (ICM) studies were also excluded because the components of this model have been defined in very different ways. In some cases, ICM programs seem to meet many of the components of ACT except that caseloads are not shared, yet in other studies it resembles the other extreme, the Broker model (Curtis et al., 1992; Hornstra et al., 1993). Because of the variance in conceptualization and practice in ICM model programs, it was decided not to include these studies in our review.

Third, studies in which the primary research participants were homeless individuals were excluded. Many studies on homeless persons with psychiatric disabilities used approaches that were short term (Susser et al., 1997), incorporated housing vouchers, and served populations that had significantly fewer people with schizophrenia than non-homeless studies. In addition, attrition rates are generally high and some studies referred people to ACT programs after the initial intervention, thereby confounding follow-up findings.

Twenty-one studies on case management were selected for this review. This included sixteen randomized controlled studies (Bond, Miller, Krumwied, & Ward, 1988; Bond et al., 1990; Bush, Langford, Rosen, & Gott, 1990; Chandler, Meisel, McGowan, Mintz & Madison, 1996; Essock & Kontos, 1995; Fekete et al., 1998; Godley, Hoewing-Roberson & Godley, 1994; Jerrell & Hu, 1989; Macias, Kinney, Farley, Jackson, & Vos, 1994; Marx, Test, & Stein, 1973; Modrcin, Rapp, & Poertner, 1988; Mulder, 1982; Quinlivan et al., 1995; Rosenheck, Neale, Leaf, Milstein, & Frisman, 1994; Stein & Test, 1980; Test, 1992) and five non-randomized studies (Bond, Pensec et al., 1991; Bond, Witheridge, Dincin, & Wasmer, 1991; Macias, Farley, Jackson, & Kinney, 1997; Sands & Cnaan, 1994; Stanard, 1999). These reflect studies conducted on ACT and the Strengths model.

Tables 1 and 2 summarize the results of seventeen ACT and four Strengths model studies. The numerical values correspond to the number of studies reporting that outcomes were either better, no different, or worse than a comparison group (in most cases a brokered form of case management). Reports of effects significant at $p < .05$ were used to code the results indicating a better outcome than the comparison group. For studies with mixed results on a particular outcome domain, the decision of how to tally the result was based upon the overall pattern of the findings (e.g., did subscales on a particular variable favor the experimental group over the comparison group). Both authors coded each of the articles independently then met together to resolve any discrepancies, using previous articles that have coded these studies (Bond et al., 2001; Mueser et al., 1998) as a guide.

The research on ACT is the most extensive, with 17 studies qualifying for inclusion. Of all the models, ACT shows the best results for reducing psychiatric hospitalization. It has also shown impressive results in keeping people engaged in treatment. These results are more impressive when one considers that the people served in these studies were often those "most-in-need." On the other hand, the results suggest very uneven results in quality of life related outcomes (see Table 1).

Table 1. Statistically Significant Outcomes for Assertive Community Treatment in 17 Studies

Outcome	Effectiveness of ACT Compared with Control Conditions		
	Better	No Different	Worse
Hospitalization	10	7	0
Housing	3	4	1
Symptoms	3	4	0
Social Functioning	2	2	0
Vocational	4	6	0
Quality of Life	1	5	0
Substance Use	1	3	0
Satisfaction with Services	3	0	0
Self-Esteem	0	3	0
Leisure Time	1	2	0
Social Contact	2	4	0
Satisfaction with Life	1	2	0

Note: See Appendix A for list of studies reviewed and their individual results

The Strengths model research is limited to four experimental or quasi-experimental studies, therefore some caution is needed. While the impact on hospitalization outcomes was not as significant as it was in the ACT studies, there is an overall trend showing the impact of Strengths on non-hospitalization outcomes (e.g., housing, symptoms, etc.) (See Table 2). The ratio of significant results in non-hospitalization outcomes for the strengths model condition versus no differences is about 2:1. A recent non-experimental study (Barry, Zeber, Blow, & Valenstein, 2003) compared the outcomes of veterans who received ACT versus Strengths model services.

The results found that both groups reduced inpatient days and were "clinically improved," but persons receiving Strengths model services were significantly better in terms of improvement of symptoms.

Table 2. Statistically Significant Outcomes for Strengths Model in 4 Studies

	Effectiveness of Strengths Compared with Control Conditions		
Outcome	Better	No Different	Worse
Hospitalization	1	2	0
Housing	2	0	0
Symptoms	2	0	0
Social Functioning	1	1	0
Vocational	1	1	0
Quality of Life ·	1	1	0
Satisfaction with Services	0	1	0
Leisure Time	1	0	0
Social Contact	1	0	0

Note: See Appendix B for list of studies reviewed and their individual results

ACTIVE INGREDIENTS OF CASE MANAGEMENT

Determining the "critical ingredients" that are involved in effective case management is a difficult task. Several factors regarding the research literature contribute to this difficulty. First, the studies are not equivalent in terms of stringency in research design or methodology. Though we included only studies that were experimental or quasi-experimental, there was considerable variation in terms of sample size, follow-up rates, attrition, and sample demographics. Second, outcome measures were not equivalent in the studies. Third, reported outcomes in many studies were mixed. For example, the experimental intervention may have produced significant differences in terms of reducing hospitalization from the control group, but other outcomes (e.g., symptoms, quality of life, and housing) were not significantly different. Fourth, the control and comparison groups in the studies were not equivalent across studies with some being "no service condition," others being "usual services" (often not defined), and still others being other forms of case management. Fifth, and probably most important to our review, individual components of case management were not singled out while holding other elements constant. This made it difficult to conclude that one specific component was associated with the outcome achieved.

With these limits in mind, the approach taken was to locate the factors that seemed common to the interventions that demonstrated some statistically significant results in favor of the experimental group. At times, these factors contrasted sharply with approaches that did not find positive results, thereby giving added credence to the factor's viability. Using this method, nine factors or common denominators have been identified. A tenth ingredient, consumer choice, has been added based on a different body of research.

Five levels were used to characterize the evidence in support of a particular mental health practice. These levels are:

- Level 1: At least 6 published studies with scientifically rigorous designs (RCT, well-controlled quasi-experimental) using a variety of meaningful outcomes;

- Level 2: Less than five published scientifically rigorous studies and/or studies using less meaningful outcomes;

- Level 3: Published studies of less rigorous design (e.g., pre/post with no control group, consumer self-report of perceived changes following receipt of services/program participation);

- Level 4: Multiple organizational "case studies" with reported outcomes published in peer-reviewed journals;

- Level 5: Expert panel recommendations based on empirical research evidence but not including consensus (e.g., based on "surveys" of expert clinicians, surveys of consumer's preferences, unpublished program evaluations).

ACTIVE INGREDIENTS OF EFFECTIVE CASE MANAGEMENT

#1—Case managers should deliver as much of the "help" or service as possible, rather than making referrals to multiple formal services. (Level 1)

The evidence of the importance of this factor is substantial. This ingredient was present in each of the 21 studies reviewed. Common to each of the Brokerage model studies is the reliance on referral, with an emphasis on mental health services (Curtis et al., 1992; Franklin et al., 1987; Hornstra et al., 1993). In fact, Curtis et al. (1992) instructed the experimental case managers "not to assume direct responsibility for care but to help the patient enroll in a day hospital program, adult mental health clinic, rehabilitation program, or alcohol treatment program" (p. 896). These studies uniformly found poor outcomes. The poor results are true even when Brokerage model services have other desirable features like small caseloads (Hornstra at al., 1993) and perform their duties in an outreach mode (Curtis et al., 1992).

In contrast, ACT and Strengths models prescribe that the case managers should directly provide most of the services. For example, both models initially focus on the provision of assistance with the basics of housing, income and entitlements, medication and health. In their study of the Strengths model, Macias et al. (1994) reported that people received direct case management assistance in a wide range of financial, daily living and personal problem areas. Bond et al. (1990) recognized the importance of staff focusing on concrete problem-solving as part of their interventions.

ACT programs that had the most success with independent living and employment (Marx et al., 1973; Mulder, 1982; Stein & Test, 1980) were ones in which the team members themselves worked intensively in-vivo with people in these areas, rather than referring people to other services (Bond et al., 1988; Chandler et al., 1996; Hoult, Reynolds, Charbonneau-Powis, Weekes & Briggs, 1983). Brokerage has been the only variable negatively related to satisfaction with services (Huxley & Warner, 1992). The treatment condition that fared the best was that in which case managers provided the most services directly and had "minimal contact with community based direct service providers other than for medication review" (Rydman, 1990).

#2—Natural community resources are the primary partners. (Level 1)

A second and related ingredient concerns the resources identified and used by case managers. ACT and Strengths model case managers are expected to work with landlords, employers, ministers, neighbors, teachers, art clubs, community colleges and coaches on behalf of the people they serve. As people pursue vocational, socialization, living skills, etc., the two models encourage the case manager to do this rather than make referrals to specialized programs. For example, the case manager may work with employers to find and maintain employment rather than refer the person to vocational rehabilitation, teach the living skills rather than refer the person to a day treatment or partial hospital program; and arrange socialization opportunities rather than relying on mental health programs. The ACT fidelity guide includes "work with informal support system: family, landlords, employers" as one of the items. The Strengths model goes even further in explicitly requiring the exploration and use of non-mental health and professionally driven resources prior to consideration of these formally organized services (Rapp, 1998). The need for such an approach is obvious in rural areas that typically lack formal services. The results in rural areas of this approach for both ACT and Strengths found significantly lower rates of hospitalization and high rates of goal achievements in most life domains (Rapp & Wintersteen, 1989; Santos et al., 1993). The primacy placed on natural community resources is also consistent with the recovery literature, which underscores the need to build a life apart from the mental health system (Ridgway, 2001).

#3—Work is in the community. (Level 1)

ACT and Strengths prescribe an outreach mode with in-vivo service delivery (Rapp, 1993; Test, 1992; Witheridge, 1991) and this ingredient was present in all studies reviewed. The reasons include: removes problems of generalization; minimizes dropout and enhances engagement; allows more complete and accurate assessments; and provides more opportunity to locate and use individual and community strengths. Rapp (1993) adds that client self-determination, if taken seriously, would alone make outreach visits the norm since most people prefer it.

The average rate of keeping people engaged in services for at least a year is 84% across ACT studies, which produces a highly significant ($\chi^2 = 60.5$, $p < .001$) difference from control subjects (Bond, McGrew, & Fekete, 1995). The over 80% retention rate for a year greatly exceeds traditional aftercare where retention rates seldom exceed 50% for even 6 months (Axelrod & Wetzler, 1989; Bond et al., 1995).

This is no small achievement given the historical difficulty in engaging and retaining people diagnosed with severe psychiatric disabilities in service. Bond et al. (1990) found that individuals "who are frequently hospitalized, those who do not become involved in treatment often continue their revolving-door pattern" (p. 885).

Another study found a number of assertive outreach variables, including frequency of out-of-office visits, were correlated with the person's satisfaction with service accessibility (Huxley & Warner, 1992). Bond (1991) commented that "one program using office visits because of a reluctance to make home visits had minimal success until it changed its treatment strategy" (p. 75). Rosenheck, Neale, Leaf, Milstein, and Frisman (1995) found in a study of veterans in ten sites that one site that provided intensive services, but did not provide them in community settings actually increased both inpatient usage and costs by more than 50%. McGrew and Bond (1995) found nearly unanimous agreement of ACT experts on the importance of outreach and in-vivo service delivery. The failure of the Brokerage model, which is usually office-bound, and the fact that many of the control groups for ACT and Strengths research were office or facility-bound services argues for the criticalness of an outreach mode of operation.

#4—Individual and team case management works. (Level 1)

The use of interdisciplinary or otherwise configured teams has been a hallmark of ACT and has often been used as a point of demarcation with other models. The arguments for a team approach include: reduced burnout (Boyer, 1991; Boyer & Bond, 1999; Salyers, Masterton, Fekete, Picone, & Bond, 1998) enhanced continuity of care (Bond, Witheridge et al., 1991; Test, 1979; Ware, Tugenberg, Dickey, & McHorney, 1999); increased availability of someone who knows the person (Bachrach, 1992); and more creative service planning (Test, 1979). The advantages of individual case managers that have been proffered include: A single point of accountability, more efficiency of time through fewer meetings (Bond, Pensec, et al., 1991; Degan, Cole, Tamayo, & Dzerovych, 1990), increased clarity of task assignment (Degan et al., 1990), and one person to develop a professionally intimate relationship (Bachrach, 1992).

The team vs. individual dichotomy tends to camouflage the similarities between ACT and Strengths. For example, since its inception the Strengths model has stipulated a group supervision/team approach for the purpose of creative planning, problem-solving, sharing knowledge of resources, and support to team members (Modrcin et al., 1988; Rapp & Chamberlain, 1985; Rapp & Wintersteen, 1989). Responsibility for actual service delivery is lodged with an individual case manager although the supervisor, or even other team members, often acts as backup. The distinction between models is further blurred when one considers that several of the reported sites for ACT research were dominated by single case manager service provision (Bond, McDonel, Miller & Pensec, 1991; Borland, McRae, & Lycan, 1989; Santos et al., 1993).

The evidence of effectiveness for team-delivered services is equivocal. McGrew, Bond, Dietzen and Salyers (1994) found that "shared caseloads" were significantly correlated with a reduction in days hospitalized. In the one study that sought to examine this variable, Bond, Pensec, et al., (1991) found less burnout and staff turnover for teams than individuals, and reduced hospitalization as time went on although overall no differences were found on program dropouts and hospital admissions. Bond, McGrew, and Fekete (1995) hypothesized that lack of overall differences may be attributable to the control group also receiving intensive case management, although not using a team approach. In another study, Sands and Cnaan (1994) compared two team approaches where a difference was "corporate responsibility" for persons served versus "individual caseloads with team backup." There were no outcome differences although the authors commented that both groups of participants were "faring relatively well." The criticalness of a team approach in service delivery also gets tempered by the favorable outcomes found in the Strengths model research that uses individually delivered case management.

One report (Degan et al., 1990) from a project that used the team approach reflected:

> The team method of case management is time consuming and manpower intensive. Staff over-saturation with frequently changing information often results in long or incessant meetings, or communication attempts that are sometimes spurious. Staff has a tendency to "tune out" because of over-arousal or overflow. Additionally, another problem with team case management is accountability in a system where there is no primary case manager except for charting, with resultant ambiguity about who will do the follow-up after treatment planning (p. 268).

Teams also may be impractical for rural areas (McGrew & Bond, 1995; Santos et al., 1993). In one rural project that found significant outcomes, "shared caseloads and daily team meetings were greatly modified" (Santos et al., 1993).

The conclusion is that both models prescribe a team approach under the leadership of a seasoned professional for the purposes of planning and support. They differ however, in that service delivery is the responsibility of a single case manager in the Strengths model with supervisory backup, but shared responsibility in ACT. The evidence suggests team delivered services are no more successful in producing positive outcomes than individually delivered services. But the consensus is that the team is needed for backup, support, and service planning ideas. ACT experts surveyed by McGrew and Bond (1995) "rated shared caseloads for treatment planning as more important than shared caseloads for treatment provision" (p. 117). Seventy-four percent rated "treatment planning" as "very important to the model" while "treatment provision" garnered only a 58% rating. In fact, only two other items were rated lower (McGrew & Bond, 1995).

#5—Case managers have primary responsibility for a person's services. (Level 1)

The preference of these models is to have the ultimate service responsibility for people assigned to the case managers rather than sharing responsibility with other programs or agencies. The Wisconsin (PACT) and Kansas (Strengths) programs were started as semi-autonomous alternatives to the then current service systems. As Turner and Shifren (1979) argued: Case management is the "integrative mechanism at the client level" (p. 9). Fragmented responsibility is generally the rule and the polar opposite of integration. This does not mean that referrals to other programs do not occur (although the Strengths model prioritizes non-programmatic resources), but that authority is not delegated. As Bond (1991) concluded: "Outreach teams are likely to have less impact if they are viewed as components of a mental health system than if they have functional autonomy" (p. 77).

One of the criticisms of ACT research argues that the positive results in reducing psychiatric hospitalization could be due to the influence and authority the teams have over the hospitalization decisions rather than the nature of the service delivery (Gomory, 2001). Rosenheck et al. (1995) stated that one significant factor that probably limited the impact of the intervention at several sites was that teams did not have the final decision-making authority to admit or discharge from the hospital. In contrast, Bond et al. (1990) found that ACT services reduced hospital admissions even though staff did not have control over the channels of admissions. Since most ACT studies do include enhanced responsibility for critical decisions and the results are positive, the conclusion is that this is a critical ingredient.

#6—Case managers can be para-professionals. Supervisors should be experienced and fully credentialed. (Level 1)

Both ACT and Strengths use teams of "generalists" with consultation by medical professionals and other experts as needed. The Strengths model sees

B.A. or B.S.W. level case managers as adequate. In fact, in three Strengths model studies (only Modrcin et al. [1988] is included in this report), the case managers were undergraduate or graduate students in social work. The PACT model (Wisconsin variant of ACT) prescribes interdisciplinary teams including psychiatrists (recommended team leader), nurses, and social workers, and could include vocational counselors, substance abuse counselors, a member with a psychiatric disability, etc.

ACT research has found that only the degree of nurse participation on the team was correlated with positive outcomes (McGrew et al., 1994). The study of ACT experts found "relatively low interjudge agreement for the team subscale with wide variance in size, make-up, and operation" (McGrew & Bond, 1995).

Reports of persons with psychiatric disabilities as case managers or as case manager extenders seem promising (Sherman & Porter, 1991; Solomon & Draine, 1994, 1995, 2001). Both Solomon and Draine (1994) and Kisthardt (1993) found persons with psychiatric disabilities value the interpersonal characteristics (emotional engagement, personal support) as more important than credentials, or consumer/non-consumer status.

The evidence is that case managers can be selected from a wide pool of people (professionals, B.A. level generalists, students, consumers) but need high quality supervision from a seasoned professional, and easy access to medical personnel and other experts. The research in supported employment (Bond, 1998) and dual diagnosis treatment (Drake, Mercer-McFadden, Mueser, McHugo, & Bond, 1998) strongly suggests that a specialist of each should be assigned to each case management team. Considerable pre-service and in-service training and technical assistance has been recommended (Bond, Witheridge et al., 1991; Modrcin et al., 1988; Sullivan & Rapp, 1991).

#7—Caseload size should be small enough to allow for a relatively high frequency of contact. (Level 1)

The expectations concerning the direct provision of services, the outreach mode of service delivery, involvement with crises, highly individualized service, the breadth of life domains to be attended to, and the work with naturally occurring community resources inevitably requires a rather low consumer to staff ratio. Low ratios received virtually unanimous agreement of ACT experts (McGrew & Bond, 1995). The ACT programs recommended a 10:1 ratio (Test, 1992; Witheridge, 1991). The Strengths model suggests caseload sizes between 12:1 (Rapp & Wintersteen, 1989) and 20:1 (Macias et al., 1994). No study, however, has found positive outcomes with caseloads exceeding 20:1. In most studies, the comparison site had high caseloads (typically between 40:1 and 100:1).

In two studies where the comparison group to the ACT team had lower caseloads (Bond, Pensec, et al., 1991; Sands & Cnaan, 1994), there were no significant differences in hospitalization outcomes.

Both approaches suggest tailoring caseload size to the needs presented by people and the outcomes or benefits sought by the intervention (Witheridge, 1991). For example, a ratio of 20:1 seems effective when it is comprised of people normally distributed in terms of severity (Macias et al., 1994) and 30:1 if comprised of people who are stable and more independent (Salyers et al., 1998).

While not the only reason, small caseload sizes are prescribed to allow increased intensity of contact with the person. King, Le Bas and Spooner (2000) found that caseload size was inversely associated with personal efficacy. With higher caseloads, a case manager's efficacy in areas of knowledge of people's home environment, acute response, linkage to community resources and advocacy was greatly reduced. Rife, Greenlee, Miller, and Feichter (1991) found that the strongest predictor of successful engagement was frequency of contacts. People who received more frequent contact were more likely to remain engaged in services and remain living independently (Rife et al., 1991). Similarly, Quinlivan et al. (1995) found a strong inverse association between frequency of contact and inpatient utilization. Another study (Dietzen & Bond, 1993) found that the four [ACT] programs with moderate or substantial impact in reducing hospital days also had moderate to high levels of service intensity, together averaging 11 contacts per month. The three programs that had minimal impact on hospital use had moderate to low service intensities, together averaging 6.3 contacts per month (Dietzen & Bond, 1993). Programs delivering very low frequencies of service were ineffectual in reducing hospital use. This same study found, however, no significant correlations between frequency of contact and hospital use for the combined sample of 155 participants.

Bond et al. (1990) speculates that brief visits may be more valuable than less frequent but longer visits. Others (McGrew et al., 1994) found that number of contacts, not number of hours of contact, were significantly related to hospital outcomes. This study also found a significant relationship between frequency of telephone contacts and contacts with collaterals, and hospital outcomes.

Three conclusions seem warranted: First, frequency of contact rather than hours of contact makes a difference; the use of telephone may be a helpful supplement, not a replacement. Second, frequency of contact and hospital outcomes will never be truly linear since those who are most in need will often receive the most contact but may also have higher rates of hospitalization (even if reduced compared to similar control groups). The third conclusion is that the quality of the contact, not just frequency, may be a mitigating factor. For example, small caseloads employing ineffective methods or skill-deficit case managers would probably be ineffective. The study by Hornstra et al. (1993) is illustrative whereby a brokerage model intervention with small caseloads and significantly more case-manager contact produced no outcome differences compared to the control group.

#8 Case management service should be time-unlimited (if necessary). (Level 1)

Each of the models prescribes time-unlimited case management services although intensity at any point in time would vary. Psychiatric disabilities are often lifelong with cyclical exacerbation of symptoms. Because of serious and ongoing difficulties, people are likely to need lifelong or very long-term access to a broad range of services and resources, delivered in a highly personalized fashion to maintain previous gains and make further progress (Ridgway & Zipple, 1990; Talbott, 1988). In the study of ACT experts (McGrew & Bond, 1995), "time-limited services for some clients was rated very low (3.7), reflecting the experts' opinions that short-term services were contrary to the ACT model" (p. 118).

The evidence suggests that short-term case management can produce short-term outcomes in hospitalization prevention, acquiring stable housing, and adequate money management (Bond, 1991). Impressive results have been attained with the Strengths model for as little as 6 months worth of services (Modrcin, et al., 1988; Rapp & Chamberlain, 1985). However, most research strongly suggests that while immediate gains can be made, without long-term services, gains can evaporate and others do not have time to occur (Goering, Wasylenki, Farkas, Lancee, & Ballantyne, 1988; McGrew et al., 1994; Strauss, Hafey, Lieberman, & Harding, 1985). The seminal work by Stein and Test (1980) showed that when PACT services were removed, many people relapsed or showed loss of gain.

With each of these studies, case management was withdrawn abruptly with little attention given to the transfer process and only brief follow-up periods after transfer. In contrast, Salyers et al. (1998) studied the Harbinger Step-Down program for recipients of ACT services. This effort was designed to preserve continuity of care through a selective and orderly transfer process:

1. individualized transfer of persons
2. single agency responsible
3. continuity of staffing
4. continuity of basic service model
5. gradual transfer
6. communication between teams

Persons with psychiatric disabilities moved to a 3-person team with a consumer-staff ratio of 30:1 where previously the ACT team had 7 members each with an 8:1 ratio. The new team did not have daily meetings and were not available 24 hours a day, 7 days a week like the ACT team. Intensity of service was reduced by a third. The results found that more stable persons actually continued to improve.

The conclusion is that case management services should be of indefinite duration. Given the importance of continuity of relationship and service, the case manager or team should be constant; not requiring people to switch to different case managers as needs change. However, the Salyers study (1998) suggests that rather stable persons with psychiatric disabilities can be transferred to lower intensity services quite successfully if a well-planned process is employed.

#9—People need access to familiar persons 24 hours a day, 7 days a week. (Level 1)

Each model argues that case managers should be accessible 24 hours a day, 7 days a week and most experimental conditions included this element. One of the reasons for team approaches is to spread this responsibility across team members. The ACT experts, however, reached relatively low levels of agreement on this element while the early Wisconsin efforts and some subsequent ACT programs adhere to this rigidly. Some ACT programs are 9 to 5. Even with great variation in this dimension across studies, positive outcomes have been reported regardless of the structure employed; therefore this specific component of service seems optional.

What is not optional is that people need access to crisis and emergency services 24 hours a day, 7 days a week. The effectiveness of crisis services is enhanced by access to staff who have familiarity and a relationship with the person and who are committed to avoiding hospital care when possible (Carlson, Gowdy, & Rapp, 1998). This would necessarily include the case manager, the team leader or supervisor, the team members, or in some (probably rural) areas the crisis staffs themselves.

#10—Case managers should foster choice. (Level 1)

The freedom to choose has been a stated value of community services for over a decade. In fact, self-determination and choice has been one of six principles of the Strengths model since its inception in the early 1980s. There is an increasing body of research suggesting that choice is also associated with improved outcomes. In supported employment, interventions that base admissions merely on a person's desire to work and who individualize job seeking to positions conforming with people's preferences produce higher rates of competitive employment (Abrams, DonAroma, & Karan, 1997;

Becker, Drake, Farabaugh, & Bond, 1996; Gowdy, Carlson & Rapp, 2003; Mueser, Becker, & Wolfe, 2001).

In a review of supported housing research, Ridgway and Rapp (1997) found that when people had subsidies and options, most moved into independent living situations (Depp et al., 1986; Dixon, Krauss, Myers, & Lehman, 1994; Newman, Reschovsky, Kaneda, & Hendrick, 1994). In a ten-site pre-post national evaluation, increased sense of choice at baseline was found to be associated with improved satisfaction with housing and improved residential stability at follow-up (Livingston, Gordon, King & Srebnick, 1991; Srebnick, 1992).

The importance of choice is also seen in motivational interviewing strategies used in integrated dual diagnosis treatment (Carey, 1996; Drake, Essock et al., 2001; Miller & Rollnick, 2002; Ziedonis & Trudeau, 1997). The importance of choice also resounds from the hundreds of first person accounts of recovery.

CONCLUSIONS AND LIMITATIONS

Each of the ten principles warranted Level 1 status: at least six published studies with scientifically rigorous designs using a variety of meaningful outcomes. Based on the current empirical evidence, these principles should act as the indispensable core for designing case management services. The evidence strongly suggests that all persons with psychiatric disabilities should have a case manager (if they choose) whose practice conforms to the 10 ingredients. The Broker model of case management should be abandoned and resources reallocated. The results of the studies of the Broker model overwhelmingly find either no differences compared to control groups or differences in favor of the control group.

The research suggests that ACT is the most effective approach if one is primarily concerned with reduction of psychiatric hospitalization use. In fact, given that ACT is relatively expensive, both Len Stein, the originator of PACT, and Gary Bond, the principle researcher for ACT, have concluded that ACT should be available to the 10 to 20% of those with the highest service need (Gary Bond, personal communication, 2002). In certain situations, ACT will need to be adapted to fit local conditions. For example, rural areas often require alterations in individual versus team delivered services and composition of teams. The research suggests that while compromises may need to be made in the "pure" ACT model, the ten principles should not be compromised. Similarly, a Strengths model program may decide to use a team delivered approach in order to better provide 24/7 coverage. However, in other ways conformity to the ten ingredients should be maintained.

In contrast to ACT, the Strengths model has demonstrated a rather positive pattern in affecting non-hospitalization outcomes. In fact, the one study comparing the two models found the only significant difference was in terms of improving symptoms and it favored the Strengths model. Since eight of the ten principles are common to ACT and Strengths (team vs. individual and consumer choice are possible exceptions), it would be interesting to test the effectiveness of an ACT structure using the key clinical methods from the Strengths model (e.g., strengths assessment, personal planning, hope-inducing engagement). It is possible that such a synthesis could positively affect both hospitalization and quality of life-type outcomes.

While the studies examined in this review meet the qualifications for Level 1 evidence as stated by Sackett et al. (2000), no attempts to rate the methodological rigor of each of the studies was performed. Therefore we cannot assume that each study reported is equivalent in terms of the evidence provided for the effectiveness of a particular intervention. There was considerable variation in sample sizes, follow-up rates, attrition, and sample demographics in each of the studies.

The intervention reported in each of these articles was a specific program model and individual components of case management were not isolated. This made it difficult to conclude that one specific component was associated with the outcome achieved. Dismantling of the various models to assess impact of specific program components would be needed.

Another limitation is that outcome measures were not equivalent in the studies and results in many studies were mixed. The defining outcome measure for ACT studies has been the reduction of hospitalization. Effectiveness in other key outcome areas, though, has been mixed. This, in a sense, privileges this particular outcome area and gives it primacy in determining evidence-based practices for case management. A question arises as to whether or not this outcome area should be given as much prominence, considering evidence-based practice research has shown little effect on outcomes identified as most meaningful to people for recovery (Anthony, 2003). We should not consider these active ingredients as static elements, but as ones that seem to indicate effectiveness based upon particular outcomes. As outcome areas of interest change, so too may the active ingredients used to obtain them.

Acknowledgments
The paper was commissioned and supported by the Texas Department of Mental Health and Mental Retardation.

Appendix A—ACT Studies (*n* = 18)

Author(s)	Research Design	Sample	Attrition	Follow-up Duration	Outcomes
Marx et al. (1973)	Experimental	CTG (21) RUC (20) OUC (20)	2%	29 months	HD: CTG<RUC, OUC HO: CTG>RUC, OUC CE: CTG>RUC, OUC PS: CTG=RUC, OUC SE: CTG=RUC, OUC
Stein & Test (1980)	Experimental	ACT (65) S (65)	13%	1 year	HD: ACT<S HO: ACT>S VF: ACT>S CE: ACT=S LT: ACT=S SC: ACT>S SE: ACT=S SL: ACT>S PS: ACT<S
Mulder (1982)	Experimental	ACT (59) S (62)	41%	30 months	HD: ACT<S HO: ACT>S VF: ACT>S SF: ACT>S SA: ACT=S
Bond et al. (1988)	Experimental	ACT (84) (3 sites) S (83)	21%	6 months	HA: ACT<S HD: ACT<S QL: ACT=S
Jerrell & Hu (1989)	Experimental	ACT, S (35 total)	Unknown	2 years	HD: ACT=S SC: ACT=S SL: ACT=S
Bond et al. (1990)	Experimental	ACT (45) DIC (43)	34%	1 year	HA: ACT<DIC HD: ACT<DIC HO: ACT=DIC PS: ACT<DIC SC: ACT=DIC QL: ACT=DIC CE: ACT=DIC SS: ACT>DIC SF: ACT=DIC
Bush et al. (1990)	Experimental	ACT (14) S (14)	Unknown	1 year	HD: ACT<S

(continued)

Note: For abbreviations see footnote at end of Appendix A.

Appendix A—ACT studies *(continued)*

Author(s)	Research Design	Sample	Attrition	Follow-up Duration	Outcomes
Test (1992)	Experimental	ACT (75) S (47)	Unknown	2 years	HD: ACT<S
Godley et al. (1994)	Experimental	ACT (25) S (23)	3%	2 years	HA: ACT=S PS: ACT=S SF: ACT=S SA: ACT<S VF: ACT=S
Rosenheck et al. (1994)	Experimental	ACT (454) S (419)	0%	2 years	HD: ACT<S
Essock & Kontos (1995)	Experimental	ACT (131 – 3 sites) S (131)	5%	18 months	HD: ACT<S QL: ACT>S PS: ACT=S VF: ACT=S SL: ACT=S LT: ACT=S SC: ACT>S
Quinlivan et al. (1995)	Experimental	ACT (30) S (30) No CM (30)	0%	2 years	HD: ACT=S ACT<No CM
Chandler et al. (1996)	Experimental	ACT (217 – 2 sites) S (222)	Unknown	1 year	HD: ACT<S PS: ACT=S HO: ACT=S SC: ACT=S QL: ACT=S LT: ACT>S SS: ACT>S VF: ACT>S SE: ACT=S SA: ACT=S
Fekete et al. (1998)	Experimental	ACT (78) S (75)	15%	2 years	HD: ACT=S PS: ACT<S HO: ACT<S QL: ACT=S VF: ACT=S SS: ACT>S

(continued)

Note: For abbreviations see footnote at end of Appendix A.

Author(s)	Research Design	Sample	Attrition	Follow-up Duration	Outcomes
Bond, McDonel et al. (1991)	Quasi	ACT (31) RG (23) S (43)	42%	18 months	HD: ACT=S HO: ACT=S QL: ACT=S VF: ACT=S
Bond, Pensec et al. (1991)	Quasi	ACT (30) SrCM (10)	25%	2 years	HA: ACT=SrCM (in final quarter there was sig. diff.) HD: ACT=SrCM
Sands & Cnaan (1994)	Matched groups	ACT (30) ICM (30)	0%	12 months	HD: ACT=ICM HO: ACT=ICM SF: ACT›ICM SA: ACT=ICM CE: ACT=ICM SC: ACT=ICM

Note. Abbreviations used:

ACT= assertive community treatment
CE = competitive employment
CTG = continuous treatment group
DIC = Drop-in Center
HA = hospital admissions
HD = days hospitalized
HO = housing
ICM = intensive case management
LT = leisure time
OUC = other unit control
PS = psychiatric symptoms
QL = quality of life
RG = reference group
RUC = research unit control
S = standard case management
SA = substance abuse
SC = social contact
SE = self-esteem
SF = social functioning
SL = satisfaction with life
SrCM = senior case management
SS = satisfaction with services
VF = vocational functioning

Appendix B—Strengths Model Studies (*n*=4)

Author(s)	Research Design	Sample	Attrition	Follow-up Duration	Outcomes
Modrcin et al. (1988)	Experimental	STR (23) S (21)	51%	4 months	HA: STR=S VF: STR=S LT: STR>S QL: STR=S SF: STR>S
Macias et al. (1994)	Experimental	STR+PR (20) PR (21)	17%	18 months	HA: STR<PR PS: STR<PR SF: STR=PR SS: STR=PR
Macias et al. (1997)	Quasi	STR (48) S (49)	24%	9 months	HO: SCM>S PS: SCM<S SC: SCM>S
Stanard (1999)	Quasi	STR (29) S (15)	9%	3 months	HA: SCM=S HD: SCM=S QL: SCM>S VF: SCM>S HO: SCM>S

Note. Abbreviations used:

CE = competitive employment
HA = hospital admissions
HD = days hospitalized
HO = housing
LT = leisure time
PS = psychiatric symptoms
S = Standard case management
SA = substance abuse
SC = social contact
SF = social functioning
SS = satisfaction with services
STR = Strengths Model case management
QL = quality of life
VF = vocational functioning

REFERENCES

Abrams, K., DonAroma, P., & Karan, O. C. (1997). Consumer choice as a predictor of job satisfaction and supervisor ratings for people with disabilities. *Journal of Vocational Rehabilitation, 9,* 205–215.

Anthony, W. A. (2003). Expanding the evidence base in an era of recovery. *Psychiatric Rehabilitation Journal, 27* (1), 1–2.

Anthony, W. A., Rogers, E. S., Farkas, M. (2003). Research on evidence-based practices: Future directions in an era of recovery. *Community Mental Health Journal, 39*(2), 101–114.

Axelrod, S., & Wetzler, S. (1989). Factors associated with better compliance with psychiatric aftercare. *Hospital and Community Psychiatry, 40,* 397–401.

Bachrach, L. L. (1992). Case management revisited. *Hospital and Community Psychiatry, 43*(3), 209–210.

Barry, K. L., Zeber, J. E., Blow, F. C., & Valenstein, M. (2003). Effect of strengths model versus assertive community treatment model on participant outcomes and utilization: Two-year follow-up. *Psychiatric Rehabilitation Journal, 26*(3), 268–277.

Becker, D. R., Drake, R. E., Farabaugh, A., & Bond, G. R. (1996). Job preferences of clients with severe psychiatric disorders participating in supported employment programs. *Psychiatric Services, 47,* 1223–1226.

Bigelow, D. A., & Young, D. J. (1991). Effectiveness of a case management program. *Community Mental Health Journal, 27,* 115–133.

Bond, G. R. (1991). Variations in an assertive outreach model. *New Directions in Mental Health Services, 52,* 65–80.

Bond, G. R. (1998). Principles of the individual placement and support model: Empirical support. *Psychiatric Rehabilitation Journal, 22*(1), 11–23.

Bond, G. R., Drake, R. E., Mueser, K. T., & Latimer, E. (2001). Assertive community treatment for people with severe mental illness: Critical ingredients and impact on patients. *Disease Management and Health Outcomes, 9,* 141–159.

Bond, G. R., McDonel, E. C., Miller, L. D., & Pensec, M. (1991). Assertive community treatment and reference groups: An evaluation of their effectiveness for young adults with serious mental illness and substance abuse problems. *Psychosocial Rehabilitation Journal, 15*(2), 31–43.

Bond, G. R., McGrew, J. H., & Fekete, D. (1995). Assertive outreach for frequent users of psychiatric hospitals: A meta-analysis. *Journal of Mental Health Administration, 22,* 4–16.

Bond, G. R., Miller, L. D., Krumwied, R. D., & Ward, R. S. (1988). Assertive case management in three CMHCs: A controlled study. *Hospital and Community Psychiatry, 39,* 411–418.

Bond, G. R., Pensec, M., Dietzen, L. L., McCafferty, D., Giemza, R., & Sipple, H. W. (1991). Intensive case management for frequent users of psychiatric hospitals in a large city: A comparison of team and individual caseloads. *Psychosocial Rehabilitation Journal, 15*(1), 90–98.

Bond, G. R., Witheridge, T. F., Dincin, J., & Wasmer, D. (1991). Assertive community treatment: Correcting some misconceptions. *American Journal of Community Psychology, 19,* 41–51.

Bond, G. R., Witheridge, T. F., Dincin, J., Wasmer, D., Webb, J., & De Graaf-Kaser, R. (1990). Assertive community treatment for frequent users of psychiatric hospitals in a large city. *American Journal of Community Psychology, 18,* 865–891.

Borland, A., McRae, J., & Lycan, C. (1989). Outcomes of five years of continuous intensive case management. *Hospital and Community Psychiatry, 40,* 369–376.

Boyer, S. L. & Bond, G. R. (1992). A comparison of assertive community treatment and traditional case management on burnout and job satisfaction. *Outlook, 2* (2), 13–15.

Boyer, S. L., & Bond, G. R. (1999). Does assertive community treatment reduce burnout? A comparison with traditional case management. *Mental Health Services Research, 1,* 31–45.

Burns, B. J., & Santos, A. B. (1995). Assertive community treatment: An update of randomized trials. *Psychiatric Services, 46,* 669–675.

Bush, C. T., Langford, M. W., Rosen, P., & Gott, W. (1990). Operation Outreach: Intensive case management for severely psychiatrically disabled adults. *Hospital and Community Psychiatry, 41,* 647–649.

Carey, K. (1996). Substance use reduction in the context of outpatient psychiatric treatment: A collaborative, motivational, harm reduction approach. *Community Mental Health Journal, 32*(3), 291–306.

Carlson, L., Gowdy, E., & Rapp, C. A. (1998). *Best practice in reducing hospitalization.* Lawrence, KS: University of Kansas School of Social Welfare.

Chandler, D., Meisel, J., McGowan, M., Mintz, J., & Madison, K. (1996). Client outcomes in two model capitated integrated service agencies. *Psychiatric Services, 47,* 175–180.

Curtis, D. L., Millman, E. J., Struening, E., & D'Ercole, A. (1992). Effect of case management on rehospitalization and utilization of ambulatory care services. *Hospital and Community Psychiatry, 43,* 895–899.

Degan, K., Cole, N., Tamayo, L., & Dzerovych, G. (1990). Intensive case management for the seriously mentally ill. *Administration and Policy in Mental Health, 17*(4), 265–269.

Depp, F. C., Dawkins, J. E., Selzer, N., Briggs, C., Howe, R., & Toth, G. (1986). Subsidized housing for the mentally ill. *Social Work Research and Abstracts,* 3–7.

Dietzen, L. L., & Bond, G. R. (1993). Relationship between case manager contact and outcome for frequently hospitalized psychiatric clients. *Hospital and Community Psychiatry, 44*(90), 839–843.

Dixon, L., Krauss, N., Myers, P., & Lehman, A. F. (1994). Clinical treatment correlates of access to Section 8 certificates for homeless mentally ill persons. *Hospital and Community Psychiatry, 45*(12), 1196–1200.

Drake, R. E., Essock, S. M., Shaner, A., Carey, K., Minkoff, K., & Kola, L. (2001). Implementing dual diagnosis services for recipients with severe mental illness. *Psychiatric Services, 52*(4), 69–76.

Drake, R. E., Goldman, H. H., Leff, H. S., Lehman, A. F., Dixon, L., Mueser, K. T., et al. (2001). Implementing evidence-based practices in routine mental health service settings. *Psychiatric Services, 52*(2), 179–182.

Drake, R. E., Mercer-McFadden, C., Mueser, K. T., McHugo, G., & Bond, G. R. (1998). A review of integrated mental health and substance abuse treatment for patients with dual disorders. *Schizophrenia Bulletin, 24*(4), 589–608.

Edwards, D. V., Nikkel, B., & Coiner, B. (1991). *Final report of the National Institute of Mental Health Young Adult Dual Diagnosis Oregon Demonstration Project.* Unpublished manuscript, Oregon Mental Health and Developmental Disability Division.

Essock, S. M., & Kontos, N. (1995). Implementing assertive community treatment teams. *Psychiatric Services, 46,* 679–683.

Fekete, D., Bond, G. R., McDonel, E. C., Salyers, M. P., Chen, A., & Miller, L. D. (1998). Rural assertive community treatment: A field experiment. *Psychiatric Rehabilitation Journal, 21,* 371–379.

Franklin, J. L., Solovitz, B., Mason, M., Clemons, J. R., & Miller, G. E. (1987). An evaluation of case management. *American Journal of Public Health, 77,* 674–678.

Godley, S. H., Hoewing-Roberson, R., & Godley, M. D. (1994). *Final mentally ill substance abusers report: Technical report.* Bloomington, IL: Chestnut Health Systems.

Goering, P., Wasylenki, D., Farkas, M., Lancee, W., & Ballantyne, R. (1988). What difference does case management make? *Hospital and Community Psychiatry, 39,* 272–276.

Gomory, T. (2001). A critique of the effectiveness of assertive community treatment. *Psychiatric Services, 52,* 1394.

Gowdy, E., Carlson, L., & Rapp, C. A. (2003). Practices differentiating high performing from low performing supported employment programs. *Psychiatric Rehabilitation Journal, 26*(3), 232–239.

Holloway, F., Oliver, N., Collins, E., & Carson, J. (1995). Case management: A critical review of the outcome literature. *European Psychiatry, 10,* 113–128.

Hornstra, R. K., Bruce-Wolfw, V., Sagduyu, K., & Riffle, D. W. (1993). The effect of intensive case management on hospitalization of patients with schizophrenia. *Hospital and Community Psychiatry, 44,* 844–847.

Hoult, J., Reynolds, I., Charbonneau-Powis, M., Weekes, P., & Briggs, J. (1983). Psychiatric hospital versus community treatment: The results of a randomized trial. *Australian and New Zealand Journal of Psychiatry, 17,* 160–167.

Huxley, P. J., & Warner, R. (1992). Case management for long term psychiatric patients: A study of quality of life. *Hospital and Community Psychiatry, 43*(8), 799–802.

Intagliata, J. (1982). Improving the quality of community care for the chronically mentally disabled: The role of case management. *Schizophrenia Bulletin, 8*(4), 655–674.

Jerrell, J., & Hu, T.-W. (1989). Cost-effectiveness of intensive clinical and case management compared with an existing system of care. *Inquiry, 26,* 224–234.

Jerrell, J., & Ridgely, M. S. (1995). Comparative effectiveness of three approaches to serving people with severe mental illness and substance abuse disorders. *Journal of Nervous and Mental Disease, 183,* 566–576.

King, R., Le Bas, J., & Spooner, D. (2000). The impact of caseload on the personal efficacy of mental health case managers. *Psychiatric Services, 51*(3), 364–368.

Kisthardt, W. (1993). The impact of the strengths model of case management from the consumer perspective. In M. Harris & H. C. Bergman (Eds.), *Case management: Theory and practice* (pp. 112–125). New York: Longman.

Lehman, A. F., Postrado, L. T., McNary, S. W., & Goldman, H. H. (1994). Continuity of care and client outcomes in the Robert Wood Johnson Foundation program on chronic mental illness. *Milbank Quarterly, 72,* 105–122.

Levine, I., & Fleming, M. (1985). *Human resource development: Issues in case management.* College Park, MD: Center of Rehabilitation and Manpower Services, University of Maryland.

Livingston, J. A., Gordon, L. R., King, D. A., & Srebnick, D. S. (1991). *Implementing the supported housing approach: A national evaluation of NIMH supported housing demonstration projects.* Burlington, VT: The Center for Community Change through Housing and Support, Trinity College of Vermont.

Macias, C., Farley, O. W., Jackson, R., & Kinney, R. (1997). Case management in the context of capitation financing: An evaluation of the Strengths model. *Administration and Policy in Mental Health, 24*(6), 535–543.

Macias, C., Kinney, R., Farley, O. W., Jackson, R., & Vos, B. (1994). The role of case management within a community support system: Partnership with psychosocial rehabilitation. *Community Mental Health Journal, 30,* 323–339.

Marx, A. J., Test, M. A., & Stein, L. I. (1973). Extrahospital management of severe mental illness: Feasibility and effects of social functioning. *Archives of General Psychiatry, 29,* 505–511.

McGrew, J. H., & Bond, G. R. (1995). Critical ingredients of assertive community treatment: Judgement of the experts. *Journal of Mental Health Administration, 22,* 113–125.

McGrew, J. H., Bond, G. R., Dietzen, L. L., & Salyers, M. P. (1994). Measuring the fidelity of implementation of a mental health program model. *Journal of Consulting and Clinical Psychology, 62,* 670–678.

Miller, W. R., & Rollnick, S. (2002). *Motivational interviewing: Preparing people for change (second ed.).* New York: Guilford Press.

Modrcin, M., Rapp, C. A., & Poertner, J. (1988). The evaluation of case management services with the chronically mentally ill. *Evaluation and Program Planning, 11,* 307–314.

Mueser, K. T., Becker, D. R., & Wolfe, R. (2001). Supported employment, job preferences, and job tenure and satisfaction. *Journal of Mental Health, 10,* 411–417.

Mueser, K. T., Bond, G. R., Drake, R. E., & Resnick, S. G. (1998). Models of community care for severe mental illness: A review of research on case management. *Schizophrenia Bulletin, 24*(1), 37–74.

Mulder, R. (1982). *Evaluation of the Harbinger Program.* Unpublished manuscript, Grand Rapids, MI.

Muller, J. (1981). Alabama community support project evaluation of the implementation and initial outcomes of a model case manager system. *Community Support System Journal, 4,* 1–4.

Newman, S. J., Reschovsky, J. D., Kaneda, K., & Hendrick, A. M. (1994). The effects of independent living on persons with chronic mental illness: An assessment of the Section 8 certificate program. *Milbank Quarterly, 72,* 171–198.

Quinlivan, R., Hough, R., Crowell, A., Beach, C., Hofstetter, R., & Kenworthy, K. (1995). Service utilization and costs of care for severely mentally ill clients in an intensive case management program. *Psychiatric Services, 46,* 365–371.

Rapp, C. A. (1993). Theory, principles, and methods of the strengths model of case management. In M. Harris & H. C. Bergman (Eds.), *Case management for mentally ill patients: Theory and practice.* Langhorne, PA: Hardwood Academic Publishers.

Rapp, C. A. (1998). The active ingredients of effective case management: A research synthesis. *Community Mental Health Journal, 34*(4), 363–380.

Rapp, C. A. (1998). *The Strengths Model: Case management with people suffering from severe and persistent mental illness.* New York: Oxford University Press.

Rapp, C. A., & Chamberlain, R. (1985). Case management services for the chronically mentally ill. *Social Work, 30,* 417–422.

Rapp, C. A., & Wintersteen, R. (1989). The Strengths Model of case management: Results from twelve demonstrations. *Psychosocial Rehabilitation Journal, 13,* 23–32.

Ridgway, P. (2001). Re-storying psychiatric disability: Learning from first person narrative accounts of recovery. *Psychiatric Rehabilitation Journal, 24*(4), 335–343.

Ridgway, P., & Rapp, C. A. (1997). *The active ingredients of effective supported housing: A research synthesis.* Lawrence, KS: University of Kansas School of Social Welfare.

Ridgway, P., & Zipple, A. M. (1990). The paradigm shift in residential services: From the linear continuum to supported housing approaches. *Psychosocial Rehabilitation Journal, 13,* 11–31.

Rife, J. C., Greenlee, R. W., Miller, L. D., & Feichter, M. A. (1991). Case management with homeless mentally ill people. *Health and Social Work, 16*(1), 58–67.

Rosenheck, R., Neale, M., Leaf, P., Milstein, R., & Frisman, L. (1994). Issues in estimating the cost of innovative mental health programs. *Psychiatric Quarterly, 66,* 1–23.

Rosenheck, R., Neale, M., Leaf, P., Milstein, R., & Frisman, L. (1995). Multisite experimental cost study of intensive psychiatric community care. *Schizophrenia Bulletin, 21*(1), 129–140.

Rossler, W., Loffler, W., Fatkenheuer, B., & Riecher-Rossler, A. (1992). Does case management reduce the hospitalization rate? *Acta Psychiatrica Scandinavica, 86*, 445–449.

Rydman, R. J. (1990). More hospital or more community? *Administration and Policy in Mental Health, 17*(4), 215–234.

Sackett, D. L., Straus, S. E., Richardson, W. S., Rosenberg, W., & Haynes, R. B. (2000). *Evidence-based medicine: How to practice and teach EBM.* London: Churchhill Livingstone.

Salyers, M. P., Masterton, T. W., Fekete, D., Picone, J. J., & Bond, G. R. (1998). Transferring clients from intensive case management: Impact on client functioning. *American Journal of Orthopsychiatry, 68*, 233–245.

Sands, R. G., & Cnaan, R. A. (1994). Two modes of case management: Assessing their impact. *Community Mental Health Journal, 30*, 441–457.

Santos, A. B., Deci, P. A., Lachance, K. R., Dias, J. K., Sloop, T. B., Hiers, T. G., et al. (1993). Providing assertive community treatment for severely mentally ill patients in a rural area. *Hospital and Community Psychiatry, 44*, 34–39.

Scott, J. E., & Dixon, L. (1995). Assertive community treatment and case management for schizophrenia. *Schizophrenia Bulletin, 21*(4), 657–668.

Sherman, P. S., & Porter, R. (1991). Mental health consumers as case management aides. Hospital and Community Psychiatry, 42, 494–498.

Solomon, P. (1992). The efficacy of case management services for severely mentally disabled clients. *Community Mental Health Journal, 28*, 163–180.

Solomon, P., & Draine, J. (1994). Satisfaction with mental health treatment in a randomized trial of consumer case management. *Journal of Nervous and Mental Disease, 182*, 179–184.

Solomon, P., & Draine, J. (1995). The efficacy of a consumer case management team: 2-year outcomes of a randomized trial. *Journal of Mental Health Administration, 22*, 135–146.

Solomon, P., & Draine, J. (2001). The state of knowledge of the effectiveness of consumer provided services. *Psychiatric Rehabilitation Journal, 25*, 20–27.

Srebnick, D. S. (1992). *Perceived choice and success in community living for people with psychiatric disabilities.* Unpublished dissertation, Trinity College, Burlington, VT.

Stanard, R. P. (1999). The effect of training in a Strengths model of case management on outcomes in a community mental health center. *Community Mental Health Journal, 35*(2), 169–179.

Stein, L. I., & Test, M. A. (1980). Alternative to mental hospital treatment: I. Conceptual model, treatment program, and clinical evaluation. *Archives of General Psychiatry, 37*, 392–397.

Strauss, J. B., Hafey, H., Lieberman, P., & Harding, C. E. (1985). The course of psychiatric disorder, III: Longitudinal principles. *American Journal of Psychiatry, 142,* 289–296.

Sullivan, W. P., & Rapp, C. A. (1991). Improving client outcomes: The Kansas technical assistance consultation project. *Community Mental Health Journal, 27*(5), 327–336.

Susser, E., Valencia, E., Conover, S., Felix, A., Tsai, W. Y., & Wyatt, R. J. (1997). Science and homelessness: Critical time intervention for mentally ill men. *American Journal of Public Health, 87,* 256–262.

Talbott, J. A. (1988). The chronically mentally ill: What do we now know, and why aren't we implementing what we know? In J. A. Talbott (Ed.), *The Perspective of John Talbott* (37 ed., pp. 43–58). San Francisco: Jossey-Bass.

Test, M. A. (1979). Continuity of care in community treatment. In L. I. Stein (Ed.), Community support systems for the long-term patient: *New directions for mental health services* (pp. 15–23). San Francisco: Jossey-Bass.

Test, M. A. (1992). Training in community living. In R. P. Liberman (Ed.), *Handbook of psychiatric rehabilitation* (pp. 153–170). New York: Macmillan Press.

Thornicroft, G. (1991). The concept of case management for long-term mental illness. *International Review of Psychiatry, 3,* 125–132.

Turner, J. E., & Shifren, I. (1979). Community support systems: How comprehensive? *New Directions in Mental Health Services, 2,* 1–23.

Ware, N. C., Tugenberg, T., Dickey, B., & McHorney, C. A. (1999). An ethnographic study of the meaning of continuity of care in mental health services. *Psychiatric Services, 50*(3), 395–400.

Witheridge, T. F. (1991). The "active ingredients" of assertive outreach. *New Directions in Mental Health Services, 52,* 47–64.

Ziedonis, D. M., & Trudeau, K. (1997). Motivation to quit using substances among individuals with schizophrenia: Implications for a motivation-based treatment model. *Schizophrenia Bulletin, 23*(2), 229–238.

Ziguras, S., & Stuart, G. M. (2000). A meta-analysis of the effectiveness of mental health case management over 10 years. *Psychiatric Services, 51,* 1410–1421.

Integrated Mental Health and Substance Abuse Treatment for Severe Psychiatric Disorders

Kim T. Mueser, Robert E. Drake, and Douglas L. Noordsy

At the time of original publication, Kim T. Mueser, PhD, Robert E. Drake, MD, PhD, and Douglas L. Noordsy, MD, were with the New Hampshire-Dartmouth Psychiatric Research Center, Concord, NH.

This article was published previously in the *Journal of Practical Psychiatry and Behavioral Health,* May 1998, 4, 129–139, and is reprinted with permission.

Abstract: Widespread recognition of the problem of dual disorders, defined here as coexisting substance use disorder (substance abuse or substance dependence) and severe mental illness, has led to the development of programs that integrate mental health and substance abuse treatments. In this article, the authors provide a brief summary of problems related to traditional treatment approaches for persons with dual disorders. They then define integrated dual-disorders treatment and describe common components of these programs: assertive outreach, comprehensiveness, long-term perspective, shared decision-making, stage-wise treatment, and pharmacotherapy. The authors elaborate on the concept of stages of treatment (engagement, persuasion, active treatment, relapse prevention), including the specific goals of each stage, and provide examples of clinical interventions for achieving designated goals. Research on integrated treatment is then briefly summarized.

Over the past two decades, there has been a growing awareness of the problem of dual disorders, which refer to co-occurring substance use disorder (abuse or dependence) and severe mental illness (such as schizophrenia and bipolar disorder). As evidence has accumulated demonstrating that traditional, separate services for individuals with dual disorders are ineffective, new treatment approaches have been developed based on the theme of integrating previously disparate treatment services.

In this article, we provide an overview of integrated treatment as it has evolved over the past decade. We begin with a brief review of the prevalence of substance use disorders in persons with severe mental illness, followed by a discussion of common clinical correlates of substance use disorders in this population. We briefly discuss the natural history of dual disorders and review the problems associated with traditional approaches to treating dually diagnosed patients. After defining integrated treatment, we describe common elements of effective integrated treatment programs, with special emphasis on the concept of stages of dual diagnosis treatment. Last, we provide a brief summary of research on integrated dual diagnosis treatment and conclude with a discussion of future directions for clinical work and research in this area.

PREVALENCE OF SUBSTANCE USE DISORDERS IN SEVERE MENTAL ILLNESS

Numerous studies have shown that persons with severe mental illness are at increased risk for having comorbid substance use disorders (Cuffel, 1996). In the most comprehensive study of comorbidity in severe mental illnesses conducted to date, the Epidemiologic Catchment Area (ECA) study, the rate of lifetime substance use disorders in the general population was 17%, compared to 48% among persons with schizophrenia and 56% among persons with bipolar disorder (Regier et al., 1990). The ECA study found that, in general, all psychiatric disorders were associated with higher rates of substance use disorders compared to the general population, with individuals with severe mental illness having the highest rates.

In addition to the high rate of lifetime substance use disorders in persons with severe mental illness, rates of recent alcohol and drug use disorders are also high. Most studies suggest that between 25% and 35% of persons with severe mental illness have had a substance use disorder during the past 6 months (Mueser, Bennett, & Kushner, 1995). Thus, substance use disorders are common among persons with severe mental illness, with about half of all patients experiencing problems related to substance use at some time in their lives, and about one quarter to one third of patients having an active substance use disorder.

The prevalence and incidence rates of substance use disorder in the psychiatric population can vary as a function of sampling location and the demographic characteristics of the population. Persons with severe mental illness who are homeless, in jail, or who are assessed in an emergency room or acute care setting are more likely to have substance use disorders than other patients (Galanter, Castaneda, & Ferman, 1988). In addition, substance use disorders tend to be more common in patients who are male, young, single, less educated, and have a family history of substance use disorder (Barry et al., 1996; Lambert, Griffith, & Hendrickse, 1996; Menezes et al., 1996; Mueser, Bennett, & Kushner, 1995). To the extent that any sample of persons with severe mental illness is overrepresented among those with these demographic characteristics, patients may be more likely to have comorbid substance use disorders.

CLINICAL CORRELATES OF DUAL DIAGNOSIS

Substance use disorders in persons with severe mental illness have been correlated with a wide range of negative outcomes. In fact, there is some evidence suggesting that substance abuse simply exacerbates all the negative outcomes that frequently occur in persons with severe mental illness. More specifically, substance use disorders have been found to be associated with higher rates of relapse and rehospitalization, medication noncompliance, violence, suicide, financial strain, family difficulties, HIV risk behaviors, and legal problems (Caton et al., 1994; Dixon, McNary, & Lehman, 1995; Drake & Brunette, 1998; Lindqvist & Allebeck, 1989; Linszen, Dingemans, & Lenior, 1994).

As a consequence of the clinical and social effects of substance use disorders in this population, dually diagnosed patients tend to utilize more psychiatric services then singly diagnosed patients, especially costly services such as emergency room visits and inpatient hospitalizations (Dickey & Azeni, 1996). Because of the high prevalence of substance use disorders in persons with severe mental illness, the wide ranging negative effects of substance abuse on the course of illness and the high cost of treatment, the development of more effective treatment programs for dual diagnosis has been a high priority since the mid-1980s.

NATURAL HISTORY OF DUAL DISORDERS

Although few studies have examined the long-term course of dual disorders, the available evidence suggests that, for most dual-disorder patients, substance use disorders are persistent with low rates of spontaneous remission (Drake et al., 1996). Bartels and colleagues (1995) followed up a cohort of 148 patients in an intensive case management program 7 years later and found a stable rate of current substance use disorder. Using data from the ECA study described above (Regier et al., 1990), Cuffel and Chase (1994) found very similar rates of active substance use disorder in persons with schizophrenia assessed twice over a 1-year period. In the longest follow-up study to date, Kozaric-Kovacic et al. (1995) found remarkable persistence of alcoholism in a sample of 312 patients with schizophrenia followed up after approximately 20 years in Croatia.

Thus, the limited available evidence suggests the long-term persistence of substance use disorders in this population. Since most of the patients in these follow-up studies have received standard psychiatric care, their poor long-term outcome provides an indirect indictment of traditional treatment practices for dual disorders. Indeed, as discussed in the next section, numerous problems with traditional approaches to the treatment of dual diagnosis have been documented.

PROBLEMS WITH TRADITIONAL TREATMENT OF DUAL DIAGNOSIS

In the United States and abroad, there has for many years been a division between mental health and substance use disorder treatment services.

Consequently, two different treatment systems oversee and provide services for these two types of disorders. Education, training, and credentialing procedures differ between the two systems; eligibility criteria for patients to receive services also differ. Because of this separation of mental health and substance use disorder services, two general approaches to the treatment of dual diagnosis have predominated until recently: the sequential treatment approach and the parallel treatment approach. Each of these approaches is associated with a variety of problems.

The *sequential treatment* approach is a common clinical justification for exclusion from treatment rather than an explicit treatment model. In this approach, dually diagnosed patients are told they are not eligible for treatment in one part of a nonintegrated system until they resolve the other problem first. This approach defends programmatic boundaries while ignoring individual patients and larger systems needs. For example, an individual with schizophrenia and an alcohol use disorder might be informed by a substance abuse counselor that his alcohol problem cannot be effectively treated until the schizophrenia has been successfully treated or stabilized. Alternatively, an individual with bipolar disorder and a concurrent substance use disorder presenting for treatment to a mental health professional might be informed that it is unsafe to prescribe medications for her bipolar disorder until she stops using substances. Because substance use disorders rarely remit spontaneously and can worsen the course of psychiatric illness, and the severity of psychiatric illness can contribute to substance abuse (e.g., acute mania can increase substance abuse), attempts to treat one disorder before attending to the other are invariably doomed to failure.

In the *parallel treatment* approach, mental health and substance use disorders are treated simultaneously by different professionals, who usually work for different agencies. In theory, providers of separate services should attempt to coordinate their services by regular contacts and reaching consensus concerning the essential elements of the treatment plan. In practice, however, parallel treatment services have not involved such collaboration between professionals, and the burden of integration has either fallen on the patient, or, more likely, has not occurred at all. Although a variety of explanations may account for the poor integration of services in the parallel treatment approach, one possible factor is the different philosophies of treatment held by mental health and substance abuse treatment providers. For example, the use of affectively charged, confrontational approaches has been common among substance abuse treatment providers, while there is a general consensus that such emotionally charged approaches are counterproductive when working with individuals with severe mental illnesses such as schizophrenia and bipolar disorder.

In addition to the problems inherent in the sequential and parallel treatment approaches, dually diagnosed patients have often encountered funding barriers that interfere with access to treatment for one or the other of their disorders. Nonintegrated approaches generally rely on the dually diagnosed patient seeking treatment from both the mental health and substance abuse treatment systems. However, many individuals lack awareness of or motivation for treatment for one or both of their disorders. Consequently, some individuals with a dual diagnosis have failed to receive services for one of their disorders. Other individuals have failed to receive services for *either* disorder, "falling between the cracks" of available services as mental health and substance abuse service providers have deemed such individuals inappropriate for their type of service.

By the end of the 1980s, several comprehensive literature reviews had documented these and other problems with traditional dual diagnosis treatment services (e.g., Ridgely, Goldman, & Willenbring, 1990). By that time, there was also overwhelming evidence documenting the poor prognosis for dually diagnosed patients and suggesting higher rates of costly service utilization (Dickey & Azeni, 1996). As these facts became more widely recognized new programs began to be developed with the primary aim of integrating mental and substance abuse services in order to improve the long-term outcome for persons with a dual diagnosis.

INTEGRATED MENTAL HEALTH AND SUBSTANCE ABUSE TREATMENT

An *integrated treatment program* can be defined as a program in which the same clinician (or team of clinicians) provides treatment for both the mental illness and the substance use disorder at the same time. This clinician assumes responsibility for integrating the mental health and substance abuse treatments so that the interventions are selected, modified, combined, and tailored for the specific patient. Because the educational and prescriptive message is integrated, there is no need for the patient to reconcile two messages—the approach appears seamless to the patient. It should be clear that integration does not mean that two agencies or programs merely agree to collaborate.

A variety of different integrated treatment programs have been developed in recent years to meet the needs of dually diagnosed patients. Many of these programs share a common philosophy, as well as core components of intervention. The essential components of integrated treatment programs for dually diagnosed patients are: assertive outreach, comprehensiveness, shared decision making, long-term commitment, stage-wise treatment; and pharmacotherapy. We describe each of these components in the following sections.

Assertive Outreach

Assertive outreach refers to the provision of services in patients' natural living environments, rather than in the clinic. Assertive outreach is an essential component of integrated treatment because many dually diagnosed patients tend to drop out of outpatient treatment due to the chaos in their lives, cognitive impairment, or low motivation. If these patients are to be engaged in treatment and progress is to be made towards reducing substance use and related outcomes, clinicians must reach out to patients by providing more community-oriented services and fewer clinic-based services. In addition to facilitating the engagement process, assertive outreach is helpful in monitoring the course of dual disorders since it can provide clinicians with more information about patients' functioning, as well as about social and other environmental factors that may influence the outcome of the disorders. Without assertive outreach, many dually diagnosed patients never receive the integrated services necessary to improve their disorders.

Comprehensiveness

Although a fundamental goal of integrated treatment is to decrease and eliminate substance abuse, achieving this goal typically involves more than changing behaviors directly related to substance use. To achieve long-term abstinence, individuals must not only stop using alcohol and other drugs but must also learn to lead an abstinent life. Maintaining abstinence for more than a few days is difficult precisely because it involves changing habits, activities, expectations, beliefs, friendships, and ways of dealing with internal distress—indeed, almost everything about one's life. Individuals who are dually diagnosed typically have a wide range of needs, such as improving the quality of their family and social relationships, work, capacity for independent living, leisure and recreational pursuits, and ability to manage anxiety and depression. Competent integrated treatment programs are necessarily *comprehensive* because they assume that the recovery process occurs longitudinally in the context of making many life changes and they address this broad range of needs.

In fact, every stage of treatment involves a comprehensive approach. Clients can make progress even before they acknowledge their substance abuse or develop motivation to reduce alcohol and drug use by improving their skills and supports. These improvements will increase their hopefulness about making positive changes and will facilitate their subsequent efforts to attain abstinence. As they attempt to live their lives without alcohol and drugs, they must be able to handle distress, to find meaningful activities, to have a constructive social network including rewarding friendships, and to live in a safe setting. Otherwise, they are very unlikely to maintain abstinence.

Shared Decision Making

A fundamental value of the integrated treatment approach is its goal of shared decision making among all critical stakeholders. A major premise of integrated treatment is that dually diagnosed patients, like others with severe mental illness, are capable of playing a critical role in the management of their disorders and in making progress towards achieving their goals. Such a philosophy is consistent with the recent emphasis on consumerism, illness self-management, community integration, quality of life rehabilitation, and recovery for persons with severe mental illness.

Shared decision making also recognizes the critical role that many families play in the lives of persons with severe mental illness. Since they are often involved as caregivers and serve to buffer patients from many of the negative effects of stress, families also need to be engaged and involved in making decisions.

For a number of medical illnesses, shared decision making has resulted in better educated patients, greater treatment compliance, higher satisfaction with care, and improved biomedical outcomes (Wennberg, 1991). Similar benefits are expected in mental health care. Making decisions collaboratively requires that patients and their families have as much information as possible about illnesses and treatments to facilitate better decisions. Providers assume the burden of getting information to patients and their families so that they can become more effective participants in the treatment process. Shared decision making maximizes the chances that treatment plans will be followed since different stakeholders are involved in selecting and implementing solutions to identified problems. Over the long run, patients and families become more able to advocate for themselves and to work collaboratively with professional providers. The goal, of course, is for the person with dual disorders to become responsible for recognizing and managing his or her own illnesses, using families for support and professionals for specific consultations and treatment. Patients and families are satisfied with care as they learn more and take responsibility for implementing care plans that they understand and have chosen. Shared decision making assumes that more knowledge, greater choice of treatment, increased responsibility for self-management, and higher satisfaction with care will produce better outcomes, including less severe symptoms, better social and vocational functioning, and a better quality of life.

Long-Term Commitment

If left untreated or treated by traditional service approaches, the longitudinal course of dual disorders is both chronic and severe. Available research on integrated treatment programs suggests that these programs can have a beneficial effect on decreasing substance use disorders and related negative outcomes in dually diagnosed patients.

However, research also suggests that integrated treatment programs do not produce dramatic changes in most patients over short periods of time; rather, patients gradually improve over time, with approximately 10 to 20% per year achieving stable remission of their substance use disorders (Drake et al., 1998). These findings are consistent with other data on recovery, including longitudinal research on attaining stable remission from alcoholism (Vaillant, 1983) and on the long-term effects of rehabilitation for those with severe mental illness (Bellack & Mueser, 1993). Learning to lead an abstinent lifestyle, just like developing the skills and supports needed to manage one's illnesses and to attain satisfaction with activities and relationships, requires major life changes over months and years. It makes no sense to believe that recovery from two intertwined disorders might be faster than from either one alone.

Stage-Wise Treatment

A central feature of integrated treatment is the concept of stages of treatment. Clinicians and researchers have for a long time proposed that changes in maladaptive behavior occur in a series of different stages (Mahoney, 1991; Prochaska, 1984). Stages differ in terms of patients' motivational states, orientation towards change, goals, and the interventions that are most likely to be effective. Recognition of the stages of treatment can provide clinicians with valuable information as to which interventions are most likely to be successful at a particular point in the course of recovery from a dual diagnosis.

Based on observations of the natural course of recovery of individuals with a dual diagnosis, Osher and Kofoed (1989) described four common stages: 1) engagement, 2) persuasion, 3) active treatment, and 4) relapse prevention.

Osher and Kofoed observed that most patients who recovered progressed through each stage (although relapses and return to prior stages were common). Each of the different stages can be defined in terms of the patient's use of alcohol or drugs and the nature of their relationship with a dual diagnosis clinician. By determining a patient's stage of treatment, appropriate treatment goals can be identified. Clinicians have a variety of different treatment options they can use at each stage to help patients achieve a particular goal. The different stages of treatment have been operationalized in behavioral terms with a rating scale to facilitate reliable ratings between clinicians (McHugo et al., 1995).

In what follows, we define each stage of treatment, describe the goals of that stage, and provide examples of interventions that can be used to achieve those goals. Table 1 summarizes the definitions and goals of each stage.

Tables 2–5 outline possible clinical interventions at each stage. After describing the four stages, we briefly highlight the clinical utility of the stages concept.

Table 1. Stages of Treatment

Stage	Definition	Goal
Engagement	Patient does not have regular contact with dual diagnosis clinician	To establish a working alliance with the patient
Persuasion	Patient has regular contact with clinician, but does not want to work on reducing substance abuse	To develop the patient's awareness that substance use is a problem and create motivation to change
Active Treatment	Patient is motivated to reduce substance use as indicated by reduction in substance use for at least 1 month but less than 6 months	To help the patient further reduce substance use and, if possible, attain abstinence
Relapse Prevention	Patient has not experienced problems related to substance use for at least 6 months (or is abstinent)	To maintain awareness that relapse could happen and to extend recovery to other areas (e.g., social relationships, work)

Table 2. Examples of Clinical Interventions for the Engagement Stage

Outreach

Practical assistance (e.g., housing, benefits, transportation, medical care)

Crisis intervention

Support and assistance to social networks

Stabilization of psychiatric symptoms

Table 3. Examples of Clinical interventions for the Persuasion Stage

Individual and family education

Motivational interviewing

Peer groups (e.g., "persuasion" groups)

Social skills training to address situations not related to substance use

Structured activity

Sampling constructive social and recreational activities

Psychological preparation for lifestyle changes necessary to achieve remission

Safe "damp" housing (i.e., tolerant of some substance abuse)

Select medications to treat psychiatric illness that may have a secondary effect on craving/addiction (e.g., selective serotonin reuptake inhibitors, tricyclic antidepressants, atypical antipsychotics, buspirone, buproprion)

Table 4. Examples of Clinical Interventions for the Active Treatment Stage

Family problem solving
Peer groups (e.g., "active treatment" groups)
Social skills training to address substance-related situations
Self-help groups (e.g., Alcoholics Anonymous)
Individual cognitive-behavioral counseling
Substituting activities (e.g., work, sports)
Pharmacologic treatments to support abstinence (e.g., disulfiram, naltrexone)
Safe housing
Outpatient or inpatient detoxification
Contingency management

Table 5. Examples of Clinical Interventions for the Relapse Prevention Stage

Supported or independent employment
Peer groups (e.g., "active treatment" groups)
Self-help groups
Social skills training to address other areas
Family problem solving
Lifestyle improvements (e.g., smoking cessation, healthy diet, regular exercise, stress management techniques)
Independent housing

Engagement. Engagement is defined by the lack of a working alliance between the patient and the dual diagnosis clinician. Because the clinician cannot help the patient modify his or her substance use behavior without a therapeutic relationship, the goal of the engagement stage is to establish such an alliance, which is operationally defined as meeting voluntarily on a regular (at least weekly) basis. Patients who are not actively engaged in dual diagnosis treatment often attend clinics on an inconsistent, sporadic basis and never establish a trusting relationship with a single clinician. Therefore, outreach is often necessary in order to establish a therapeutic relationship with a patient.

The process of engagement typically begins with practical assistance in securing food, clothing, shelter, crisis intervention, or support. While rendering practical assistance, sensitivity and skill are required to understand and respond to the patient's language, behavior, and unspoken needs so that some trust and openness develop. During the engagement stage, the clinician typically does not address substance use directly, focusing instead on learning about the patient's world and developing a relationship that will later serve as a basis for modifying substance use behavior. Premature attempts to push patients into abstinence are often unsuccessful because they fail to recognize that the patient must develop the motivation, skills, and supports to lead an abstinent lifestyle. By the end of the engagement stage, the therapeutic alliance should allow discussion of the client's substance use and mental illness symptoms to facilitate the work of the persuasion stage.

Persuasion. After establishing regular contact and a working relationship with a dual diagnosis clinician, many patients still do not acknowledge that substance use has negative effects nor do they attempt to modify their substance use behavior. These behavioral steps of acknowledgment and modification constitute motivation; patients who are behaviorally unmotivated are in the persuasion stage. The goals of persuasion are to help the patient recognize that substance use is problematic, develop hopefulness that life can be improved by reducing substance use, and demonstrate motivation by attempting to change behavior. The tasks of persuasion are distinguished from directly helping the patient to acquire skills and supports for reducing substance use, which occurs during the next stage of treatment.

A variety of different strategies can be used to help patients understand that their substance use is a problem. Active psychiatric symptoms are stabilized at the same time as the patient receives substance abuse counseling to minimize interference from grandiosity, psychosis, or thought disorder. Patients and family members often benefit from education regarding psychiatric illness, substances of abuse, interactions between psychiatric illness and substances, and principles of treatment. Individual counseling is based on motivational interviewing (Miller & Rollnick, 1991) which enables patients to identify their own personal goals and to discover how their use of substances interferes with attaining those goals. Group interventions help many patients to develop motivation to address substance-related problems (Ridgely, 1990). Persuasion groups are designed to provide an open forum in which patients can discuss their experiences with alcohol and drugs, both positive and negative, with peers. Family interventions and the sampling of healthy recreational and social activities are also frequently used as strategies during persuasion.

Coercive interventions such as involuntary hospitalizations, guardianship, or commitment to community treatment are sometimes necessary to stabilize the dangerously ill dually diagnosed patient. It is important to recognize that the prevention of harm and compulsory compliance that involuntary measures may provide do not constitute treatment and that such controls can only hold a patient static at best (O'Keefe, Potenza, & Mueser, 1997). The most helpful aspects of involuntary measures may be increased access to the patient and psychiatric stabilization. For the patient to progress through the persuasion process, the clinician must still establish a therapeutic alliance and proceed with motivational development.

The term *persuasion* is sometimes misleading. The essence of persuasion is empowering the patient to have the insight, courage, and desire to change his or her substance disorder, not forcing the patient into abstinence by instituting behavioral controls. Motivation for abstinence must reside *in the patient,* not in the clinician or family. This distinction is often misunderstood and frequently leads to frustration on the part of dual diagnosis clinicians.

Understanding that motivation must exist in the patient helps providers recognize that many other important changes may occur during the persuasion stage. For example, it is possible to improve social skills, constructive activities, and social supports before there is any expressed motivation for abstinence; these changes will help to nurture motivation and will be needed by the patient in developing an abstinent lifestyle down the road. Note that the emphasis is on empowering the patient to make healthful changes rather than on coercive or involuntary interventions.

Active Treatment. A patient is defined as motivated to reduce substance use, and hence in the active treatment stage, when he or she has changed behaviors by significantly reducing substance use for more than 1 month and by actively seeking to sustain or enhance reductions.

The goal of this stage is to help the patient reduce substance use to the point of eliminating negative consequences or to attain abstinence for a prolonged period of time. Although research data indicate that abstinence is a much more successful remission strategy than occasional or moderate use (Drake et al., 1998), the decision to pursue abstinence must come from the patient.

A wide variety of different clinical strategies can be used to help patients further reduce their substance use or attain abstinence. These strategies involve the traditional rehabilitation dyad of increasing skills and improving supports, and they can be accomplished in a variety of settings. Individual counseling uses behavioral techniques for enhancing abstinence skills and networks that support abstinence (Monti et al., 1989). Active treatment groups and social skills training groups can help patients reduce substance use by developing skills for dealing with high-risk situations or compensatory skills for meeting needs in ways other than using substances (Mueser & Noordsy, 1996).

Self-help groups, such as Alcoholics Anonymous, can be useful for patients who endorse abstinence as a goal and wish to take advantage of the wide availability of such groups in most communities. Patients may affiliate most readily with self-help groups tailored to the dually diagnosed population (e.g., "Double-Trouble" or "Dual Recovery" groups). Family problem solving can be used to identify possible triggers of substance use, to help patients get involved in alternative activities, to structure their time in order to decrease opportunities to use substances, and to provide behavioral rewards for achieving target goals. Contingency management strategies, such as monetarily reinforcing patients for not using substances (Shaner, et al., 1997), can be useful in helping patients reduce substance use and experience the benefits of sobriety.

Although the explicit goal during this stage is to reduce substance use, clinicians recognize that sustained behavioral change involves more than avoiding substances; it includes all the lifestyle changes described above under comprehensiveness. Therefore, interventions during active treatment may need to address the broader changes needed to achieve a different lifestyle that does not rely on drugs. Clinicians expand upon the persuasion process to develop patients' recognition of and motivation for addressing these changes. This process determines which areas are addressed during active treatment and which are saved for future work.

Relapses or slips back into active substance use are common in the active treatment stage. Relapses are not viewed as failures, but rather as part of the course of the chronic illness. Relapses are used as opportunities to learn more about what each individual will need to achieve sustained abstinence. The patient and clinician examine the relapse in microscopic detail, gleaning information about relapse triggers and the sequence of events leading to substance use. They use this information to refine their active treatment interventions and to identify new areas of lifestyle change that need attention.

If the patient has a relapse into sustained active substance use, the clinician should shift back into persuasion-stage work, only returning to active treatment interventions when the patient again demonstrates motivation for abstinence or reduced substance use. Many patients will choose to reduce substance use rather than to adopt abstinence during early active treatment. This strategy often fails to sustain remission, but the experience can be helpful in the long-term process of recovery because the patient learns experientially that moderate use of alcohol or drugs is not viable, thereby developing motivation to pursue abstinence.

Relapse Prevention. The patient is defined as having reached the relapse prevention stage when he or she has not experienced negative consequences related to substance use (or has been abstinent) for at least 6 months. The goals of this stage are to maintain an awareness that relapse of the substance use disorder could still happen, to prepare to respond to relapse, and to continue to expand the recovery to other areas of functioning, such as social relationships, work, and health. After abstinent patients achieve an extended period of sobriety, they often develop the confidence that they can resume controlled substance use. This strategy usually fails, since few patients with severe mental illness are capable of sustaining moderate use of alcohol or drugs without incurring negative consequences (Drake & Wallach, 1994). Helping patients in the relapse prevention stage maintain an awareness of their high vulnerability to relapse and developing monitoring strategies are critical goals of this stage of treatment. As is true at every stage, the patient's choices are paramount in how these goals are accomplished. Some patients will attend self-help groups, some will continue in dual diagnosis groups, some will review their status with their clinicians, and some will use other community-integrated support networks.

The overarching goal of this stage is to develop a meaningful recovery process. Clinicians facilitate a shift in focus from giving up substances to gaining a healthy life. When a remission of the substance use disorder has lasted for over 6 months, it becomes increasingly important to help patients achieve goals in other areas of functioning. The more patients are able to derive natural rewards from normative activities such as work, social relationships, and leisure pursuits, the less susceptible they will be to relapses of their substance use disorder. Therefore, strategies such as supported employment and social skills training may be used to help patients to achieve these goals.

At the same time, preparing for relapse is also an important skill during relapse prevention. The patient must know how to accept relapse and begin working on abstinence right away rather than experiencing failure, developing hopelessness, and giving in to a prolonged relapse. Education and knowledge about the long-term process of recovery may be helpful in preparing for relapse.

Clinical Utility of the Stages of Treatment. The most important feature of the concept of stages of treatment is that it helps clinicians identify appropriate goals and strategies at a particular point of treatment. Paying attention to the stage of treatment ensures that interventions will be optimally timed to fit a patient's current motivational state. For example, if a clinician attempts to help a patient discover that his or her substance use is destructive (a goal of the persuasion stage) before a therapeutic relationship with the patient has been established (engagement stage), he or she may unwittingly drive the patient away from treatment. Similarly, if the clinician tries to help the patient reduce his or her substance use (a goal of the active treatment stage) before the patient sees substance use as a problem (persuasion stage), the patient may become disenchanted and convinced that the clinician does not really "understand" him, and drop out of treatment. Therefore, the concept of stages helps clinicians increase the chances of selecting interventions with the greatest immediate relevance for patients at a particular point during their treatment.

Pharmacotherapy

Medications for both psychiatric illness and substance disorder should be integrated with psychosocial interventions in a complementary approach. Failure to prescribe needed medications or undermedication of severe psychiatric illness can promote psychiatric deterioration and/or relapse of substance use disorder. Because of the potential risks of medication abuse and of interactions between medications and drugs of abuse, however, caution is generally encouraged in prescribing psychoactive medications. In addition, due to the high rate of medication nonadherence in dually diagnosed patients, close monitoring of medication adherence in the community, for example by outreach nurses, is often recommended.

The Center for Substance Abuse Treatment has developed several guidelines for integrating pharmacotherapy with psychosocial approaches (Center for Substance Abuse Treatment, 1994):

1. Begin with nonpharmacologic approaches to manage emerging symptoms of a less severe nature, such as anxiety and mild depression and add medications if the symptoms do not respond. At the same time, recognize that acute and severe symptoms associated with mania, psychotic depression, and schizophrenia require immediate medications.

2. Encourage the use of medications with a low abuse potential. This conservative dictum should again be moderated by the dangers of acute and severe symptoms.

3. Be aware of specific interactions between drugs of abuse or withdrawal syndromes and medication effects. For example, alcohol intoxication and withdrawal can disturb electrolyte balance and affect lithium levels.

Specific pharmacotherapies for dual diagnosis are only now emerging. One experimental trial showed that schizophrenic patients with cocaine disorder did better with adjunctive desipramine (Ziedonis et al., 1992). Two nonexperimental reports suggest that clozapine may be superior to other antipsychotic drugs for dually diagnosed patients with schizophrenia by exerting a specific effect on substance use (Drake et al., 2000; Zimmet et al., 2000). Clinicians often recommend parenteral antipsychotic drugs (i.e., long-acting injections) for dually diagnosed patients who are seriously nonadherent, but we are unaware of any research on this practice. Anecdotally, clinicians have also reported success in using disulfiram or naltrexone with individual dual-diagnosis patients, but there are no controlled studies of these medications either (Koefed et al., 1986).

RESEARCH ON INTEGRATED TREATMENT

With the proliferation of integrated treatment programs for dually disordered patients over the past decade, the effectiveness of these programs has become the subject of substantial research. Early studies on integrated treatment usually involved before and after treatment assessments (i.e., no experimental control group) or quasi-experimental control groups. Although the research methods employed in these studies were limited, and many programs were relatively brief in duration, several trends were evident (Drake, Mercer-McFadden et al., 1998). First, research suggested that integrated dual diagnosis programs were capable of engaging the vast majority of dually diagnosed patients in treatment and retaining them in treatment for 1 year or more. Second, engagement in integrated treatment programs was associated with greater improvement in substance use outcomes compared to patients who were not engaged or who dropped out. Third, brief, intensive programs and programs that failed to use motivation-based interventions tended to have poor outcomes.

More recent research on integrated treatment programs has employed appropriate control groups and has evaluated programs over longer periods of time (e.g., 1.5–3 years). Research from these studies has provided further encouragement concerning the effectiveness of integrated treatment programs (Drake, Mercer-McFadden et al., 1998). Research on integrated treatment that is provided over a period of several years has shown that dually diagnosed patients demonstrate a consistent gradual progression towards substance use reduction and abstinence. Most research on traditional (parallel or sequential) treatment approaches for dual disorders indicate annual rates of sustained remission of less than 5%. In comparison, recent research on integrated treatment programs suggests significantly higher rates of remission, with 10% to 20% of dually diagnosed patients achieving stable remission per year. These remission rates approximate those seen among people with substance use disorders without mental illness in substance abuse treatment, suggesting that integrating treatment for dual disorders may eliminate the adverse effect of mental illness on remission from substance abuse. There is also evidence that improvements in substance use outcomes are associated with gains in a variety of other areas, such as enhanced quantity and quality of community residence, decreased victimization, and increased life satisfaction (Drake, McHugo et al., 1998). Finally, research on integrated treatment suggests that most dually diagnosed patients can be engaged in treatment for extended periods of time, well beyond the relatively brief intervals studied in earlier research (e.g., less than 1 year).

SUMMARY AND RECOMMENDATIONS

The treatment of dually diagnosed individuals has evolved tremendously over the past two decades, and advances continue to be made in this newly emergent field. There are several practical implications of this new growth in knowledge for clinicians who treat individuals with dual disorders.

First, clinicians must be aware of the high prevalence of substance use disorders in patients with severe mental illness. Substance use disorders can be hidden and may develop at any time during the life cycle. Therefore, assessment for substance use disorders must be ongoing. In order to detect dual disorders, clinicians need to be familiar with the common consequences of substance use in patients with severe mental illness, including relapse and rehospitalization, legal problems, family conflict, homelessness, money problems, suicidality, and violence. Due to the biological vulnerability that is presumably the basis of major mental illnesses, negative consequences may occur in these patients following even small amounts of substance use.

Second, clinicians need to strive to provide *integrated mental health and substance use disorder treatment* to individuals who are dually diagnosed. At the most basic level, integrated treatment means that the clinician or treatment team treats both disorders simultaneously, with an eye towards addressing the possible interactions between disorders. The clinician, not the patient, assumes the burden of integrating treatments. When skillfully done, such integration is seamless.

Third, clinicians who treat dually diagnosed patients need to be mindful that effective integrated treatment requires several core elements, including *assertive outreach* to patients in their natural environments, *comprehensiveness* (i.e., addressing areas such as work, housing, and social relationships), *shared decision making* (including patients, families, and significant others), *pharmacotherapy* to treat severe mental illness and (possibly) addiction, and *long-term commitment* (i.e., years rather than months). The success of an integrated treatment program rests on the incorporation of these basic components.

Fourth, integrated treatment programs that embrace the concept of stages of treatment *(engagement, persuasion, active treatment, and relapse prevention)* will optimize the timing of interventions by matching them to patients' current motivational states. The four stages of treatment are behaviorally defined with respect to patients' use of substances, and each stage has a unique goal that is the clinician's primary therapeutic aim. Multiple treatment options exist for clinicians to help patients accomplish the goal of each stage.

The lives of dually diagnosed patients are often miserable; these patients create havoc in their social relationships with relatives and others and are challenging and sometimes frustrating to treat. However, as the technology of integrated treatment has developed over the past decade, the outlook for dually diagnosed persons has brightened considerably. Many of these individuals enjoy positive outcomes and a favorable prognosis with the concerted efforts of dedicated clinicians. We are encouraged by both research and clinical experience that integrated treatment is a valuable approach for helping dually diagnosed patients progress towards a healthier lifestyle and achieve personally valued goals.

REFERENCES

Barry, K. L., Fleming, M. F., Greenley, J. R., Kropp, S., & Widlak, P. (1996). Characteristics of persons with severe mental illness and substance abuse in rural areas. *Psychiatric Services, 47,* 88–90.

Bartels, S. J., Drake, R. E., & Wallach, M. A. (1995). Long-term course of substance use disorders among patients with severe mental illness. *Psychiatric Services, 46,* 248–251.

Bellack, A. S. & Mueser, K. T. (1993). Psychosocial treatment for schizophrenia. *Schizophrenia Bulletin, 19,* 317–336.

Caton, C. L. M., Shrout, P. E., Eagle, P. F., Opler, L. A., Felix, A., & Dominguez, B. (1994). Risk factors for homelessness among schizophrenic men: A case-control study. *American Journal of Public Health, 84,* 265–270.

Center for Substance Abuse Treatment (1994). *Assessment and treatment of patients with coexisting mental illness and alcohol and other drug abuse. Treatment improvement protocol (TIP) series 9.* Rockville, MD: U.S. Department of Public Health.

Cuffel, B. J. & Chase, P. (1994). Remission and relapse of substance use disorder in schizophrenia: Results from a one-year prospective study. *Journal of Nervous and Mental Disease, 182,* 342–348.

Cuffel, B. J. (1996). Comorbid substance use disorder—Prevalence, patterns, of use and course. In R. E. Drake & K. T. Mueser (Eds.), Dual diagnosis of major mental illness and substance abuse, Vol. 2: Recent research and clinical implications. *New Directions for Mental Health Services* (pp. 93–105). San Francisco: Jossey-Bass.

Dickey, B. & Azeni, H. (1996). Persons with dual diagnoses of substance abuse and major mental illness: Their excess costs of psychiatric care. *American Journal of Public Health, 86,* 973–977.

Dixon, L., McNary, S., & Lehman, A. (1995). Substance abuse and family relationships of persons with severe mental illness. *American Journal of Psychiatry, 152,* 456–458.

Drake, R. E., Musser, K. T., Clark, R. E., & Wallach, M. A. (1996). The course, treatment, and outcome of substance disorder in persons with severe mental illness. *American Journal of Orthopsychiatry, 66,* 42–51.

Drake, R. E. & Brunette, M. E. (1998). Complications of severe mental illness related to alcohol and drug use disorders. In M. Galanter (Ed.), *Recent developments in alcoholism, Vol. 14: The consequences of alcohol.* New York: Plenum.

Drake, R. E. & Wallach, M. A. (1994). Moderate drinking among people with severe mental illness. *Hospital and Community Psychiatry, 44,* 780–782.

Drake, R. E., McHugo, G. J., Xie, H., Teague, G. B., Mueser, K. T., & Vaillant, G. E. (1998). *The five-year course of treated substance use disorder in patients with severe mental illness.* Manuscript submitted for publication.

Drake, R. E., Mercer-McFadden, C., Mueser, K. T., McHugo, G. J., & Bond, G. R. (1998). A review of integrated mental health and substance abuse treatment for patients with dual disorders. *Schizophrenia Bulletin, 24*(4), 589–608.

Drake, R. E., Xie, H., McHugo, G. J., & Green, A. I. (2000). The effects of clozapine on alcohol and drug use disorders among patients with schizophrenia. *Schizophrenia Bulletin, 26*(2), 441–449.

Galanter, M., Castaneda, R., & Ferman, J. (1988). Substance abuse among general psychiatric patients. *American Journal of Drug and Alcohol Abuse, 14,* 211–235.

Koefed, L., Kania, J., Walsh, T., & Atkinson, R. M. (1986). Outpatient treatment of patients with substance abuse and coexisting psychiatric disorders. *American Journal of Psychiatry, 42,* 948–949.

Kozaric-Kovacic, D., Folnegovic-Smalc, V., Folnegovic, Z., & Marusic, A. (1995). Influence of alcoholism on the prognosis of schizophrenic patients. *Journal of Studies on Alcohol, 56,* 622–627.

Lambert, M. T., Griffith, J. M., & Hendrickse, W. (1996). Characteristics of patients with substance abuse diagnoses on a general psychiatry unit in a VA medical center. *Psychiatric Services, 47,* 1104–1107.

Lindqvist, F. & Allebeck, P. (1989). Schizophrenia and assaultive behaviour: The role of alcohol and drug abuse. *Acta Psychiatrica Scandinavica, 82,* 191–195.

Linszen, D. H., Dingemans, P.M., & Lenior, M. E. (1994). Cannabis abuse and the course of recent-onset schizophrenic disorders. *Archives of General Psychiatry, 51,* 273–279.

Mahoney, M.J. (1991). *Human change processes: The scientific foundations of psychotherapy.* Delran, NJ: Basic Books.

McHugo, G.J., Drake, R.E., Burton, H.L., & Ackerson, T.H. (1995). A scale for accessing the stage of substance abuse treatment in persons with severe mental illness. *Journal of Nervous and Mental Disease, 183,* 762–767.

Menezes, P. R., Johnson, S., Thornicroft, G., et al. (1996). Drug and alcohol problems among individuals with severe mental illnesses in South London. *British Journal of Psychiatry, 168,* 612–619.

Miller, W. R. & Rollnick, S. (1991). *Motivational interviewing: Preparing people to change addictive behavior.* New York: Guilford Press.

Monti, P. M., Abrams, D. B., Kadden, R. M., & Cooney, N. L. (1989). *Treating alcohol dependence.* New York: Guilford Press.

Mueser, K. T. & Noordsy, D. L. (1996). Group treatment for dually diagnosed clients. In R. E. Drake & K. T. Mueser (Eds.) Dual diagnosis of major mental illness and substance abuse, Vol. 2: Recent research and clinical implications. *New Directions for Mental Health Services No. 70.* (pp. 33–51). San Francisco: Jossey-Bass.

Mueser, K. T., Bennett, M., & Kushner, M. G. (1995). Epidemiology of substance abuse among persons with chronic mental disorders. In A.F. Lehman, L. Dixon (Eds.), *Double jeopardy: Chronic mental illness and substance abuse* (pp. 9–25). New York: Harwood Academic Publishers.

O'Keefe, C., Potenza, D. P., & Mueser, K. T. (1997). Treatment outcomes for severely mentally ill patients on conditional discharge to community-based treatment. *Journal of Nervous and Mental Disease, 185,* 409–411.

Osher, F. C. & Kofoed, L. L. (1989). Treatment of patients with psychiatric and psychoactive substance abuse disorders. *Hospital and Community Psychiatry, 40,* 1025–1030.

Prochaska, J. O. (1984). *Systems of psychotherapy. A transtheoretical analysis.* Homewood, IL: Dorsey.

Regier, D. A., Farmer, M. E., Rae, D. S., et al. (1990). Comorbidity of mental disorders with alcohol and other drug abuse. *Journal of the American Medical Association, 264,* 2511–2518.

Ridgely, M. S., Goldman, H. H., & Willenbring, M. (1990). Barriers to the care of persons with dual diagnoses: Organizational and financing issues. *Schizophrenia Bulletin, 16,* 123–132.

Shaner, A., Roberti, L. J., Eckman, T. A., et al. (1997). Monetary reinforcement of abstinence from cocaine among mentally ill patients with cocaine dependence. *Psychiatric Services, 48,* 807–810.

Vaillant, G. E. (1983). *The natural history of alcoholism revisited.* Cambridge, MA: Harvard University Press.

Wennberg, J. E. (1991). Outcomes research, patient preferences, and the primary care physician. *Journal of the American Board of Family Practice, 4,* 365–367.

Ziedonis, D. M., Richardson, T., Lee, E., Petrakis, I., & Kosten, T. (1992). Adjunctive desipramine in the treatment of cocaine abusing schizophrenics. *Psychopharmacology Bulletin, 28,* 309–314.

Zimmet, S. U., Strous, R. D., Burgess, E. Kohnstamm, S., & Green, A. E. (2000). Effects of clozapine on substance use in patients with schizophrenia and schizoaffective disorder: A retrospective study. *Journal of Clinical Psychopharmacology 20*(1), 94–98.

Transitional Employment and Psychosocial Rehabilitation

Thomas J. Malamud and Dennis J. McCrory

This article was published previously in Jean Ciardiello and Morris D. Bell (Eds.), *Vocational Rehabilitation of Persons with Prolonged Psychiatric Disorders*, pp 150–162. © 1988, Johns Hopkins University Press and reprinted with permission from Johns Hopkins University Press.

Abstract: The psychosocial rehabilitation program developed at Fountain House, New York City, has had a long-standing influence on the development of many similar club-house programs throughout the United States. Malamud and McCrory give a detailed account of transitional employment as it is practiced at Fountain House. They describe the philosophical assumptions underlying the model, as well as the ways in which its various elements interface with a general psychosocial model. Results of an evaluation of transitional employment are used to suggest new directions for research and program development.

There has been increased interest in the vocational rehabilitation of the mentally ill in recent years owing to deinstitutionalization. Work, it has been established, is of vital importance for the reintegration of the "chronically mentally ill" in the community.

Vocational rehabilitation is a process that enables transitions to higher levels of productivity for people disabled by medical and/or psychiatric conditions. In practice, it is often a series of transitions. The number of steps, the course and duration of the process, and the long-term outcomes vary greatly from individual to individual.

Sadly, for persons with severe psychiatric impairments, vocational rehabilitation services are often not available in a timely fashion. Sometimes, such impaired individuals and their families, therapists, and rehabilitation counselors cannot imagine their holding down a fulltime job. They are assumed to be "too sick." At other times, it is held that they simply need a period of time for convalescence or treatment to regain their mental health, and they resist referral to programs that serve obviously handicapped psychiatric clients. They are "not sick enough" that is, until long periods of unemployment or repeated failures to (re)enter the work force, regressions, and rehospitalizations increase their residual disabilities, erode their hope, and again make them appear "too sick." Lastly, there are times when services or a sequence of services that would meet their needs are not offered in local communities.

Thus, there has developed a stereotype, which has become a self-fulfilling prophecy, that the chronically mentally ill cannot be gainfully employed and instead should declare themselves "permanently and totally disabled" and apply for Social Security benefits. The risk of loss of these benefits then becomes a disincentive to the further pursuit of work. The person who may have valued work, may have developed occupational skills, and may indeed have "rehabilitation potential" has now become a chronic mental patient, with little likelihood of employment.

This state of affairs was well described by Gruenberg (1967) as the social breakdown syndrome. Not only does the person have to contend with the symptoms and impairments of his illness, but he has also lost hold of his life structure and must live with a changed set of expectations of himself, reinforced by the concern of the significant others in his life. He has lost the sense of "can do" which White (1963) has termed *effectance:* "energies... which seem to perform the service of maintaining and expanding an effective interaction with the environment." He has also lost his sense of belonging in the community as a productive member of society, a wage earner, a breadwinner, a taxpayer.

In a review of the relevant vocational rehabilitation literature, Anthony, Cohen, and Vitalo (1978) reported low employment rates, from 10 to 30%, following patient discharge and at the end of a 1-year followup. By contrast, it is clear that there is a higher percentage for other, nonpsychiatrically disabled groups (Skelley, 1980).

We believe that this process of dishabilitation is neither inevitable nor irreversible, and in this article we develop another point of view: when offered opportunity, support, and sufficient time, many persons with prolonged mental illness can successfully engage in a vocational rehabilitation process.

One salient factor in the review by Anthony and colleagues is the length of follow-up periods for collecting data. Most of the studies had a 6- to 12-month follow-up period, and there are indications that there is a positive correlation between client attendance at a particular training program and employment outcome. For instance, a longitudinal study was done in Vermont of 269 patients with chronic mental illness who became involved in a psychosocial and vocational rehabilitation program (Harding et al., 1983, 1987). Subjects were hospitalized for 6 continuous years on the average and were "ill" for 16 years. They were discharged from the hospital into the community in the mid-1950s, and after 20 to 25 years, results showed that 50% of those employable (not retired), were working productively, many on farms. Seventy-three percent of the sample showed little or no evidence of symptomatology, and 82% were self-sufficient, requiring little or no help with basic living routines.

Sheltered workshops in general and other inpatient programs such as work therapy have been charged with creating dependency and not facilitating the movement towards competitive employment (Barber, Berry, & Micek, 1969; Carpenter & Black, 1986). Further, although the literature involving work stations in industry is very limited, such research has concluded that work stations are more effective than workshops in increasing self-esteem, competence, and vocational skills (Conte, 1983b; Rapp, 1979).

The transitional employment (TE) model is an alternative method for placing psychiatrically disabled persons in competitive industrial employment. The TE model is a narrower form within the work stations (Conte, 1983a) and differs from the latter in that it has a short period of placement, while work stations involve a long-term job setting.

Rutman and Armstrong (1985) identified and evaluated 114 provider agencies in the United States of which 95 agencies were currently providing transitional employment programs, while 19 other agencies were not. Results showed that the average number of days on TE was significantly related to employment outcome. Partial correlations were used to control for past work history. It was estimated that about 35% of the persons studied were employed 6 months after transitional employment; of these, 19% were working full time and 16% part time in competitive employment.

Thus, over the past 30 years, there has developed a variety of approaches that can be conceptualized as a continuum of work experiences: hospital work programs, volunteer employment, short-term sheltered employment, extended sheltered employment, prevocational program in day treatment and day training centers, transitional employment, supported work, and on-the-job training.

This article focuses on one of these approaches, transitional employment (TE). The clubhouse model as practiced in Fountain House will be described. The general development and practice of TE will also be presented. Results of a recently completed long-term retrospective study of TE will be presented to support its efficacy. Implications for practice will be drawn, and directions for further program development and research will be suggested.

TRANSITIONAL EMPLOYMENT IN THE COMMUNITY CONTEXT: THE FOUNTAIN HOUSE MODEL

From an ecological perspective, human needs and problems can be seen as generated by transactions between people and their environments, calling for practices which will focus on both releasing the adaptive capacities of individuals and improving their environments. A rehabilitative method must engage people's strengths and the forces pushing toward growth as well as influence organizational structures, social systems, and physical settings so they will be more responsive to individual needs. This perspective, and the method used to implement it, compose the "life model."

In the life model, as described by Germain and Gitterman (1980), individuals' needs and predicaments are located at the interface of person and environment. Professional interventions are directed to creating healthy processes at that interface. In the relationship between the individual and work, where each brings the influences of interacting life-space forces, goals are set to strengthen adaptive capacity and increase environmental responsiveness.

The clubhouse model of prevocational rehabilitation and TE facilitates such transactions between prolonged mentally ill persons and their environments. Skills for community adjustment are facilitated by engaging individuals in real work both in the clubhouse and on the job site. This is an ecological-systems approach where the entire process of planning is rooted in the real needs of the member population (Auerswald, 1968).

Fountain House, a nonprofit psychiatric rehabilitation center, was established in 1948 for the express purpose of facilitating the social and vocational rehabilitation of men and women, called "members" (rather than patients or clients), following hospitalization in public and private mental institutions. Fountain House occupies a homelike clubhouse located just a few blocks from Times Square in New York City, and is attended each day by 375 individuals who participate in its comprehensive rehabilitative programs.

These programs are organized around the concept of the "clubhouse model." It is an environment in which an individual's presence is clearly needed and celebrated, where there is emphasis on mutual help and self-help. There are opportunities to engage in a wide range of restorative activities concerned with the operation and management of the clubhouse program. Staff and members work side by side. The clubhouse is open 7 days a week throughout the year. The daytime hours are utilized to prepare members for independent employment through a prevocational program directed toward those activities required to keep the clubhouse operational. These activities include preparing a noontime meal, a wide variety of clerical functions, cleaning and maintenance work in the clubhouse, receiving and touring visitors, putting out a daily newspaper, running an in-house TV station, computer programming, and fundraising.

Fountain House also provides housing alternatives for 170 members either in fully supervised community residences, partially supervised apartment settings, or independently shared satellite apartments. During the evenings and on weekends and holidays, social and recreational activities are available.

A fourth program area is the employment alternative known as transitional employment (TE). As part of the day program, transitional employment is a vocational service that was initiated in 1958 (Beard, 1982) and provides any member the opportunity to work in commerce and industry.

Fundamental to creating TE placements is the clubhouse's need to fill such placements. The practice has always been to create work opportunities first, rather than preparing members first and then locating placements later, in the belief that work must be important for the experience to be rehabilitative. Each day 110 members go to work on TE, and an estimated 450 members will have a TE experience over the course of a year. A large number of severely disabled individuals are provided a real work experience, and Fountain House communicates to its men and women the actual need for them to work at these placements.

The operating dynamic at Fountain House, therefore, is a continual encouragement for members to try TE. Crucial to the integrity of this dynamic are the provisions of ongoing supports and easy reentry back to Fountain House. Since membership may be life long, members realize that neither job success nor job failure leads to rejection by the clubhouse. This policy permits members to try placements without the fear of success or the burden of failure. Members may start TE within a month of agency intake or may take weeks, months, or even years to reach the point of trying TE.

Movement on and off placement is freer, because members will return to the day program for further services prior to returning to TE once again. Many times "success" is the simple act of trying a placement, the "surviving" of one day on placement. Ease of access in and out of Fountain House and TE also allows for success to be defined as increasing time on TE and decreasing time in the day program between placements. Of course, success can also be defined as movement on to independent employment, school, or other rehabilitation programs. This broader definition of success and consequent easy reentry to Fountain House allows for more liberal standards with reference to symptomatology. Staff members do not view job readiness as necessarily related or equivalent to absence of symptoms.

TRANSITIONAL EMPLOYMENT PROGRAMS BASED ON THE FOUNTAIN HOUSE MODEL

By the end of 1985, a total of 135 community-based rehabilitation facilities in 35 states, the District of Columbia, and two foreign countries were providing TE programs. In partnership with the business community, these programs facilitate the work adjustment of the vocationally disabled, financially dependent psychiatric patient. Based on the Fountain House model of TE, each of these 135 programs had in common certain basic characteristics. All placements for the severely disabled mentally ill are located in normal places of business, ranging from large, nationally recognized corporations to small local firms employing only a few individuals.

TE placements are essentially entry-level employment requiring minimal training or job skills. All employers provide the prevailing wage rate for each job position, ranging from the minimum wage to over $6 an hour, with a few positions paying up to $8 an hour. Almost all jobs are worked on a half-time basis so that one full-time job can serve two members at a time. This allows the member to be at the clubhouse half of each day. Many programs provide weekly or bi-weekly dinner meetings for TE members to get together.

Most TE positions are on an individual basis. The member works in the presence of other employees. Some placements, however, are performed on a group basis where six to ten members work together, relating primarily with each other. All placements are temporary or "transitional," providing employment for as little as 3 months to as long as a year.

TE is a guaranteed opportunity to work on temporary, entry-level jobs in normal places of business and to continue employment through a series of TE placements or to use the job as a step toward eventual fulltime, independent employment. Placements are maintained only if the individual meets the work requirements of the employer. Employers do not adjust or lower work standards. Job failures are viewed as experiences that the vocationally disabled member, in most instances, must undergo to eventually achieve a successful work adjustment. In the work experiences of nondisabled individuals, failure or withdrawal from entry-level employment often occurs. TE employers emphasize that job turnover rates are not typically greater for the mentally ill on TE than the rates for the nondisabled employee.

New placements are first performed by a staff worker for a few hours to assess the requirements of the job. The staff is therefore able to evaluate the work environment and its compatibility to the needs of the disabled individual, as well as the degree of acceptance by other employees on the work site. Because of this familiarity with the work environment, staff have immediate access to the work site when starting new members. Whenever vocational difficulties or crises occur, staff can make a prompt assessment of a member's performance. In the training phase, staff are able to provide on-the-job guidance to the member.

The employer assigns placements to the rehabilitation facility. The selection process by which placements are filled rests with staff and the individual member it serves. The employer pays wages without any subsidy. This collaboration between the business community and the rehabilitation facility is not a charitable act by the employer. It is an agreement of mutual benefit to employer and member.

TE programs provide an opportunity to enrich and expand the evaluation of vocational potential. Assessment in a normal work environment has advantages over evaluations in sheltered environments or those based on personal interviews and psychological assessment.

In short, TE programs successfully remove or circumvent barriers common to employment for psychiatrically disabled individuals. These barriers include a history of psychiatric disorders, an inability to pass a job interview, the absence of a work history, motivational deficits, and many others.

In each of the 135 community-based rehabilitation facilities throughout the nation that provide TE programs, the vocationally disabled member has the easily accessible opportunity to go to work part time in an entry-level job in a normal place of business. This is an integral part of the vocational adjustment process.

These work opportunities show the member that mental illness is not the sole or even primary explanation of vocational disability. Rather, mental illness is a personal experience that typically has prevented the member from entering the real world of work and developing the capacity to perform work productively and meet job requirements.

AN EVALUATION OF THE TRANSITIONAL EMPLOYMENT PROGRAM

Having described the context and the components of TE, we now present an evaluation of the program. This retrospective evaluation was completed in 1985 (Malamud, 1985). The basic design followed was a single-group time-series quasi-experimental design as described by Huck, Cormier, and Bounds (1974). The design included observations at agency intake, at study intake, and at a number of points following placement on TE.

Observations measured the amounts and kinds of rehabilitation services or other community services each subject received. The instrument developed to record these observations is called Categories of Community Adjustment, or COCA (for a description see Malamud, 1985). Thus, changes in program experiences constituted the independent variable, and the dependent variables were measures of functional capacity observed at various intervals.

TE is an opportunity available to all Fountain House members, and as such, all participants have met the general agency eligibility criteria:

1. They are age 16 or older.

2. Their primary presenting problem is not alcoholism, drug abuse, severe developmental disability, or acting-out behavior.

3. They are able to participate in Fountain House unattended.

Data were collected on all members who secured a TE placement during the 42-month period from July 1, 1980, through December 31, 1983. An examination of 21 demographic, social, clinical, and vocational variables gathered at intake showed that the TE sample of 527 individuals were representative of the Fountain House population. Thus, findings from this study may be generalized to similar groups of severely disabled psychiatric patients.

Identification of Patterns of Adjustment

Subjects in the sample underwent a large number of changes in their levels of community adjustment, averaging better than one change every three months. While the frequency of these changes may not differ for those severely disabled individuals in the community who do not have access to programs like Fountain House, it is expected that for such nonmembers the character of such changes might be substantially different. Instead of being isolated and withdrawn from the community and undergoing psychiatric rehospitalization, a situation typical of nonmembers, the great majority for the Fountain House sample were moving in and out of the day program, TE, and independent employment.

The day program was the most frequently used experience. Over 40% of all movement was into the day program, over 80% of all members had some day program experience during the follow-up, and 28% of the sample were in the day program at the end of the follow-up.

We found that 174 subjects, or a third of the sample, had a least one independent employment experience following a TE placement, and that about 15% of the total time during our study was spent on fulltime jobs. Further, we found that independent employment rates increased as time in the program increased. Thus, by the 42nd month, nearly 36% of those completing 42 months of follow-up time were independently employed, a rate higher than typically reported in the literature. An additional 7% were employed on TE at the 42nd month, so that a 43% employment rate had been achieved. If the few people who were lost to follow-up at the 42nd month were dropped and the remaining rates prorated, then the independent employment rate would be 40% and the TE rate would be 9%, so that just under 50% of the known sample were employed at the end of 42 months.

During the time of the study, for all 527 subjects a total of 140,975 days were spent on TE, an average length of 8¾ months. Of greater interest, the sample spent a total of 69,927 days independently employed for an average length of just less than 4½ months. As the average length of time in the study is 29½ months, the more than 13 months spent employed represents about 45% of the total study time available.

Psychiatric hospitalizations occurred relatively infrequently during the study, and no more than 3.4% of the sample were hospitalized at any one time. With respect to duration, a total of 13,790 days were spent in the hospital during the study, or an average for the whole sample of 26 days during the 42-month period.

Identification and Definition of Subgroups

From the analysis of data certain subgroupings emerged. One of these consisted of 148 subjects who were in a psychiatric hospital at some point during the study. For those 148, the average time spent in the hospital was 93 days, or 3 months. Three-fifths were hospitalized once, and half were in the hospital for less than 30 days.

Compared with intake data, time in hospital was reduced. It appears that length of hospitalization during the study was less for those subjects on a TE or day program. Over 70% of the hospitalizations that followed a TE placement and nearly 60% of those following a period in the day program were less than 30 days in duration. In comparison, 70% of rehospitalizations following involvement in some other rehabilitation program and two-thirds of those following a period withdrawn in the community not involved in any rehabilitative activity were longer than 30 days in length. The difference between length of hospitalization and preceding adjustment experience was found to be statistically significant (chi square = 16.08, df = 4, p <.01). Background characteristics did not distinguish between those hospitalized and those not hospitalized during the study.

A second group consists of those securing independent employment. Length of time on fulltime jobs for those employed averaged 400 days, or just over 13 months. Nearly three-fifths of those employed had jobs of over 3 months in length, while one-quarter of the jobs were from 1 year to 38 months. With so much time independently employed, many members who had been receiving either SSI or SSDI have had their entitlements affected, including removal from the rolls, reduction in benefits, or extension of time as the 9-month trial work period had been surpassed.

The data document that the process of rehabilitation can be a long one. Results indicated that the length of time from agency intake to the securing of fulltime gainful employment could take 5 years or longer. Groups that had been in the study the longest were composed of subjects with more time in Fountain House prior to study intake. These groups and those subjects had the highest rates of independent employment (66% for those 104 members with over 2 years following Fountain House intake and 42 months of study follow-up time), as well as the highest proportion of study time spent on fulltime jobs. This leads to the conclusion that the rest of the study sample might achieve equally high employment rates once sufficient time has been allowed for them to be in the day program and TE.

Over a third of all instances of independent employment were immediately preceded by TE, and the length of time spent on TE is positively and significantly correlated to the obtaining of fulltime gainful employment (t = 2.154, df = 525, p < .025). We conclude, therefore, that the length of time required for securing a fulltime job might be shortened substantially by providing more opportunities for TE placements. Analysis of background characteristics did not significantly differentiate the 174 individuals who had an independent placement from the 353 others who did not obtain full-time employment during the study.

Implications for Practice and Future Trends

In his chapter in *The Chronic Mental Patient,* Peterson (1978), a member currently on staff at Fountain House, personally witnessed the value of transitional employment for both himself and his fellow members. These members can be eloquent about their experiences (Schmidt, Nessel, & Malamud, 1969, pp. 95–102):

> I began working less and less until...I just stopped completely for 2½ years. It was just a matter of not being able to function any more. Employment is very important. People don't realize this but as long as you are busy this is a great thing for the mind. It keeps your mind off a lot of other things that are really of no value....The more time that you have to think, why of course, you can just retrogress, which isn't very good.

> It makes you forget a little bit of your emotional problems and your nerves and your worries. It gets you with people who are well instead of sitting here talking all day—"Oh, I've been sick for 10 years, I've been sick for 20 years." This is discouraging. When you're working, you're with healthy people...You're interested in what they're saying. You're trying to keep up with them in clothes and your appearance. Since I have been working, I'm setting my hair, showering, ironing, washing, cleaning the apartment. I'm functioning so much better...because I feel that I'm doing something.

> It gets your life going. It gives you responsibility and also makes you feel different, makes you feel that you can face the outside world. And also makes you feel that you are important. Important to your people, important to your friends, because you are earning money. You're making your own penny, your own dollar bill...And when you walk into the

store, you feel, well, I can buy this and I can buy that, because it's your money, and it's a wonderful feeling. And I'm glad to be working.

When I first went to work there, I didn't know anything about the...business. I started part time...I helped set up the routine and I helped serve the customers. The bosses are pleasant to work for and the people are pleasant to associate with. I think people do benefit from its being in existence. It gives them a feeling of usefulness and it helps them to feel that they are accomplishing something, and it increases their own general knowledge. It's an honest day's labor for an honest day's pay. Helps you sleep nights.

This TE study has gone beyond such intuitive and anecdotal evidence of the effectiveness of TE as practiced at Fountain House. Our goal in sharing these experiences is threefold: to help correct the stereotype that persons with prolonged mental illness cannot work; to broadcast one rehabilitation model that had been clearly defined, replicated, and studied; and to stimulate the development of similar programs and studies.

While Fountain House believes that the clubhouse model supports TE, it recognizes that TE can be offered in conjunction with sheltered workshops and day treatment programs, and actually gives these basic programs more of a transitional nature. TE is also offered as an independent program although some programs identified as TE resemble the supported work model, whose goal is to "roll over" the transitional position into full-time permanent employment. All such programs need to define their activities and study their effectiveness over a prolonged periods of time. Through this precision and inquiry the contributions of differing models will be discovered, so that their differential usefulness will emerge. Currently, for example, Fountain House is conducting a national evaluation of the levels of vocational and residential adjustment in a sample of 1,800 individuals connected with 25 clubhouse programs.

CONCLUSION

Given opportunity, support, and time, a substantial number of persons with severe psychiatric disabilities can benefit from a vocational rehabilitation process.

This finding is very much in keeping with the results of the 20-year retrospective study, cited earlier, of patients discharged from Vermont State Hospital in the middle 1950s. Indeed, an emerging finding is that the diagnosis of major mental illness is more compatible with healthy vocational and social functioning than traditional wisdom had believed, provided that support, opportunity, and time are available. As Peterson (1978) stated,

There are places where the chronic patient becomes less chronic, and I hope we can prove what can be accomplished, so that there will be fewer people in the mental health field who seem to feel hopeless about the chronic patient. We need people to believe in us and what we can accomplish...Most important is to stop looking at us as chronic.

For 10 years, Fountain House has offered a national training program for those wishing to start their own clubhouse and TE programs. By the end of 1985, over 630 colleagues from 340 agencies throughout the United States and 11 foreign countries have attended this training program, with the result that some 180 new clubhouse programs have emerged.

There are now 135 TE programs nationwide, giving 1,756 individuals the opportunity to return to work, earning, in collective annualized wages, $6,992,387—a small, but substantial beginning. The hope is to encourage further local expressions of this approach. Regional training centers at appropriate clubhouse programs are planned to help in this process. Such training centers have already been established at Beach House, Virginia Beach, Virginia; Independence Center, St. Louis, Missouri; and Rainbow House, Rome, New York.

Given the chance, members have been able to make efforts to direct their energies to real-life challenges, not just to cope with the vicissitudes of their mental illness. They have been able to organize themselves to meet the demands of real jobs that have given them the real and immediate rewards of money, status, and enhanced self-esteem. The need for and recognized value of their work has given them more reason to struggle with their conflicts and symptomatology and demonstrate a mastery of themselves that has helped to change their "patient" roles into "worker" roles. This has, of course, represented hard work for them and those who have supported them. All were not successful in their first efforts; their were regressions and rehospitalizations, albeit remarkably few. Not everybody reached a level of sustained competitive employment. Many needed to work at the process for what seemed like a very long time.

It is also clear that the success of members in their ability to commit themselves has depended not just on their individual efforts supported by their supervisors, but also on the support of their peers, families, clinicians, and employers. Particularly noteworthy is the support of fellow members, whether by reaching out, by informal sharing, or at member meetings and TE dinners.

There are certainly questions that require further study. The study reported here spanned nearly 4 years. What trends will appear over a longer follow-up period? Can employment rates be expected to continue increasing? Members had opportunities to (re)join the work force initially on entry levels. What difference would it make to have a more active placement program? What sorts of skill development and career advancement will occur after members begin to work competitively? What substantive changes will occur in the entitlements such individuals have been receiving? Low hospitalization rates were found during the study. What are the implications for long-term prognosis for psychiatric illness with participation in a Fountain House type program? TE is available to all clubhouse members. What are the criteria for persons with prolonged mental illness who can benefit from TE but may not be clubhouse members? These and other questions deserve further inquiry and will be certainly followed up with interest by Fountain House and, it is to be hoped, by other rehabilitation programs as well.

REFERENCES

Anthony, W. A., Cohen, M. R., & Vitalo, R. (1978). The measurement of rehabilitation outcome. *Schizophrenia Bulletin, 4,* 365–383.

Anthony, W., & Jansen, M. (1984). Predicting the vocational capacity of the chronically mentally ill: Research and policy implications. *American Psychologist, 39,* 537–544.

Auerswald, E. H. (1968). Interdisciplinary vs. ecological approach. *Family Process, 7,* 205.

Barber, M., Berry, K., & Micek, L. (1969). Relationship of work therapy to psychiatric length of stay and readmission. *Journal of Consulting and Clinical Psychology, 33,* 735–738.

Beard, J. H. (1982). *Industry and the vocational rehabilitation of the disabled mental patient.* Paper presented to the annual meeting of the President's Committee on Employment of the Handicapped, Washington, D.C.

Carpenter, M., & Black, B. (1986). Review of research and evaluation. In B. Black (ed.), *Work as therapy and rehabilitation for the mentally ill.* New York: Altro Health and Rehabilitation Services.

Conte, L. (1983a). Sheltered employment and disabled citizens: An analysis of the work stations in the industry model. *Dissertation Abstracts International, 43,* 2976A.

Conte, L. (1983b) Sheltered employment services and programs. *Rehabilitation Research Review, Monograph no. 11.* Washington, DC: National Rehabilitation Information Center.

Germain, C., & Gitterman, A. (1980). *The life model of social work practice.* New York: Columbia University Press.

Gruenberg, E. (1967). The social breakdown syndrome: Some origins. *American Journal of Psychiatry, 123,* 1481–1489.

Harding, C., Brooks, G., Ashikaga, T., & Strauss, J. (1983). *Overview: The long-term course of chronic patients.* Paper presented at the annual meeting of the American Psychiatric Association, New York.

Harding, C., Brooks, G., Ashikaga, T., & Strauss, J. (1987). The Vermont longitudinal study of persons with severe mental illness, I: Methodology, study sample, and overall current status. *American Journal of Psychiatry, 144,* 718–726.

Huck, S., Cormier, W., & Bounds, W. G. (1974). *Reading statistics and research.* New York: Harper and Row.

Malamud, T. J. (1985). *Evaluation of a clubhouse model: Community-based psychiatric rehabilitation.* New York: Fountain House. Mimeographed.

Peterson, K. J. (1979). Assessment in the life model: A historical perspective. *Social Casework (Family Service Association of America), 60,* 590.

Peterson, R. (1978). What are the needs of chronic mental patients? In J. A. Talbott (Ed.), *The chronic mental patient.* Washington, DC: American Psychiatric Association.

Rapp, R. E. (1979). A normalization approach to the vocational training of mentally retarded adults. (Doctoral dissertation, University of Arizona, 1979). *Dissertation Abstracts International, 40,* 1410A.

Rutman, I., & Armstrong, K. (1985). *A comprehensive evaluation of transitional employment programs in the rehabilitation of chronically mentally disabled clients.* A Mary E. Switzer Research Fellowship Project, 1983–1984.

Schmidt, J. R., Nessel, J. J., & Malamud, T. J. (1969). *An evaluation of rehabilitation services and the role of industry in the community adjustment of psychiatric patients following hospitalization* (Final report, RD1281-p). Washington, DC: Rehabilitation Services Administration.

Skelley, T. (1980). National developments in rehabilitation: A rehabilitation services administration perspective. *Rehabilitation Counseling Bulletin, 24,* 22–33.

White, R. W. (1963). *Ego reality in psychoanalytic theory.* New York: International Universities Press.

Evolving Perspectives on Individual Psychotherapy for Schizophrenia

Wayne S. Fenton

At the time of original publication, Wayne S. Fenton, MD, was Deputy Director of Clinical Affairs, Division of Mental Disorders, Behavioral Research and AIDS, National Institute of Mental Health, National Institutes of Health, Bethesda, MD.

This article was published previously in the *Schizophrenia Bulletin,* 2000, 26(1), 47–72, and is reprinted with permission.

Abstract: Some form of individual psychotherapy, in combination with the prescription of antipsychotic medications, is likely the most common treatment for patients with schizophrenia. In the absence of empirical data supporting the efficacy of a particular approach, psychotherapy has often been guided by ideology and deference to authority. In recent years, a reformulation of schizophrenia as a disorder requiring individualized, comprehensive treatment has allowed the development and empirical testing of new targeted and illness-phase-specific individual psychotherapies. This report reviews randomized clinical trials that have evaluated individual psychotherapy of schizophrenia in the context of changing contemporaneous beliefs about the disorder's etiology and treatment. A general approach to individual treatment, termed *flexible psychotherapy,* derived from historical approaches but consistent with available clinical and research perspectives, is outlined.

With virtually no data to support its efficacy, individual psychotherapy has been the cornerstone of treatment for schizophrenia for decades. Even in today's era of evidence-based medicine, some form of individual psychotherapy in combination with antipsychotic medications is likely the most common treatment offered to patients with schizophrenia (Dixon et al., 1999). Furthermore, surveys of patients and their families consistently rank individual psychotherapy among the most highly valued services provided by mental health practitioners (Coursey et al., 1991, 1995; Hatfield et al., 1996; Perreault et al., 1996).

What is psychotherapy? Who is qualified to provide it? How does psychotherapy differ from case management? From adequate clinical care? What is the difference between psychotherapy and the monitoring necessary for good pharmacotherapy? Who needs psychotherapy? For what problems, and when?

In their 1995 evidence-based review of treatment efficacy, the Schizophrenia Patient Outcomes Research Team (PORT) defined individual psychotherapy structurally, as interventions with one-to-one contact between a patient and a therapist (Scott & Dixon, 1995). Assuming patients were receiving adequate clinical care, individual psychological interventions were found to lack an adequate base of demonstrated efficacy (Lehman et al., 1995). With ample conflicting opinions but no real data, the practicing clinician was left to define exactly what was "adequate clinical care" on a case-by-case basis.

Hundreds of studies have evaluated pharmacological agents in schizophrenia, but very few controlled clinical trials of individual psychotherapy have been conducted. Often initiated in the context of factionalism between psychologically and biologically oriented psychiatry, these trials have generally been of greater value in dislodging passionately held beliefs about the effectiveness of specific types of individual psychotherapy than in pointing to what does work.

Over the past 5 years, however, researchers in the United States and United Kingdom have made significant steps in alleviating some of the intractable problems of defining and studying individual psychotherapy for schizophrenia. This progress had to await a shift away from ideological disputes about what was the best treatment for schizophrenia to a consensus that no single treatment can ameliorate the myriad symptoms and disabilities associated with the disorder. As articulated in the American Psychiatric Association's "Practice Guidelines for the Treatment of Patients with Schizophrenia" (1997), therapeutic efforts must be comprehensive, multimodal, and empirically titrated to the individual patient's response and progress. In a context that presupposes the need for comprehensive treatment, recent trials of one-to-one interventions have begun to generate rigorous empirical support for disorder-specific, targeted individual psychotherapeutic approaches that can help inform clinical practice.

The purpose of this article is:

1. To provide an overview of major historical trends in the psychotherapy of schizophrenia, and

2. To review randomized clinical trials that have evaluated individual psychotherapy for schizophrenia.

Studies are described and evaluated in the context of changing contemporaneous beliefs about the disorder's etiology and treatment. While data generated to date do not unambiguously endorse any single approach to psychotherapy for schizophrenia, a general strategy, termed *flexible psychotherapy,* derived from historical approaches but consistent with available clinical and research perspectives, is outlined.

METHODS

The clinical and theoretical literature on the psychotherapy of schizophrenia is vast. Because clinical trials of individual psychotherapy for schizophrenia are best understood in historical context, a brief overview of the traditions of investigative and supportive psychotherapy is provided. Individual psychotherapy is defined as a one-to-one psychosocial intervention, delivered alone or in combination with other treatments, designed to improve symptoms, functioning, and quality of life or to forestall or prevent relapse. Primary randomized clinical trials (RCTs) of individual psychotherapy predating 1990 were selected based on their inclusion in one or more reviews assessed by the Schizophrenia PORT (Mosher & Keith, 1980; Heinrichs & Carpenter, 1981; Gomez-Schwartz 1984; Mueser & Berenbaum, 1990). More recent RCTs that evaluate individual psychotherapy were identified from the English language psychiatric and psychological literature with the aid of computer searches, using keywords such as individual psychotherapy, psychological treatment, and schizophrenia. Studies comparing models of case management, social skills training, and cognitive retraining methods, and studies designed primarily to evaluate other psychosocial treatments (e.g., group therapy) that use individual psychotherapy as a treatment as usual comparison were not included for review. Methodological aspects of psychotherapy research have been extensively considered by others (Heinrichs & Carpenter, 1981; Aveline & Shapiro, 1995). This review aims to emphasize the clinical implications of available data and to describe the evolution and current status of this treatment modality.

BACKGROUND

Investigative and Supportive Psychotherapy

In the early decades of the 20th century schizophrenia was viewed as untreatable. "Organic" psychiatry as represented by Emil Kraepelin saw schizophrenic personality disintegration as an inevitable product of neurological deterioration. Following Freud, most psychoanalysts considered dementia praecox to be a "narcissistic neurosis," where transference and analytic treatment were impossible. The diagnosis of dementia praecox most often led to therapeutic nihilism and recommendation of lifelong institutional care (Rothman, 1971).

Despite the misgivings of Freud, early psychoanalysts such as Brill advocated an active effort to promote "rapport" and arouse the patient's interest in his or her own malady. In time, Brill observed, confidence in and a "passive attachment" to the physician could develop so that the doctor could become a bridge between the patient and reality (Brill, 1929).

Between 1922 and 1930, Harry Stack Sullivan organized a small treatment unit for male patients with schizophrenia at Sheppard and Enoch Pratt Hospital in Towson, Maryland. Sullivan staffed his unit with introverted male attendants and, stressing that patients' difficulties were similar to those of so-called normals, promoted development of benevolent intimacy in this milieu. He observed that providing an experience of reciprocal trust—which he hypothesized many patients missed during important periods of development—could be beneficial, by allowing a "validation of all components of personal worth" (Sullivan, 1931, 1970; Perry, 1982).

Observing the difficulties patients had in maintaining relationships led Sullivan to formulate the paradigm of "interpersonal psychiatry." Psychopathology was viewed as difficulties in living arising largely from personal and social relations, and as personality warps thought to be the lasting residue of earlier unsatisfactory interpersonal experiences. Sullivan elaborated these ideas in a series of seminars at Chestnut Lodge Hospital, in Rockville, Maryland, where a group of psychoanalysts and social scientists interested in the intensive study of schizophrenia assembled during the 1940s (Rioch et al., 1984). Here, it was observed that covert staff tension and disagreements often appeared to be associated with worsening of patients' psychotic symptoms; likewise, improvement followed when those tensions were resolved (Stanton & Schwartz, 1954). These observations suggested that the illness itself might be caused and cured by psychosocial means. Frieda Fromm-Reichmann's *Principles of Intensive Psychotherapy* (1950) was the first systematic elaboration of what became known as intensive psychodynamic psychotherapy. The predecessors of ego and self psychology (Greenberg & Mitchell, 1983), "interpersonal psychiatry" and "psychodynamic psychotherapy," became dominant paradigms in American psychiatry in the 1940s, 1950s, and 1960s (Klerman, 1984).

Investigative Psychotherapy: Theory and Practice

The goal of intensive, or investigative, psychotherapy is alleviation of the patient's emotional difficulties and elimination of symptoms. This is accomplished by undertaking a thorough scrutiny of the patient's life history, reviewing in close detail the realities of the patient's current relationships and life situation, and understanding the historical roots and current ramifications of maladaptive interpersonal patterns as reflected in the doctor-patient relationship and in daily life. This process is expected to result in modification of maladaptive interpersonal patterns and personality growth.

The literature on intensive psychotherapy emphasizes the influence of the environment in the etiology of schizophrenia. Characteristic difficulties among patients with schizophrenia are said to include:

1. A basic mistrust and expectation of harm from others.

2. A marked ambivalence in relationships, with oscillations between longing for merger based on intolerance of loneliness and withdrawal and isolation based on terror of closeness.

3. Weak or absent ego boundaries with resulting difficulty differentiating one's own thoughts and impulses from those of others (McGlashan, 1983).

The central conflict of schizophrenia patients was described as "that of a small child dependent on a person by whom he feels persecuted and who is, in his opinion, unstable and uncertain" (Hill, 1955). This position was thought to represent the patient's conviction concerning the nature of human relationships.

"Process" refers to expected developments in the doctor-patient relationship as it evolves over time. "Transference" is the manner in which the perception of others in the present is shaded or distorted by important past relationships. It is thought of as a natural, but often unconscious, aspect of all human relationships. Examining transference in the doctor-patient relationship is a major task in investigative (as opposed to supportive) psychotherapy—this examination is expected to be useful in allowing the patient to better understand his or her current difficulties and respond more realistically to people in his or her current life.

"Countertransference" refers to all of the therapist's thoughts and feelings about the patient. Some of these are distortions arising from the therapist's past, but others derive from current interaction with the patient. Feelings that arise in work with schizophrenia patients can be particularly intense and may include discouragement, fear, worthlessness, guilt, rage, envy, or lust. In view of this, awareness of countertransference and the ability through introspection to understand its sources are crucial functions for the psychotherapist. In the tradition of investigative psychotherapy, countertransference also serves as a source of information about the patient's state of mind, and as an indicator for understanding how others typically react and respond to the patient (Searles, 1965, 1979). Successful management of countertransference allows the therapist to create a "holding" or "containing" relationship with the patient that is postulated to be central to the action of psychotherapy (Pao, 1979; Levine & Wilson, 1985).

The literature on intensive psychotherapy describes interventions that correspond to different phases of therapy:

1. Establishing a relationship with the patient,

2. Elucidating the patient's experience,

3. Tolerating mobilized transference and countertransference,

4. Integrating the patient's experiences into an expanded perspective of the self, and

5. Working through. The accomplishment of earlier tasks allows greater attention to be paid to subsequent ones (McGlashan, 1983; McGlashan & Keats, 1989).

Establishing a relationship with a schizophrenia patient can be challenging. Therapist attributes seen as important are an interest in and capacity to tolerate intense affect, dependency, and ambiguous communication. Basic respect for the patient is a prerequisite. Aloofness, rigidity, and critical pomposity are especially discouraged. The psychotherapist should be flexible, creative, and willing to admit when he or she is wrong. Frequency of visits can range from one to five per week, and free association is discouraged as aggravating disorganization and thought disorder. Within bounds, a reasonable degree of self-disclosure on the therapist's part can help counter distortions by allowing the patient to get a fix on the therapist as a person. A relationship should be sought on the patient's terms. If the initial encounters are traversed successfully, a background feeling of security and predictability will increasingly characterize the therapy.

Semrad viewed the three core tasks of psychotherapy as helping the patient acknowledge, bear, and put into perspective his feelings and painful life experiences (Rako & Mazer, 1980). Acknowledging the patient's feelings and painful experiences becomes pertinent once a relationship has been established. Acknowledging requires elucidating affects, employing strategies such as listening, narrowing the focus, seeking concrete detail, acknowledging feelings (especially loss, anger, and sadness), and naming or labeling affects. The therapist conveys to the patient that experiencing emotions will neither overwhelm the patient nor hurt others. Psychotic symptoms, when expressed, are considered to signal an affective reaction to some actual event that patient and doctor do not yet understand. Examining the patient's day-to-day life in detail will allow the therapist to develop a more vivid picture of the patient's difficulties, frustrations, and characteristic reactions to others. If successful, therapist and patient will share a common language with which to communicate about the latter's difficulties.

Tolerating affects, transference, and countertransference corresponds to Semrad's concept of "bearing" painful feelings. Simply stated, patients experience themselves being accepted, negative emotions and all, and, learning from the therapist's example, become better able to accept unwanted aspects of themselves. Thus, the patient's identification with the therapist and his or her functioning is seen as a major factor in the therapeutic action of psychotherapy.

Broadening patients' understanding of themselves and their situation corresponds to the third part of Semrad's triad: helping patients put into perspective their painful affects, life experiences, and maladaptive solutions. Thus, providing insight is another way in which psychotherapy is thought to be useful, complementing identification with the therapist. Integrating the patient's experience entails a change in therapeutic relationship and enlists interpretation as its major technical tool. Emotional insight, gained by direct experience in the doctor-patient relationship, is emphasized. This derives from interpretations pointing out the transferential nature of the patient's feelings toward the doctor, including their origin in the patient's past experience and their inappropriate application in the patient's current everyday life. If traversed successfully, this phase of therapy will leave patients with a more accepting and complex view of themselves experiencing the full range of human emotions. The patient will recognize that continued progress depends on willingness to attempt new solutions, both inside and outside of treatment.

With improvement in psychosis and maturation of the patient's nonpsychotic personality, the phase of integrating evolves into the last phase of working through. The patient becomes better able to help the therapist perform his or her functions and eventually becomes capable of performing these functions independently.

Supportive Psychotherapy: Theory and Practice

Supportive psychotherapy has been favored by biologically and pharmacologically-oriented clinicians. In theory and technique it is grounded in the medical model where the patient is seen as suffering from an organically based illness requiring treatment from a physician.

As described by Talcot Parsons (1951), the medical model implies essential elements of expected behavior for both the physician and patient. These elements define the physician's and patient's roles, relationship, and responsibilities. The physician's role is characterized by four key qualities: 1) universalistic, 2) functionally specific, 3) affectively neutral, and 4) collectivity oriented. The universalistic norm requires the physician to treat all patients alike according to scientific and medical standards. The role is functionally specific in that the physician is seen as a specialist in health and disease and is expected to limit attention to circumscribed medical matters. Affective neutrality prevents the doctor from entering too sympathetically into the patient's situation; this allows for steadfastness of judgment and the exercise of emotional control. Finally, collectivity orientation, as opposed to self-orientation, demands that the doctor treat the patient according to the patient's needs and the health standards of the community.

The role of the patient, like the role of the physician, is defined by expected behavior that involves both rights and obligations. First, the person who is ill is exempt from normal social responsibilities and excused from customary obligations so he or she may attend to the process of getting well. A second right is exemption from responsibility for illness—the illness is not considered the patient's fault, and the patient has the right to receive care. At the same time, the patient has the obligation to want to get well, to obtain technically competent help, and to cooperate with treatment.

In contrast to the ambitious aim of personality change associated with the intensive therapy tradition, the short- and long-term goals of supportive psychotherapy are comparatively modest. They include the following:

1. Relief from the immediate crisis or direct reduction of acute disequilibrium,

2. Removal of symptoms to premorbid levels,

3. Reestablishment of psychic homeostasis through a strengthening of defenses,

4. Sealing over psychotic experiences and conflicts,

5. The circumscribed fostering of adaptation, and

6. Mobilization and preservation of healthy aspects of the patient to enable optimal functioning and minimize the impact of persistent deficits (McGlashan, 1982; Gilbert & Ugelstad, 1994).

Supportive therapy uses the physician-patient relationship to create a background of adequate clinical care to support the prescription of effective pharmacological interventions. Functional or social recovery, rather than personality change, is the primary aim of treatment.

The overall technical approach of supportive psychotherapy is one of pragmatism in which the physician, based on medical and psychiatric expertise, helps the patient interpret and adapt to reality (Winston et al., 1986). As such, the therapist employs techniques that include defining reality, offering direct reassurance, giving advice on current problems of living, urging modification of expectations, and actively organizing the environment for patients who cannot do so themselves (Zahniser et al., 1991). To help stabilize the patient's environment, the therapist often maintains close contact with the patient's family or others providing treatment and may intervene on the patient's behalf with family, employers, and social agencies.

Eliciting and tracking symptomatology and targeting symptoms for psychopharmacological intervention is a major focus for the supportive psychotherapist. Psychopathology is interpreted in a medical context as the unwanted emergence of signs of illness. The basic content of psychotherapy focuses on teaching and relearning—the patient is educated regarding the nature of the illness, taught to monitor symptoms, and act promptly to suppress his or her exacerbation. The therapist fosters positive transference as a benign authority; positive feelings are regarded as real. Negative transference is avoided. The therapist may become active in helping the patient learn new ways of adapting and may use or prescribe cognitive, behavioral, or social skill training techniques.

EMPIRICAL STUDIES

Efficacy of Individual Psychotherapy: Trials in the Drugs Versus Psychotherapy Paradigm (1960–1975)

Following the introduction of phenothiazines, psychiatry became increasingly divided into adherents of the "psychodynamic" or "biological" approaches. Disagreement concerning the value of intensive psychotherapy and medications was a focal point of acrimonious ideological and scientific debates. Randomized clinical trial methodology demonstrated the value of pharmacological interventions in schizophrenia and was recognized as the optimal standard for evaluating all treatments (Klerman, 1984). In this context, six controlled trials conducted during the 1960s and 1970s attempted to assess the efficacy of various forms of individual psychotherapy compared with treatment programs not specifically featuring psychotherapy (May & Tuma, 1964; Rogers et al., 1967; Grinspoon et al., 1968; Messier, 1969; Karon & Vandenbos, 1972, 1982; Hogarty et al., 1973, 1974a, 1974b; May et al., 1976a, 1976b, 1981). Reflecting the then-salient drugs versus psychotherapy debate, most include a no-medication cell.

As indicated in Table 1, each study conducted during this period had unique methodological strengths and weaknesses. The Karon and Vandenbos (1972) and Grinspoon et al. (1968) studies of psychoanalytic treatment are particularly difficult to interpret because psychotherapy was provided in special research units while nonpsychotherapy comparison group patients were transferred to or treated in different wards of state hospitals (May & Tuma, 1972). Although all studies were criticized by proponents of investigative psychotherapy on a number of methodological grounds (Dyrud & Holzman, 1973; Feinsilver & Gunderson, 1975; Wexler, 1975), together the results of these trials suggested the following conclusions:

Table 1. Clinical Trials of Psychotherapy Predating 1980

	May and colleagues 1964, 1 976a, 1 976b	Rogers et al. 1967	Grinspoon et al. 1968; Messier et al. 1969	Karon and Vandenbos 1972, 1982	Hogarty et al. 1973, 1974a, 1974b	Hogarty et al. 1979
Treatment/ Comparison Group	1) Individual psychotherapy (ego-supportive) alone; 2) Drugs alone; 3) Psychotherapy and drugs; 4) ECT: 19–25 sessions; 5) Milieu "good public"	1) Client-centered therapy; 2) Usual hospital care	1) Analytically oriented psychotherapy; 2) Psychotherapy and drugs; 3) Usual care at different hospital	1) Psychoanalysis alone; 2) "Ego-analytic" and drugs; 3) Drugs only (in different hospital)	1) MRT; 2) MRT and placebo; 3) Drug no MRT; 4) No MRT and placebo	1) Fluphenazine decanoate + intensive social therapy; 2) Oral fluphenazine + intensive social therapy; 3) Fluphenazine decanoate + routine care; 4) Oral fluphenazine and routine care
Patients	228 first-admission inpatients, mid-range prognosis	32 inpatients	20 inpatients with chronic schizophrenia	32 patients, two-thirds first admission	374 discharged patients	105 discharged patients
Design	Random assignment, assessed after treatment and naturalistic followup	Random, stratified by duration of hospitalization and sex, with 1- yr followup	Selected patients compared with controls (n = 20) in different hospital	Random, but usual treatment group in different facility, with 2-yr followup	Random, stratified	Random
Therapists	Residents with 6 mos to 6 yrs experience, supervised one-half hr per wk	1 to 25 yrs' experience, not supervised	Senior analysts	2 experienced analysts and 10 trainees	Social workers	Social workers with more than 10 yrs' experience

Table 1. Clinical Trials of Psychotherapy Predating 1980 (continued)

	May and colleagues 1964, 1976a, 1976b	Rogers et al. 1967	Grinspoon et al. 1968; Messier et al. 1969	Karon and Vandenbos 1972, 1982	Hogarty et al. 1973, 1974a, 1974b	Hogarty et al. 1979
Therapy Duration/ Intensity	2 hrs/wk for 1 yr (mean of 46 sessions)	2 hrs/wk for 2 to 30 mos	2 times/wk 2 yrs controlled 3-yr followup	1) 5 times/wk until discharge; 2) 3 times/wk until discharge; After discharge, 1 time/wk for 20 mos	At least monthly, varied by need 2-yr duration	Varied by need 2-yr duration
Medications	2) Stelazine 10–120 mg; 3) Stelazine 4–120 mg, controlled during inpatient phase	Not controlled	2) Thioridazine 300–1000 mg daily	2) Chlorpromazine 150–600 mg; 3) Chlorpromazine 300–1600 mg	1,2): Chlorpromazine at least 100 mg daily; mean of 270 mg	1,3): 12.5 mg to 125 mg biweekly; 2,4): mean 10 mg daily
Outcome Domains	LOS, SOC, VOC, PSY, BEH, SX	BEH, PSY, SX	SX, BEH, LOS, REHOSP	LOS, SX, PSY, REHOSP	REHOSP, SX, PSYCH, VOC, SOC	REHOSP, SX, VOC, SOC
Results	End of treatment: drugs alone or drugs and psychotherapy > ECT> therapy alone > milieu; At 3–5-yr followup: drugs alone or ECT = best; psychotherapy alone = worst	No significant differences between therapy and controls, but trend favors therapy; Better outcome for patients who rated therapist as empathic; Patient's, but not therapist's, view of relationship quality associated with outcome	End of treatment: drugs and psychotherapy > psychotherapy alone; no value for psychotherapy alone; At 3–5-yr followup, no significant difference between psychotherapy and no psychotherapy	End of treatment: psychotherapy and drugs > usual treatment; At 2-year followup: psychotherapy and drugs same as usual care; psychotherapy > usual care, experienced therapists only	Relapse: Placebo 80%, drug 48%, MRT and drug 37%, MRT and drug, better adjustment at 24 mos	No significant difference in group relapse rate; Near significant interaction: decanoate and social therapy has lowest relapse rate

Table 1. Clinical Trials of Psychotherapy Predating 1980 *(continued)*

	May and colleagues 1964, 1976a, 1976b	Rogers et al. 1967	Grinspoon et al. 1968; Messier et al. 1969	Karon and Vandenbos 1972, 1982	Hogarty et al. 1973, 1974a, 1974b	Hogarty et al. 1979
Methodological Strengths	Large sample; Sophisticated design; Multiple outcome measures	Focus on patient's perception of helpfulness; Aspects of process related to outcome	Senior therapists; Long duration of treatment	Large sample; Sophisticated design; Multiple outcome measures	Large *n*; Multiple outcome domains; Adequate treatment duration	Adequate duration of treatment
Methodological Weaknesses	Inexperienced therapists; Treatment uncontrolled during followup; Results limited to inpatient psychotherapy	Mainly concerned with process; Medication uncontrolled and confound results	Nonrandom patient selection; Control patients in different hospital; Small *n*	Inconsistent medication across groups; Usual treatment group transferred to state hospital	Treatment vaguely specified; Overlap in psychosocial treatment groups	Inadequate power to test interactions; Social treatment vaguely specified

Note.
BEH = ward behavior
ECT = electroconvulsive therapy
LOS = length of stay
MRT = major role therapy
PSY psychological testing
REHOSP = rehospitalization rate
SOC social functioning
SX = symptom measures
VOC vocational functioning

1. No study provided evidence to support the efficacy of any type of individual psychotherapy as a sole treatment for schizophrenia: When pharmacological treatment was controlled, medication-treated groups always demonstrated superior outcome, whether or not psychotherapy was offered to non-medication-treated comparison groups.

2. Studies of psychoanalytic psychotherapy that included a followup component (May & Tuma, 1964; Grinspoon et al., 1968; Karon & Vandenbos, 1972) indicated no clear advantage for psychoanalytic therapy plus drugs versus drugs alone, with the possible exception of the one finding of a better outcome among patients of two very experienced therapists (Karon & Vandenbos, 1982).

3. Two methodologically sophisticated and carefully conducted investigations suggested an additive effect on both relapse and functioning for a pragmatic problem-oriented therapy termed Major Role Therapy (Hogarty et al., 1973, 1974a, 1974b, 1979). This was described as an individual problem-solving method focused on the resolution of personal or environmental problems or both that directly affected the patient's functioning (Hogarty et al., 1974b).

These conclusions were further supported by the results of long-term followup studies of patients treated with intensive psychodynamic psychotherapy at Chestnut Lodge and the Columbia New York State Psychiatric Institute. The majority of patients in both followup cohorts remained seriously disabled by chronic schizophrenia (McGlashan, 1984, 1988), and both groups experienced significant rates of death from suicide (Fenton et al., 1997; Stone, 1986).

Efficacy of Individual Psychotherapy Combined with Medication Versus Supportive Versus Investigative Psychotherapy (circa 1980)

The Boston Psychotherapy Study (Gunderson et al., 1984; Stanton et al., 1984) aimed to compare the effectiveness of expressive insight-oriented (EIO) individual psychotherapy and reality-adaptive supportive (RAS) psychotherapy against a backdrop of high quality inpatient, outpatient, and pharmacological treatment provided to both patient groups. Designed to remedy methodological deficiencies identified in the first generation RCTs in schizophrenia, advances incorporated into this investigation included 1) well-defined treatments; 2) experienced and ideologically committed therapists; 3) process and treatment adherence measures; 4) reliable diagnostic, prognostic, and outcome measures; 5) adequate pharmacological treatment for both patient groups; and 6) sufficiently large sample and duration of treatment to detect effects. The EIO and RAS therapies evaluated in this study were designed to approximate high quality insight-oriented (average three times per week) and supportive (average once per week) psychotherapy as they had evolved over the preceding decades.

Following discharge from one of three Boston area hospitals, patients (mean age = 22) were randomly assigned to EIO or RAS psychotherapy. Treatment groups did not differ with respect to amount of antipsychotic medication prescribed or use of other treatment modalities.

Contrary to the investigators' expectations (an advantage for EIO was expected), neither treatment emerged as markedly superior, although differential effects across outcome domains were noted: The less intensive RAS was preferentially effective in reducing rehospitalization and improving vocational adjustment; EIO exerted a non-significant preferential effect on ego functions and cognition. Treatments were comparable in their impact on symptoms.

Significant among the findings from the Boston Psychotherapy Study was the degree to which, despite theoretical differences, the actual techniques employed by the EIO and RAS therapists tended to converge. Both therapies were found to employ substantial supportive elements (Gunderson et al., 1984). Sobering, but also significant, were the substantial attrition rates for both types of therapy. Those who remained in therapy continued to accrue benefits, but by the end of 1 year more than half (56%) and by the end of 2 years more than two-thirds (69%) of all patients had unilaterally dropped out of treatment.

Having found few differences in overall outcome between patients treated with EIO and RAS therapy, investigators searched for common factors in the treatments associated with positive therapeutic change and good outcome. Results indicated that independent of severity of psychopathology, patients able to form a good alliance with the therapist within the first 6 months of treatment were more likely to remain in therapy and comply with medication. These patients achieved better outcomes at 2 years and used less medication than those who did not form a therapeutic alliance (Frank & Gunderson, 1990). Across both therapies, a strong positive correlation was found between reductions in patient denial of illness and retardation and apathy, and the therapists' demonstration of a sound dynamic understanding and accurate attunement to the patients' underlying concerns. Directive activity was associated with reductions in anxiety and depression. (Glass et al., 1989).

Findings from the Boston Psychotherapy Study have been reviewed and debated (Carpenter, 1984; Docherty, 1984; Karon, 1984; May, 1984); generally, the following conclusions have been suggested:

1. Individual cases notwithstanding (A Recovering Patient, 1986; Stone, 1986; Fenton & McGlashan, 1987), for most patients no empirical evidence supports the efficacy of intensive investigative psychotherapy combined with medications over less intensive and less costly individual therapy approaches.

2. A convergence of techniques among therapists with different ideologies suggests that the distinction between supportive and insight-oriented therapy may not be meaningful or salient.

3. Independent of severity of psychopathology, a positive therapeutic alliance supported by a sound attunement to patients' needs is associated with better medication compliance and better outcome. These results are consistent with numerous studies that indicate that a patient's feeling of being listened to and understood by the physician is a strong predictor of medication compliance (Fenton et al., 1997).

The disappointing results of randomized clinical trials and followup studies contributed to a decline in prestige and influence of the psychodynamic paradigm generally and intensive individual psychotherapy of schizophrenia in particular. As a result, individual psychotherapy research and psychological theorizing concerning schizophrenia slowed to a near halt (Mueser & Berenbaum, 1990), and several influential reviews emphasized the potentially toxic effect of ill-timed and overly demanding psychodynamic interventions (Drake & Sederer, 1986; Stone, 1986; Mueser & Berenbaum, 1990). Lacking credible scientific support, psychosocial theories of etiology were rejected as harmful and erosive of patients,' families,' and professionals' efforts to work collaboratively (Dolnick, 1998). The biological paradigm decisively gained ascendancy as the most influential in the field.

Reappraisals of Individual Psychotherapy (1985–1995)

In the context of advances in biological therapeutics, family-based interventions, and community support technologies, investigators in the United States and abroad called for a reappraisal of the role of individual psychotherapy in the treatment of schizophrenia.

Carpenter (1986) noted that parochialism undermined efforts to integrate what ought to be complementary approaches. He described the clinical relationship as a foundation for treating schizophrenia, providing continuity of care, and integrating treatment modalities based on a phenomenological understanding of the patient's individual needs. According to Carpenter, illness heterogeneity dictated that treatment would need to be individualized. Drake and Sederer (1986) identified the development of a trusting alliance as the crucial step in all psychological treatments, warned against overly intrusive intervention, and advocated supporting the patient's role as an active agent in managing his or her own illness.

Coursey (1989) proposed a redefinition of the aims and goals of individual psychotherapy in view of unequivocal evidence of schizophrenia's biological determinants. He identified the following as appropriate foci for individual psychotherapy:

1. The human issues raised by having a chronic debilitating disorder,

2. Efforts to help patients learn about and self-manage the disorder, and

3. Attention to the problems of living that people with schizophrenia have to deal with.

Coursey advocated an eclectic approach, including education, crisis intervention, empowerment, support for existential anguish, practical advice, and insight.

Dingman and McGlashan (1989) proposed broadly reformulating psychotherapy to refer to the relationship between clinician and patient. Acknowledging the validity of clinical descriptions of schizophrenia patients' difficulties observed during the era of investigative psychotherapy, they identified the vulnerability-stress model as best guiding psychotherapeutic efforts. Relationship building, administration (coordinating other prescribed psychosocial interventions), and one-to-one interaction using both supportive and investigative techniques as dictated by the patient's situation were described as key elements in Dingman and McGlashan's broadly conceived psychotherapy.

Katz (1989) urged selectivity in both the target symptoms for psychotherapy and timing of interventions over the illness course. Sarti and Cournos (1990) pointed out that medication noncompliance, high relapse rates, and social disability defined the limits of a strictly pharmacological approach to schizophrenia. They emphasized the utility of integrated, practically oriented treatment that aimed fundamentally to strengthen the physician-patient alliance and educate the patient about the illness.

Also guided by the vulnerability-stress model, Falloon (1992) described efforts to strengthen patients' coping capacity as the appropriate target of psychotherapeutic strategies in schizophrenia. Beyond education and stress management for patients (and caregivers), he advised that the choice and amount of other psychological interventions be determined by the patient's particular illness type. Alanen (Alanen et al., 1991; Alanen, 1997) used the term "need-adapted treatment" to describe a comprehensive therapeutic approach developed over three decades in Turku, Finland, that attempted to integrate dynamically informed individual psychotherapy, pharmacological, and rehabilitative efforts. Perris (1989) described the integration of cognitive-based individual psychotherapy with pharmacotherapy and rehabilitation in a comprehensive treatment approach provided in ideologically supportive specialized group homes (cognitive behavioral centers) in the Umea, Sweden, region. Individual psychotherapy in this approach emphasizes relationship building, problem identification, and correction of dysfunctional cognition that impedes interpersonal interactions and social skills acquisition.

Although psychodynamic theories of the *etiology* of schizophrenia hold no currency in reformulations of psychotherapy, Dingman and McGlashan (1989) and Sarti and Coumos (1990) viewed *clinical* psychodynamic concepts such as countertransference as helping clinicians avoid inappropriate power struggles or other damaging reactions in the course of treating patients with schizophrenia. Others view psychodynamic understanding as facilitating management of clinical problems such as paranoia and denial (Weiden & Havens, 1994), medication noncompliance (Diamond, 1983; Book, 1987), establishment of clinical contact (Huszonek, 1987), and tracking of suicidality and maintenance of self-esteem (Drake et al., 1984; Cotton et al., 1985; Drake & Cotton, 1986; Hingley, 1997).

Disorder-Specific and Targeted Individual Psychotherapies

Personal psychotherapy. Informed by reappraisals of individual psychotherapy over the preceding decade, Gerald Hogarty and his colleagues at the University of Pittsburgh developed personal therapy (PT) as a disorder-specific individual psychotherapy that could both accommodate individual patient differences yet be operationalized for empirical testing (Hogarty et al., 1995). PT is designed for recently discharged outpatients with chronic or subchronic schizophrenia. Its objective is to enhance personal and social adjustment and forestall late (third year) relapse. A graduated approach accommodates neuropsychological aspects of schizophrenia and attempts to avoid the adverse effect of poorly timed interventions.

Individual-specific stress, often interpersonal, is seen as precipitating affective dysregulation in vulnerable patients. This loss of control over mood is seen as resulting in poorly reasoned dysfunctional behavior that negatively influences the reciprocal behavior of others in a cycle that may end in relapse. Based on individual patients' needs and preferences, PT uses a range of interventions to promote patients' self-awareness and foresight and equip them with adaptive strategies that facilitate self-monitoring and self-control of affect.

PT includes three phases, each with explicitly defined goals and corresponding interventions. The achievement of these goals is carefully assessed before the patient advances to the next level of treatment. Phases of treatment, goals, and operational criteria defining readiness to move to more advanced phases are summarized in Table 2. Within each phase, the exposure

Table 2. Personal Therapy: Goals, Techniques, and Criteria For Advancement

	Initiation Criteria	Goals	Techniques
Phase I (3–6 months)	Hospital discharge	Therapeutic joining; Stabilization; Treatment contract; Basic psychoeducation (stress-vulnerability model); Establish lowest effective medication dose	Supportive techniques (acceptance, empathy, problem solving); Basic stress identification and avoidance; Support gradual resumption of responsibilities; Basic social skills training; Basic psychoeducation workshop
Phase II (6–18 months)	Positive symptoms stable; Maintenance dose of medication achieved; Ability to maintain attention for 30 minutes; Basic understanding of illness; Regular appointment attendance; Appropriate basic social skills	Self-awareness of affective, cognitive, and behavioral states; Awareness of individual stressors, internal cues of stress; Self-protective strategies learned; Awareness of individual dysfunctional responses to stress; Improved social perception and functioning	Individualized psychoeducation; Encouragement of self-reflection; Exploration of individual vulnerabilities, stresses; Teaching of basic relaxation techniques (if patient is interested); Exercises to improve social perception, teaching of basic conflict management (role-play)
Phase III (18–36 months)	Continued clinical stability; Recognition of role of stress as potential precipitant of psychosis; Regular participation in role-playing exercises (if social skills deficit present); Evidence of accurate social perception; Identification of at least one affect and physical or cognitive cue of vulnerability; Basic relaxation techniques learned	Learn relationship between life circumstance and internal state; Learn relationship between felt affect and expressions of affect; Learn to predict significant other's reactions to expressions of affect; Learn criticism management; Recognize prodrome, need for prophylactic medication—avoid late relapse	Investigation of individual-specific responses to stress; Exploration of individual strengths and persistent limitations; Carefully timed vocational and resocialization initiatives; Advanced relaxation and social skills exercises

of patients to specific interventions is varied based on individual need. While the therapy was designed to be given over a 3-year time span, patients spend as much time at each level as required to meet advancement criteria and not all patients progress through all three phases. PT is administered against a backdrop of psychopharmacological treatment that aims to minimize side effects by using the lowest medication dose needed to prevent symptom exacerbation (Hogarty & Ulrich, 1998).

Investigators at the University of Pittsburgh have completed two 3-year randomized clinical trials of PT for newly discharged patients with schizophrenia and schizoaffective disorders (Hogarty et al., 1997a, 1997b). Patients residing with their families were assigned to supportive therapy, personal therapy, family psychoeducation/management, or a combination of the latter two treatments. Patients living alone, who were generally more disabled, were assigned to personal therapy or supportive therapy.

Results indicated that PT was remarkably well accepted by patients participating in the trials. Over 3 years, only 8% of patients receiving PT, and 23% of patients in contrasting treatments, were dropped for noncompliance or administrative reasons. Eight percent of patients remained in basic-phase PT, 38% of patients entered but did not progress beyond intermediate-phase PT, and 54% of patients progressed to advanced-phase PT over the 3-year trial period.

The efficacy of PT in relapse reduction was tied to residential status. Patients receiving PT who were living with family experienced fewer relapses. The more impaired group of patients receiving PT, who were living alone, experienced a greater relapse rate. Consistent with the clinical dictum that psychologically oriented treatments can be futile or harmful when applied before basic human service needs are addressed, PT patients who relapsed were more likely to have unstable housing and difficulty securing food and clothing. Independent of relapse reduction, PT produced substantial differential improvements in social adjustment and role performance. While improvements in social adjustment among patients receiving supportive and family therapy reached a plateau at 12 months, the personal adjustment of PT patients continued to improve in the second and third postdischarge years with no evidence of a plateau. Relative to supportive and family therapy, individual psychotherapy was superior in promoting a progressive improvement in psychosocial adjustment.

From a clinical perspective, it is important to recognize that while structured, PT is not a tightly prescriptive manualized treatment. Rather, PT outlines a set of principles and priorities that leave considerable room for individualization (Fenton & McGlashan, 1997).

Phase-specific cognitive-behavioral therapy: Targeted individual psychotherapy. While PT is organized as a broad strategic outline for psychotherapy for schizophrenia patients following hospital discharge, empirical support for the efficacy of briefer and more targeted disorder-specific individual psychotherapies come from a series of RCTs of individual cognitive-behavioral therapy (CBT) from the United Kingdom. These treatments are time limited, illness phase specific, and they target specific clinical problems that may be experienced by subpopulations of schizophrenia patients.

Acute phase. Table 3 summarizes RCTs of three targeted individual CBT interventions for inpatients in the acute phase of illness. Compliance therapy, conceptually based in motivational interviewing (Rollnick et al., 1992), is an effective four- to six-session intervention for acutely ill inpatients that targets improved attitude toward medication and postdischarge compliance as treatment goals (Kemp et al., 1996a, 1996b; Kemp et al., 1998). Drury et al. (1996a, 1996b) found intensive (3 hours per week) CBT designed to reduce duration of acute psychosis and level of residual positive symptoms to be effective in combination with family intervention and structured activities during inpatient treatment. Haddock et al. (1999) compared short-term CBT to supportive counseling and education in a small number of recent-onset acute inpatients and found comparable efficacy for both treatments. In contrast to Drury et al.'s (1996a, 1996b) intensive program that included continued treatment for at least 8 weeks postdischarge, most patients treated with the short-term CBT evaluated by Haddock et al. did not participate in aftercare "booster sessions."

Postacute phase. CBT targeting delusions and hallucinations that have not fully responded to pharmacological treatment has also been developed and tested for outpatients at a postacute phase of illness (Table 4). Conceptually, these treatments are based on the observation that patients are able to discover, learn, and use coping strategies to reduce symptom severity or distress associated with medication-resistant symptoms (Falloon & Talbot, 1981; Breier & Strauss, 1983). Techniques employed derive from individualized assessment and vary based on individual patient preference. They may include belief modification; self-management techniques; and coping strategy enhancements such as attention switching, attention narrowing, increasing or decreasing social activity, modifying sensory input, using relaxation strategies, and psychoeducation. In vivo practice and homework assignments are often prescribed, and an overall attempt is made to build on coping methods already used by the patient (Tarrier 1992a, 1992b; Haddock et al., 1994; Beck & Rector, 1998; Tarrier et al., 1998b).

Tarrier et al. (1993a, 1993b) compared the efficacy of coping strategy enhancement to problem solving among stable outpatients with residual

Table 3. Controlled Trials of Targeted Cognitive-Behavioral Psychotherapy: Acute Illness Phase

	Drury 1996a, 1996b	Kemp et al. 1996a, 1996b, 1998	Haddock, 1999
Goals	Reduce duration of acute psychosis; Reduce level of residual positive symptoms	Improve compliance with medication after discharge; Improve attitude toward treatment and insight into illness	Increase rate and amount of acute symptom reduction
Treatment/Comparison	Cognitive therapy (individual and family) vs. matched hrs of recreational therapy and informal support	Compliance therapy vs. nonspecific counseling	Short-term CBT vs. supportive counseling and psychoeducation
Patients	40 inpatients with functional psychosis	74 inpatients with psychosis	21 inpatients with *DSM-IV* schizophrenia or schizoaffective, ill < 5 yrs, with hallucinations disorder or delusions present
Design	RCT stratified by predictors, with 9-mo followup	RCT with 18-month postdischarge followup	RCT (pilot) with 2-yr chart followup
Therapists	Research psychologists	Research psychiatrist and clinical psychologist	Two expert clinical psychologists
Therapy duration and intensity	Mean 3 1-hr individual and group CBT sessions and 1–2 family interventions for 12 wks and structured activity program, integrated with intensive aftercare for 8 wks	4–6 sessions 10–60 min each	10 50-min sessions, over 5 wks or until discharge, with 4 postdischarge boosters offered
Medications	"Routine" pharmacotherapy; Pharmacotherapy and length of stay determined by psychiatrist blind to treatment, groups comparable to stelazine equivalents	Typical antipsychotics; PO and De-canoate Mean dose = 977 CPZ equivalents for compliance therapy group, 698 for control	Prescribed by medical consultants blind to treatment

Table 3. Controlled Trials of Targeted Cognitive-Behavioral Psychotherapy: Acute Illness Phase *(continued)*

	Drury 1996a, 1996b	Kemp et al. 1996a, 1996b, 1998	Haddock, 1999
Outcome measures	PAS; Self-report of delusional conviction; Time to recovery; Days in hospital	Composite compliance measure; Social functioning; BPRS modified; GAF; Insight; Drug Attitude Inventory	BPRS; Psychiatric Symptom Rating Scale; Time to discharge; 2-yr relapse and rehospitalization
Results	Faster rate of positive symptom reduction for CBT; Greater positive symptom reduction for CBT, persisted at followup; Less delusional conviction for CBT group; CBT group had 50% time in hospital relative to controls; Lower relapse rate for CBT over 9 mos	Better compliance with intervention group; Better attitude toward treatment and insight with intervention group; Longer community survival for intervention group at 18-mo followup	Both treatments associated with acute symptom improvement; No significant difference in length of stay, relapses, rehospitalization; Nonsignificant trend for fewer relapses with CBT
Predictors of good outcome	Female; Shorter duration of illness; Shorter average untreated illness	Higher IQ; Voluntary status; Fewer EPS	Not reported
Comments	Of 62 randomized, 22 excluded as not suitable; Requires patients to be willing and able to engage in dialogue about symptoms; Nonblind assessors	30% nonparticipation rate	One-third eligible refused treatment; Independent assessors; Poor patient compliance with postdischarge booster session

Note. BPRS = Brief Psychiatric Rating Scale
CBT = Cognitive-behavioral therapy
CPZ = chlorpromazine
EPS = extrapyramidal symptoms
GAF = global assessment of functioning
PAS = Psychiatric Assessment Scale
RCT = randomized clinical trial

Table 4. Controlled Trials of Targeted Cognitive-Behavioral Psychotherapy: Postacute Phase

	Tarrier et al. 1993a, 1993b	Haddock 1996	Garety et al.; Kuipers et al. 1997, 1998	Tarrier 1998b, 1999
Treatment/ Comparison	CSE vs. problem solving	Focusing technique vs. distraction technique vs. waiting-list control	CBT and standard care vs. standard care (case management and medication)	Intensive CBT and routine care vs. supportive counseling and routine care vs. routine care alone
Patients, *n*	27 with *DSM-III-R* schizophrenia, medication nonresponsive, with delusions or hallucinations	34 with > 2–3 auditory hallucinations/wk for > 6 mos, experienced as unpleasant	60 with psychosis (schizophrenia, schizoaffective, delusional disorder), with at least one positive symptom that was distressing, unremitting for 6 mos, and medication resistant	87 with *DSM-III-R* schizophrenia, schizoaffective, or delusional disorder, with persistent hallucinations or delusions for 6 mos despite medication, stable at least 1 mo
Design	RCT with 6-mo followup	RCT	RCT Three sites, 18- month followup	RCT stratified by symptom severity, sex, with 12-mo followup
Therapists	4 research psychologists	Expert psychologist	Experienced clinical psychologist	3 experienced clinical psychologists using protocol manual
Therapy duration and intensity	2 1-hr sessions/wk for 5 wks	1 hr/wk	1 hr/wk (flexible), then 2 times/mo for 9 mos	2 hrs/wk in clinic for 10 wks
Medications	"Regular and stable neuroleptic medications"	Prescribed by medical consultants	As prescribed by treatment team; No group differences at trial onset	Approximately 425–500 CPZ equivalents, no differences across groups

Table 4. Controlled Trials of Targeted Cognitive-Behavioral Psychotherapy: Postacute Phase *(continued)*

	Tarrier et al. 1993a, 1993b	Haddock 1996	Garety et al.; Kuipers et al. 1997, 1998	Tarrier 1998b, 1999
Goals	Reduce delusions and hallucinations that have been unresponsive to medication; Teach coping strategies to reduce symptom and distress	Medication-resistant auditory hallucination	Reduce distress from positive symptoms; Reduce depression, anxiety, hopelessness; Promote self-regulation of relapse risk and social disability	Treat delusions and hallucinations resistant to medication; Teach patients means of reducing distress associated with symptoms
Outcome measures	BPRS; Symptom change score; Psychiatric Assessment Scale; Social Functioning Scale; Coping skills and problem solving; Subjective benefit of treatment	PSE; Self-report hallucinations; Anxiety/depression scale; Self-esteem	BPRS; Maudsley Assessment of Delusions; Beck Depression Inventory; Beck Anxiety Inventory; Social functioning scale; Insight Assessment (Amdur); Self-concept and attitude scales; Self-report of symptom severity	Present State Exam; BPRS; SANS; Hospital days

Table 4. Controlled Trials of Targeted Cognitive-Behavioral Psychotherapy: Postacute Phase *(continued)*

	Tarrier et al. 1993a, 1993b	Haddock 1996	Garety et al.; Kuipers et al. 1997, 1998	Tarrier 1998b, 1999
Results	Both groups showed improved symptoms at end of treatment and followup; Advantage for CSE in total delusions, symptom improvement; Expectancy not associated with outcome (therapists' high or low expectation of improvement); Treatment-specific skill improvement in coping or problem solving	Both groups show reduction in frequency of hallucinations and life disruption; No change in attribution of voices	CBT had significantly greater decrease in BPRS than controls; No change in other outcomes; 21% of CBT vs. 3% of controls dropped 10 points in BPRS; CBT had low (11%) dropout; 80% highly satisfied; Cost of CBT offset by reduced use of inpatient services	CBT group showed greater improvement in positive symptom number and severity; CBT group more likely to have 50% symptom reduction; Routine care alone patients spent more days in hospital; Advantage of CBT on positive symptoms maintained at 12 mos, differences less clinically significant
Predictors of good outcome	Patients with higher pretreatment scores improved most	No report	"Chink of insight at baseline"; Acknowledge possibility of being mistaken; cognitive flexibility; Greater number of admissions in last 5 yrs, other baseline measures (e.g., IQ) *not predictive*	Shorter duration of illness; Less severity at baseline; Male, low IQ, unemployed, low education most likely to drop out
Comments	Of 48 suitable patients, 27 (56%) continued to posttreatment, 23 (48%) to 6-mo followup	Narrow focus on alternate strategies for auditory hallucinations, high attrition over trial	50% of patients responded to treatment Independent assessors	87/138 treated after allocation; Assessors blind to treatment assignments; Booster sessions advisable?

Note. BPRS = Brief Psychiatric Rating Scale; CBT= cognitive-behavioral therapy; CPZ = chlorpromazine; CSE = coping strategy enhancement; PSE = Present State Exam; RCT = randomized clinical trial; SANS = Scale for the Assessment of Negative Symptoms.

positive symptoms. Symptoms experienced by patients in both treatment groups improved relative to waiting-list controls, and changes in coping were significantly related to decreases in psychotic symptoms during treatment. A second larger trial of more intensive CBT combined training in coping, problem solving, and relapse prevention. This trial found that CBT added to routine care (medication and outpatient management) reduced residual positive symptoms, exacerbations, and days spent in hospital relative to generic supportive counseling and routine care (Tarrier et al., 1998b). A significant effect of CBT on residual positive symptoms remained at 12-month followup (Tarrier et al., 1999).

Following a small pilot trial (Garety et al., 1994), the efficacy of CBT for medication-resistant symptoms in the stable plateau illness phase (including evidence for the durability of improvement and cost-effectiveness over 18 months) has recently been independently validated by Garety and her colleagues (Garety et al., 1997; Kuipers et al., 1997, 1998). A detailed clinical and empirical overview of cognitive-behavioral treatment for medication resistant symptoms is provided by Garety et al. (2000).

Results of RCTs consistently demonstrate an advantage of adding time-limited illness-specific cognitive-behavioral therapies to usual care for schizophrenia patients at both the acute and stable plateau phases of illness. At the same time, substantial initial dropout or refusal rates, following randomization indicate that these treatments will not be appropriate for all patients. Those studies that have evaluated predictors of response have pointed to subjective distress associated with symptoms and some pretreatment insight as predictors of patients most likely to benefit from targeted CBT interventions.

CURRENT CLINICAL PRACTICE

How can available research concerning effective approaches to individual psychotherapy inform clinical practice? The techniques employed in empirically tested therapies differ based on the treatment's specific goals. However, all effective individual psychotherapies share the following characteristics: 1) schizophrenia is understood as a biologically based disorder that can be partially managed by learned and practiced coping strategies; 2) a vulnerability-stress model is used to explain symptoms and illness course; 3) a therapeutic alliance is established as a prerequisite for all other activities; 4) a focus on understanding the patient's subjective experience and strengthening natural coping mechanisms is emphasized; 5) treatment is flexibly based on individual patient needs and capacities; and 6) each intervention presupposes that the patient is receiving ongoing supportive care and management, including attention to pharmacological treatment, human service needs, and rehabilitation.

In an effort to outline practice that reflected various reappraisals of psychotherapy, Fenton and McGlashan (1995) defined "flexible psychotherapy," a disorder-specific treatment informed by current scientific conceptions of schizophrenia. This pragmatic approach to psychotherapy relies on a variety of strategies applied flexibly depending on the individual patient's type of schizophrenia and phase of illness. At various times, supportive, directive, educational, or insight-oriented activity is provided in the context of a stable doctor-patient relationship. Dogmatic adherence to a single technique applied to all patients is considered least likely to be helpful. Flexible psychotherapy can be described in terms of assumptions, clinical tasks, and interventions and likely approximates how most patients are treated in current practice (Kane & McGlashan, 1996).

Flexible Psychotherapy: Assumptions

A flexible approach to psychotherapy is based on assumptions about schizophrenia that recognize the joint contributions of biological, psychological, and social/environmental factors:

1. The vulnerability-stress model represents the best available integration of data pertinent to the etiology, course, and outcome of schizophrenia. This model postulates that schizophrenia results from a dynamic interaction between environmental or experiential stress in a person who is "vulnerable" to react to this stress with schizophrenic symptom formation (Meehl, 1962; Zubin, 1981; McGlashan, 1986). Aspects of vulnerability are undoubtedly genetic, although some may be acquired biologically through intrauterine, birth, and postnatal complications (Falloon, 1992; Hollister et al., 1996; Olin & Mednick, 1996; Susser et al., 1996). At the same time, vulnerability is not static but shaped epigenetically over time by environmental influences. A "stress" sufficient to precipitate relapse at one time, for example, may be less likely to do so at a later point when new coping strategies or better supports have been acquired (Strauss et al., 1985).

2. The stress side of the vulnerability-stress model postulates that a variety of stressors (internal or external events requiring adaptation) can precipitate the emergence of symptoms in a vulnerable individual. Given biologically based vulnerability, the onset, course, and outcome of an individual's disorder may be shaped by interactions between the person and the environment. Among psychosocial factors, stressful life events, cultural milieu (egocentric vs. sociocentric), social class, social network size and density, and emotional quality of the living environment have been demonstrated to be associated with the onset and

course of schizophrenia (Nuechterlein & Dawson, 1984; McGlashan, 1986; Lin & Kleinman ,1988; Wyatt et al., 1988).

3.   Schizophrenia is heterogeneous, as are individuals afflicted with it. The clinical diversity of schizophrenia in relation to vulnerabilities and risk factors, age and type of onset, manifest signs and symptoms, longitudinal course, and long-term outcome suggest that the disorder may be heterogeneous in regard to underlying etiology. This heterogeneity may be partially captured by currently available subtyping systems such as deficit versus nondeficit schizophrenia, but at a minimum, schizophrenic illnesses of greater and lesser severity and "virulence" can be identified and the "biological" vulnerability of individuals may differ (McGlashan & Fenton, 1993). As with the illness itself, individuals afflicted with schizophrenia differ substantially in adaptive capacities, intelligence, and instrumental and verbal competence.

4.   Schizophrenia is often phasic in course. Systematic investigation of longitudinal course has only recently begun, and our understanding of illness phases is preliminary (Strauss et al., 1985). Phases may include the following: a) prodromal periods, during which time a highly individualized constellation of symptoms that represent early manifestation of clinical decompensation emerge; b) acute or active phases, often associated with the full-blown emergence of positive symptoms superimposed onto preexisting deficits; c) subacute, convalescent, or stabilization phases, characterized by gradual restoration of some functioning perhaps associated with postpsychotic depression; d) moratoriums or adaptive plateaus, characterized by a gradual reconstitution of identity, gathering of support, and strengthening of skills; e) change points or shifts in functioning over a relatively brief period of time, initiated by the patient's own desires or pressure from others and associated with the potential for either quantum improvement or decompensation; or f) end state or stable plateaus, relatively enduring periods of stability characterized by greater or lesser fixed deficits, chronic levels of positive symptoms, or both.

Flexible Psychotherapy: Clinical Tasks and Technical Strategies

To treat schizophrenia, the therapist must use a variety of interventions and strategies. The crucial question becomes which interventions are of potential value for a particular individual at a particular phase of illness. The range of therapeutic tasks and associated goals and interventions can be roughly ordered hierarchically. Although attention to issues such as relationship building cuts across all phases of therapy, as outlined in Table 5, different therapeutic tasks are of particular importance during different illness phases. In addition, while some tasks are clearly relevant for all patients, others, particularly those relating to the goals of intensive psychotherapy, are pertinent for only a small subgroup. This model assumes the therapist's capacity to "shift gears" flexibly and change roles with all patients based on changing circumstances, always holding in mind the goal of helping the patient accept, learn about, and self-manage what may often be a chronic and devastating illness.

Consideration of the patient's schizophrenia subtype, current and premorbid functioning, and self-defined treatment goals are all relevant to the determination of appropriate treatment tasks. For patients with severe hebephrenic and deficit forms of schizophrenia, for example, the most humane and practical goal may be establishing a supportive ongoing treatment within a sheltered setting that minimizes stress and provides for basic human needs. For the majority of patients who reside in the community, some psychoeducation and rehabilitative tasks should be planned with the aim of minimizing acute relapses and promoting maximal functioning and quality of life. A focus on investigative tasks is reserved for motivated patients who have established a good therapeutic relationship and exhibit an interest in and ability to make constructive use of such techniques. Attunement to psychological concerns may be particularly important for patients who have a dramatic response to new medications (Duckworth et al., 1997).

The use of multiple treatment modalities is anticipated and creates the need for someone to orchestrate and coordinate them. As is true in medicine generally, the quality of the individual doctor-patient relationship is viewed as a major factor in the success of all prescribed therapies. Thus, a focus on the skillful use of this relationship usefully informs all tasks at all levels. Here, removed from its outmoded etiologic assumptions and overly ambitious aims, the substantial clinical knowledge derived from the tradition of investigative psychotherapy can be applied pragmatically in a contemporary context.

Depending upon the administrative structure in which treatment is provided, many of the tasks outlined in Table 5 may overlap with the concerns and expertise of other service providers. All, however, should be the concern of the individual psychotherapist and a focus for individual psychotherapy (Jeffries, 1995). A focus on higher level educational and psychological tasks is generally inappropriate in the presence of overwhelming difficulties at the level of basic human services. Thus, the necessary first goal of psychotherapy with a homeless person may be direct assistance in finding housing. Although other professionals may be relied upon to accomplish specific tasks, the individual psychotherapist should consider himself or herself responsible for ensuring the results of these efforts. While the majority of therapeutic time may be spent "sitting in an office talking," this approach assumes that the therapist should be prepared to participate in outreach, family consultation and education, and environmental intervention to an extent required by individual circumstances and the ability and availability of other treatment team members. The therapist operating in the way described here should be prepared to directly participate in environmental interventions when needed.

The following general treatment strategies are common to all of the specific therapeutic tasks outlined: evaluation, continuous reevaluation, timing, titration, and integration with psychopharmacology.

Evaluation

A thorough evaluation of the patient initiates the treatment process and should include a determination of whether other treatments of demonstrated efficacy such as family psychoeducation or assertive outreach are indicated. During medical assessment and stabilization, evaluation includes ruling out identifiable physical conditions, assessing competence to consent to treatment and dangerousness, and determining the responsiveness of symptoms to acute pharmacological intervention. Psychosocial assessment inventories available support and aim to measure the degree to which the patient's adaptive capacities measure up against the stresses and demands of his or her living environment. Efforts to establish a supportive ongoing treatment test the patient's capacity to trust and rely upon another human being for support and guidance. When applicable, psychoeducational, rehabilitative, and investigative interventions are preceded by an assessment of the patient's cognitive strengths and deficits, allowing interventions to be formulated that match the patient's talents.

Continuous Reevaluation

The fluid nature of schizophrenia and an individual's adaptation to it over time demands periodic reassessment of course, prognosis, phase of illness, and target problems. As these change, so do treatment goals. Providing concrete support in the form of a ride to work may be helpful early in the effort to promote vocational rehabilitation, but later may promote unwarranted dependency and prolong disability.

Timing

The phasic natural history of schizophrenia requires attention to when particular therapeutic tasks are attempted. For many patients, in order to minimize stress and forestall relapse, relatively little beyond assessment, stabilization with medication, and establishment of a supportive ongoing treatment should be attempted during the first 6 to 12 months following an acute

Table 5. Flexible Psychotherapy: Phase-Specific Tasks, Intervention, and Goals

Therapeutic Task	Illness Phase	Clinical Focus	Interventions	Goals
Medical and psychiatric assessment and stabilization	Prodromal, acute	Crisis intervention; Psychiatric/medical diagnosis; Safety; Acute symptom management	Clinical, medical, neurological assessment; Hospitalization or community alternative acute care; Directive and supportive communication, limit setting; Acute pharmacologic treatment	Diagnose or rule out medical, neurological disorders; Ensure safety; Minimize effect of acute episode on life situation (housing, job, family); Effect rapid symptom reduction
Psychosocial assessment and case management	Subacute, convalescent, stabilization	Stress and vulnerabilities; Social supports; Living arrangements, daily activities; Adaptive capacities; Access to economic and treatment resources	Skilled psychological and psychosocial assessment; Evaluation of human service needs; Linkage with social service, human service, and community support services	Mobilize social support; Assess postepisode psychosocial service needs, including day treatment, supportive housing if needed; Ensure access to all required entitlements; Enlist cooperation of family or other caregivers
Establishment of supportive treatment	Early maintenance, moratorium, or adaptive plateau	Treatment relationship and alliance; Denial, suspiciousness, disorganization; Self-esteem	Continued medication—attention to complaints and medication side-effects; Support, positive regard, reassurance, bolstering defenses; Promote comfort with therapist and treatment—encourage benign positive transference; Assertive outreach (if needed) and direct assistance with situational problems	Encourage sufficient acceptance of illness to allow cooperation with treatment; Promote trust in therapist and comfort with therapeutic routine; Support strengths, adaptive defenses; Monitor for relapse

Table 5. Flexible Psychotherapy: Phase-Specific Tasks, Intervention, and Goals *(continued)*

Therapeutic Task	Illness Phase	Clinical Focus	Interventions	Goals
Psychoeducation	Maintenance, moratorium, change points	Understanding and acceptance of illness; Human concerns associated with disability; Self-management of illness	Teaching and support Identification of individual-specific stresses; Awareness of individual-specific prodromal and active symptoms; Determine lowest effective prophylactic medication dose	Prevent relapse; Teach stress management strategies; Achieve self-recognition of prodromal symptoms; Establish maintenance regime; Achieve collaborative self-management of illness
Rehabilitation or habilitation	Maintenance, end state, stable plateau	Social, vocational, self-care skills; Learning or relearning; Establishing realistic expectations; Adaptation to deficits	Attention to details of daily self-care, social and occupational functioning; Modeling and practice of new skills; Cognitive, problem-solving, and social skills enhancement; Environmental intervention, family education, supported employment	Promote highest adaptive functioning within limitations imposed by defeats; Promote activities that enhance self-esteem through accomplishment and productivity; Encourage activities that improve quality of life; Promote attainment of self-defined goals; Learn strategies that allow functioning despite deficits; Enhance cognitive flexibility
Investigative and insight-oriented tasks	Selected and motivated patients during stable periods	Conflicts, transference, countertransference, life goals, motivations	Exploration of feelings, conflicts, ambivalence; Focus on unconscious, past events, life history, hidden meanings; Examination of important relationships, including relationship with therapist; Interpretation	Integrate psychosis into expanded concept of self; Construct life narrative; Work through conflicts; Improve capacity for intimacy and productivity

episode. Once the patient is asymptomatic and shows signs of revitalization, rehabilitation and more complex psychoeducational elements may be gradually introduced.

Titration

Treatment interventions should be applied with graded increases of intensity and complexity. Higher level therapeutic tasks should be attempted and higher levels of work or social functioning expected only after completion and consolidation of earlier gains. Substantial rehabilitation, for example, will rarely be possible until progress has been made in attaining a stable supportive treatment relationship. Likewise, there is evidence that early, active, and ambitious psychologically oriented treatment may be disorganizing or toxic for certain patients. In general, treatment changes should be pursued cautiously, modifying only one element at a time.

Integration with Psychopharmacology

Each of the tasks outlined above assumes most patients will be prescribed acute and prophylactic neuroleptic drugs. Control and prevention of psychotic symptoms using the lowest effective dosage of medication is the overall treatment goal. Decisions regarding pharmacological management are often linked to the relative success or failure of accomplishing various psychotherapeutic tasks. Considerable psychoeducation, for example, should be accomplished before attempting maintenance medication dose reduction or the initiation of a targeted (intermittent) medication strategy. Long-acting injectable neuroleptics may be useful for patients unable to tolerate the daily reminder of illness associated with oral medication and for patients unable to maintain a reliable treatment relationship.

DISCUSSION

As noted by Carpenter (1986), in clinical practice the irreducible essence of our interest in schizophrenia is the nature of another person's experience. One-to-one interaction between physician or therapist and patient has characterized efforts to treat schizophrenia throughout much of the century. In the absence of a firm empirical grounding, individual therapy as practiced was most often guided by ideology and deference to authority. Research advances were hampered by a focus on global questions such as the relative merits of drugs versus psychotherapy or supportive versus investigative techniques.

For a long period, empirical research on one-to-one intervention virtually ceased. A reformulation of schizophrenia as a disease requiring individualized, comprehensive treatment has allowed the development and empirical testing of new targeted and illness-phase-specific individual psychotherapies.

In these models, each component of a comprehensive treatment plan for a patient with schizophrenia targets specific aspects of the disease and its common sequelae. Individual psychotherapy addresses the human aspects of adaptation to a serious psychiatric illness and targets problems such as residual symptoms, relapse prevention, denial, demoralization, treatment compliance, personal relationships, and self-esteem. Its focus is on understanding the patient's beliefs, attitudes, aspirations, and experiences. The coordination, timing, and titration of all specific treatment elements is informed by this understanding and by an ongoing assessment of individual patient needs that can often best be achieved within a long-term physician-patient or therapist-patient relationship.

Defining individual psychotherapy for research continues to be problematic. If individualization and integration of multiple modalities are the core features of effective therapy, it is unlikely that a search for a single effective ingredient common to successful psychotherapy will be fruitful; in fact, it could once again lead to a rancorous focus on minutia.

Empirical studies validate two seemingly divergent approaches to further development of evidence-based individual psychotherapy for schizophrenia. Hogarty's PT is a broadly defined strategic outline that sequentially organizes the focus of therapeutic interaction across illness phases over a period of years. It resembles case management when human service needs are most pressing, but changes focus over time to accommodate changing patient needs. Like PT, flexible psychotherapy provides a broad outline of what might be considered adequate clinical care in the context of a one-to-one psychotherapeutic relationship. The challenge for future development of approaches such as these is to outline sequenced interventions with sufficient specificity to allow them to be operationalized, taught, and measured, while retaining sufficient flexibility to accommodate patient heterogeneity. This will require description of therapeutic approaches at a level intermediate between a tightly prescriptive process and global strategic outline—along with identification of measurable quality indicators associated with adherence to the treatment model. These indicators will include the therapist's provision or prescription of other effective interventions (such as outreach and family psychoeducation) when required.

In contrast to global strategic approaches, British CBT models are time limited, illness phase specific, and targeted toward specific medication-resistant symptoms and distress. These interventions involve application of specific and more readily defined therapeutic techniques. The major challenge in their development appears to be better definition of the specific patient subgroups for whom these interventions are effective: specification of what works for whom. A psychotherapist operating within a broad strategic outline might then be in a position to select or prescribe from a menu of effective, targeted, time-limited interventions for particular patients at particular times. Targeted approaches to medication-resistant hallucinations and delusions are already validated. Depression, impaired self-concept, and substance abuse may be appropriate targets for future CBT methodology.

With or without data to inform it, clinicians will continue to practice individual psychotherapy. New antipsychotic agents with greater efficacy and fewer side effects raise the functional ceiling previously imposed on many patients treated with first generation medications. Effectiveness studies that include use of new medications are clearly required to test the generalizability of both broad and targeted psychotherapy approaches. Moving studies validated in the laboratory to myriad real world settings where patients and therapists meet will define the standard of care for schizophrenia treatment for the future.

REFERENCES

A Recovering Patient. (1986). "Can we talk?" The schizophrenic patient in psychotherapy. *American Journal of Psychiatry, 143,* 68–70.

Alanen, Y. O. (1997). *Schizophrenia: Its origins and need-adapted treatment.* London, England: H. Karnac.

Alanen, T. O., Lehtinen, K., Rakkolainen, V., & Aaltonen, J. (1991). Need-adapted treatment of new schizophrenic patients: Experiences and results of the Turku project. *Acta Psychiatrica Scandinavica, 83,* 363–372.

American Psychiatric Association. (1997). Practice guidelines for the treatment of patients with schizophrenia. *American Journal of Psychiatry, 154(Supp).*

Aveline, M., & Shapiro, D. A., (Eds.). (1995). *Research foundations for psychotherapy practice.* New York, NY: John Wiley and Sons.

Beck, A. T., & Rector, N. A. (1998). Cognitive therapy for schizophrenic patients. *The Harvard Mental Health Letter, 15,* 4–6.

Book, H. E. (1987). Some psychodynamics of non-compliance. *Canadian Journal of Psychiatry, 32,* 115–117.

Breier, A., & Strauss, J. S. (1983). Self-control in psychotic diseases. *Archives of General Psychiatry, 40,* 1141–1145.

Brill, A. A. (1929). Schizophrenia and psychotherapy. *American Journal of Psychiatry, 9,* 519–541.

Carpenter, W. T. (1984). A perspective on the Psychotherapy of Schizophrenia Project. *Schizophrenia Bulletin, 10*(4), 599–603.

Carpenter, W. X. (1986). Thoughts on the treatment of schizophrenia. *Schizophrenia Bulletin, 12*(4), 527–538.

Cotton, P. G., Drake, R. E., & Gates, C. (1985). Critical treatment issues in suicide among schizophrenics. *Hospital and Community Psychiatry, 36,* 534–536.

Coursey, R. D. (1989). Psychotherapy with persons suffering from schizophrenia: The need for a new agenda. *Schizophrenia Bulletin, 15*(3), 349–353.

Coursey, R. D., Farrell, E. W., & Zahniser, J. H. (1991). Consumers' attitudes towards psychotherapy, hospitalization, and aftercare. *Health and Social Work, 16,* 155–161.

Coursey, R. D., Keller, A. B., & Farrell, E. W. (1995). Individual psychotherapy and persons with serious mental illness: The client's perspective. *Schizophrenia Bulletin, 21*(2), 283–301.

Diamond, R. J. (1983). Enhancing medication use in schizophrenic patients. *Journal of Clinical Psychiatry, 44,* 7–14.

Dingman, C. W., & McGlashan, T. H. (1999). Psychotherapy. In A. S Bellack (Ed.), *A clinical guide for the treatment of schizophrenia.* New York, NY, and London, England: Plenum Press.

Dixon, L., Lyles, A., Scott, J., Lehman, A., Postrado, L., Goldman, H., & McGlynn, E. (1999). Services to families of adults with schizophrenia: From treatment recommendations to dissemination. *Psychiatric Services, 50,* 233–238.

Docherty, J. P. O. Tempora, O. Mores. (1984). Directions in research on the psychotherapeutic treatment of schizophrenia. *Schizophrenia Bulletin, 10*(4), 621–623.

Dolnick, E. (1998). *Madness on the couch: Blaming the victim in the heyday of psychoanalysis.* New York, NY Simon and Schuster.

Drake, R. E., & Cotton, P. G. (1986). Depression, hopelessness, and suicide in chronic schizophrenia. *British Journal of Psychiatry, 148,* 554–559.

Drake, R. E., Gates, C., Cotton, P. G., & Whitaker, A. (1984). Suicide among schizophrenics: Who is at risk? *Journal of Nervous and Mental Disease, 172,* 613–617.

Drake, R. E., & Sederer, L. I. (1986). The adverse effects of intensive treatment of chronic schizophrenia. *Comprehensive Psychiatry, 27,* 313–326.

Drury, V., Birchwood, M., Cochrane, R., & MacMillan, F. (1996a). Cognitive therapy and recovery from acute psychosis: A controlled trial: I. Impact on psychotic symptoms. *British Journal of Psychiatry, 169,* 593–601.

Drury, V., Birchwood, M., Cochrane, R., & MacMillan, F. (1996b). Cognitive therapy and recovery from acute psychosis: A controlled trial: II. Impact on recovery time. *British Journal of Psychiatry, 169,* 602–607.

Duckworth, K., Nair, V., Patel, J. K., & Goldfinger, S. M. (1997). Lost tune, found hope and sorrow: The search for self, connection, and purpose during "awakenings" on the new antipsychotics. *Harvard Review of Psychiatry, 5,* 227–233.

Dyrud, J. E., & Holzman, P. S. (1973). Evaluation of psychotherapy: The psychotherapy of schizophrenia: Does it work? *American Journal of Psychiatry, 130,* 670–673.

Falloon, I. R. H. (1992). Psychotherapy of schizophrenia. *British Journal of Hospital Medicine, 48,* 165–170.

Falloon, I. R. H., & Talbot, R. E. (1981). Persistent auditory hallucinations: Coping mechanisms and implications for management. *Psychological Medicine, 11,* 329–339.

Feinsilver, D. B., & Gunderson, J. G. (1975). Psychotherapy for schizophrenics: Is it indicated? In J. G. Gunderson and L. R. Mosher, (Eds.), *Issues and controversies in the psychotherapy of schizophrenia,* (pp. 403–430). Northvale, NJ: Jason Aronson.

Fenton, W. S., Blylef, C. R., & Heinssen, R. K. (1997). Determinants of medication compliance in schizophrenia: Clinical and empirical correlates. *Schizophrenia Bulletin, 23*(4), 637–651.

Fenton, W. S., & McGlashan, T. H. (1987). Sustained remission in drug free schizophrenics. *American Journal of Psychiatry, 144,* 1306–1309.

Fenton, W. S., & McGlashan, T. H. (1995). Schizophrenia: Individual psychotherapy. In H. I. Kaplan & B. J. Sadock (Eds.), *Comprehensive textbook of psychiatry. Vol. 6,* (pp. 1007–1018). Baltimore, MD: Williams and Wilkins.

Fenton, W. S., & McGlashan, T. H. (1997). We can talk: Individual psychotherapy for schizophrenia. *American Journal of Psychiatry, 154,* 1493–1495.

Fenton, W. S., McGlashan, T. H., Victor, B. J., & Blyler, C. R. (1997). Symptoms, subtype, and suicidality in patients with schizophrenia spectrum diseases. *American Journal of Psychiatry, 154,* 199–204.

Frank, A. F., & Gunderson, J. G. (1990). The role of the therapeutic alliance in the treatment of schizophrenia: Relationship to course and outcome. *Archives of General Psychiatry, 47,* 228–236.

Fromm-Reichmann, E. (1950). *Principles of intensive psychotherapy.* Chicago, IL: University of Chicago Press.

Garety, P., Fowler, D., & Kuipers, E. (2000). Cognitive-behavioral therapy for medication-resistant symptoms. *Schizophrenia Bulletin, 26*(l), 73–86.

Garety, P, Fowler, D., Kuipers, E., Freeman, D., Dunn, G., Bebbington, P., Hadley, C., & Jones, S. (1997). London–East Anglia randomised controlled trial of cognitive-behavioural therapy for psychosis: II. Predictors of outcome. *British Journal of Psychiatry, 171,* 420–426.

Garety, P., Kuipers, L., Fowler, D., Chamberlain, F., & Dunn, G. (1994). Cognitive behavioural therapy for drug-resistant psychosis. *British Journal of Medical Psychology, 67,* 259–271.

Gilbert, S., & Ugelstad, A. (1994). Patients' own contribution to long-term supportive psychotherapy in schizophrenic diseases. *British Journal of Psychiatry, 164(Suppl 23),* 84–88.

Glass, L. L., Katz, H. M., Schnitzer, R. D., Knapp, P. H., Frank, A. F., & Gunderson, J. G. (1989). Psychotherapy of schizophrenia: An empirical investigation of the relationship of process to outcome. *American Journal of Psychiatry, 146,* 603–608.

Gomez-Schwartz, B. (1984). Individual psychotherapy of schizophrenia. In A. Bellack (Ed.), *Schizophrenia: Treatment, management, and rehabilitation,* (pp. 307–335). New York, NY: Grune and Stratton.

Greenberg, J. R., & Mitchell, S. A. (1983). *Object relations in psychoanalytic theory.* Cambridge, MA, and London, England: Harvard University Press.

Grinspoon, L., Ewalt, J. R., & Shader, R. (1968). Psychotherapy and pharmacotherapy in chronic schizophrenia. *American Journal of Psychiatry, 124,* 1645–1652.

Gunderson, J. G., Frank, A. F., Katz, H. M., Vannicelli, M. L., Frosch, J. P., & Knapp, P. H. (1984). Effects of psychotherapy in schizophrenia: II. Comparative outcome of two forms of treatment. *Schizophrenia Bulletin, 10*(4), 564–598.

Haddock, G., Bentall, R. P., & Slade, P. D. (1996). Psychological treatment of auditory hallucinations: Focusing or distraction? In G. Haddock & P. Slade (Eds.) *Cognitive-behavioural interventions with psychotic diseases,* (pp. 45–70). London, England: Routledge.

Haddock, G., Sellwood, W., Tarrier, N., & Yusupoff, L. (1994). Developments in cognitive-behavioural therapy for persistent psychotic symptoms. *Behavior Change, 11,* 200–212.

Haddock, G., Tarrier, N., Morrison, A.P., Hopkins, R., Drake, R., & Lewis, S. (1999). A pilot study evaluating the effectiveness of individual inpatient cognitive-behavioural therapy in early psychosis. *Social Psychiatry and Psychiatric Epidemiolog, 34,* 254–258.

Hatfield, A. B., Gearson, J. S., & Coursey, R. D. (1996). Family members' ratings of the use and value of mental health services: Results of a national NAMI survey. *Hospital and Community Psychiatry, 27,* 825–831.

Heinrichs, D. W., & Carpenter, W. T. (1981). The efficacy of individual psychotherapy: A perspective and review emphasizing controlled outcome studies. In S. Arieti & H. K. Brodie (Eds.), *American Handbook of Psychiatry,* (pp. 586–613). New York, NY: Basic Books.

Hill, L. B. (1955). *Psychotherapeutic intervention in schizophrenia.* Chicago, IL: University of Chicago Press.

Hingley, S. M. (1997). Psychodynamic perspectives on psychosis and psychotherapy: II. Practice. *British Journal of Medical Psychology, 70,* 313–324.

Hogarty, G. E., Kornblith, S. J., Greenwald, D., DiBarry, A. L., Cooley, S., Flesher, S., Reiss D., Carter, M., & Ulrich, R. (1995). Personal therapy: A disorder-relevant psychotherapy for schizophrenia. *Schizophrenia Bulletin, 21*(3), 379–393.

Hogarty, G. E., Kornblith, S. J., Greenwald, D., DiBarry, A. L., Cooley, S., Ulrich, R. F., Carter, M., & Flesher, S. (1997a). Three year trials of personal therapy among schizophrenic patients living with or independent of family: I. Description of study and effects on relapse rates. *American Journal of Psychiatry, 154,* 1504–1513.

Hogarty, G. E., Goldberg, S. C., & the Collaborative Study Group. (1973). Drug and sociotherapy in the aftercare of schizophrenic patients: One year relapse rates. *Archives of General Psychiatry, 28,* 54–64.

Hogarty, G. E., Goldberg, S. C., Schooler, N. R., & the Collaborative Study Group. (1974a). Drug and sociotherapy in the aftercare of schizophrenic patients: III. Adjustment of nonrelapsed patients. *Archives of General Psychiatry, 31,* 609–618.

Hogarty G. E., Goldberg, S. C., Schooler, N. R., Ulrich, R. F., & the Collaborative Study Group. (1974b). Drug and sociotherapy in the aftercare of schizophrenic patients. *Archives of General Psychiatry, 31,* 603–608.

Hogarty, G. E., Greenwald, D., Ulrich, R. F., Kornblith, S. J., DiBarry, A. L., Cooley, S., Carter, M., & Flesher, S. (1997b). Three year trials of personal therapy among schizophrenic patients living with or independent of family: II. Effects on adjustment of patients. *American Journal of Psychiatry, 154,* 1514–1524.

Hogarty, G. E., Schooler, N. R., Ulrich, R., Mussare, F., Ferro, P., & Herron, E. (1979). Fluphenazine and social therapy in the aftercare of schizophrenic patients. Relapse analyses of a two-year controlled study of fluphenazine decanoate and fluphenazine hydrochloride. *Archives of General Psychiatry, 36,* 1283–1294.

Hogarty, G., & Ulrich, R. F. (1998). The limitations of antipsychotic medications on schizophrenia relapse and adjustment and the contributions of psychosocial treatment. *Journal of Psychiatric Research, 32,* 243–250.

Hollister, J. M., Laing, P., & Mednick, S. A. (1996). Rhesus incompatibility as a risk factor for schizophrenia in male adults. *Archives of General Psychiatry, 53,* 19–23.

Huszonek, J. J. (1987). Establishing therapeutic contact with schizophrenics: A supervisory approach. *American Journal of Psychotherapy, 16,* 185–193.

Jeffries, J. J. (1995). Working with schizophrenia: A clinician's personal experience. *Canadian Journal of Psychiatry, 40,* S22–S25.

Kane, J. M., & McGlashan, T. H. (1996). Treatment of schizophrenia. *Lancet, 346,* 820–825.

Karon, B. P. (1984). The fear of reducing medication, and where have all the patients gone? *Schizophrenia Bulletin, 10*(4), 613–617.

Karon, B. P., & Vandenbos, G. R. (1972). The consequences of psychotherapy for schizophrenic patients. Psychotherapy: *Theory, Research and Practice, 9,* 111–119.

Karon, B. P., & Vandenbos, G. R. (1982). *Psychotherapy of schizophrenia: The treatment of choice.* New York, NY Jason Aronson.

Katz, H. M. (1989). A new agenda for psychotherapy of schizophrenia: Response to Coursey. *Schizophrenia Bulletin, 15*(3), 355–359.

Kemp, R., David, A., & Haywood, P. (1996a). Compliance Therapy: An intervention targeting insight and treatment adherence in psychotic patients. *Behavioural and Cognitive Psychotherapy, 24,* 331–350.

Kemp, R., Hayward, P., Applewhaite, G., Everitt, B., & David, A. (1996b). Compliance therapy in psychotic patients: A randomized controlled trial. *British Medical Journal, 312,* 345–349.

Kemp, R., Kirov, G., Everitt, P., Haywood, P., & David, A. (1998). Randomized controlled trial of compliance therapy: 18-month follow-up. *British Journal of Psychiatry, 172,* 413–419.

Klerman, G. L. (1984). Ideology and science in the individual psychotherapy of schizophrenia. *Schizophrenia Bulletin, 10*(4), 608–612.

Kuipers, E., Fowler, D., Garety, P., Chisholm, D., Freeman, D., Dunn, G., Bebbington, P., & Hadley, C. (1998). London-East Anglia randomised trial of cognitive-behavioural therapy for psychosis: III. Follow-up and economic evaluation at 18 months. *British Journal of Psychiatry, 173,* 61–68.

Kuipers, E., Garety, P., Fowler, D., Dunn, G., Bebington, P., Freeman, D., & Hadley, C. (1997). London-East Anglia randomized controlled trial of cognitive-behavioural therapy for psychosis: I. Effects of the treatment phase. *British Journal of Psychiatry, 171,* 319–327.

Lehman, A. F., Carpenter, W. T., Goldman, H. H., & Steinwachs, D. M. (1995). Treatment outcomes in schizophrenia: Implications for practice, policy and research. *Schizophrenia Bulletin, 21*(4), 669–676.

Levine, I. L., & Wilson, A. (1985). Dynamic interpersonal processes and the inpatient holding environment. *Psychiatry, 48,* 341–357.

Lin, K. M., & Kleinman, A. M. (1988). Psychopathology and clinical course in schizophrenia: A cross cultural perspective. *Schizophrenia Bulletin, 14*(4), 555–567.

May, P. R. A. (1984). A step forward in research on psychotherapy of schizophrenia. *Schizophrenia Bulletin, 10*(4), 604–607.

May, P. R. A., & Tuma, A. H. (1964). The effect of psychotherapy and stelazine on length of hospital stay, release rate and supplemental treatment of schizophrenia patients. *Journal of Nervous and Mental Disease, 139,* 362–369.

May, P. R. A., & Tuma, A. H. (1972). Methodological problems in psychotherapy research: Observations on the Karon Vandenbos study of psychotherapy and drugs in schizophrenia. In R. Cancro (Ed.), *Annual review of the schizophrenic syndrome.* New York, NY Bruner-Mazel.

May, P. R., Tuma, A. H., & Dixon, W. J. (1976a). Schizophrenia: A follow-up study of results of treatment: I. Design and other problems. *Archives of General Psychiatry, 33,* 464–478.

May, P. R. A., Tuma, A. H., & Dixon, W. J. (1981). Schizophrenia: A follow-up study of the results of five forms of treatment. *Archives of General Psychiatry, 38,* 776–784.

May, P. R., Tuma, A. H., Yale, C., Potepan, P., & Dixon, W. J. (1976b). Schizophrenia: A follow-up study of results of treatment: II. Hospital stay over two to five years. *Archives of General Psychiatry, 33,* 481–486.

McGlashan, T. H. (1982). DSM-III schizophrenia and individual psychotherapy. *Journal of Nervous and Mental Disease, 170,* 752–757.

McGlashan, T. H. (1983). Intensive individual psychotherapy of schizophrenia: A review of techniques. *Archives of General Psychiatry, 40,* 909–920.

McGlashan, T. H. (1984). The Chestnut Lodge Follow-up Study II: Long-term outcome of schizophrenia and affective disorders. *Archives of General Psychiatry, 41,* 586–601.

McGlashan, T. H. (1986). Schizophrenia: Psychosocial treatments and the role of psychosocial factors in its etiology and pathogenesis. In A. Frances & R. Hales (Eds.), *Annual review of psychiatry. Vol. 4.* Washington, DC: American Psychiatric Press.

McGlashan, T. H. (1988). A selective review of recent North American long-term followup studies of schizophrenia. *Schizophrenia Bulletin, 14*(4), 515–542.

McGlashan, T. H., & Fenton, W. S. (1993). Subtype progression and pathophysiologic deterioration in the course of early manifest schizophrenia. *Schizophrenia Bulletin, 19*(l), 71–84.

McGlashan, T. H., & Keats, C. J. (1989). *Schizophrenia: Treatment process and outcome.* Washington, DC: American Psychiatric Press.

Meehl, P. E. (1962). Schizotaxia, schizotypy, schizophrenia. *American Psychologist, 17*, 827–838.

Messier, M., Finnerty, R., Botvin, C. S., & Grinspoon, L. (1969). A follow-up study of intensively treated chronic schizophrenic patients. *American Journal of Psychiatry, 125*, 1123–1127.

Mosher, L. R., & Keith, S. J. (1980). Psychosocial treatment: Individual, group, family and community support approaches. *Schizophrenia Bulletin, 6*(l), 10–41.

Mueser, K. T., & Berenbaum, H. (1990). Psychodynamic treatment of schizophrenia: Is there a future? *Psychological Medicine, 20*, 253–262.

Nuechterlein, K. H., & Dawson, M. E. (1984). A heuristic vulnerability/stress model of schizophrenic episodes. *Schizophrenia Bulletin, 10*(2), 300–312.

Olin, S. S., & Mednick, S. A. (1996). Risk factors of psychosis: Identifying vulnerable populations premorbidly. *Schizophrenia Bulletin, 22*(2), 223–240.

Pao, P-N. (1979). *Schizophrenic disorders.* New York, NY: International Universities Press.

Parsons, T. (1951). *The social system.* Glencoe, IL: The Free Press. Chapter 10.

Perreault, M., Rogers, W.L., Leichner, P., & Sabourin, S. (1996). Patient requests and satisfaction with services in an outpatient psychiatric setting. *Psychiatric Services, 47*, 287–292.

Perris, C. (1989). *Cognitive therapy with schizophrenic patients.* New York, NY: Guilford.

Perry, H. S. (1982). *Psychiatrist of America: The life of Harry Stack Sullivan.* Cambridge, MA, and London, England: The Belknap Press of Harvard University Press.

Rako S., & Mazer, H., (Eds.). (1980). *Semrad: The heart of a therapist.* New York, NY: Jason Aronson.

Rioch, D. M., Dexter Bullard, Sr., & Chestnut Lodge. (1984). *Psychiatry, 47*, 1–8.

Rogers, C. R., Gendlin, E. G., Kiesler, D. J., & Truax, C .B. (1967). *The therapeutic relationship and its impact.* Madison, WE University of Wisconsin Press.

Rollnick, S., Heather, N., & Bell, A. (1992). Negotiating behavior change in medical settings: The development of brief motivational interviewing. *Journal of Mental Health, 1*, 25–37.

Rothman, D. J. (1971). *The discovery of the asylum: Social order and disorder in the New Republic.* Boston, MA: Little Brown and Company.

Sarti, P., & Coumos, F. (1990). Medication and psychotherapy in the treatment of chronic schizophrenia. *Psychiatric Clinics of North America, 13*, 215–228.

Scott, J. E., & Dixon, L. B. (1995). Psychological interventions for schizophrenia. *Schizophrenia Bulletin, 21*(4), 621–630.

Searles, H. F. (1965). *Collected papers on schizophrenia and related subjects.* New York, NY: International Universities Press.

Searles, H. F. (1979). *Countertransference and related subjects.* New York, NY. International Universities Press.

Stanton, A. H., Gunderson, J. G., Knapp, P. H., Frank, A. F., Vannicelli, M. L., Schnitzer, R., & Rosenthal, R. (1984). Effects of psychotherapy in schizophrenia: I. Design and implementation of a controlled study. *Schizophrenia Bulletin, 10*(4), 520–563.

Stanton, A. H., & Schwartz, M. S. (1954). *The mental hospital.* New York, NY: Basic Books.

Stone, M. H. (1986). Exploratory psychotherapy in schizophrenia spectrum patients: A reevaluation in the light of long-term follow-up of schizophrenic and borderline conditions. *Bulletin of the Menninger Clinic, 50,* 287–306.

Strauss, J. S., Hafez, H., Lieberman, P., & Harding, C. M. (1985). The course of psychiatric disorder: III. Longitudinal principles. *American Journal of Psychiatry, 142,* 289–296.

Sullivan, H. S. (1931). The modified psychoanalytic treatment of schizophrenia. *American Journal of Psychiatry, 89,* 519–540.

Sullivan H. S. (1970). *The psychiatric interview.* New York, NY: W.W. Norton and Company.

Susser, E., Neugebauer, R., Hosk, H. W., Brown, A. S., Lin, S., Labovitz, D., & Gorman, J. M. (1996). Schizophrenia after prenatal famine. *Archives of General Psychiatry, 53,* 25–3l.

Tarrier, N. (1992a). Management and modification of residual positive psychotic symptoms. In M. Birchwood and N. Tarrier (Eds.), *Innovations in the psychological management of schizophrenia.* New York, NY: John Wiley and Sons.

Tarrier, N. (1992b). Psychological treatment of positive schizophrenic symptoms. In Kavanagh, (Ed.), *Schizophrenia: An overview and practical handbook.* London, England: Chapman and Hall.

Tarrier, N., Beckett, R., Harwood, S., Baker, A., Yusupoff, L., & Ugarteburu, I. A. (1993a). Trial of two cognitive-behavioural methods of treating drug-resistant residual psychotic symptoms in schizophrenic patients: I. Outcome. *British Journal of Psychiatry, 162,* 524–532.

Tarrier, N., Sharpe, L., Beckett, R., Harwood, S., Baker, A., & Yusopoff, L. (1993b). A trial of two cognitive behavioural methods of treating drug-resistant residual psychotic symptoms in schizophrenic patients: II. Treatment-specific changes in coping and problem-solving skills. *Social Psychiatry and Psychiatric Epidemiology, 28,* 5–10.

Tarrier, N., Wittkowski, A., Kinney, C., McCarthy, E., Morris, J., & Humphreys, L. (1999). Durability of the effects of cognitive-behavioural therapy in the treatment of chronic schizophrenia: 12-month follow-up. *British Journal of Psychiatry, 174,* 500–504.

Tarrier, N., Yusupoff, L., Kinney, C., McCarthy, E., Gledhill, A., Haddock, G., & Morris, J. (1998b). Randomized controlled trial of intensive cognitive behaviour therapy for patients with chronic schizophrenia. *British Medical Journal, 317,* 303–307.

Weiden, P., & Havens, L. (1994). Psychotherapeutic management techniques in the treatment of outpatients with schizophrenia. *Psychiatric Services, 45,* 549–555.

Wexler, M. (1975). Comment on the five-treatment comparative study. In J. G. Gunderson & L. R. Mosher (Eds.). *Issues and controversies in the psychotherapy of schizophrenia,* (pp.431–433). Northvale, NJ, and London, England: Jason Aronson.

Winston, A., Pinsker, H., & McCullough, L. (1986). A review of supportive psychotherapy. *Hospital and Community Psychiatry, 37,* 1105–1114.

Wyatt, R. J., Alexander, R.C., Egan, M. F., & Kirch, D. G. (1988). Schizophrenia: Just the facts. What do we know, how well do we know it? *Schizophrenia Research, 1,* 3–18.

Zahniser, J. H., Coursey, R. D., & Hershberger, K. (1991). Individual psychotherapy with schizophrenic outpatients in the public mental health system. *Hospital and Community Psychiatry, 42,* 906–913.

Zubin, J., & Steinhauer S. (1981). How to break the log-jam, in schizophrenia: A look beyond genetics. *Journal of Nervous and Mental Disease, 169,* 477–492.

Acknowledgment

The views expressed in this article are those of the author and do not necessarily reflect the official views of the National Institute of Mental Health, the National Institutes of Health, or any other branch of the U.S. Department of Health and Human Services.

Cognitive-Behavioral Therapy for Medication-Resistant Symptoms

Philippa A. Garety, David Fowler, and Elizabeth Kuipers

At the time of original publication, author affiliations were as follows: Philippa Garety, MA, MPhil, PhD, FBPsS, is Professor of Clinical Psychology, The Guy's, King's and St. Thomas' Medical and Dental School, King's College, London, United Kingdom; David Fowler, MSc, CPsychol, AFBPsS, is Consultant Clinical Psychologist, Norfolk Mental Health Care Trust and School of Health Policy and Practice, University of East Anglia, Norwich, United Kingdom; Elizabeth Kuipers, BSc, MSc, PhD, FBPsS, is Professor of Clinical Psychology, Institute of Psychiatry, London, United Kingdom.

This article was published previously in the *Schizophrenia Bulletin,* 2000, 26(1), 73–86, and is reprinted with permission.

Abstract: Cognitive-behavioral therapy for psychosis is described. It draws on the cognitive models and therapy approach of Beck and colleagues, combined with an application of stress-vulnerability models of schizophrenia and cognitive models of psychotic symptoms. There is encouraging evidence for the efficacy of this approach. Four controlled trials have found that cognitive-behavioral therapy reduces symptoms of psychosis, and there is some evidence that it may contribute to relapse reduction. Studies that have examined factors that predict treatment response are reviewed. There is preliminary evidence that a good outcome is partially predicted by a measure of cognitive flexibility or a "chink of insight." People who present with only negative symptoms may show poorer outcome. However, there is no evidence that intelligence or symptom severity is associated with outcome. Implications for selecting patients and for optimal duration of treatment are discussed. Finally, the importance of taking account of the heterogeneity of people with psychosis, so that individual treatment goals are identified, is discussed.

In recent years, particularly in the United Kingdom, there has been a growing interest in developing cognitive-behavioral therapy for those people with psychosis who continue to experience psychotic symptoms despite efforts to treat those symptoms with antipsychotic medication. It is estimated that between one quarter and one half of people with a diagnosis of schizophrenia experience medication-resistant persistent symptoms such as delusions and hallucinations, which cause distress and interference with functioning (Fowler et al., 1995). The need for an effective psychological intervention for psychotic symptoms also arises from the reluctance of many patients to take long-term medication, with its unpleasant and even disabling side effects, and the fact that relapse occurs commonly, even in patients who do adhere to medication regimes (Roth & Fonagy, 1996).

Unlike certain other psychological interventions for people with schizophrenia spectrum disorders (hereafter referred to as "psychosis"), such as social skills training or cognitive remediation approaches, cognitive-behavioral therapy takes as its central focus the experiences of psychosis (i.e., the symptoms) and the person's attempts to understand them. In recent years, three books have been published providing detailed descriptions of cognitive-behavioral therapy for people with psychosis (Kingdon & Turkington 1994; Fowler et al., 1995; Chadwick et al., 1996). There are some differences of emphasis, but there is agreement concerning the goals and main methods of therapy; indeed, there has been a fruitful cross-fertilization of ideas. The principal aim of cognitive-behavioral therapy for medication-resistant psychosis is to reduce the distress and interference with functioning caused by the psychotic symptoms. The thoughts, beliefs, and images experienced by people are the core material with which cognitive-behavioral therapists work. The approach draws extensively on the cognitive therapy of Beck and colleagues (e.g., Beck et al., 1979), both in terms of therapeutic style and of content. In terms of style, the therapist works collaboratively, setting agendas and therapy goals, and takes an actively enquiring stance toward the clients' accounts of their experiences. The content of therapy involves identifying thoughts and beliefs, reviewing evidence for these beliefs, encouraging self-monitoring of cognitions, relating thoughts to mood and behavior, and identifying thinking biases. However, the standard cognitive therapy approach must be modified to effectively address the particular problems of psychosis, including the special difficulties of establishing a therapeutic relationship, the complexity and severity of the problems presented, the need to take account of neurocognitive deficits, and the importance of working on the subjective understanding of psychosis. In this article, we will describe cognitive-behavioral therapy for psychosis, review the evidence for its effectiveness, and discuss which patients might benefit from this approach.

COGNITIVE-BEHAVIORAL THERAPY

Theoretical Background

A number of theoretical models and hypotheses provide a theoretical underpinning to cognitive-behavioral therapy for psychosis. In general, psychoses are viewed as heterogeneous and multifactorial and as best understood within a biopsychosocial framework. It is assumed that there are different degrees to which biological vulnerability, psychological processes, and the social environment have contributed in the individual case to the expression of psychosis (Garety & Hernsley, 1994; Fowler et al., 1995). This is consistent with widely accepted "stress-vulnerability" models (Zubin & Spring, 1977; Strauss & Carpenter, 1981). These posit that the individual has an enduring vulnerability to psychosis, possibly but not necessarily of genetic or neurodevelopmental origin, a vulnerability that may be heightened by childhood experiences, whether social, psychological, or biological. The psychosis becomes manifest on subsequent exposure to a range of additional stresses, which again may be social, psychological, or biological, such as adverse environments, major life transitions, or drug misuse. A further set of factors may be important in maintaining the illness in the longer term (such as the meaning attributed to psychotic experiences, loss of social roles, or the use of medication). In applying the stress-vulnerability framework in the context of cognitive-behavioral therapy, the key implication is that there are different factors exerting their influence in different cases and at different times. The therapist aims to develop an individual account of a person's vulnerabilities, stresses, and responses, and to help the person to modify cognitions and behavior accordingly (Fowler et al., 1998). "Personal therapy," an approach developed and evaluated in the United States by Hogarty and colleagues, also draws on the stress-vulnerability framework and in some respects is similar to the cognitive-behavioral approaches developed in the United Kingdom (Hogarty et al., 1995, 1997). Personal therapy emphasizes working on the identification of the experience of stress and its modification, with a clear focus on enhancing personal and social adjustment and on relapse prevention; this emphasis is shared by cognitive-behavioral therapy. However, personal therapy directs less attention to the symptoms of psychosis. Cognitive-behavioral therapy, because it is grounded in cognitive models of psychotic symptoms, focuses on such symptoms as a key component of therapy.

The core symptoms and experiences of psychosis are manifest as disturbances of cognition, both in basic cognitive processes concerned with information processing, resulting in anomalies of perception and experience of the self (e.g., hallucinations), and in conscious appraisals and judgments leading to unusual beliefs (delusions). Cognitive psychology, applying an understanding of cognitive processes involved in the general population, has found evidence of disruptions and biases in processes that are thought to contribute to the development and persistence of psychotic symptoms (Garety & Freeman, 1999).

There are several competing cognitive theories to explain psychotic symptoms (Nuechterlein & Subotnik, 1998). Theorists such as Hemsley (1994) and Frith (1992) have suggested that some of the primary anomalous experiences associated with delusions result from cognitive neuropsychological deficits and probably a brain dysfunction. For example, Frith (1992) has proposed that a deficit in the self-monitoring of thoughts and intentions to act (a cognitive process occurring outside conscious awareness) gives rise to the symptoms of thought insertion and alien control. Others have suggested that delusions may arise as reasonable attempts to explain puzzling anomalous experiences (Maher, 1988), while Garety and Hernsley (1994) have identified that delusions are associated with a "jumping to conclusions" style of reasoning that may play a role in their formation or persistence. Still other theorists have suggested that delusions are motivational in origin and may serve the function of defending a person against threats to self-esteem (Freud, 1915; Bentall et al., 1994). We have argued that it is probable that there is no single pathway to delusions or other psychotic symptoms. In some cases, careful assessment may suggest that one type of process may satisfactorily explain the presence of the symptom, but in other cases symptoms appear to be the product or final common pathway of several interacting processes, be they biological, psychological, or social.

Cognitive accounts have also considered how psychotic experiences, however they arise, may be negatively appraised by individuals. These experiences may then result in emotional disturbance, such as depression or anxiety, or in negative evaluations of the self, which jointly contribute to the development and maintenance of symptoms and distress (Chadwick & Birchwood, 1994; Close & Garety, 1998). The hypothesized role of emotional processes such as depression and anxiety in the maintenance and the onset of psychosis leads to the direct application of cognitive therapy techniques for these problems (Birchwood & Iqbal, 1998; Freeman & Garety, 1999).

Cognitive-behavioral therapy for psychosis draws on accounts of cognitive and emotional processes, in psychosis, in people with emotional problems and in the general population. The central assumption is that people with psychosis, like all of us, are attempting to make sense of the world and their experiences. The meanings attributed to their experiences and the way they process their experiences, together with their earlier personality development, will influence the expression and development of symptoms, emotional responses, and behavior. Helping people to become aware of the processes that influence their thoughts and emotions and to reevaluate their views of themselves and the psychosis is therefore central to therapy. Cognitive-behavioral therapy combines approaches based on these cognitive models with interventions grounded in the stress-vulnerability model.

However, in placing cognitive accounts of psychosis within broader stress-vulnerability models, it is clear that there is a role for a range of different interventions for people with psychosis. We see individual cognitive therapy as only one approach in an array of potentially beneficial methods of treatment and support, including biological treatments (i.e., antipsychotic medication) and many psychosocial interventions.

The Therapeutic Approach

The broad aims of cognitive-behavioral therapy for people with medication-resistant psychosis are threefold (Fowler et al., 1995):

1. To reduce the distress and disability caused by psychotic symptoms.

2. To reduce emotional disturbance.

3. To help the individual arrive at an understanding of psychosis that promotes his or her active participation in reducing the risk of relapse and levels of social disability.

The general approach is concerned with understanding and making sense, and with achieving collaboration between the individual and the therapist, rather than employing didactic, interpretative, or confrontational styles. It is important to note that psychodynamically oriented therapies have different goals and methods than cognitive-behavioral therapy. These goals and methods have not been demonstrated to be effective for people with schizophrenia in well-controlled trials; one possible reason for this is that traditional psychodynamic approaches are too emotionally intense for at least some patients (Gunderson et al., 1984; Mueser & Berenbaum, 1990).

Cognitive-behavioral therapy is a structured and time-limited therapy, although the duration and frequency of therapy sessions will vary according to the nature and severity of the patient's problems. In patients with relatively stable medication-resistant symptoms, we have generally offered 9 months of therapy, on a weekly or biweekly basis, averaging about 20 sessions. However, this may range from 12 to 30 sessions, over 6 months to more than 1 year, as needed. Booster sessions may also be offered over a longer time period, or we may offer a brief period of more intense work if problems reemerge. Our recent therapy trial (Kuipers et al., 1997) was conducted on the basis of 9 months of therapy. Cognitive-behavioral therapy is normally offered alongside a range of other treatments and services, such as medication, day or vocational services, and case management. Indeed, optimal care requires integration of such interventions (Fenton & McGlashan, 1997). However, engagement in services is variable. Cognitive-behavioral therapy can be offered to people who do not engage in other services or who do not take medication.

We have conceptualized therapy as a series of six components or stages (Table 1), although we do not intend that they should be viewed as an inflexible linear sequence. In practice, engagement issues (the first "stage") may be readdressed at various times as required, while the work described in the final "stage" may be considered earlier. The six stages should therefore be seen as a guiding framework to be applied flexibly (Fowler et al., 1995). In describing the therapeutic techniques, we will also highlight the particular adaptations of cognitive-behavioral therapy required by working with this client group.

Table 1. Stages of Cognitive-Behavioral Therapy for Psychosis

Stage	Task
1	Engagement and assessment
2	Coping strategy work
3	Developing an understanding of the experience of psychosis
4	Working on delusions and hallucinations
5	Addressing mood and negative self-evaluations
6	Managing the risk of relapse and social disability

Building and Maintaining a Therapeutic Relationship: Engagement and Assessment

Cognitive-behavioral therapy begins with a period of building and establishing a collaborative therapeutic relationship in which enabling the client to feel understood is of paramount importance. While establishing a therapeutic alliance is an important predictor of therapy success in general (Horvath & Symonds, 1991), it is particularly relevant to working with people with psychosis. In the initial stages of therapy, people with psychosis may be suspicious, may be angry with mental health services, or may deny the relevance of therapy for their problems. If attention is not paid to these issues, early dropout is likely. Our solution is a flexible approach to therapy, which is accepting of the client's beliefs and emotions and starts by working from the client's own perspective. Particularly at this stage, we emphasize checking and discussing carefully with clients how they experience the sessions and their thoughts about the therapist's role. If a client finds sessions arousing or disturbing, we recommend shortening sessions or changing the topic to a less distressing subject. The primary aim is to ensure that the sessions are tolerable, always explicitly discussing this with the client. The occurrence of psychotic symptoms during the session, such as hallucinations or paranoid ideas, are acknowledged and gently discussed. This collaborative and gentle style clearly contrasts with the past conventional wisdom, which held that it was important to confront and not collude with a person's delusions. Clinical experience and research evidence indicate, however, that the direct challenging of beliefs as false, unlikely, or unfounded, with counterarguments, is not helpful. Indeed, such an approach will generally increase the strength of conviction and will potentially lead to distress and dropout (see Milton et al., 1978).

Gradually the therapist moves from empathic listening to more structured assessment interviewing, in which the therapist attempts to clarify the particular life circumstances, events, and experiences that provided the context for the onset of psychosis and makes a detailed analysis of specific distressing symptoms and other problems. Over a period of approximately six sessions (although this can be longer or shorter), the therapist carries out a detailed assessment, covering past history and present circumstances, while also aiming to develop rapport and trust. By the end of this period, some preliminary shared goals for therapy should be developed. These must be relevant to the client and expressed in the client's own terms, while being compatible with what the therapy can hope to achieve. For example, goals might be "to feel less paranoid while out of the house," "to cope better with the voices when at the day center," or "to feel less upset and angry with myself if the day goes badly." Such limited goals can be elaborated or changed as therapy progresses. The intervention that follows will be individualized and will focus on problems identified in collaboration with the client.

Cognitive-Behavioral Coping Strategies

Work on coping strategies follows directly from the assessment, in which current distressing symptoms and experiences have been identified, such as episodes of hearing voices and feeling anxious or suspicious when out. A range of cognitive and behavioral strategies, including activity scheduling, anxiety reduction, and attention control, has been shown to reduce the occurrence or duration of such problems (Fowler & Morley, 1989; Tarrier, 1992). Yusupoff and Tarrier (1996) describe these methods as essentially pragmatic and emphasize identifying what works in the individual case by undertaking a detailed assessment of existing strategies and of the antecedents and consequences of current symptoms. The goal is to manipulate any factors that contribute to symptom maintenance. Finding an approach that is helpful generally requires trial and error, since opposite strategies may be effective for different individuals or for different contexts (e.g., in response to hallucinations, an effective strategy might be either talking to someone or, alternatively, withdrawing from social contact). Developing an effective coping strategy can bring particular relief in cases where symptoms are experienced as overwhelming and uncontrollable, resulting, for example, in self-harm or disturbed behavior. The aim is to foster feelings of control and hope and to provide practical help in the early stages of therapy.

Implementing a new coping strategy may involve asking the client to undertake a homework task, such as keeping a record of the occurrence of the target symptom. Here adjustments to standard cognitive-behavioral practice may be needed. Clients with low IQ, literacy problems, or the specific neurocognitive deficits found in psychosis (such as deficits in memory or planning) may have difficulties with such tasks. Our approach is to take account of the client's cognitive abilities and to tailor tasks accordingly. For example, self-monitoring diaries can be set up to minimize literacy demands by use of prepared recording sheets with individualized multiple choice questions, while prompt cards can aid memory for use of a self-instruction strategy.

Developing a New Understanding of the Experience of Psychosis

Discussion of the experience and meaning of psychosis is an important element of cognitive-behavioral therapy. Most patients, at this stage of therapy, maintain strong conviction in their delusions and would be regarded as having poor insight in the formal sense (i.e., they do not recognize that they have a mental illness or do not recognize the contribution of specific symptoms to their illness). However, it is our experience that, nonetheless, the experience of psychosis is recognized by most as some kind of personal dysfunction, however caused, for which an explanation is required. A key first step in helping a client reevaluate beliefs is to construct a new model of events that is acceptable and makes sense to the client. This can provide the foundation for reevaluation of more specific ideas and beliefs subsequently. This work is similar to the "psychoeducation" component of other psychosocial approaches to psychosis, such as family work (reviewed by Penn & Mueser, 1996). However, in cognitive-behavioral therapy, the focus is not so much on "education about schizophrenia" as on developing an individualized account that draws on knowledge of psychosis but aims to make sense of the particular history and perspective of the client. Constructing a new model of psychosis therefore starts with exploring the client's current understanding of the disease, building on the acknowledgment, however tentative, of the experience of personal dysfunction. We explore the questions of whether clients see themselves as ill, stressed, or, perhaps, suffering from schizophrenia. We discuss their views of what caused their problems and what helps them. We ask how they view the future. Building on the clients' views and the information gained from the assessment, the therapist will aim tentatively to offer an individualized formulation, within a broad stress-vulnerability framework, but emphasizing an explanation of the person's subjective experience of psychosis. The formulation will make links between the client's life history and any identified vulnerability factors, stressful events that may have been precipitating factors at the onset of psychosis, and processes that may be maintaining the symptoms. Evidence that psychotic experiences occur in the general population under certain stressful conditions (e.g., sensory and sleep deprivation) is used to "normalize" psychosis (Kingdon & Turkington, 1994). Depending on the ability and interest of the client, we discuss biopsychosocial theories of psychosis and cognitive models of symptoms. The possible mechanisms of antipsychotic medication are often usefully discussed and set within the broader stress-vulnerability framework. In fostering a new or fuller understanding of the experience of psychosis, the therapist aims to reduce the guilt or denial associated with it and to provide a rationale for engaging in behaviors that reduce the risk of relapse and enhance functioning.

Working on Delusions and Hallucinations

It is not assumed that simply discussing a formulation will lead to delusional belief change. Where delusions and beliefs about voices are well-established, they are typically maintained by repeated misinterpretations of specific events, by ongoing anomalous experiences, and by cognitive and behavioral patterns that preferentially seek out confirmation and prevent disconfirmation of existing beliefs (Garety & Hernsley, 1994). For example, there is strong evidence that some people with delusions "jump to conclusions" on the basis of little evidence and that they have a biased attributional style in which other people are blamed for negative events (Bentall, 1994; Garety & Freeman, 1999). The beliefs may also serve the function of protecting self-esteem, and at the least, will have made subjective sense of disturbing or puzzling experiences. Therefore, the emotional consequences of changing strongly held beliefs need to be explored. After discussing in general terms how events may be misinterpreted as a result of cognitive biases and how inner experiences (thoughts or images) may be misattributed to external sources, a detailed analysis of day-to-day experiences and judgments is made. In each session, over a number of weeks or months, these are reviewed and alternatives generated. Chadwick et al. (1996) have provided a full account of this work with delusional beliefs, while Chadwick and Birchwood (1994) have developed approaches to auditory hallucinations that show that changing the beliefs held about voices (e.g., about their identity or powerfulness) will reduce distress.

This central work of identifying and changing the distressing and disabling delusions and hallucinations, by a systematic process of reviewing the evidence and generating alternatives, draws on standard cognitive approaches. However, there are some differences of method. First, as will have been noted, we only undertake this work once the therapeutic relationship is firmly established. By this we mean that the therapy should have progressed at least to the point that agreed goals have been articulated (as at the end of stage one) and preferably also that there has been some discussion of a model of psychotic experience on which the more detailed examination of individual symptoms can draw. It may therefore often be that this detailed discussion of delusions and hallucinations will take place in the second half of therapy. Second, the approach is gentle and non-confrontational; the therapist must carefully judge whether and how far to challenge the client's interpretations. Also, perhaps more commonly than in standard cognitive therapy, the therapist may supply alternative interpretations rather than always seek to ensure the client generates them. This helps to compensate for the cognitive inflexibility or impairment of some clients. Third, despite our best efforts, some clients firmly resist reevaluating their beliefs; in these cases, we aim to "work within" the delusions, identifying possible ways of reducing distress and disability despite the continuance of the belief. For example, one of us worked with a person who believed that the voice of God commanded her to jump out of the window. She had, in fact, more than once jumped out of an upstairs window, causing serious harm. However, she was not willing or able to reevaluate the evidence for the belief that she had a special relationship with God and heard his voice. Instead, it was possible to retain the belief that God talked to her in this way, but to discuss whether a benevolent God would wish her to do herself harm. The consequences of acting and not acting on such commands were explored, together with anxiety-reduction strategies to manage the high levels of arousal she experienced at such times.

Addressing Negative Self-Evaluations, Anxiety, and Depression

Low self-esteem is common in people with medication-resistant symptoms of psychosis (Freeman et al., 1998). Furthermore, links between the content of delusions or hallucinations and the characteristics of threatening and traumatic events in earlier life may have been identified in the assessment and formulation stages. These links may indicate that a patient has long-standing unresolved difficulties and associated negative self-evaluations (e.g., believing him or herself to be evil or worthless). Such self-evaluations are likely to be factors in the maintenance of delusions and voices, for example, by being congruent with and thereby appearing to confirm the accuracy of abusive voices (Close & Garety, 1998). After negative evaluations have been identified, standard cognitive therapy approaches are often applicable, to review the history of the development of these ideas over the life span and to reevaluate the evidence. Many people with psychosis have experienced very adverse life events and circumstances, including the psychosis itself and its consequences. In such cases, reappraisal may take the form of assisting the client to view him or herself as not, for example, "a total failure" or "a worthless person," but as someone who has struggled heroically with adversity.

The impact of the experience of psychosis is also relevant not only to specific evaluations, but also more generally to depression and anxiety. Birchwood et al. (1993) have documented how people experience demoralization and feelings of loss of control as a result of the onset of psychosis, while McGorry et al. (1991) have identified traumatic reactions to onset. Anxiety is often severe in people with psychosis, but is often overlooked (Freeman & Garety, 1999). Standard cognitive approaches of identifying automatic thoughts and dysfunctional assumptions and exploring alternative appraisals are recommended.

Managing Risk of Relapse and Social Disability

The final stage of therapy involves reviewing the work done and looking to the future. The understanding clients have of psychosis (discussed earlier) influences their engagement with services and supports and their attitudes toward medication. This is reviewed and discussed further as appropriate. Although aspects of social functioning will have been discussed throughout therapy (e.g., difficulties in social and family relationships, work, or other activities), short- and medium-term plans are discussed further, in light of what has been learned in therapy. The approach is not didactic, but aims to help the person weigh the advantages and disadvantages of different strategies and plans. At this stage, if the client is vulnerable to symptom exacerbations or relapses, it is helpful to review what has been learned about the specific individual precursors of relapse and to discuss again strategies to reduce the risk of relapse (Birchwood, 1996).

OUTCOME RESEARCH

Over the past 10 years there has been a growing number of published reports of evaluations of cognitive-behavioral therapy with people with medication-resistant symptoms. Some reports have focused on working with a particular symptom, such as delusions (Chadwick & Lowe, 1990; Alford & Beck, 1994) or hallucinations (Morrison, 1994; Haddock et al., 1996). Some also use a more restrictive range of therapeutic techniques than described above, such as the earlier coping strategy enhancement work of Tarrier and colleagues (1993). In general, these more specific approaches are increasingly being integrated into a more comprehensive therapeutic approach, along the lines of the description of the therapy above.

The studies discussed here concern cognitive-behavioral therapy with people with "medication-resistant" psychosis. There is variability in the way the concept of medication resistance is defined, or if it is defined at all. Generally, the studies do offer some criteria. For example, Kuipers et al. (1997) specify that the psychotic symptoms must have persisted for at least 6 months despite trials at recommended dosage of at least two antipsychotic medications. In practice, the participants in these studies have often experienced persisting symptoms for much longer than 6 months, and most have been in contact with services for many years.

Bouchard et al. (1996) reviewed 15 studies of "cognitive restructuring" in the treatment of schizophrenia, most of which were individual case studies or small case series using cognitive-behavioral approaches with medication-resistant delusions or hallucinations. Of these, they considered five studies, including one small controlled trial (Garety et al., 1994), to be both methodologically rigorous and also performed with people with schizophrenia. Bouchard et al. (1996) focused on changes in positive symptoms as the main measure of outcome. They concluded that these studies suggest that cognitive approaches are effective to reduce or eliminate delusions and hallucinations in people with schizophrenia. In a detailed examination of the studies, however, they found that the effect may be greater on delusions than hallucinations, the former reliably showing substantial changes.

Randomized controlled trials, despite having limitations (such as generalizing from research to clinical settings), are more conclusive than case reports or case series as valid tests of the efficacy of various forms of therapy. Two randomized controlled trials with patients with medication-resistant psychosis have recently been completed (Kuipers et al., 1997, 1998; Tarrier et al., 1998, 1999). A systematic review of cognitive-behavioral therapy for psychosis, just published, includes these studies together with two other studies of cognitive-behavioral therapy with acute inpatients (Jones et al., 1998). This is a small data base from which to draw conclusions; our knowledge base will be much improved when further ongoing and new studies publish their reports (Kingdon, 1997).

Table 2 shows details of the published randomized controlled trials, together with two earlier controlled trials undertaken by the same two research groups. The most consistent finding is that there are significant benefits in terms of symptom reduction, particularly in positive symptoms, as a result of cognitive-behavioral therapy. This is found in all cases where the cognitive-behavioral therapy plus standard treatment group is compared with a standard-treatment-only control group. These benefits are sustained at followup, up to 1 year posttreatment. In one study (Kuipers et al., 1998), there was some evidence of further improvement in the cognitive-behavioral therapy group after treatment, while the control group reverted to baseline. There is also a preliminary indication that cognitive-behavioral therapy may reduce days in hospital. Effects are not only apparent in positive symptoms, although these findings are less consistent: Tarrier et al. (1998) showed a reduction in negative symptoms, while Garety et al. (1994) found reductions in depression scores. Overall, therefore, there is good evidence, from controlled trials, that cognitive-behavioral therapy is effective in terms of psychotic symptom reduction, and there is preliminary evidence that it may contribute to relapse reduction. These same conclusions are drawn by Jones et al. (1998) in their recent systematic review of cognitive-behavioral therapy for schizophrenia, a review that also includes two trials of therapy in the acute episodes (Drury et al., 1996; Kemp et al., 1996). However, social functioning has not been found to improve, despite it being targeted in therapy. Furthermore, in the study where cognitive-behavioral therapy was compared with another psychosocial intervention, supportive counseling (Tarrier et al.,

1999), there are few advantages, particularly at followup, to cognitive-behavioral therapy.

It is a truism, but noteworthy nonetheless, that statistical significance does not equate to clinical significance. Both Kuipers et al. (1997) and Tarrier et al. (1998) examined clinically significant changes. Kuipers et al. defined a reliable clinical change as a change of five points or greater on the Brief Psychiatric Rating Scale (BPRS). (This equates to an improvement of at least 20% on the scale score.) At followup, 15 of 23 in the cognitive-behavioral therapy group showed a reliable clinical improvement compared with 4 of 24 of the control group (Kuipers et al., 1998). Tarrier et al. (1998) found a significant advantage of the cognitive-behavioral therapy group over the other two groups (supportive counseling and standard treatment) at the end of treatment in terms of 50% or greater improvement in positive symptoms, with supportive counseling in an intermediate position.

PREDICTORS OF GOOD OUTCOME FROM COGNITIVE-BEHAVIORAL THERAPY

Research studies, and particularly randomized controlled trials, have demonstrated that people with medication-resistant symptoms of psychosis can benefit from cognitive-behavioral therapy. However, not all people show improvements. In the studies reviewed above, only about 50 to 60% of participants receiving therapy benefit significantly, while up to 50% show limited or no improvement. Which clients will respond to cognitive-behavioral therapy is therefore an important clinical question. It also has theoretical relevance: variables that predict outcome may direct our attention to the processes of therapeutic change and thus help us to understand how cognitive-behavioral therapy works and who it helps.

A small number of studies have examined this question. Tarrier et al. (1993) examined the effect of pretreatment scores on treatment outcome; those with higher symptom scores improved more, a result that could simply reflect regression to the mean. This finding was not replicated by Tarrier et al. (1998); they found that shorter duration of illness and less severe symptoms at entry to the study predicted improvement. However, neither of these studies investigated the variables that specifically predicted improvement in response to cognitive-behavioral therapy. Rather, these were the variables that were associated with improvement in general, whichever intervention was offered.

Two small case study series report interesting findings that may point to factors that are more specific to cognitive approaches. First, Chadwick and Lowe (1990) used a cognitive intervention with six clients with delusions and a diagnosis of schizophrenia. During the baseline phase, they tested the participants' response to a hypothetical contradiction of their delusions—a plau-

Table 2. Controlled Trials of Cognitive-Behavioral Therapy with Medication-Resistant Psychosis

Study	Diagnosis (Total n)	Duration of Illness	Design	Treatment Conditions	Treatment Duration (mean n of sessions) and Followup	Outcome
Tarrier et al., 1993	Schizophrenia (27)	12.2 yrs (SD = 9.2)	Controlled trial (nonrandom allocation)	1) Cognitive-behavioral coping strategy enhancement and standard treatment; 2) Problem solving and standard treatment; 3) Standard treatment waiting list	5 wks (? sessions) Followup at 6 mos	Both treatment groups significantly improved in total symptoms over standard treatment group; CB coping strategy group showed greater improvements in delusions and anxiety
Garety et al., 1994	Schizophrenia and schizoaffective disorder (20)	For CBT group, 16.5 yrs (range 6–30); For control group, 10.9 yrs (range 5–20)	Waiting list, nonrandom allocation	1) CBT and standard treatment; 2) Standard treatment waiting list	6 mos (15 sessions) No followup	Significant improvements in CBT group in total symptoms (BPRS), delusions (conviction and action), depression, and subjective appraisal of problems
Kuipers et al., 1997, 1998	Schizophrenia-spectrum psychoses (60)	13.1 yrs (range 1–33)	RCT	1) CBT and standard treatment 2) Standard treatment	9 mos (18 sessions) Followup at 9 mos	Significant improvement in CBT group over standard treatment in total symptoms (BPRS), delusions (distress), and hallucinations (frequency); Economic evaluation indicates cost of CBT offset by reduced use of services, particularly inpatient days

(continued)

Table 2. Controlled Trials of Cognitive-Behavioral Therapy with Medication-Resistant Psychosis *(continued)*

Study	Diagnosis (Total *n*)	Duration of Illness	Design	Treatment Conditions	Treatment Duration (mean *n* of sessions) and Followup	Outcome
Tarrier et al., 1998	Schizophrenia (87)	14.2 yrs (SD = 9.9)	RCT	1) CBT and standard treatment; 2) Supportive counseling and standard treatment; 3) Standard treatment	10 wks (20 sessions) Followup at 12 mos	CBT and supportive counseling showed significant improvement over standard treatment for positive symptoms and negative symptoms; CBT showed significant improvements maintained at 12 months' followup, for positive symptoms; Some advantages for CBT over supportive counseling at end of treatment, but not at followup

Note.
BPRS = Brief Psychiatric Rating Scale
CBT = cognitive-behavioral therapy
RCT = randomized controlled trial
SD = standard deviation

sible but contradictory hypothetical occurrence—where they were asked if this would alter their belief in any way (Brett-Jones et al., 1987). Chadwick and Lowe reported that the response to hypothetical contradiction seemed of potential benefit in predicting outcome. Four of the clients who were most responsive to hypothetical contradiction were also the most sensitive to the intervention, whereas the two clients whose delusional conviction scores were least changed by the intervention also entirely rejected the possibility of belief disconfirmation.

A second series of six single cases investigated delusional phenomenology in detail over time and in response to cognitive therapy (Sharp et al., 1996). Six individuals with a diagnosis of delusional disorder were treated, of whom three showed a positive response to treatment, defined in terms of a reduction in delusional belief conviction. The Maudsley Assessment of Delusions Schedule (MADS), a multidimensional assessment of delusional phenomenology, was used, modified for weekly administration (Wessely et al., 1993). Although the study did not set out to investigate predictors of outcome, an analysis of the correlations between different dimensions of delusions during baseline and intervention phases yielded some interesting data. Strikingly, strong correlations were found between delusional conviction and the "belief maintenance factors" during the baseline phase. This subscale assesses the reasons individuals give for holding their beliefs and their ability to consider an alternative view. These belief maintenance factors covaried with therapeutic improvement, changing as the individuals who responded to cognitive therapy came to doubt their delusions. Sharp et al. (1996) suggest that their study demonstrates that these factors do truly maintain the delusional belief and must change for therapy to be effective. If this is so, then these variables may also be relevant to predicting change.

Building on these earlier studies, our group set out to investigate which factors predicted a positive response to cognitive-behavioral therapy in the context of a randomized controlled trial with 60 participants (Kuipers et al., 1997, described above). The predictors of outcome study investigated whether response to therapy was predicted by demographic variables, IQ, insight or other aspects of cognitive functioning, current symptom presentation, symptom severity, or responses to MADS items at the initial assessment (Garety et al., 1997). Since this is the first comprehensive study of this kind we will consider it in some detail. Outcome was defined as improvement on the BPRS. Using analysis of variance and covariance, tests were conducted for differential effects of predictor variables as opposed to overall prognostic effects common to both groups. The study found that the variables that predicted response to treatment differed between the cognitive-behavioral therapy plus standard treatment group and the standard treatment-only control group.

A positive response to cognitive therapy was predicted at baseline by the following four variables:

1. The response to the MADS "possibility of being mistaken," where acknowledging that another view of the delusion may be possible is associated with better outcome.

2. Scores on a test sensitive to frontal lobe damage, the Cognitive Estimates Test, where a higher error score predicts good outcome;

3. The number of admissions in 5 years, where having more admissions is associated with better outcome; and, finally,

4. Insight-approached significance, where better insight correlated with better outcome.

These variables were entered into a multiple regression model. Because the MADS variable only applies to people with delusions, two analyses were conducted—for the group with delusions and for the larger total group (which included patients with hallucinations or other psychotic symptoms without delusions).

The first analysis found that two variables, accounting for a total of 74% of the variance, predicted outcome to cognitive-behavioral therapy. These variables were the MADS "possibility of being mistaken" and the number of admissions in 5 years. The second analysis found that the predictor variables for the whole group were insight and the number of admissions in 5 years, accounting for 52% of the variance.

Outcome was less predictable in the control group. A positive response to standard treatment only (the control group) was predicted at baseline by poorer social functioning and greater hopelessness. However, these variables together accounted for only 24% of the variance. A number of baseline variables did not predict outcome in either group. These included demographic and clinical variables, intelligence and other cognitive functioning measures, affect, symptom severity, or measures of the strength of delusional conviction or preoccupation.

The findings of this study offer intriguing pointers to understanding treatment response to cognitive-behavioral therapy. Most notably, response to therapy for those patients with delusions (the majority) was strongly predicted by a combination of the response to the MADS question about the possibility of being mistaken and having had a greater number of recent admissions. The MADS finding confirms our hypothesis, based on earlier work by Chadwick and Lowe (1990) and Sharp et al. (1996), that a response, at baseline, to the "mistaken" question, which admits of the possibility of an alternative view of the delusion, would predict a good response. It seems that cognitive-behavioral therapy for delusions may be more effective where there is a "chink of insight." It is important to note that this does not imply that those who responded well were not deluded. They met well-established criteria for delusions, including asserting their beliefs with high conviction. Furthermore, outcome was not predicted by delusional conviction, which was carefully assessed. For those without delusions, a conventional measure of insight predicted a positive response to therapy. It certainly makes sense that the capacity to discuss and review alternative ways of viewing one's situation inherent in this therapy is predicted by some awareness that one may have a mental illness and an awareness of its social consequences. Furthermore, the fact that good outcome is predicted by a cognitive measure also suggests that a good outcome in cognitive-behavioral therapy is due at least in part to the specific effects of cognitive therapy on delusional thinking.

Despite the finding that having a chink of insight predicts outcome, it is important to note that IQ did not predict outcome. From this study, it appears that high IQ, or intact cognitive functioning, is not required for cognitive-behavioral therapy to be effective. In fact, the results suggested that poorer cognitive functioning in some respects (the responses on the Cognitive Estimates Test) predicted better outcome. It is possible, although this is highly speculative, that this therapy may provide compensatory methods that assist in reevaluating beliefs for those people whose cognitive biases may tend to lead to delusions.

The other variable that predicted outcome in response to therapy was the number of recent admissions. We had not anticipated this from our review of the literature. Two possible explanations warrant consideration. First, a greater number of admissions over a 5-year period may suggest that the psychosis is unstable and has proved more disruptive to the individual. This, in turn, may heighten motivation for change. Alternatively, a more unstable psychosis may be inherently more modifiable by cognitive therapy, perhaps because it is less firmly entrenched in a person's belief system. However, as a novel finding, without a clear theoretical basis, this result needs to be replicated before it is incorporated into our understanding of cognitive-behavioral therapy for psychosis.

Although the finding that an identifiable cognitive flexibility concerning their delusions, which was present in 50% of patients, predicted better outcome at the end of treatment, the prediction did not hold as strongly at 9-month posttherapy followup (Kuipers et al., 1998). At this stage, we found that those participants who admitted the possibility that they might be mistaken responded more quickly and to a greater extent to therapy than the others, but that the others appeared to benefit in the end, albeit to a lesser extent, from the therapy. From these data, it seems we cannot conclude that certain people will not benefit from cognitive-behavioral therapy, although we may be able to predict which people will benefit more quickly and to a greater extent.

Finally, there is some evidence that points to one group of people with psychosis who may not respond well to cognitive-behavioral therapy, and that explains our emphasis on working with positive symptoms. In developing the work described above, one of us (Fowler) conducted pilot studies with 19 patients with schizophrenia (Fowler, 1992). This group consisted of 7 patients presenting with negative symptoms only, 10 with positive symptoms, and 2 with mixed positive and negative symptoms only. Fowler found that the subgroup with negative symptoms only responded poorly, in that they did not report changes in the subjective experience of their symptoms. There were severe difficulties in establishing and maintaining a therapeutic relationship with this group, in part because distress about their symptoms was not always present. It was, as a result, rarely possible to implement structured cognitive-behavioral procedures. Sporadic signs of improvement were not maintained and formal measures showed no consistent or reliable therapy gains. As a result of this pilot work, we have not included people with only negative symptoms in our subsequent studies. In general, cognitive-behavioral therapy for psychosis has targeted people with persistent positive symptoms.

NEW DEVELOPMENTS OF COGNITIVE-BEHAVIORAL THERAPY

Although most of the work in cognitive-behavioral therapy for psychosis has been targeted at people with medication-resistant positive symptoms, a recent innovation has been the formal application of this approach to the acute episodes of psychosis (Drury et al., 1996). The aims of this are to hasten the resolution of positive symptoms and to promote full recovery, reducing the severity of residual symptoms. It is also hoped that by reducing the distress associated with the psychotic episode itself, subsequent traumatic responses and depression may be lessened. Drury et al. (1996) report a randomized controlled trial of an intensive psychosocial intervention, including individual cognitive-behavioral therapy combined with cognitive group therapy and a brief family intervention, delivered during approximately 12 weeks of an inpatient admission. The results are impressive. The patients in the cognitive therapy condition showed a significantly faster and more complete recovery from their psychotic episodes. At 9-month followup, 95% of the cognitive therapy group and 44% of the activity control group reported no or only minor hallucinations or delusions. The cognitive therapy group also had a significantly shorter stay in hospital. This is an exciting study, which indicates that intensive multimodality cognitive-behavioral work with people during their acute episodes may be beneficial and cost-effective. Further research is now being conducted, particularly targeting people with early episodes of psychosis (see McGorry, 1998).

APPLYING COGNITIVE-BEHAVIORAL THERAPY
OUTSIDE THE RESEARCH CONTEXT

A number of questions arise when considering how to offer cognitive-behavioral therapy to people with medication-resistant psychoses in the setting of ordinary clinical services. These concern selection of patients, frequency and duration of therapy, components of therapy to emphasize, and integration of therapy with other interventions.

It is apparent that cognitive-behavioral therapy for medication-resistant psychosis is most effective for the key targets of therapy: persistent positive symptoms. To engage patients, we have found it helpful to identify with them how their symptoms are distressing or interfere with their own goals. In the clinical setting, we therefore focus our resources on those people who report distress or interference with achieving their goals as a result of experiencing positive symptoms. As indicated above, this excludes people who only experience negative symptoms. It also suggests that those patients who report no distress or personal difficulties may not engage well with therapy, for example, those patients whose delusions are mainly grandiose in content, especially if they also deny problems arise from their beliefs or experiences. Clinically, it is likely that a good time to offer therapy is when a person expresses some interest in having some further help. This is also consistent with the finding discussed earlier that people with a "chink of insight" may do better. However, it is important to emphasize again that this does not mean that we cannot work effectively with people who are fully convinced of their delusions or who are formally rated as having poor insight.

Our research has focused on people with medication-resistant symptoms, and in practice, they have had many years of illness. Starting to work with people earlier, within the first 5 years since onset, is both therapeutically and theoretically indicated. We are currently working with this typically younger group and think that the extension of the work to this group offers promise.

In terms of the duration and frequency of therapy, although the duration of therapy in the research studies has varied, most have offered a median of approximately 20 sessions. In clinical settings, it is our experience that therapy is best delivered over a period of between 6 months and 1 year, preferably starting weekly and reducing to biweekly for the greater part of the period. However, monthly sessions may be offered toward the end and continued for selected patients for a much longer period, if resources allow. Although there is no research to confirm this, it is possible that people with a vulnerability to relapse or very unstable belief systems may be helped by such continued contact. Alternatively, it may be practicable to make a full and careful transition to another mental health worker who is in regular contact with the patient and who can offer cognitively informed ongoing support.

As we have emphasized, given the heterogeneity of the problems presented by people with psychosis, cognitive-behavioral therapy involves a detailed assessment, an individualized formulation, and individually selected therapy goals. It follows that for each person the therapy will focus on specific elements of the six "stages" listed above. Although it is clear that the first stage, developing a therapeutic relationship, is common to all, it is not known which of the other elements are necessary or most effective in particular cases. In practice we find that for medication-resistant symptoms the stages of developing an understanding of psychosis and working on delusions and hallucinations form the core of the work, while developing coping strategies and work on negative self-evaluations or mood disturbance may be less relevant to certain patients. Nonetheless, the disappointing lack of clear benefits in the studies in reducing depression suggests that further work is needed to improve the therapeutic approach to achieve this. For people with a more favorable response to medication but a relapsing course, there will be a stronger emphasis on the specific issues described above·in the sixth stage: working on relapse prevention and enhancing social functioning.

People with medication-resistant psychoses are generally in contact with a variety of mental health services. Although most patients are prescribed antipsychotic medications concurrently with therapy, an area yet to be researched is how cognitive-behavioral therapy interacts with medication or with other forms of psychosocial intervention. In practice, it seems that cognitive-behavioral therapy can be helpful in facilitating patients' engagement with other services, such as vocational or social programs; it may also enhance medication or other treatment adherence in individual cases (although this has not been demonstrated). Of particular interest for patients living with families is whether the outcome is improved when this individual approach is offered in addition to a family intervention, which has previously been shown to be beneficial (Penn & Mueser, 1996). This has not been systematically studied. Especially with younger patients, whose psychosis is of recent onset, a combined individual cognitive-behavioral and family approach may be beneficial and we are currently piloting this in the clinical setting.

CONCLUSIONS

Cognitive-behavioral therapy is emerging as an effective approach for the relief of symptoms not optimally helped by antipsychotic medication. This therapy has been shown to reduce positive psychotic symptoms, and there is evidence that it may contribute to relapse reduction (Jones et al., 1998). One study has shown that improvements were sustained or even increased at followup, suggesting that the approach can transmit skills of self-management (Kuipers et al., 1998). It is also likely to prove cost-effective, especially if the evidence that it delays relapse proves robust. However, not all patients are helped by this approach. Further work is needed on this question; at present, it appears that people who report distress as a result of their symptoms and who show what we have called a "chink of insight" may engage more readily or, possibly, benefit more quickly or to a greater extent. Finally, although we have discussed medication-resistant psychosis, there is some evidence that cognitive approaches can help people with acute and early psychosis. Indeed, an intervention that focuses on the beliefs and the understanding that a person develops in the context of the experience of psychosis is very likely to be more helpful if offered early. However, given the complexity and heterogeneity of psychosis, optimal care will require offering a range of interventions described in this special issue of the *Schizophrenia Bulletin* (2000, 26[1]) as desired by patients and their caretakers and as judged appropriate. Cognitive-behavioral therapy should be considered as one possible component of a comprehensive treatment plan.

REFERENCES

Alford, B. A., & Beck, A. T. (1994). Cognitive therapy of delusional beliefs. *Behaviour Research and Therapy, 32*, 369–380.

Beck, A. T., Rush, A.J., Shaw, B. F., & Emery, G. (1979). *Cognitive therapy of depression.* New York, NY: Guilford.

Bentall, R., Kinderman, P., & Kaney, S. (1994). The self, attributional processes and abnormal beliefs: Towards a model of persecutory delusions. *Behaviour Research and Therapy, 32*, 331–341.

Bentall, R. P. (1994). Cognitive biases and abnormal beliefs: Towards a model of persecutory delusions. In A. S. David & J. Cutting, J., (Eds.), *The neuropsychology of schizophrenia* (pp. 337–360). Hove, England: Lawrence Erlbaum.

Birchwood, M. (1996). Early interventions in psychotic relapse: Cognitive approaches to detection and management. In G. Haddock & P. Slade (Eds.), *Cognitive-behavioural interventions with psychotic disorders,* (Chapter 10). London, England: Routledge.

Birchwood, M., & Iqbal, Z. (1998). Depression and suicidal thinking in psychosis: A cognitive approach. In T. Wykes, N. Tarrier & S. Lewis (Eds.), *Outcome and innovation in psychological treatment of schizophrenia,* (Chapter 5). Chichester, England: John Wiley and Sons.

Birchwood, M., Mason, R., MacMillan, F., & Healy, J. (1993). Depression, demoralisation and control over psychotic illness: A comparison of depressed and non-depressed patients with a chronic psychosis. *Psychological Medicine, 23,* 387–395.

Bouchard, S., Valliéres, A., Roy, M. A., & Maziade, M. (1996). Cognitive restructuring in the treatment of psychotic symptoms in schizophrenia: A critical analysis. *Behavior Therapy, 27,* 257–277.

Brett-Jones, J., Garety, P., & Hernsley, D. (1987). Measuring delusional experiences: A method and its application. *British Journal of Clinical Psychology, 26*(4), 257–265.

Chadwick, P., & Birchwood, M. (1994). The omnipotence of voices: A cognitive approach to auditory hallucinations. *British Journal of Psychiatry, 164,* 190–201.

Chadwick, P. D. J., Birchwood, M., & Trower, P. (1996). *Cognitive therapy for delusions, voices and paranoia.* Chichester, England: John Wiley and Sons.

Chadwick, P. D. J., & Lowe, C. F. (1990). Measurement and modification of delusional beliefs. *Journal of Consulting and Clinical Psychology, 58,* 225–232.

Close, H., & Garety, P. A. (1998). Cognitive assessment of voices: Further developments in understanding the emotional impact of voices. *British Journal of Clinical Psychology, 37*(2), 173–188.

Drury, V., Birchwood, M., Cochrane, R., & MacMillan, F. (1996). Cognitive therapy and recovery from acute psychosis: A controlled trial: 1. Impact on psychotic symptoms. *British Journal of Psychiatry, 169,* 593–601.

Fenton, W., & McGlashan, T. H. (1997). We can talk: Individual psychotherapy for schizophrenia. *The American Journal of Psychiatry, 154,* 1493–1495.

Fowler, D. G. (1992). Cognitive behaviour therapy for psychosis: Preliminary studies. In A. Werbart & J. Cullberg (Eds.), *The psychotherapy of schizophrenia: Facilitating and obstructive factors.* Oslo, Norway: Scandinavian University Press.

Fowler, D., Garety, P., & Kuipers, E. (1995). *Cognitive-behaviour therapy for people with psychosis.* Chichester, England: John Wiley and Sons.

Fowler, D., Garety, P., & Kuipers, E. (1998). Cognitive therapy for psychosis: Formulation, treatment, effects and service implications. *Journal of Mental Health, 7,* 123–133.

Fowler, D., & Morley, S. (1989). The cognitive-behavioural treatment of hallucinations and delusions: A preliminary study. *Behavioural Psychotherapy, 17,* 267–282.

Freeman, D., & Garety, P. A. (1999). Worry, worry processes and dimensions of delusions: An exploratory investigation of a role for anxiety processes in the maintenance of delusional distress. *Behavioural and Cognitive Psychotherapy, 27,* 47–62.

Freeman, D., Garety, P. A., Fowler, D., Kuipers, E., Dunn, G., Bebbington, P., & Hadley, C. (1998). The London-East Anglia randomized controlled trial of cognitive-behavioural therapy for psychosis: IV. Self-esteem and persecutory delusions. *British Journal of Clinical Psychology, 37*(4), 415–430.

Freud, S. A (1915/1956). *Case of paranoia running counter to the psychoanalytic theory of disease, Vol. 2.* London, England: Hogarth.

Frith, C. D. (1992). *The cognitive neuropsychology of schizophrenia.* Hove, England: Lawrence Erlbaum.

Garety, P., Fowler, D., Kuipers, E., Freeman, D., Dunn, G., Bebbington, P., Hadley, C., & Jones, S. (1997). The London-East Anglia randomised controlled trial of cognitive-behavioural therapy for psychosis: II. Predictors of outcome. *British Journal of Psychiatry, 171,* 420–426.

Garety, P. A., & Freeman, D. (1999). Cognitive approaches to delusions: A critical review of theories and evidence. *British Journal of Clinical Psychology, 38*(2), 113–154.

Garety, P. A., & Hernsley, D. R. (1994). Delusions: investigations into the psychology of delusional reasoning, *Maudsley Monograph.* Oxford, England: Oxford University Press.

Garety, P. A., Kuipers, E., Fowler, D., Chamberlain, F., & Dunn, G. (1994). Cognitive behavioural therapy for drug resistant psychosis. *British Journal of Medical Psychology, 67*(3), 259–271.

Gunderson, J. G., Frank, A. F., Katz, H. M., Vannicelli, M. L., Frosch, J. R, & Knapp, P. H. (1984). Effects of psychotherapy in schizophrenia: II. Comparative outcome of two forms of treatment. *Schizophrenia Bulletin, 10*(4), 564–598.

Haddock, G., Bentall, R. P., & Slade, P. D. (1996). Psychological treatment of auditory hallucinations: Focusing or distraction? In G. Haddock & P. D. Slade (Eds.), *Cognitive-behavioural interventions with psychotic disorders* (pp. 45–70). London, England: Routledge.

Hernsley, D. R. (1994). Perceptual and cognitive abnormalities as the bases for schizophrenic symptoms. In A. S. David & J. C. Cutting, J.C. (Eds.), *The neuropsychology of schizophrenia* (pp. 97–116). Hove, England: Lawrence Erlbaum.

Hogarty, G. E., Kornblith, S. J., Greenwald, D., DiBarry, A. L., Cooley, S., Flesher, S., Reiss, D., Carter, M., & Ulrich, R. (1995). Personal therapy: A disorder-relevant psychotherapy for schizophrenia. *Schizophrenia Bulletin, 21*(3), 379–393.

Hogarty, G. E., Komblith, S. J., Greenwald, D., DiBarry, D., Cooley, S., Ulrich, R. F., Carter, M., & Flesher, S. (1997). Three-year trials of personal therapy among schizophrenic patients living with or independent of family: 1. Description of study and effects on relapse rates. *American Journal of Psychiatry, 154,* 1504–1513.

Horvath, A. O., & Symonds, B. D. (1991). Relationship between working alliance and outcome in psychotherapy: A meta analysis. *Journal of Consulting and Clinical Psychology, 38,* 139–149.

Jones, C., Cormac, I., Mota, J., & Campbell, C. (1998). Cognitive-behaviour therapy for schizophrenia (Cochrane Review). *The Cochrane Library.* Oxford, England: Update Software.

Kemp, R., Hayward, R, Applewhaite, G., Everitt, B., & David, A. (1996). Compliance therapy in psychotic patients: Randomised controlled trial. *British Medical Journal, 312,* 345–349.

Kingdon, D. (1997). *The wellcome study of cognitive therapy for "treatment resistant" schizophrenia*. Paper presented at the Psychological Treatments for Schizophrenia Conference, Oxford, England.

Kingdon, D., & Turkington, D. (1994). *Cognitive-behavioural therapy for schizophrenia*. Hove, England: Lawrence Erlbaum.

Kuipers, E., Fowler, D., Garety, P., Chisolm, D., Freeman, D., Dunn, G., Bebbington, P., & Hadley, C. (1998). The London East Anglia randomised controlled trial of cognitive behavioural therapy for psychosis: III. Follow-up and economic evaluation at 18 months. *British Journal of Psychiatry, 173,* 61–68.

Kuipers, E., Garety, R, Fowler, D., Dunn, G., Bebbington, P., Freeman, D., & Hadley, C. (1997). The London-East Anglia randomised controlled trial of cognitive-behavioural therapy for psychosis: 1. Effects of the treatment phase. *British Journal of Psychiatry, 171,* 319–327.

Maher, B.A. (1988). Anomalous experience and delusional thinking: The logic of explanations. In T. F. Oltmanns & B. A. Maher (Eds.), *Delusional belief* (pp. 15–33). New York, NY: John Wiley and Sons.

McGorry, P., (Ed.) (1998). Verging on reality. *British Journal of Psychiatry, 172*(Suppl 33).

McGorry, P. D., Chanen, A., & McCarthy, E. (1991). Posttraumatic stress disorder following recent onset psychosis: An unrecognized postpsychotic syndrome. *Journal of Nervous and Mental Disease, 179,* 253–258.

Milton, R, Patwa, V. K., & Hafner, R. J. (1978). Confrontation vs. belief modification in persistently deluded patients. *British Journal of Medical Psychology, 51,* 127–130.

Morrison, A. P. (1994). Cognitive behaviour therapy for auditory hallucinations without concurrent medication: A single case. *Behavioural and Cognitive Psychotherapy, 22,* 259–264.

Mueser, K. T., & Berenbaum, H. (1990). Psychodynamic treatment of schizophrenia: Is there a future? *Psychological Medicine, 20,* 253–262.

Nuechterlein, K. H., & Subotnik, K. L. (1998). The cognitive origins of schizophrenia and prospects for intervention. In T. Wykes, N. Tarrier & S. Lewis (Eds.). *Outcome and innovation in psychological treatment of schizophrenia* (pp. 17–43). Chichester, England: John Wiley and Sons.

Penn, D. L., & Mueser, K. T. (1996). Research update on the psychosocial treatment of schizophrenia. *American Journal of Psychiatry, 153*(5), 607–617.

Roth, A., & Fonagy, P. (1996). Schizophrenia. In A. Roth & P. Fonaghy (Eds.), *What works for whom? A critical review of psychotherapy research* (Chapter 10). New York, NY: Guilford Press.

Sharp, H. M., Fear, C. F., Williams, M. G., Healy, D., Lowe, C. F., Yeadon, H., & Holden, R. (1996). Delusional phenomenology-Dimensions of change. *Behaviour Research and Therapy, 34,* 123–142.

Strauss, J. S., & Carpenter, W. T. (1981). *Schizophrenia*. New York, NY: Plenum.

Tarrier, N. (1992). Management and modification of residual positive psychotic symptoms. In M. Birchwood & N. Tarrier (Eds.), *Innovations in the psychological management of schizophrenia*. Chichester, England: John Wiley and Sons.

Tarrier, N., Beckett, R., Harwood, S., Baker, A., Yusupoff, L., & Ugarteburu, (1993). 1. A trial of two cognitive-behavioural methods of treating drug-resistant residual psychotic symptoms in schizophrenic patients: 1. Outcome. *British Journal of Psychiatry, 162,* 524–532.

Tarrier, N., Wittkowski, A., Kinney, C., McCarthy, E., Morris, J., & Humphreys, L. (1999). Durability of the effects of cognitive-behavioural therapy in the treatment of chronic schizophrenia: 12-month follow-up. *British Journal of Psychiatry, 174,* 500–504.

Tarrier, N., Yusupoff, L., Kinney, C., McCarthy, E., Gledhill, A., Haddock, H., & Morris, J. (1998). Randomised controlled trial of intensive cognitive behaviour therapy for chronic schizophrenia. *British Medical Journal, 317,* 303–307.

Wessely, S., Buchanan, A., Reed, A., Cutting, J., Everitt, B., Garety, P., & Taylor, T.J. (1993). Acting on delusions: 1. Prevalence. *British Journal of Psychiatry, 163,* 69–76.

Yusupoff, L., & Tarrier, N. (1996). Coping strategy enhancement for persistent hallucinations and delusions. In G. Haddock & P. D. Slade (Eds.), *Cognitive-behavioural interventions with psychotic disorders* (Chapter 5). London, England: Routledge.

Zubin, J., & Spring, B. (1977). Vulnerability—A new view on schizophrenia. *Journal of Abnormal Psychology, 86,* 103–126.

Strategies that Foster Collaboration Between Consumers and Providers

Tonya M. Mestemaker

At the time of original publication, Tonya M. Mestemaker was affiliated with University of Chicago's Center for Psychiatric Rehabilitation.

This article was published previously in *Psychiatric Rehabilitation Skills*, 1(1), 16–20, and is reprinted with permission.

Abstract: This article focuses on the development of a collaborative working relationship between the consumer and clinician in which the responsibility for treatment falls on both parties. Due to high dropout rates during psychosocial treatment by persons with schizophrenia, it is inferred that there are many barriers that prevent consumers from starting and continuing mental health treatment (Corrigan, Liberman, & Engel, 1990). Past literature has focused on consumer behaviors as the cause for treatment noncompliance. However, this paper addresses treatment barriers as challenges that both the consumer and the provider need to overcome together as a team.

Several factors can effect the collaborative relationship, factors related to the treatment regimen, the consumer, the therapist, the consumer's family and the relationship between the consumer and the therapist (see Table 1). This paper addresses these factors and identifies strategies to overcome them.

Perhaps at the most fundamental level, the clinician can model a cooperative stance by being receptive to the consumer's comments. In addition, clinicians can provide realistic and comprehensive information about the illness, negotiate treatment contracts with the consumer, and provide the consumer with explicit feedback about treatment progress, drug side effects, and the attainment of goals.

PROBLEMS WITH THE WAY TREATMENT IS EXPLAINED

One of the major barriers to collaboration between consumers and professionals is the way treatment itself is presented to the consumer. Treatment-related barriers include side effects, treatment plans that are too difficult for the consumer to understand, and treatment that is too lengthy. Several strategies can alleviate medication and psychosocial treatment side effects. These strategies include teaching consumers to identify and monitor the severity level of side effects, persistent symptoms, and warning signs. This knowledge can lead to a greater sense of control, as well as place the consumer in a better position to collaborate with the clinician during the next clinic visit (Corrigan, Liberman, & Engel, 1990).

Another treatment-related barrier is treatment plans that are complex and difficult to understand. Polydrug protocols, confusing psychosocial program schedules, and difficult-to-follow behavior therapy prescriptions all decrease the likelihood of understanding and following the treatment plan. Professionals can use creative methods to eliminate these barriers such as providing each consumer with a program card. This card can contain information about the times and places of programming, the types of medications the consumer is taking, the time to take medications, possible medication side effects, and other important information. Decreasing the complexity of the treatment protocol can also be addressed by training professionals to use simple language, which is free of technical jargon, when they are educating consumers about medication and program regimens.

Lengthy treatment can also lead to consumer non-compliance. Consumers are constantly reminded about their mental illness and this can lead to feelings of hopelessness. Some psychosocial programs have incorporated vacations which give consumers a break from continuous treatment (Corrigan, Davies-Farmer, & Lome, 1988). Consumers look forward to these breaks because they alleviate pressures related to having to attend a never-ending rehabilitation program. Consumers and staff can use this vacation time to assess consumer progress and to evaluate and improve programming.

PROBLEMS THERAPISTS HAVE THAT IMPEDE COLLABORATION

Barriers to treatment adherence can also stem from the consumer-clinician relationship. Consumers who experience positive therapeutic relationships with clinicians are more likely to adhere to treatment regimens (Frank & Gunderson, 1990). Clinicians are unlikely to foster positive relationships with their clients if they have negative attitudes about their ability to enhance a consumer's life. Mirabi and colleagues (1985) found that 85% of clinicians preferred not to treat chronic consumers; 68% believed that they were not adequately trained to address this population's needs. Many professionals may believe that consumers are "untreatable." This view, which results from a lack of effective training, can lead clinicians to feel inadequate and frustrated.

Clinicians can work toward a more cooperative stance by talking with consumers and families about their experiences with medical and psychosocial regimens. Additionally, clinicians can facilitate cooperation with treatment by developing interpersonal skills that improve the quality of the therapeutic relationship. Janis (1983) found improved therapist-consumer collaboration among consumers whose therapist provided consistent positive feedback while gently eliciting moderate levels of self-disclosure. For example, during social and coping skills training groups, group leaders are trained to give consumers positive feedback. When this occurs, consumers feel accepted, which leads to more self-disclosure, improved self-esteem, and a positive consumer-clinician relationship. In addition, clinicians can ease their feelings of frustration and hopelessness by setting realistic, modest, and incremental goals for their consumers.

Table 1. Factors That Impair Consumer-Provider Collaboration

Factor	Examples
The Treatment Regimen	Inadequate presentation of the treatment plan
	Inadequate knowledge about side effects
	Difficult-to-understand treatment plans
	Rehabilitation treatment that is too lengthy
The Clinician	Negative attitudes about consumer prognosis
	Clinician feels that they are not adequately trained
	Clinician has an aversive interpersonal style
	Clinician does not provide the consumer with positive feedback for achievements
	Clinician sets unrealistic goals which do not coincide with the consumer's idea about treatment
	Clinician ignores the consumer's dissatisfaction with treatment
	Frequent changes in providers
	Clinician fosters consumer dependence on the mental health system, instead of teaching the consumer skills which will lead to independent living
The Consumer	Consumer does not understand their mental illness and the need for treatment.
	Cognitive disorganization
	Fatalistic attitudes
The Family	Lack of support from the family
	Negative attitudes (e.g., overconcern, overburdened, or detached)
	Inadequate education about mental illness
	Unrealistic expectations
	Family feels unsupported
	Misunderstandings of consumer behaviors

Many of the traditional ways in which treatment is delivered are perceived as aversive by consumers, which leads them to stop treatment regimens when they are unsupervised. Liberman and Davis (1975) designed a program to enrich the experiences of persons with chronic schizophrenia who attended a medication clinic once a month at a typical community mental health center. The clinic was organized as a social hour in a comfortably furnished room where consumers and their relatives were served a luncheon buffet as music played in the background. The psychiatrist mingled with the consumers like a host at a party, observing their mental status, interviewing them and their caregivers about symptoms and side effects, and noting the need for changes in prescriptions. A randomly assigned control group of persons with schizophrenia received more traditional interventions where the psychiatrist only met monthly with the consumer for 15 minutes. Liberman et al. (1975) found that the experimental group showed significantly better attendance rates, higher compliance levels with medication, and more favorable attitudes about medications when they were compared to the control group.

Frequent changes in primary clinicians or case managers can undermine a consumer's commitment to the treatment program. For example, it may take a consumer a year to feel comfortable with a therapist and the program. If the therapist leaves the agency, the consumer may experience feelings of loss and abandonment which can lead to frequent program absences. These changes usually occur when students who are clinicians move to other educational activities, when the rate of staff turnover is high, or when consumers are discharged or transferred to another agency for services. There is an improvement in treatment adherence when continuity of care which includes an enduring consumer-therapist relationship is fostered.

Many of the barriers to treatment adherence can be circumvented by encouraging therapists to actively engage consumers in the management and control of their illnesses. For example, a series of modules for training social and independent living skills have been developed and used in comprehensive treatment programs for persons with schizophrenia (Wirshing, Eckman, Liberman, & Marder, 1991). Two of the modules taught in these programs were medication and symptom management. This type of training provides consumers with the knowledge and skills they need to take a greater role in their own treatment.

PROBLEMS CONSUMERS HAVE THAT IMPEDE COLLABORATION

Other barriers that prevent treatment adherence are related to characteristics of the consumer. Major blocks to adherence can occur if there is a lack of understanding by the consumer regarding the symptoms of the disorder, the effect that these symptoms have on this individual's social life, and the need for treatment (Falloon, Boyd, & McGill, 1984; Liberman, 1979; Marder, Swann, Winslade, Van Putten, Chien, & Wilkins, 1984). McEvoy and colleagues (1981) found that 40% of a sample of persons with severe mental illness demonstrated only fair insight into their disease. In this sample, 98% accurately reported that they were taking medications, but only 47% believed they needed them and 56% said they would be able to discontinue the medications in the future.

Difficulties with treatment plans are magnified by the consumer's cognitive disorganization. Many consumers with schizophrenia have greater difficulty processing information. Instructions are more likely to be followed when they are written down, divided into small steps, and repeated back to the consumer (Corrigan, Liberman, & Engel, 1990). For more confused consumers, a trusted and reliable third party, such as a roommate, relative, or caregiver, can be enlisted to prompt the consumer when needed. Educational programs provide consumers with a better understanding of their illness. However, consumers may need to learn cognitive rehabilitation techniques in order to improve disorders in thinking before they can start an educational program. For example, Liberman and his colleagues (1986) designed techniques to improve attention during conversation skills training. These techniques include observing others modeling the targeted behaviors, acting out the behaviors by role playing, providing positive feedback to peers concerning the role plays, and moving toward mastery of the targeted behaviors through shaping. These techniques may prove useful in helping thought-disordered and distractible consumers improve collaboration with treatment.

Consumers may have a fatalistic attitude towards themselves and treatment due to their beliefs about mental illness. Consumers may experience feelings of passivity and loss of control and, as a result, express autonomy by not cooperating with treatment. Cognitive restructuring methods that address these attitudes can be useful. For example: a consumer who feels that medication makes him "more crazy" could be asked to talk about these thoughts and feelings with higher-functioning consumers who have had similar experiences (Corrigan et al., 1990).

PROBLEMS FAMILIES HAVE THAT IMPEDE COLLABORATION

A lack of family support can also prevent consumers from adhering to treatment. Consumers who receive emotional support from family members and friends are more likely to participate in treatment than consumers who do not receive this support (Falloon, Boyd, & McGill, 1984). Sweeney and colleagues (1984) found that 80% of a sample of consumers with chronic mental illness who were accompanied to an outpatient appointment by family members followed through with treatment prescriptions, while only 55% of a sample of unaccompanied consumers adhered to the treatment regimen.

Family-related barriers can arise from overconcern about the consumer's treatment and feeling burned out by the illness which can lead to detachment. Family members can be helped to cope with the consumer's disorder through education and support from practitioners. Falloon and colleagues (1984) developed an education program for consumers and their families. This program educated participants, in layperson's language, about the basic facts that describe schizophrenia. Meeting with family members and consumers together allowed them to have the opportunity to share their experiences and enhanced the families' understanding of consumer behaviors. Teaching problem-solving techniques to family members may also help to overcome treatment barriers. Family members, along with the consumer, can learn communication and problem-solving skills which will help them identify, brainstorm, evaluate, and try out different solutions to everyday problems.

SUMMARY

The clinician can improve collaboration by assuming some responsibility for improving the consumer-clinician relationship. An array of strategies were described in this article which address the barriers arising from treatment techniques such as the consumer-practitioner relationship, lapses and discontinuities in the service delivery system, characteristics of family members and friends, and consumer characteristics. Through the application of these strategies, and the creation of a positive consumer-practitioner relationship, clinicians and consumers can forge better working relationships to address the impact of the disorder.

REFERENCES

Corrigan, P. W., Davies-Farmer, R. M., & Lome, H. B. (1988). A curriculum-based, psychoeducational program for the mentally ill. *Psychosocial Rehabilitation Journal, 12,* 71–73.

Corrigan, P. W., Liberman, R. P., & Engel, B. A. (1990). From noncompliance to collaboration in the treatment of schizophrenia. *Hospital and Community Psychiatry, 41,* 1203–1211.

Falloon, I. R. H., Boyd, J. L., & McGill, C. W. (1984). *Family care of schizophrenia.* New York: Guilford.

Frank, A. F., Gunderson, J. G. (1990). The role of the therapeutic alliance in the treatment of schizophrenia: Relationship to course and outcome. *Archives of General Psychiatry, 47,* 228–238.

Janis, I. L. (1983). The role of social support in adherence to stressful decisions. *American Psychologist, 38,* 143–160.

Liberman, R. P. (1979). Social and political challenges to the development of behavioral programs in organizations. In P. O. Sjoden, W. S. Dockens, & S. Bates (Eds.), *Trends in Behavior Therapy.* New York: Academic Press.

Liberman, R. P., & Davis, J. (1975). Drugs and behavior analysis. *Progress in Behavior Modification, 1,* 307–330.

Liberman, R. P., Mueser, K. T., & Glynn, S. (1988). Modular strategies in behavior family therapy. In I. R. H. Falloon (Ed.), *Handbook of Behavioral Family Therapy* (pp. 27–50). New York: Guilford.

Liberman, R. P., Mueser, K. T., Wallace, C. J., Jacobs, H. E., Eckman, T., & Massel, H. K. (1986). Training skills in the psychiatrically disabled: Learning coping and competence. *Schizophrenia Bulletin, 12,* 631–647.

McEvoy, J. P., Aland, J., Jr., Wilson, W. H., Guy, W., & Hawkins, L. (1981). Measuring chronic schizophrenic patients, attitudes towards their illness and treatment. *Hospital and Community Psychiatry, 32,* 856–858.

Marder, S. R., Swann, E., Winslade, W. J., Van Putten, T.,Chien, C., & Wilkins, J. N. (1984). A study of medication refusal by involuntary psychiatric patients. *Hospital and Community Psychiatry, 35,* 724–726.

Mirabi, M., Weinman, M. L., Magnetti, S. M., & Keppler, K. N, (1978). Professional attitudes toward the chronic mentally ill. *Hospital and Community Psychiatry, 36,* 404–405.

Sweeny, J. A., Von Bulow, B., Shear, M. K., Friedman, R., & Plowe, C. (1984). Compliance and outcome of patients accompanied by relatives to evaluations. *Hospital and Community Psychiatry, 35,* 1037–1038.

Wirshing, W. C., Eckman, T., Liberman, R. P., & Marder, S. R. (1991). Management of risk of relapse through skills training of chronic schizophrenics. In C.A. Tamminga & S.C. Schulz (Eds.), *Schizophrenia Research: Advances in neurochemistry and psychopharmacology* (pp. 255–267). New York: Raven Press.

Citizenship Rights and Psychiatric Disability

Judi Chamberlin

Judi Chamberlin is a founder of the Ruby Rogers Advocacy and Drop-In Center in Somerville, Massachusetts, and is affiliated with the Center for Psychiatric Rehabilitation, Boston University.

This article was published previously in the *Psychiatric Rehabilitation Journal,* 1998, 21(4), and is reprinted with permission. The article was adapted from a presentation at the World Mental Health Day Conference, Stockholm, Sweden, October 10, 1996.

Discussions of rights and rights protection for people labeled "mentally ill" are often termed "the rights of the mentally ill," as if being "mentally ill," or carrying that label, means that this group has special, or different rights than other people. Documents concerning the "rights" of "the mentally ill" usually begin (and often end) with "treatment rights": the "right" to treatment that is decent, respectful, adequate, and so forth. I submit to you that this is the wrong way to think about rights.

By rights, I mean those fundamental expectations that govern the relationship between individuals and societies. In modern, western societies, rights of individuals are conceptualized as protections against arbitrary power, so that individuals retain the rights of personal choice and decision-making. Autonomy is a key underlying value; the adult individual is free to make choices that differ from social norms or expectations, so long as those choices do not bring the individual into conflict with established civil or criminal law. Rights can only be abridged, in theory, when individuals come into conflict with society according to established laws, and then only after certain procedural safeguards have been met.

These practices evolved over long periods of time, and mark an advancement in social relations from absolute rule by a monarch or by the state (which, of course, still continue in many parts of the world). The right of the individual to be free from arbitrary exercise of state power is perhaps the key difference between the democratic nations of the world and those that operate under other systems. The cross-cultural value of individual rights is recognized by documents such as the Universal Declaration of Human Rights, which hold that all adults, anywhere in the world, should be free to make basic life choices for themselves.

Why, then, does the supposedly medical diagnosis of "mental illness" carry with it such a profound effect on the rights of those so labeled? People with psychiatric labels can, in almost every country of the world, regardless of its political and social system, be deprived of their liberty and put into mental institutions against their will, often indefinitely. They can be required to take psychiatric drugs, be given electroshock treatments, even be lobotomized. They can lose their civil rights, such as the right to marry, the right to enter into contracts, the ability to work in their chosen professions, and the right to custody of their children. Often, they are socially ostracized, and such stigma may extend to their relatives. Such things don't happen only in so-called "backward" countries. Last year in the U.S.A., for example, it was revealed that leading medical organ transplant centers maintained "blacklists" of people deemed "not suitable for transplantation"; these lists included people who had been diagnosed with mental illness, and people with mental illness in their family history.

Involuntary commitment, forced treatment, and psychiatric control over decision making are really not complicated issues, despite the efforts to make them seem so. The fundamental question is this: Why do we take one group of people, those labeled "mentally ill," and deny them basic rights? The common justifications include "special needs," "vulnerabilities," "at-risk populations," and other terms designed to obscure this fundamental question: Is it ethically justifiable to confine people against their will, to subject them to procedures against their will, or to overrule their life choices, on the basis of an ostensibly medical diagnosis? I believe that until we frame this question properly, as a human rights question, we will continue to make the simple complicated. I believe that my views about choice and voluntariness are applicable to any person, regardless of label (or lack of label), who can express his or her own wishes and desires, no matter how irrational they may appear to others. All people deserve to have their choices respected. Only those who are genuinely incapable of such expression fall beyond the scope of my argument. By genuinely incapable, I mean people who are comatose or otherwise unable to communicate, not those who are clearly communicating what others may not want to hear.

Supposedly, we live under the rule of law. Just because we believe that someone is likely to commit a crime, we cannot put that person in prison. The reasons why we may believe that someone is a likely criminal often have to do with that person's membership in a class. Nearly every society has its minority groups, whether they are racial, ethnic, or otherwise defined, that are often believed by the dominant culture to be dangerous and deviant. It's all right to abridge their rights, in this way of thinking, since, left to their own devices, they will undoubtedly commit crimes or otherwise upset the social order. I believe this is a basic injustice.

A similar analysis applies to the mental health system. We are told that certain individuals are vulnerable to "mental illness" and that psychiatric interventions are what they "need." Is it justifiable, therefore, to ignore their expressed wishes and proceed on the basis of the supposedly superior wisdom of those who have the power to make the definitions, and to enforce the consequences? I believe that this, too, is a basic injustice.

According to psychiatrists, most people at some point show some "symptoms" of "mental illness," and large numbers of people are seriously "ill," yet most of them manage quite well without psychiatric interventions. Most psychiatrists seem to think that a little psychiatry would be good for everyone, and that not knowing that you are "ill" is one of the "symptoms" of the "illness," and so people need to be coerced. But this is not the way things are supposed to work in a free society.

The ethical system (if I can call it that) that drives the involuntary treatment system is paternalism, the idea that one group (the one in power, not oddly) knows what is best for another group (which lacks power). The history of civilization is, in part, the struggle against paternalism and for self-determination. People in power are always saying that they know what is best for those they rule over, even if those poor unfortunate individuals think they know best what they want. The powerful seldom cast their own motives in anything but benevolent terms. Rulers and slave masters like to think (or to pretend) that their subjects love them and are grateful to them, often having to ignore much evidence to the contrary. The struggle for freedom has always been seen by the powerful as a denial of the obvious truth of the superiority of the rulers.

All of us should be free to follow our own dreams. The U.S. Declaration of Independence states that basic rights include "life, liberty, and the pursuit of happiness." As we each pursue happiness, most of us seek economic stability, good and comfortable places to live, choices of daily activities, and satisfying companions for friendship and love. As the irrational, fallible human beings we are, our lives are an endless series of steps and missteps in pursuit of those dreams. Those who would overrule, on the basis of "incompetence," the dreams of others, are usually concerned with safety issues, with little regard to happiness. If we are truly concerned with protecting people we may deem to be incompetent, surely we must zealously protect their right to pursue happiness as well as their right to be safe. Otherwise, we are prescribing one standard for so-called normals, which allows (and even celebrates) the primacy of the pursuit of happiness, and another, more sober and more severe standard for those for whom we presume to decide their "best interest."

This historic confusion of medicine and power skews our language and our thinking. We hear arguments for the "medical model"; that so-called "mental illness" is an illness like any other. If psychiatrists want to be like other doctors, I believe they should do as other doctors do: wait for patients to come to them, and treat those patients as free agents. No one "chooses" to get cancer, or heart disease, or diabetes. But a person with one of these illnesses remains a free moral agent, who can choose to seek medical treatment, to enter a hospital, to undergo surgery or other medical procedures, or, equally important, who can choose not to do so. The fact that a person has cancer (a real illness) does not give us, as a society, the right to lock that person up and treat him or her if that person's choice is to go to a faith-healer, or a practitioner of alternative healing, or even to ignore the situation.

Contrast the situation of the person who is diagnosed as "mentally ill" (a theoretical illness). Typically, the "illness" consists of behavior that the person may or may not find distressing, but which is distressing to people around him or her. This individual is not free to choose treatment or to reject it. Clearly, something very different is going on here, despite the rhetoric of "illness" and "treatment." It is public safety and social control that are the real reasons that mental patients are subjected to involuntary interventions while medical patients are not.

Supposedly, the difference is "competence." We allow people we deem competent to make irrational or wrong decisions, while assuming a paternalistic stance toward so-called "incompetents," to protect them from their own shortcomings. But I believe that competence, like beauty, lies very much in the eye of the beholder. Take, for example, teenagers who choose to smoke cigarettes. Almost by definition, teenagers are unable to judge long-term consequences, or to see themselves as old, and so many discount anti-smoking education that focuses on the development of disease 20 or 30 years down the line. Are these teenagers incompetent, or are they simply showing some very human traits, putting current gratification above future considerations? I believe that most so-called incompetent decision making is this same process at work, viewed through the lens, however, of a person's label.

Adults, too, often act against their own best interests, with the full legal right to do so (providing they have not been labeled "mentally ill"). Overeating, not exercising, taking up dangerous hobbies (such as skydiving), driving too fast, and getting drunk are all common behaviors that certainly are not in the best interests of the individual, or of society as a whole. Yet we respect people's individual choices to engage in these activities, as I believe we should. If you are considered normal, you have the right to be wrong.

Therefore, whether or not there is or is not an underlying genetic or biochemical cause of "mental illness" is irrelevant. Despite all the research and all the theorizing, the schizophrenia gene or the schizophrenia germ has never been demonstrated. I believe that it never will; we can no more find the "cause" of complex human behavior in brain chemistry than we can find the "cause" of poetry. But even if there were real, biological diseases, psychiatrists wouldn't therefore derive the power to lock people up and treat them against their will, or to overrule their personal life decisions. These are legal and, ultimately, moral decisions, not medical ones.

What, then, is the best way to help people who are confused, who are behaving in non-ordinary ways, who seem to be out of contact with the ordinary world and society's expectations? This is another point where discussion usually gets muddled; opponents of involuntary psychiatric interventions are supposed to propose "alternatives," as if a better way to deal with these problems was the solution to the problem. It's like asking what the alternative is to slavery. Are opponents of slavery supposed to suggest "better" ways of "dealing with" a troublesome population? The ethical position toward slavery is to see it as a moral wrong, and freedom not as a "treatment" or an "alternative," but as a moral imperative. Similarly, the "alternative" to psychiatric domination is also freedom. Freedom does not mean that the problems of the former slave, or the former patient, disappear, but it does mean that the power over the individual that was formerly held by the slave master or the psychiatrist does disappear. Only then can people approach one another as equals, face difficulties, and search for solutions.

Defining a person's difficulties as psychiatric is a rejection of the reality of people's experiences. Psychiatric diagnosis is, in part, a process of decontextualization, of denying the real meaning that supposedly dysfunctional behavior has to the individual. A person may behave in ways that other people can't understand, but in ways that have meaning and value for that person in the context of his or her life. Turning behavior, thoughts, and feelings into "symptoms" actually gets in the way of understanding and helping. What is really helpful is contextualization, helping the person to understand that thoughts, feelings, and emotions do have meaning within the context of that person's own life and experiences. Unlike involuntary psychiatric treatment, this kind of real, individualized help is impossible without the active participation of the individual being helped.

I have written at great length about the self-help alternatives that have been developed by the patients' movement as a way of helping people to deal with the pain that is often a significant part of life, as have other activists in the psychiatric survivor movement. (Chamberlin, 1977; Chamberlin, 1987). It is not the job of the consumer/survivor movement to solve social problems that have led to the present unjust system. Instead, it is our job to serve as the moral focus of this debate, to represent the powerless in our struggle for fundamental justice. It is clear that we cannot leave our fate in the hands of lawyers, judges, and psychiatrists, who seem quite willing to sacrifice our freedom in the name of benevolent paternalism. The struggles against slavery, against the subjugation of women, and against racial and ethnic discrimination are, ultimately, moral issues. As people who have been labeled with "mental illness," we, too, are fighting for our rights. We cannot wait for the lawyers and judges to decide when or if we are "ready" for freedom. Wanting to be free is not a delusion.

In many countries of the world, people who have experienced psychiatric treatment are speaking out about these issues. Our organizations represent people who are refusing to remain voiceless and powerless. We are no longer willing to let others speak for us, whether those others are psychiatrists, lawyers, relatives, or politicians. We are citizens of our countries, and we want to be treated as equal to other citizens. We have joined together because we recognize our own humanity when others have denied it. We have found support and friendship from others who have shared our experiences. Often, we have been lone voices speaking out about problems other people don't want to think about. It's easy for others to assume that the issues of mental illness and its treatment are being dealt with by experts. But the experts have not experienced our pain and our determination to change the conditions we have experienced. Our expertise comes from our lives.

In my years of activism in the patients' movement, I've seen many changes. Not too many years ago, former patients were not invited to participate in forums and organizations that hold power over our lives. Today, our participation is welcomed in at least some of those forums, our opinions are solicited, our voices are being heard. But the continued existence of involuntary commitment, of prison-like mental institutions, of discrimination and segregation, shows how far we still have to go to reach our goals: full citizenship, equality, and human dignity.

REFERENCES

Chamberlin, J. (1977). *On our own: Patient controlled alternatives to the mental health system.* New York: McGraw-Hill.

Chamberlin, J. (1987). Community relations. In Zinman, S., Harp, H. & Budd, S. (Eds.), *Reaching across: Mental health clients helping each other* (pp.79–85). Sacramento: California Network of Mental Health Clients.

Chamberlin, J. (1990). The ex-patients' movement: Where we've been and where we're going. *Journal of Mind and Behavior, 11*(3&4), 323(77)–336(90).

Advocacy, Self-Help, and Consumer-Operated Services

Harriet Lefley

Harriet Lefley, PhD, is Professor, University of Miami, Department of Psychiatry.

This article was published previously in *Psychiatry, Volume 2 (2nd rev. ed.)*, edited by Allan Tasman, Jerald Kay, and Jeffrey A. Lieberman, 2003, and is reprinted by permission of John Wiley & Sons Limited.

A mentally ill woman involved with a self-help group writes to thank a peer who has helped her recover from an episode of hopelessness and despair:

> We've all known so much pain and so many years of struggling, that I feel we share a bond the likes of which the so-called "normal" world will never know. I consider it a privilege to be associated with people who have survived, and survived, and survived again, but still have the courage, the compassion, and the humanity to keep on striving and caring about themselves and reaching out to touch others in trouble. Although the rest of the world perceives us as different and pretty much useless, I think we're about as special as you can get. (Pat Deegan, 1994)

The letter captures some of the therapeutic aspects of the self-help experience. These include the feeling of not being alone, of bonding with peers who have shared the experience of mental illness. The woman is grateful for role models who have been able to reach out and help others. Viewing these examples of strength in persons with psychiatric disabilities, the writer rejects the world's stigmatization of the mentally ill and reevaluates with pride her own identity. There is a new appreciation of herself as someone able to transcend the pain and emerge as a survivor.

What is the relation of the self-help enterprise to the practice of psychiatry? Within the field of mental health, concepts such as advocacy, volunteerism, self-help, and consumerism represent interrelated activities that may share common objectives and yet differ substantially in process and impact. Each of these concepts has had some influence on psychiatric knowledge and practice. They designate extraprofessional efforts that, first of all, appear to be helpful to many patients. However, some of these concepts also describe social movements that have far-reaching effects on the funding of basic etiological research as well as services, the shape of mental health law, clinical training and patient-physician relationships, and the parameters and structures of treatment systems. Continuing research on self-help and consumerism may also add considerably to our knowledge of the mechanisms of therapeutic growth.

Advocacy and self-help cover a wide range of mental health related issues. Indeed, self-help groups are an acknowledged mechanism for striving to maintain mental health under adverse personal circumstances (Gartner & Riessman, 1984). In this article, these concepts are defined in terms of how they relate to a variety of conditions. However, the primary focus is on their application to the population of persons with major mental illnesses, that is, persons who have been psychiatrically hospitalized, have received crisis services, or have manifested functional impairment and a need for prolonged outpatient care. Much of the discussion relates to people with chronic disorders who rely on psychiatric services for extended periods of their lives. The involvement of such persons with self-help movements is of considerable interest to the psychiatrists from whom they receive their professional care.

CONCEPTUAL DISTINCTIONS

Advocacy

Advocacy groups focus on social and legal remedies to improve the lives of the particular constituency they represent. A primary focus of groups operating with a mental health agenda is legislative advocacy. This typically involves active lobbying for funding for research and services. Advocates may also work to promote legislation to protect the rights of mentally ill persons; extend entitlements; mandate insurance parity in order to ensure equal access to benefits of mentally, developmentally, and physically disabled persons; and improve standards and quality of care. Advocacy efforts may involve public education and anti-stigma campaigns and promoting and publicizing programs with innovative models of treatment and rehabilitation. Advocates may attempt to influence the agendas of federal agencies to focus on persons with serious mental illness, accompanied by budgetary advocacy to increase the funding for these agencies. Although tax exempt groups cannot engage in political sponsorship of candidates, individual members are likely to offer active support for legislators with a favorable voting record on mental health issues.

Currently there are strong initiatives to ensure that the needs of persons with chronic mental illness will not be lost in the acute care models of most managed care systems. In most cases, lay advocacy organizations will collaborate with professional associations to promote mutual agendas for standards, credentialing, clinical services, and research. This adds the considerable weight of a citizen constituency to what may be perceived as the vested interests of a practitioner group.

Volunteerism

Volunteerism, or work without renumeration, involves the participation of concerned individuals in a variety of unpaid activities that improve the lives of persons with mental illness. These are typically offered by nonprofessionals contributing their time and energy to augment professional services. However, as may be seen in some of the descriptions of citizen and consumer organizations, professionals may also act as volunteers. They may contribute their time to educate the public, lead support groups, serve on boards, or otherwise act in an unpaid advisory capacity.

Volunteerism may involve efforts devoted to the development of ancillary resources for persons with mental illness or the provision of personal services to supplement the professional system of care. A notable example is COMPEER, a nationwide program that trains volunteers to provide social companionship and role models for persons with severe and persistent mental illnesses.

Although volunteerism has been termed a uniquely US product (Greenblatt, 1985), there is increasing evidence of its application in other countries. One example is Friends of the National Institute of Mental Health and Neurosciences in Bangalore, India, a women's group that has developed and administers with volunteer help a psychosocial rehabilitation center for the institute's patients. In northern Italy, there are numerous volunteers contributing to a network of cooperative enterprises employing deinstitutionalized patients. In Japan, Zenkaren, the oldest family organization (organized in 1965), administers more than 800 sheltered workshops for persons with mental illness and in many other ways supplements the official mental health system (Mizuno & Murakami, 2001). Newly organized family advocacy groups in Europe and Asia are also beginning to augment services with a volunteer capability. Quantitatively, however, volunteerism is probably a far more significant aspect of medical and mental health care in the US. The scope of volunteer activities is suggested in some of the organizational descriptions in the following section.

Self-Help

Self-help refers to the organization of groups of individuals sharing a common problem who meet for purposes of mutual aid and support, education, and personal growth. Although advocacy may also be included in the agenda, self-help groups primarily focus on relief of personal problems through unburdening, sharing experiences and solutions to mutual problems, role modeling, positive reinforcement from peers, and information exchange. Through these activities, self-help groups improve coping skills and also provide social support. Self-help groups aim toward therapeutic growth and skill development through mutual efforts rather than through professional interventions.

In 1990 it was estimated that between 9 and 12 million US adults used self-help groups (Lieberman, 1990). Given the explosion of self-help groups in successive editions of *The Self-help Source Book* (White & Madara, 1999), there may be double that number today. Almost all of these groups deal with mental health-related problems. Included are the primary substance abuse organizations, Alcoholics Anonymous (AA), and Narcotics Anonymous (NA). AA has over 98,000 chapters. Their famous 12-step paradigm has been extended to other addictions (Overeaters Anonymous, Gamblers Anonymous, and the like). Parents Anonymous uses the self-help model for treatment and prevention of family violence. Other groups deal with bereavement; victimhood; physical and developmental disabilities; parenting; and societal status issues, such as being female, gay or lesbian, or a member of a particular racial or ethnic group. *The Self-help Source Book* currently (White & Madara, in press) lists 671 self-help organizations that deal with specific physical and mental disorders. There are also specialized groups for adoptees, adult children of alcoholic persons, victims of sexual abuse, and persons who have suffered a range of other human problems. These groups have proliferated so widely that the National Institute of Mental Health (NIMH) for years supported a National Self-help Clearinghouse (Greenblatt, 1985) with listings of self-help organizations. This clearinghouse maintained a database and information and referral system but tended to focus on training and research activities. The American Self-help Clearinghouse now of Cedar Knolls, New Jersey, focuses more on services and publishes a directory of 1071 national and model self-help programs (White & Madara, in press). Included are 169 online groups. After the World Trade Center (WTC) disaster of September 11, 2001, a surge of local face-to-face WTC groups were organized by survivors and families and friends of victims to deal with the traumatic effects (White & Madara, in press).

Included among the self-help groups outside of the professional system are those for people coping with psychiatric disorders. Prominent organizations, described in greater detail later, include Recovery Inc., GROW (not an acronym), the National Depressive and Manic-Depressive Association, and Schizophrenics Anonymous. These groups tend to be oriented toward support and mutual aid rather than political advocacy, although there is some overlapping membership in the growing movements of psychiatric consumer advocates.

Consumerism

Consumerism as applied to mental illness is the doctrine that service recipients have essential contributions to make to mental health planning, service delivery, and research. In this context, psychiatric service recipients generally refer to themselves as consumers, the most widely accepted term. However, they are also self-defined as clients, ex-patients, persons who are psychiatrically disabled, persons who are psychiatrically labeled, inmates, and survivors, depending on the orientation of the speaker.

Consumers are loosely defined by most consumer organizations as persons who have received services from a mental health system. The Center for Mental Health Services (CMHS) of the Substance Abuse and Mental Health Services Administration (SAMHSA) defines a consumer simply as "an individual, 18 years of age and older, with severe mental illness." (SAMHSA, 2001). Most persons identified as consumers typically have been psychiatrically hospitalized or have received outpatient care for a serious psychiatric condition. As persons who have experienced mental illness and who have been exposed to various treatment and rehabilitative modalities, consumers have long been considered to be valuable judges of whatever will best serve the needs of their peers, both by the CMHS (Consumer/Survivor, MHR, 1993) and the National Association of State Mental Health Program Directors (NASMHPD, 1989). Consumers who serve in this capacity may have various levels of functioning. Although some have a diagnosis of schizophrenia, they are articulate and rarely are cognitively disabled (Frese, 1998). Indeed, many have superior talents in writing, organizing capability, or in various areas of technical skill.

For more than a decade, consumer input has been solicited by government agencies at all levels of knowledge development and service building. This may range from formulating basic research questions to consumer roles in design, interviewing, and data analysis; from program monitoring and evaluation to state and local systems planning (SAMHSA, 2001; Consumer/ Survivor, MHR 2001; NASMHPD, 1989; Frese 1998; Trochim et al., 1993).

Targeted requests for grant applications from federal and state authorities solicit consumers in remission for service delivery roles both as staff members in professionally-run services and as operators of alternative consumer services for persons with mental illness. Evaluations of some of these enterprises are discussed in the section on research findings.

CITIZEN AND FAMILY ADVOCACY MOVEMENTS

In the US, many serious diseases and disabilities have long had organized constituencies of patients, families, and interested others who advocate for expanded research and services. The American Cancer Society, American Heart Organization, National Multiple Sclerosis Society, The Epilepsy Foundation, and the Alzheimer's Disease and Related Disorders Association are a few examples. Organizations devoted to developmental disabilities, such as the National Association for Retarded Citizens or the National Society for Autistic Children have advocated for state-of-the-art diagnostic and treatment procedures as well as appropriate education for children, enhanced rehabilitative resources, public information resources, and the like.

Until recent years, mental illness has been different from these other conditions in the composition of its advocacy groups. Encompassed within the framework of safeguarding human rights and the global promotion of mental health, advocacy for persons with severe psychiatric disorders was largely the province of concerned citizens rather than that of acknowledged stakeholders whose own lives are invested in treatment and cure. For many years, former patients and relatives who participated in these movements maintained a relatively low profile. Internalizing societal (and often professional) stigma, they rarely acknowledged their own experiences in public advocacy efforts or in leadership roles. The history of mental health advocacy in the US has therefore had two major developmental stages: citizen organizations, and since the late 1970s, family and consumer organizations (Table 1).

Table 1. Approaches To Improving the Lives of Those Touched by Mental Illness

Advocacy
Volunteerism
Self-help groups
Consumerism

Citizen Advocacy Organizations

National Mental Health Association. The National Mental Health Association (NMHA), with 340 affiliated mental health associations (MHAs), was the major advocacy group for persons with serious mental illness until the organization of the National Alliance for the Mentally Ill (NAMI) in 1979. Although it was founded by a former mental hospital patient, Clifford Beers, the NMHA in previous years had a limited emphasis on major mental illness, serving primarily as an education and referral resource for persons needing psychiatric help. The NMHA's mission has currently been aimed at improving mental health in the population at large, with a strong emphasis on primary prevention. Examples of activities by local branches include conferences on sexuality, police training to deal with interethnic conflict, support groups for at-risk groups such as newly widowed persons, and training volunteers to befriend troubled schoolchildren or work with victims of natural disasters.

In most areas, the local NMHA branch has been the major umbrella organization linking professionals with increased citizens, facilitating joint advocacy efforts, and providing mental health education for the public.

Mental health professionals have been actively involved in governance boards of the lay organization, and there are friendly affiliative relationships with professional societies. In contrast to self-help groups, Mental Health Association support groups traditionally were led by volunteer professionals, and persons needing further help were urged to use the mental health system. Today many more MHA affiliates are offering space and resources for peer-led groups which function independently of the host organization.

Table 2. Models of Advocacy

National Mental Health Association
Bazelon Center
State Protection and Advocacy Centers
National Alliance for the Mentally Ill
Consumer self-help and advocacy organizations
Therapeutic support groups
Political advocacy

NMHA has taken increasing interest in consumer groups and currently has a CMHS-funded Consumer Supporter Technical Assistance Center. The Center works to strengthen consumer and consumer supporter networking partnerships at local and state levels.

In 1987, the Mental Health Information Center was developed as the National Mental Health Association clearinghouse to answer personal inquiries and disseminate publications on mental illness and mental health topics. Despite their broad-based interests, MHA groups have always lobbied for legislation for persons with serious mental illness and developmental disabilities at both state and national levels. For many years they were the major citizen voice, working in tandem with professional societies and persons interested in mental health law and patients' rights.

Bazelon Center. The Judge David L. Bazelon Center for Mental Health Law, formerly the Mental Health Law Project, was organized in 1972 to halt abuse and neglect in state mental hospitals and training schools for persons with mental and developmental disabilities, and to prevent exclusion of disabled children from public funded education. Its current agenda is much more comprehensive. In addition to its basic focus on protecting patients' civil liberties, the center provides legal resources to combat exclusionary zoning and rental policies; promote patients' access to health care, social services, and income support; reform state systems of care; and help generate a continuum of community services for persons with psychiatric and developmental disabilities. Working in the courts and in legislative and policy arenas the Bazelon Center offers legal assistance to consumers, other advocacy groups, and policymakers.

State Protection and Advocacy Centers. State Protection and Advocacy Centers (P & As) have assumed some of the Bazelon Center's functions. The P & As are federally mandated to protect disabled persons from neglect and abuse and to protect their rights in institutional and community settings. Initially passed by congress in 1986 and reauthorized in 1991 (PL102-173), the legislation is now known as the Protection and Advocacy for Individuals with Mental Illness Act, extending rights already afforded to persons with developmental disabilities. The law provides grants to existing P & As for the developmentally disabled. Much of their work involves grievance casework for individuals, although they also initiate lawsuits to upgrade institutional conditions. Many P & As also view their mission as reforming the service delivery system, which may include shifting resources from institutional to community vendors.

All 50 states, the District of Columbia, and five territories have federally-funded programs under the Protection and Advocacy for Individuals with Mental Illness Act. State P & As are members of the National Association of Protection and Advocacy Systems.

The Family Movement: The National Alliance for the Mentally Ill (NAMI)

The organization of NAMI has been termed one of the most important events in the history of US psychiatry (Kaplan & Sadock, 1991). Indeed, former NIMH director Herbert Pardes has hailed the political influence of NAMI as "the single most positive event in the history of mental illness" (Flynn, 1993). For the first time the major psychiatric disorders had their own important national presence, a grassroots constituency of families with a profound commitment to improving services, research, and public awareness and to reduce the stigma of mental illness.

Although local family support groups had been organized in the 1960s, and at least one state family federation existed in 1971 (Shelter, 1986), it was not until 1979 that 284 family members convened at the University of Wisconsin, Madison, to form the national organization NAMI. Since that time NAMI has grown exponentially into a powerful movement. In 2001 NAMI reported 210,000 members and over 1200 affiliates in all 50 states as well as Puerto Rico and the Virgin Islands. Today, there is a well functioning NAMI office in Arlington, Virginia, disseminating information and lobbying for research and services at the national level as well as state NAMI organizations that work for improved services in their individual states.

Like most organizations that are formed by stakeholders rather than interested outsiders, NAMI merges self-help and advocacy. Thus, the basic armature in all localities is mutual support groups and membership education about all aspects of major mental illnesses. Most groups have also engaged in public education; resource development; anti-stigma campaigns;

and service on mental health planning, policy, and governance boards at local and national levels. Consumers and family members are trained to become effective lobbyists and advocates for patients. Professional educators within NAMI have developed models for training family education specialists. NAMI has also had an impact on clinical training. The NAMI Curriculum and Training Network focused on influencing mental health professionals to work with persons with severe mental illness and on ensuring state-of-the-art education in clinical training programs from preservice to continuing education levels. Several national conferences cosponsored by NAMI and NIMH brought together leading clinical educators, researchers, and practitioners with family member-mental health professionals for concept development and curriculum planning in the core professions (Lefley et al., 1989; Lefley & Johnson, 1990, NIMH 1990). A major phenomenon is the NAMI Family-to-Family program, developed by a psychologist-family member as a 12-week educational program on schizophrenia, bipolar disorder, and major depression (Burland, 1998). The program is carefully structured to train family members as educators. They provide some of the content of evidence-based psychoeducational intervention, such as problem-solving and communication skills, as well as understanding the patient's experience. The program also teaches families how to cope with family burden, avoid overinvolvement, set limits, and see to their own needs and those of other family members. Family-to-Family is available in numerous states with state mental health authority sponsorship, and has been administered to more than 30,000 families. NAMI also has a program for consumers, Living with Schizophrenia, which teaches them how to better live with their disorders.

On the national level, the family constituency has been powerfully influential in raising research dollars for mental illness. NAMI has successfully lobbied for substantial increases in congressional appropriations for NIMH research on the major psychiatric disorders and helped launch the National Schizophrenia and Brain Research campaign. NAMI co-founded the National Alliance for Research on Schizophrenia and Depression (NARSAD) in 1985 and has generated millions of dollars in research awards through the Ted and Vida Stanley Foundation. Because of its strong commitment to basic research on brain diseases, NAMI was an influential force in the return of NIMH to the National Institutes of Health.

NAMI-sponsored publications have had a substantial influence on mental health services. These have included *Care of the Seriously Mentally Ill: A Rating of State Programs* (Torrey et al., 1990), and *Criminalizing the Seriously Mentally Ill: The Abuse of Jails as Mental Hospitals* (Torrey et al., 1992). In collaboration with the Center for Psychiatric Rehabilitation at Boston University, NAMI began publishing in 1990 the scholarly journal *Innovations and Research* with a focus on clinical services, community support, and rehabilitation for persons with severe and persistent mental illness. *Innovations and Research* and the Boston University Center's previous *Psychosocial Rehabilitation Journal* have since been merged into the *Psychiatric Rehabilitation Journal*.

With a major stake in legislative advocacy at the federal level, NAMI was active in promoting passage of Public Law 99–660, which required all 50 states to develop a comprehensive mental health plan including provision of community care to persons with serious mental illness. The legislation for the first time required family and consumer participation on a state advisory council. Reauthorization language linked the approved state plans to the federal block grant, and local NAMI groups became active in monitoring their state's compliance with the plan's objectives. NAMI fought for the 1986 Protection and Advocacy for Individuals with Mental Illness legislation previously discussed, and the organization was a vocal advocate for the Americans with Disabilities Act. NAMI has been actively working for mental health parity legislation, and for implementation of the Wisconsin PACT program as evidence-based practice in all states (Bond et al., 2001). NAMI was also actively involved in the dissemination of the findings of the Schizophrenia Patient Outcomes Research Team (PORT), which recommended specific parameters for prescribed antipsychotic medications (Lehman & Steinwachs, 1998). NAMI produced and distributed more than 50,000 brochures highlighting these recommendations (Frese et al., 2001). NAMI was also instrumental in helping develop the *1999 Expert Consensus Treatment Guidelines for Schizophrenia,* and has widely disseminated the "Guide for Patients and Families" appended to the Guidelines (Weiden et al., 1999).

The NAMI Consumer Council is a group of primary consumers who function as a separate interest group within NAMI with a very substantial role in policy making. Frese (2001) reports that during the past several years at least one quarter of the members of NAMI's board of directors have been consumers. One of the few NAMI presidents elected for two terms was a consumer. Members of the NAMI Consumer Council generally support the NAMI agenda, but many have overlapping affiliations and common interests with other consumer organizations.

MENTAL HEALTH CONSUMER SELF-HELP AND ADVOCACY ORGANIZATIONS

Consumer self-help organizations generally merge mutual support with a focus on one of two basic objectives: political advocacy or personal problem resolution and growth. A study of 104 self-help groups of present and former psychiatric patients identified two major service models, which the author differentiated as social movement versus individual therapy. The social movement groups were oriented toward social change and offered public education, legal advocacy, information referral networking, and technical assistance to other consumers. The individual therapy groups offered more "inner-focused" individual change through mutual support meetings and various types of alternative therapies such as relaxation. The study found that almost two thirds of the groups were social movement models (Emerick, 1990).

A major consumer organization that combines both social movement and therapeutic functions, one that is most comparable to national organizations of persons suffering from major physical illnesses, is the National Depressive and Manic-Depressive Association (NDMDA), which consists of more than 400 chapters and has served more than 35,000 patients and families (White & Madara, in press). Chapters may have multiple area support groups. Like NAMI, the NDMDA views major affective disorders as biogenic, disseminates public education on the descriptions of biochemical nature of depressive illnesses, holds annual conferences with professional presentations, and tries to fight stigma and promote basic research with a variety of advocacy efforts.

The Therapeutic Support Group Model

The following organizations were given by group leaders or are adapted from *The Self-help Source Book,* (White & Madara 1998; in press). Figures are current as of fall, 2001. Just a few of the major national organizations for psychiatric patients can be mentioned, excluding groups that specifically focus on addictions.

- Schizophrenics Anonymous, founded in 1985, has more than 150 chapters nationwide. Organized and run by people with a schizophrenia-related disorder, Schizophrenics Anonymous offers fellowship, support, and information. Schizophrenics Anonymous focuses on recovery, using a 6-step program, along with medication and professional help.

- GROW is an international organization founded in Australia in 1957. They have more than 143 groups in the US, primarily located in Illinois, New Jersey, and Rhode Island. GROW has a 12-step program to provide skills for avoiding and recovering from a breakdown. They offer a caring and sharing community to attain emotional maturity, personal responsibility, and recovery from mental illness. Leadership and training are offered to new groups.

- Recovery Inc., founded in 1937, has 700 chapters nationally and offers "a self-help method of will training; a system of techniques for controlling temperamental behavior and changing attitudes toward nervous symptoms and fears" (White & Madara, 1998).

- Emotions Anonymous, with 1100 national chapters, is a "fellowship sharing experiences, hopes, and strengths with each other, using the 12-step program, in order to gain better emotional health (White & Madara, 1998). Other national self-help organizations of present or former patients are Obsessive-Compulsive Anonymous, Anxiety Disorders Association of America (national network), Agoraphobics in Motion, National Organization for Seasonal Affective Disorder, and many others (White & Madara, in press).

The Political Advocacy Model

Among some former psychiatric patients, self-help in itself is often viewed as a political statement. Zinman and colleagues (1987) gave the essential characteristics of self-help groups as self-definition of needs, equal power of members, mutual respect, voluntary participation, autonomy, and responsivity to other special populations. The self-help mission is for optimal personal independence with the option of choosing interdependence with other consumers.

For many years, self-help was incorporated in organizations of former psychiatric patients with names such as the Insane Liberation Front (Portland, Oregon) or the Mental Patients Liberation Project (New York) and publications such as *The Madness Network News* (California). These groups of former psychiatric patients were angry at a system that they thought had abused and dehumanized them rather than helped them. They tended to have strong antipsychiatry views; they were vehemently opposed to electroconvulsive therapy and often to psychotropic medications as well. Many thought that the only valid help for persons who were "psychiatrically labeled" would come from peers who had experienced a similar history of psychiatric hospitalization. Many of the pioneers of the consumer movements developed and provided models for today's consumer-operated services (Chamberlin, 1978).

Although contemporary consumer groups have a common agenda of self-determination, former psychiatric patients seem to be divided ideologically. A few still view mental illness as psychogenic or as a social construct, rejecting biogenesis, but most seem to accept a stress-diathesis model and many describe themselves as having a brain disease or "a chemical imbalance" (Kersker, 1994). Some consumers are totally opposed to any kind of forced treatment while others have stated that without it, they might not be alive today (Rogers, 1994). Some members of the consumer movement think that hospitalization is harmful and would like to eliminate all hospital beds.

However, their views are not supported empirically. In the California Well-Being Project, (Campbell, 1989) a survey of psychiatric clients designed and conducted by consumers and directed by a professional researcher-consumer, more than 50% of the respondents believed that their hospitalization had been helpful, 22% reported both positive and negative aspects, and only 20% found hospitalization harmful.

These different viewpoints were reflected in two major consumer advocacy organizations that are now no longer active at the national level. Their differences and influence, however, are evident at the nationwide Alternatives Conferences that are funded by the CMHS and bring together consumers of all persuasions on a regular basis. The more radical National Association of Psychiatric Survivors, a small but highly vocal consumer group, retained an essential protest orientation and took a formal position opposing any kind of involuntary treatment. It no longer has national meetings, but some members continue in leadership positions at national consumer conferences. The more moderate National Mental Health Consumers' Association (NMHCA) had taken no formal position on forced treatment, but its mission statement and organizing focus emphasized consumer empowerment and self-determination. They stated that recovery and healing, not social control must be the goal and outcome of the mental health system (Frese et al., 2001). Members of NMHCA acknowledged the validity of mental illness and the need for treatment and most have been absorbed in the NAMI Consumer Council.

These organizations have largely been supplanted by networking at annual conferences, coalition building, and developing local consumer-run initiatives, with support from federal and state governments. By the year 2000, there were an estimated 3000 consumer-run organizations working at the local, state, and national levels (Van Tosh & del Vecchio, 2000). As of 2001, 30 states have an Office of Consumer Affairs and most have local consumer groups and drop-in centers. The CMHS funds three Consumer Technical Assistance Centers and two Consumer Supporter Technical Assistance Centers whose purpose is "to develop and implement activities that assist in the improvement of mental health service systems at the state and local levels." (SAMHSA, 2001) One of these centers usually convenes the national Alternatives Conferences that bring together consumers from all over the country for organizational skill building and knowledge sharing. The National Mental Health Consumer Self-help Clearinghouse (NMHCSHC) in Philadelphia, under the direction of Joseph Rogers, encourages the development of consumer self-help groups and provides information, materials, and referrals on fund-raising and program development. Organized in 1986, the NMHCSHC has worked to develop the infrastructure of consumer movements nationwide. They have helped build new local and state self-help groups by providing technical assistance (TA) and disseminating information, developing consumer networks and coalitions, and generally building the capacity of consumer groups. The National Empowerment Center (NEC) in Lawrence, Massachusetts, directed by psychiatrist-consumer Daniel Fisher, similarly supplies TA to self-help groups. NEC has specific departments that focus on resource development and training conferences, consumer-run organizations, managed care and coalition building, information and referral, media relations, and training professionals on the consumer viewpoint. In an innovative Disability Awareness Workshop, mental health professionals are required to wear headphones blaring negative "voices" and to assess the effects of stimulus bombardment and vocal interference as they take a mental status examination, attend a day treatment program, undergo psychological testing, and ask directions in the community.

Consumer Organization and Networking Technical Assistance Center (CONTAC) located in West Virginia, is the third consumer TA center funded by the CMHS. In collaboration with the other centers, CONTAC works nationwide to provide informational materials, on-site training and skill-building curricula, electronic and other communication capabilities, networking, and customized TA to build leadership and teach business management skills to local consumer groups.

In addition to the Consumer TA Centers, federal funding is received for two Consumer Supporter TA Centers. The National Mental Health Association has a grant to provide TA to consumer and consumer supporter organizations in areas such as education, advocacy, systems change and, coalition building. TA is provided in the form of research, training, information, and financial support. NAMI has the other Consumer Supporter grant. Their primary purpose is to help implement the evidence-based Wisconsin PACT program in service systems throughout the nation through knowledge dissemination, training, and on-site TA.

In research centers studying self-help and psychiatric rehabilitation at Boston University, University of Illinois at Chicago, University of California, Berkeley, and University of Michigan, Ann Arbor, consumers have been involved in all phases of research including design, instrument development, interviewing, and analysis. At the Missouri Institute of Mental Health, under the direction of Dr. Jean Campbell, a consumer, a 4-year, multisite, $20 million dollar project is currently investigating the efficacy of consumer-operated services. Data already collected are presented in the section on research findings.

Government Roles in Consumer Empowerment

A major element in helping the organization of both family and consumer movements is the Community Support Program (CSP) of the federal government. Initially under the NIMH and now part of CMHS, the CSP was organized in 1978 to deal with problems of deinstitutionalization. The federal program focused on developing in each locality a comprehensive continuum of care for deinstitutionalized patients that would include all needed resources for survival, treatment, rehabilitation, and hopefully, a satisfactory quality of life (Stroul, 1989). Through targeted grants to state administrations, the CSP fostered public-academic linkages and funded research and demonstration grants for model programs, including case management, crisis services, services for homeless mentally ill persons, and other innovative community rehabilitative projects.

The CSP also had a heavy emphasis on aiding the development of state and local self-help and advocacy groups and facilitating dissemination of their ideas on a national basis. Through the years, the program promoted Learning Community Conferences to bring together researchers, service providers, family advocates, and primary consumers. More recently, CSP helped fund the annual Alternatives Conferences that bring together members of consumer organizations from all over the US to pursue a national agenda. The CSP has probably been the major catalyst in helping develop services in which former psychiatric patients are participants or primary providers.

Since its inception as a separate division of SAMHSA, the CSP's umbrella organization, CMHS has provided funding for many consumer activities over the years. In addition to providing scholarships and other support for the Alternatives conferences, CMHS also provided scholarships for consumers with affective disorders to attend annual meetings of the Depressive and Manic Depressive Association (DMDA). The CMHS has also worked with the DMDA to develop a training video for psychiatric residents called "Partners in Recovery" (Paolo del Vecchio, 2001, personal communication).

The Consumer/Survivor Mental Health Research and Policy Work Group was established in 1992 with support from the Mental Health Statistics Improvement Program and the Survey and Analysis Branch of the CMHS. The purpose was "to modify the relationships and dialogue between mental health professionals/service providers/policy administrators and consumers/survivors including fostering significant roles for consumers/survivors in all phases of mental health research, data standards development, planning, policy, and implementation of mental health services." (Consumer/Survivor, MHR, 1993).

A major focus of this work group was on outcome measures used in the CMHS-funded services research. A concept-mapping project resulted in a publication by the National Association of State Mental Health Program Directors (NASMHPD) entitled *Mapping Mental Health Outcomes from the Perspective of Mental Health Consumers* (Trochim et al., 1993). This project generated recommendations to the mental health research community on outcome measures of greatest interest to consumers in a future research agenda. NASMHPD developed a position paper in December 1989 that specifically outlined the role of "ex-patients-consumers" in state mental health systems. "Their contribution should be valued and sought in areas of program development, policy formation, program evaluation, quality assurance, system design, education of mental health service providers, and the provision of direct services (as employees of the provider system)," (NASMHPD, 1989).

A survey commissioned by NASMHPD in 1993 reported that 65.5% of state mental health agencies provided financial resources to consumer-run and family-run programs and that 19 states had consumer affairs offices (NASMHPD, 1993). In 2001, 30 states had consumer-affairs offices with the majority providing financial resources for drop-in centers and other consumer-run services (Paolo del Vecchio, 2001, personal communication).

Service Development by Family and Consumer Groups

For many years, NAMI groups in various localities developed resources to fill in gaps in their service delivery systems. Multiple housing facilities, employment opportunities ranging from thrift shops to furniture workshops, psychosocial rehabilitation programs, and even a psychiatric hospital are examples of resources developed throughout the US. However, despite continuing initiatives, many NAMI members believe that families should be investing their energies in legislative advocacy rather than in service development. NAMI's major mission is to augment and strengthen the service delivery system through encouraging the implementation of evidence-based practices, such as its current TA center grant to promote national adoption of the Wisconsin PACT program.

The consumer movements have had a different view of their role in services. Their focus is on using the experiences and skills of former psychiatric patients both within the system and its operators of consumer-run alternatives. Numerous CSP initiatives have been devoted to helping consumers achieve that end through funded model projects and inducements to the states. As of 2001 there are reportedly al least 3000 consumer-run programs and enterprises. These include housing facilities, residential placement services, case management, peer companion programs, social centers, employment services including job training, and consumer businesses, crisis respite houses, substance abuse treatment programs, and special programs for the homeless. CSP-funded demonstration projects include a variety of consumer enterprises. In 30 states today there is a Mental Health Consumer Affairs Office organized and staffed by one or more former psychiatric patients. Almost all states have networks of drop-in centers that provide socialization outlets outside of the traditional mental health system and sometimes fulfill an advocacy function as well. In many states the sponsorship of consumer drop-in centers by state hospitals and community agencies is a common practice, typically with maximal independence offered to the consumer group.

RESEARCH FINDINGS ON CONSUMER SELF-HELP

To date, most of the evaluations of therapeutic self-help groups lend to be qualitative or process research based. Some studies of efficacy are inferred from the members' satisfaction by use of normative data as a control condition. For example, a study of Recovery Inc. members, half of whom had been hospitalized for mental illness, focused on the benefits of membership to volunteer leaders of the organization. As a result of their participation, volunteer leaders gave high ratings to their overall satisfaction with life, health, work, leisure, and community. Their quality of life ratings were equivalent to the levels of satisfaction of a sample of the general public (Raiff, 1982). A collaborative study of GROW by University of Illinois researchers compared members for 9 months or more with those who had been members 3 months or less. GROW members for the longer period were significantly better off in terms of larger social networks, a higher rate of employment, and lower levels of psychosis and depression (Rappaport et al., 1984). Another quantitative study looked at patients discharged from a state psychiatric hospital who participated in a Community Network Development self-help program. The research found that 10 months after discharge, participants required 50% less rehospitalization and two thirds fewer inpatient days than a comparable group of nonparticipating patients. A significantly smaller percentage of Community Network Development ex-patients required community mental health center services than the comparison group Gordon et al. (1982).

A study of four self-help groups for families of persons with mental illness showed high congruence between what participants wanted from the group and what they reported actually happened in the group experience. Moreover, a time series analysis showed that the perceived helpfulness of the program for families was significantly related to the patients' functioning in terms of fewer number of hospitalizations and fewer total days in hospital (Biegel & Yamatani, 1986). The efficacy of the self-help sharing experience for family members has also received tangential empirical support from the work of McFarland (1994) and associates on psychoeducational interventions.

These researchers found that interventions with multiple family groups were significantly superior to individual family interventions in deterring patients' relapse, a finding attributed to the mutual support and information exchange of the group experience.

Table 3. Positive Research Findings Related to Consumer Self-Help Groups

Larger social networks	Increased empathy
Higher rate of employment	Feel needed and responsible
Lower levels of symptoms	Improved consumer employment
Fewer rehospitalizations	Improved education
Fewer in patient days	Increased independence
Less MHC services	Enhanced quality of life
Greater self-confidence	

Family members and consumers have been increasingly involved in grand rounds, as lecturers in clinical training programs, and in training service providers. A randomized evaluation of consumer versus nonconsumer training of state mental health service providers found positive reactions to the use of consumers as trainers (Cook et al., 1993).

A process evaluation of 6 consumer-run drop-in centers in Michigan found that the centers were meeting their programmatic goals to provide acceptance, social support, and problem-solving help. The study found high levels of consumer satisfaction together with the participants' reported feeling that they actually ran their centers (Mowbray et al. 1998). A 6-month survey of 9 consumer-operated drop-in centers in Pennsylvania indicated a high level of client satisfaction (Kaufmann et al., 1993). In California, the use of former patients as peer counselors on locked inpatient wards received enthusiastic evaluations from clinical staff, with most staff asking that the program be extended. The peer counselors reported personal benefits in terms of greater self-confidence, increased empathy, and feelings of being needed and responsible (McGill & Patterson, 1990). A study of a Rehabilitation Services Administration training program for consumer case manager and human service worker aides, comparing team and individual approaches with intensive case management for frequent users of psychiatric hospitals, found advantages in consumer employment (Bond et al., 1991). Family members participating in a randomized trial of consumer versus nonconsumer case management teams reported equal satisfaction with the capabilities of consumer case managers. Because many studies do not report on ethnicity, it is of interest that 86% of the respondents were African-Americans (Solomon & Draine, 1994).

Mind-Empowered Inc. is an assertive case management-supported housing program in Oregon that is completely run by consumers. Operating successfully for several years, it received a county contract to bring 30 persons out of the state hospital and keep them in the community. Preliminary data indicated that during the first 6 months of the program's operation, only 2 clients returned to the hospital. However, the evaluators admit that additional objective outcome data are needed to assess the long-term impact of the program (Nikkel et al., 1992).

A major question relates to job stress and the stability of former psychiatric patients as mental health service providers. A project in Denver, Colorado, trained consumers as case management aides in a psychiatric rehabilitation program. Of 25 trainees, 18 completed the program and 17 were employed as case management aides. At 2-year follow-up, the 15 trainees who were still employed had required a total of only 2 bed-days of psychiatric hospitalization (Mowbray et al., 1997).

Currently there are 2 overviews of consumer-run services and CSP research demonstration projects based on consumer services. A comprehensive retrospective review of federally-funded consumer/survivor-operated service programs in 13 states concluded that "Consumer/survivor-operated services are successful in increasing the overall quality of life, independence, employment, social supports, and education of consumer/survivors" (Van Tosh & del Vecchio, 2000). This study found, moreover, that 70% of the federally-funded initiatives were continued with other funding sources. The consumer recipients were objectively successful in capturing ongoing financial support, and subjectively they reported increased self-efficacy and self-esteem on standardized scales (Van Tosh & del Vecchio, 2000). An overview of consumer programs by the International Association of Psychosocial Rehabilitation Services reported similar findings and stated that "Consumer service provision may be an essential feature of a support system devoted to recovery" (Mowbray et al., 1997).

Although consumers seem to be doing well on many of the evaluated programs, there are some negative or problematic findings as well. For example, research in Chicago compared trained consumer and nonconsumer staff on mobile outreach teams for persons manifesting psychotic behavior. The findings showed that contrary to the hypothesis, consumers were significantly more likely than nonconsumer staff to certify clients for involuntary hospitalization (Lyons et al., 1993). It is unknown whether consumers were less capable of handling psychotic behavior or whether they were more knowledgeable about the limitations of voluntary interventions. According to an evaluator for the CSP, consumer alternatives were never envisioned to serve as substitutes for mental health services; they were meant to empower consumers to gain some control over their lives. A qualitative analysis based on systematic observations of consumer-run services found that many consumer alternatives fell short of these empowering principles. Power conflicts and hierarchies developed in many programs. Consumers often tried unsuccessfully to replicate services provided by the local mental health clinic rather than to offer self-help alternatives (McLean, 1994). This is an area of great interest that bears continued watching and evaluation.

Table 4. Consumer Involvement in Treatment

Consumer staff more likely to certify clients for involuntary hospitalization
Development of power conflicts and hierarchies
Less focus on consumer empowerment

RELATIONS OF PROFESSIONALS AND SELF-HELP GROUPS

Many health and mental health professionals have welcomed the advent of the self-help movement. In a Workshop on Self-help and Public Health held by the Surgeon General's Office of the Department of Health and Human Services, the major focus was on collaborative partnerships of professionals and self-help groups and a key recommendation that "exposure to the concepts and benefits of self-help should be included in the training curriculums of all helping professions" (The Surgeon General's Workshop, 1988). The APA's Task Force on Treatments of Psychiatric Disorders views self-help groups as part of the therapeutic armamentarium. In their four-volume publication on treatment, Borman (1989) noted that self-help groups redefine pathological states, provide a shift in human service paradigms, promote and maintain competence, and reinforce positive mental health.

An increasing number of community mental health centers and rehabilitation facilities are welcoming support groups of patients and families, offering organizational help and free staff facilitators. Most professionally-run substance abuse programs include participation in Alcoholics Anonymous or Narcotics Anonymous as a component of treatment. Numerous newsletters for professionals and administrators endorse mutual aid groups as an adjunct to psychotherapy and give substantial information on self-help resources (*Mental Health Weekly,* 1992).

It is obvious that under certain conditions, self-help groups may compose a parallel and sometimes competing system of care. Although many members may simultaneously use clinical services, some joined self-help groups because of dissatisfaction with professional medical or mental health treatment. Some self-help groups reduce the demand for clinical services because they offer alternatives and are hostile to professional interventions. Other groups, however, may raise awareness of deeper problems and provide referrals to preferred psychiatrists. Referrals work both ways and typically are mutually beneficial. Self-help group members learn about recommended professionals from their peers. Psychiatrists treating persons with a chronic mental illness are usually happy to learn about a local drop-in center to which they can refer their socially isolated patients.

Consumers who participate in self-help groups seem to be comfortable using dual systems of care. Of great interest is a 1996 Boston University study of 6 consumer-run self-help programs in various parts of the US. This research found that 50% of the self-help members were currently taking antipsychotic medication and that most also utilized professional mental health services such as counseling, day treatment, and inpatient care (Chamberlin, Rogers, & Ellison, 1996. Drop-in centers whose members come from the mental health system generally require that participants be under psychiatric care. Most self-help groups with seriously disabled members agree since they cannot deal with decompensation or other issues requiring clinical expertise.

Table 5. Strategies to Establish Collaborative Partnerships Between Professionals and Self-Help Groups

Welcome support groups
Endorse these groups as adjunctive to psychotherapy
Avoid setting groups up as competing systems of care
Use two-way referrals
Understand professionally-led groups can inhibit the therapeutic process
Be cognizant of issues related to disempowerment, control, and need for self-determination

---

Research suggests that self-help groups function best on their own without professional help in running the group. Emerick's (1990) study of 104 self-help groups of psychiatric patients found that more than 70% reported little to no interaction with professionals. As previously indicated, only a third of these groups were considered to have a therapeutic orientation, and as might be expected, these were more amenable to professional alliances. A study of professional involvement with members of GROW, one of the therapeutic orientation models, compared social climate data and behavioral data among members of groups led by either a mental health professional ($n = 36$) or an indigenous group member ($n = 70$). The study found no difference in members' outcomes but significant differences in perceptions and behaviors. Members of groups led by professionals showed fewer agreements and self-disclosures, had less small talk and information giving, and rated their groups lower in cohesion and higher in leader control than did members of groups with indigenous leaders. The authors surmised that the professionals' more formal approach may have discouraged behaviors that they thought were less psychologically relevant and cautioned against professionalizing mutual help groups (Toro et al., 1998).

The picture is different on an individual basis, however. First-person accounts of consumers indicate numerous favorable recollections of their interactions with professionals (Hatfield & Lefley, 1993). Many attribute the turning point of their recovery to a specific psychotherapist or to a rehabilitation specialist who helped them. Nevertheless, a number of former patients still tend to view negatively their overall experiences with the mental health system itself (Campbell, 1989; Hatfield & Lefley, 1993). In these cases, their negativity is typically related to feelings of disempowerment, external control, and loss of options for self-determination. It remains to be seen whether the new emphasis on consumer empowerment and peer-run services will have the desired therapeutic countereffect.

CONCLUSION

The growth of the family and consumer movements has had a revolutionary impact not only on service delivery systems and funding resources but also on knowledge and practice. Like the National Society for Autistic Children before it, NAMI has helped change professionals' attitudes toward families in numerous ways. By eliciting public statements and support from world-class researchers and authorities (Kaplan & Sadock, 1991; Flynn, 1993), and disseminating their information on the neurobiological substrates of major psychiatric disorders, NAMI has reinforced the changing ideas about familial roles in etiology among psychiatrists and other mental health professionals as well as the general public. The family movement has influenced clinical training curricula to provide state-of-the-art education (Lefley & Johnson, 1990; NIMH, 1990) helped attain increased funding for basic research; and through advertising, television, and other media events, accelerated the slow historical process of destigmatizing mental illness.

The advent of a powerful grassroots constituency has generated pronounced respect on the part of professional leaders and policy makers and an eagerness for political alliances. There has been consistent personal participation of APA presidents and NIMH directors at all annual NAMI conferences. Many state psychiatric associations have urged their members to join NAMI as associate members. Clinical training programs have sometimes required their students to attend local NAMI meetings as part of their training, and some psychiatric residents have regularly attended as resource persons for NAMI family support groups (Lefley, 1988).

Family members and consumers are increasingly involved on governance and advisory boards of service providers and on state mental health planning councils. In various departments of psychiatry, family members and consumers have lectured, given grand rounds, or made presentations at professional association meetings. They have also been encouraged to enter professional training programs through various NIMH training initiatives.

The growth of the consumer movement has dramatically highlighted the heterogeneity of psychiatric patients. An unexpectedly high level of organizational skill and leadership is evident among many people with histories of psychiatric hospitalizations and diagnoses of major disorders. In mental health service delivery, some former psychiatric patients are apparently able to fulfill paraprofessional staff functions ranging from crisis intervention to case management, with the added therapeutic advantage of offering role models and experiential empathy to the patients receiving their services.

The consumer movement itself has helped develop a wide range of skills and knowledge that are invaluable for psychiatric rehabilitation. These include writing, technical assistance, education in communications media, information dissemination, and decision-making skills. The political advocacy process has brought empowerment, respect, and influence on important leadership figures to individuals who believe that their residual psychological deficits were related to powerlessness, marginality, and internalized stigmas (Campbell, 1989). The job of helping one's peers brings rewards of competence, altruism, and efficacy (Van Tosh & del Vecchio, 2000; Mowbray et al., 1997). All of these would appear to be important factors in therapeutic growth.

On a policy level, the primary consumer movement has had an impact both on state services and on rehabilitation ideology. The director of Boston University's Center for Psychiatric Rehabilitation confirmed this influence by viewing recovery from mental illness as "the guiding vision of the mental health service system in the 1990s" (Anthony, 1993). In this vision, recovery is viewed as a subjective attitude change that enables one to live a life of meaning and purpose, even with the limitations imposed by mental illness. A consumer leader, director of a state network of drop-in centers, credited his psychiatrist with enabling him to fulfill the advocacy role that has shaped his recovery. He defined recovery as follows: "Recovery is not remission, nor is it a return to a preexisting state....Recovery is the development of new ego and identity structures to replace those damaged by our illnesses....Recovery takes place through creation of new patterns of behavior that make our lives more satisfying and productive. People in recovery like themselves as they are accept their disability, and enjoy the life they have. Acceptance of one's disability can lead to greater appreciation of one's own strengths and new levels of self-esteem" (Kersker, 1994).

Involvement in self-help and advocacy efforts seems to have additive therapeutic benefits, particularly for individuals adhering to a careful treatment regimen. These new developments are heuristic and warrant continuing research on the mechanisms of growth and paradigms of successful outcome in mental illness.

A group of consumer-professionals, writing in *Psychiatric Services* (Frese et al., 2001) have distinguished between categories of consumers with respect to the recovery vision. These authors note that advocacy for evidence-based practices, such as that offered by NAMI, is essential for the most seriously disabled consumers. Advocates who focus on consumer empowerment are those who are further along the road to recovery. These consumers merit increasing autonomy and input into the types of treatment and services they receive. The authors propose an integrative theory that maximizes the virtues and minimizes the weaknesses of each model. They also suggest that graduate and professional schools should be encouraged to recruit consumers in recovery for their training programs. This way the programs will benefit from consumers' experiential input and provide a scientific background for consumers to become knowledgeable mental health providers.

Consumerism is attractive to state and federal mental health authorities. This is demonstrated in the documents of the National Association of State Mental Health Program Directors (NASMHPD, 1989; Trochim et al., 1993), the allocations of funds by state program directors to support consumer-operated services, and the funding investments of the federal CMHS in developing the consumer movement. Nevertheless, there is a relatively small pool of qualified former patients who are capable of assuming meaningful roles in mental health agencies or in the development of alternative services. Consumer-operated programs for long-term patients are still a minor variable in the mental health service delivery systems of most states. These systems will clearly continue to require professionalism and particularly a psychiatric capability for all the foreseeable future. This need is acknowledged by the majority of patients and families. A consumer member of the NAMI board of directors described receiving almost 500 letters from consumers sharing their positive experiences with new medications and basing their hopes on continuing biological research (Beall, 1994).

In an era of health care reform, an alliance of NAMI, interested consumer groups, and professionals is essential for adequate coverage for mental health services. At the 1994 annual meeting of the National Association of Psychiatric Health Systems, the *Psychiatric News* reported the following message from former APA president Paul Fink:

> Not too many years ago, patient advocacy was an unknown for most therapists or one they chose to ignore....Now nobody "in their right mind" would make major policy decisions or testify before governmental bodies without including patients or their advocates in the process. (Alliances—1994)

Table 6. Summary of Advocacy Organizations

Organizations	Primary Membership	Description	Primary Goals	Functions
National Multichapter, Multifunction Organizations				
National Mental Health Association	Citizens	Broad-based organization; Prevention-focused concerns with mental health; Citizen-run lay organization with considerable involvement of volunteer mental health professionals in membership and governance	Raising mental health levels of general population; Helping persons with mental illnesses; Improving services; Decreasing stigma; Public education; Multiple legislative goals	Legislative advocacy; Public education; Anti-stigma campaigns; Special-interest support groups for various mental health related problems; Monitoring services (blue-ribbon juries); Community outreach; work in schools, jails
National Alliance for the Mentally Ill	Family members, consumers (present and former psychiatric patients)	Specifically concerned with serious mental illnesses (SMI); Primarily run by families and consumers, but welcomes professional membership and organizational co-sponsorship	Promoting research; Multiple legislative goals; Family education/support; Improving/monitoring services; Decreasing stigma; Public education; Fostering state-of-the-art clinical training, education	Legislative advocacy; Support/ self-help groups; Resource development; Public, family, and provider education on SMI; Planning, monitoring, and evaluating services; Media anti-stigma initiatives
Federation of Families for Children's Mental Health	Parents of emotionally disturbed (SED) children	Primarily run by families, welcomes professionals	Improved services for children, education, protection, advocacy, entitlements for SED children & youth, family involvement in treatment	Advocacy, lobbying, public/family education, roles in improving educational system/services
National Depressive and Manic-Depressive Association	Consumers (present and former psychiatric patients)	National organization of persons suffering from affective disorders, friends and relatives; Consumer-run but welcomes professional help and co-sponsorship	Promoting mutual support research, services, and stigma reduction for major affective disorders primarily unipolar depression and bipolar disorder	Support groups and education for members; Advocacy for research and service funding; Public education; Anti-stigma campaigns

Table 6. Summary of Advocacy Organizations *(continued)*

Organizations	Primary Membership	Description	Primary Goals	Functions
National or Local Organizations with Specific Focus				
Judge David L Bazelon Center for Mental Health Law; National Association of Protection and Advocacy Systems	Attorneys, citizens, stakeholders	Organizations specifically focused on protection of rights (typically expressed choice) and preventing abuses of persons with mental illness; Involvement of mental health professionals encouraged but tends to be limited	Guarding civil liberties of persons with mental illness; Legally ensuring access to needed services and resources	Monitoring; Education; Advocacy and lawsuits on behalf of individuals; Class-action suits
Schizophrenics Anonymous; Recovery Inc.; GROW	Present and former psychiatric patients	Nonpolitical consumer self-help; No or highly restricted professional involvement	Illness management; Self-knowledge; Personal growth; Education	Meetings and support groups
National Mental Health Consumer Self-help Clearinghouse; National Empowerment Center	Ex-patients, consumers, survivors	Consumer political advocacy and self-help; No or highly restricted professional involvement; (National Empowerment Center is run by professionals who are also consumers)	Consumer empowerment; Consumer participation in service delivery and mental health systems planning; Mutual support; Organizational skill development	Meetings; Information dissemination; Training; consumer-run services; Political advocacy

Acknowledgments

The author wishes to thank Paolo del Vecchio, Acting Director of CMHS Office of External Liaison, for information on the consumer movement and current CMHS initiatives.

REFERENCES

Alliances with advocacy groups urged as psychiatrists try to shape health Care reform. (1994). *Psychiatric News, 29*(5), 8.

Anthony, W. A. (1993). Recovery from mental illness: the guiding vision of the mental health service system in the 1990s. *Innovations and Research, 2*(3), 17–24.

Beall, M. A. (1994). Just between us. *NAMI Advocate, 16*(1), 15.

Biegel, D. E., & Yamatani, H. (1986). Self-help groups for families of the mentally ill: Research perspectives. In Goldstein (ed). *Family involvement in the treatment of schizophrenia,* (pp. 57–80). Washington DC: American Psychiatric Press.

Bond, G., Pensec, M., Dietzen, L., et al., (1991). Intensive case management for frequent users of psychiatric hospitals in a large city: A comparison of team and individual caseloads. *Psychosocial Rehabilitation Journal, 15,* 90–98.

Bond, G., Drake, R., Mueser, K., & Latimer, E. (2001). Assertive community treatment for people with severe mental illness: Critical ingredients and impact on patients. *Disability Management Health Outcomes, 9*(3), 141–159.

Borman, L.D. (1989). Self-help and mutual aid groups for adults. In *American Psychiatric Association Task Force on Treatments of Psychiatric Disorders: A Task Force Report of the American Psychiatric Association, Vol. 1,* (pp. 2596–2607). Washington DC: American Psychiatric Association.

Burland, J. (1998). Family-to-Family. A trauma and recovery model of family education. *New Directions for Mental Health Services, 77,* 33– 41.

Campbell, J. (1989). The Well-Being Project: Mental Health Clients Speak for Themselves California Department of Mental Health. In J. Campbell, (ed.). *Pursuit of wellness, Vol. 6.* Sacramento, CA: The California Network of Mental Health Clients.

Chamberlin, J. (1978). *On our own: Patient controlled alternatives to the mental health system.* New York: Hawthorn Books.

Chamberlin, J., Rogers, E. S. & Ellison, M. L. (1996). Self-help programs: A description of their characteristics and members. *Psychosocial Rehabilitation Journal, 19,* 33–42.

Consumer/Survivor Mental Health Research and Policy Work Group. (1993). *Community Support Network News, 9*(4), II.

Cook, J. A., Jonikas, J. A., & Razzano, L. (1993). *A randomized evaluation of consumer versus non-consumer training of state mental health service providers.* Thresholds, Chicago: National Research and Training Center on Rehabilitation and Mental Illness.

Deegan, P. (1994). A letter to my friend who is giving up. *Journal of the California Alliance for the Mentally Ill, 5*(3), 18–20.

Emerick, R. R. (1990). Self-help groups for former patients: Relations with mental health professionals. *Hospital and Community Psychiatry, 41,* 401–407.

Flynn, L. M. (1993). Political impact of the family-consumer movement. *National Forum, 73,* 8–12.

Frese, F. J. (1998). Advocacy, recovery, and the challenges for consumerism for schizophrenia. *Psychiatric Clinics of North America, 21,* 233–249.

Frese, F. J., Stanley, J., Kress, K. et al. (2001). Integrating evidence-based practices and the recovery model. *Psychiatric Services, 52,* 1462–1468.

Gardner, A., & Riessman, F. (1994). *The self-help revolution.* New York: Human Sciences Press.

Gordon, R. E., Edmunson, E., & Bedell, J. (1982). Reducing; hospitalization of state mental patients: Peer management and support. In S. Jeger, & A. Slotnick, (Eds.), *Community mental health.* New York: Plenum Publishing.

Greenblatt, M. (1985). Volunteerism and the community mental health worker. In H. I. Kaplan & B. J. Sadock, (eds). *Comprehensive textbook of psychiatry, Vol. IV,* (pp. 1893–1897). Baltimore, MD: Williams & Wilkins.

Hatfield, A. B., & Lefley, H. P. (1993). *Surviving mental illness: Stress, coping and adaptation.* New York: Guilford.

Kaplan, H. I., & Sadock, B. J. (1991). *Synopsis of psychiatry, 6th ed. rev.* Baltimore, MD: Williams & Wilkins.

Kaufmann, C. L., Ward-Colasante, C., & Farmer, I. (1993). Development and evaluation of drop-in centers operated by mental health consumers. *Hospital and Community Psychiatry, 44,* 675–678.

Kersker, S. (1994). The consumer perspective on family involvement. In H. P. Lefley & M. Wasow, (eds). *Helping Families Cope with Mental Illness,* (pp. 331–341). Newark, NJ: Harwood Academic Publishers.

Lefley, H. P. (1998). Training professionals to work with families of chronic patients. *Community Mental Health Journal, 24,* 338–357.

Lefley, H. P., Bernheim, K. F., & Goldman, C. R. (1989). National forum on training clinicians to work with seriously mentally ill persons and their families. *Hospital and Community Psychiatry, 40,* 460–462.

Lefley, H. P., & Johnson, D. L. (eds). (1990). *Families as allies in treatment of the mentally ill: New directions for mental health professionals.* Washington, DC: American Psychiatric Press.

Lehman, A. F., & Steinwachs, D. M. (1998). Translating research into practice: The Schizophrenia patient outcomes research team (PORT) treatment recommendations. *Schizophrenia Bulletin, 24,* 1– 10.

Lieberman, M. A. (1990). A group therapist perspective on self-help groups. *International Journal of Group Psychotherapy, 40,* 251–278.

Lyons, J. S., Cook, J., Ruth, A., ct al. (1993). *Consumer service delivery in a mobile crisis assessment program.* Thresholds, Chicago: National Research and Training Center on Rehabilitation and Mental Illness.

McFarlane, W. R. (1994). Families, patients, and clinicians as partners: Clinical strategies and research outcomes in single and multiple-family interventions. In H. P. Lefley & M. Wasow, (eds.) *Helping families cope with mental illness,* (pp. 195–222). Newark, NJ: Harwood Academic Publishers.

McGill, C. W., & Patterson, U. (1990). Former patients as peer counselors on locked psychiatric inpatient units. *Hospital and Community Psychiatry, 41,* 1017–1019.

McLean, A. (1954, Jun 2–4). *Institutionalizing the ex-patient movement in the United States: Advantages and costs.* Paper presented at the conference on Understanding of Mental Illness and Dealing with the Mentally Ill in Western Cultures. Berlin, Germany: University of Free Berlin.

Mental Health Weekly, September 14, 1992.

Mizuno, M. & Murakami, M. (2001). Strategic differences in implementing community-based psychiatry with families in Japan. In H. P. Lefley & D. Johnson (eds). *Family interventions in mental illness: International perspectives.* Westport, CT: Praeger.

Mowbray, C. T., Chamberlain, P., Jennings, M., et al. (1998). Consumer-run mental health services: Results from five demonstration projects. *Community Mental Health, 24,* 151–156.

Mowbray, C. T., Moxley, D., & Jasper, C. A., et al. (1997). *Consumers as providers in psychiatric rehabilitation.* International Assn of Psychosocial Rehabilitation Services.

National Association of State Mental Health Program Directors (I989, Dec. 13). *NASMHPD position paper on consumer contributions to mental health service delivery systems.* Alexandria. VA.

National Association of State Mental Health Program Directors (1993, March 22). *NASMHPD studies survey.* Alexandria, VA. P. 92–720.

National Institute of Mental Health and Lefley, H. P. (ed.) (1990). *Clinical training in serious mental illness,* (p. 90–1679). Superintendent of Documents, US Government Printing Office, US Department of Health and Human Services publication (ADM) Washington DC.

Nikkel, R. E., Smith, G., & Edwards, D. (1992). A consumer-operated case-management project. *Hospital and Community Psychiatry, 43,* 577–579.

Paolo del Vecchio. (2001, Aug. 11). Personal communication with Acting Director of CMHS Office of External Liaison.

Raiff, N. R. (1982). Self-help participation and quality of life: A study of the staff of Recovery. Inc. *Prev. Human Serv. 1,* 1–2.

Rappaport, J., Seidman, E., Toro, P. A., et al. (I984). Finishing the unfinished business: Collaborative research with a mutual help organization. *Social Policy 15,* 12–24.

Rogers, S. (1994, May 5–7). *A consumer's perspective on involuntary interventions.* Presentation at the National Symposium on Involuntary Interventions. Houston, TX: University of Texas. Houston Health Science Center.

Sherman, P. S., & Porter, R. Mental health consumers as case management aides. *Hospital and Community Psychiatry, 42,* 494–498.

Shetler, H. (1986). *A history of the National Alliance for the Mentally Ill.* Arlington, VA: National Alliance for the Mentally Ill.

Solomon, P., & Draine, I. (1994). Family perceptions of consumers as case managers. *Community Mental Health, 30,* 165–176.

Stroul, B. (1989). Community support systems for persons with long-term mental illness: A conceptual framework. *Psychosocial Rehabilitation Journal, 12,* 9–26.

Substance Abuse and Mental Health Administration. (2001, Mar). Center for Mental Health Services. *Guidance for Applicants (GFA) No. SM-01-003,* p. 9. Competitive Renewal for Grants to Support Consumer and Consumer Supporter Technical Assistance Centers.

The Surgeon General's Workshop on Self-help and Public Health. September 1987, US Department of Health and Human Services publication 224-250-88-1 (1998) Superintendent of Documents. Washington DC: US Government Printing Office.

Toro, P. A., Zimmerman, M.A., Seidman, E., et al. (I998). Professionals m mutual help groups: Impact on social climate and members' behavior. *Journal of Consulting and Clinical Psychology, 56,* 631–632.

Torrey, E. F., Wolfe, S. M., & Flynn, L. M. (1990). *Care of the seriously mentally ill: A rating of state programs. 3rd ed.* Arlington, VA: Public Citizens Health Research Group and National Alliance for the Mentally Ill.

Torrey, E. F., Wolfe, S. M., Flynn, L. M. (1992). *Criminalizing the seriously mentally ill: The abuse of jails as mental hospitals.* Arlington, VA: Public Citizens Health Research Group and National Alliance for the Mentally Ill.

Trochim, W., Dumont, J., & Campbell, J. (1993). *Mapping mental health outcomes from the perspective of consumers/survivors.* Alexandria, VA: National Association of State Mental Health Program Directors.

Van Tosh, L., & del Vecchio, P. (2000). *Consumer-operated self-help programs: A technical report.* Rockville, MD: Center for Mental Health Services.

Weiden, P. J., Scheifler, P. L., McEvoy, J. P., et al. (1999). Expert consensus treatment guidelines for schizophrenia: A guide for patients and families. *Journal of Clinical Psychiatry, 60 (Suppl. 11),* 73–80.

White, B. J., & Madara, E. J. (1999). *The self-help source book: Finding and forming mutual aid self-help groups. 6th ed.* Denville, NJ: American Self-help Clearinghouse.

White, B. J., & Madara, E. J. (in press). *The self-help source book: Finding and forming mutual aid self-help groups, 8th ed.* Information provided by personal communication with Barbara White, ed. 11-1-01. Cellar Knolls. NJ: American Self-help Clearinghouse.

Zinman, S., Harp, H., & Budd, S. (eds). (1987). *Reaching across: Mental health clients helping each other.* Riverside, CA: California Network of Mental Health Clients.

I Have Hope

Patrick Brown

At the time of original publication, Patrick Brown resided in Toronto, Ontario, Canada.

This article was published previously in the *Psychiatric Rehabilitation Journal*, 1999, 23(1) and is reprinted with permission.

I want to share my story because, over the years, I have gained more confidence in myself and have grown and developed skills in terms of managing my mental health. I am no longer afraid or insecure as to how people might perceive me, knowing that I have a disability. This is a story, which starts with confusion and embarrassment, and leads to a present in which I have the confidence to share my experiences.

My story starts in Jamaica when I was about 15 years old, when my mother went to Canada and I went to live with my grandmother. Up until then I lived with my mother and my brothers and sisters. Because my mother was a single parent, I always had a lot of responsibility—cooking, cleaning, getting my brothers and sisters off to school. Then my mother went to Canada, hoping to find a better life.

At my grandmother's house I felt very alone and looked around for guidance. Unfortunately I chose someone (my aunt) who not only was unable to provide me with any support or guidance, but she and her husband introduced me to something I shouldn't have had—marijuana tea. The first time I drank this I went totally berserk. I just lost it. Everything was really confusing. I was swearing. I was doing all kinds of really abnormal things. For some reason I started praying. I wasn't a religious person. The effects lasted for several hours, but the prayer had a tremendous positive outcome.

It was scary, but I didn't take it too seriously. I thought it was just a reaction to the marijuana tea, which had then worn off. A few days later, the same person was again at my aunt's place where everybody was drinking marijuana tea, and her husband gave me some again. What had happened a few days earlier wasn't even significant in my mind; maybe because I was a kid at the time and wasn't really thinking. The very same thing happened. I flipped out and I started swearing. This time it persisted and after two or three days I was hysterical, very hyper, very unusual, I was not myself, I was mad. I was having a lot of delusions and a lot of weird symptoms—what I would now call psychotic behavior.

This reaction lasted for about a month. Finally my Mom came back to Jamaica and took me to all kinds of doctors. They didn't know what was wrong, they couldn't say what happened. She also took me to spiritual doctors because in Jamaica those are often the people you turn to when unusual behavior occurs. People were saying it could be a spell that was put on me. There was a lot of speculation. I had to stop going to school. I was too sick.

After 2 or 3 months I was admitted to a mental hospital in Jamaica and I got better. In Jamaica they very seldom give you a diagnosis. In Canada, they put a label on you in order to treat you. I don't know if that's a good or bad thing, but in Jamaica I wasn't given a diagnosis. When I was discharged there was no follow-up care. I guess since I was symptom-free I was fit to leave.

Then I slipped into a real depression. It was serious. It was so bad that I slept 16 to 20 hours a day. I know from that early stage, about 20 years ago now, I slept to get away from my depression and other painful symptoms. When I was awake I experienced a depression that was unbearable, and when I slept I didn't have to face it, I could get away from it. Until very recently I had never heard anyone say that when they were depressed they slept to get away from depression. Then, a few months ago, I was talking to a co-worker about it, and she said, "Oh yes, I do that too. I sleep to escape from my depression." Back then I believed that the depression was a side effect from a pill I was taking because I was so hyper when I was ill. It was probably a tranquilizer which was really calming me down.

I came to Canada when I was 17 years old. Looking back, I think I went into culture shock. I had never seen so many tall buildings before. As a matter of fact, I thought I was being delusional because I saw these tall buildings, cars, and all these extravagant places that I was not used to. It was really different and that made it very stressful. I started school and it was a totally different system than I was used to. I sunk into a deeper depression because lots of things seemed so complicated. For example, at school I was given a locker and a locker combination, which I couldn't understand. Another thing that confused me was the class schedule I was given to follow—so I was always late for class. Things weren't explained to me. It was just totally confusing. This all added to the stress I had at school.

Looking back on my time at school I can now sort out what was happening to me and what would have helped. I remember that I was so sleepy from the medication I was taking that I couldn't stay awake in class—in fact I was asked to leave three programs because I slept in class. I got into so much trouble for this, and the school counselors would ask me if I was taking my medication. Now, I would say that a person in my situation needs counselors who are informed and understanding who could help me to cope better, and a doctor who would manage my medication better so that I wasn't so sleepy during the day.

At times my depression was so bad that I could walk outside on a bright, sunshiny day and I would think that it was midnight. That is how dark, desperate, and deep the depression was. It was so gross; it was like a thick cloud hanging over me. There were times when I was psychotic too, but it was always under control. My early episodes of depression lasted, on and off, for about 10 years. It would go on for maybe 6 months and then I would snap out of it for 2 months and then I would go right back to it. I would not wish this experience on my worst enemy.

In Canada I started searching for help. I went to different doctors, psychiatrists: they prescribed different medications. Someone else told me that spirituality can help. That was a part of my background in terms of my family, but not for me personally. But I got into that and found that spirituality really did help. With the medication, my spirituality, and support from friends and family I got better. I had a lot of support and I realized how important support is. People always stood by me, encouraged me, told me I was intelligent, that I should persist because some day I would be better. That really helped. People had confidence in me and they gave me support and encouragement. Some professionals were also very supportive.

I remember during this process that my psychiatrist kept changing my medication around and I remember being placed on something which took away some of the depression. At that time I wasn't educated about medication, and I didn't know that pills have side effects. I always thought that pills only do good for you. So I always saw pills as a positive, help-oriented thing. I didn't know that pills can actually do damage. Once, I remember, I was experiencing my eyes rolling back into my head and when I told people they would say: "Oh, it's in your mind" or "Did you take your medication?" At home I would talk to my Mom about it. I'd say, "Mom, my eyes are rolling, what's going on here?" And she also would say, "Did you take your medication?" And I always had. Sometimes when they said that to me I would take more medication because I thought that if I took more it would just go away. I thought the eye rolling was a symptom of the illness. Then one day I was talking to a case manager who is also a nurse, and I said, "I have had it with this thing, it is so uncomfortable, so unbearable. I've mentioned it to my psychiatrist and he has never done anything about it." So she said, "Tell me about it." And I explained it to her and she looked at me with her eyes wide open and said, "Oh, that's a side effect from your meds!" She spoke with my doctor, and he gave me some side-effect pills and the eye rolling stopped.

I realized then that I needed to take control of my own health, that I couldn't rely on others, including professionals and family members. I had to go out and get my own information—about my illness, about medications, what potential side-effects drugs prescribed for me might have. I decided that

I would take full, total and complete responsibility for my life. And that might mean sometimes saying no to a medication and to some health care professionals. In fact, I was once prescribed a medication, and after I read about all its possible side-effects, I decided that I wouldn't take it because the potential side-effects were worse than the actual symptoms I was experiencing. I remember the reaction of the doctor who prescribed the medication. He wasn't too pleased by my decision. But I was very frank with him and explained to him why I wouldn't take it. So based on my explanation, knowledge and reasons, he had no choice but to accept my decision.

This leads me to the second part of my story, my experiences with the professionals I have encountered because of my mental disability. There are those I think of as dinosaurs and those I think of as angels. There are three things I think of when I refer to a professional as a dinosaur. First of all, I see a dinosaur as something very ancient, and there are still people in the mental health field who continue to have outdated thinking. For example, I was recently speaking with a co-worker who told me that she said to her therapist, "I don't need to see you twice a week anymore, because I believe you are not helping me as much. I think seeing you once a week is good for me and that is what I think I need." Her therapist said, "Sorry, but I won't see you if I don't see you twice a week." To me that is a dinosaur attitude, that's an ancient practice, people should be given the choice. At the very least I would expect a therapist to be open to discussing options. Secondly, a dinosaur is a big creature, a really big monster, very powerful. And there are people in positions of authority who use it to dominate people like me, to overpower them and to make decisions that are really not beneficial to the people they are serving. And lastly, a dinosaur can be destructive. The destructiveness can happen when the person doesn't really care about the impact they actually have on people's lives. I work at a self-help organization that helps people find work and get back to work. At least once a month I meet somebody for whom I found a job, who had been told by a health care professional, either case manager, psychiatrist, or whoever, that he or she would not be able to work again. I hear that all the time. It surprises me. One person was told, "Sorry, you will not get back to work again. I want you to go home, apply for family benefits, get all the support that you can get. You will never be able to work again." And this woman is now working in a bank as a financial analyst. What does that tell me about the system? That you can't put your trust in it. A lot of people put trust and confidence in the system. That's one way of destroying a person's life, by not taking responsibility. I think doctors especially need to become more accountable, more responsible: they need to monitor their prescriptions and find out how the drugs they are prescribing are affecting people.

For a partnership or a good working relationship to develop there has to be mutual respect. People who experience mental disabilities often have low self-esteem, they have little faith in themselves, they think they are the worst thing that ever existed. And if the person who is providing care, providing a service for this person treats them as though there is no hope, then their sense of failure is perpetuated. If you are providing services you need to be able to make a difference in people's lives. I think that those who are recruiting health care professionals should look for people who are sensitive, people who have some kind of compassion. The same goes for colleges and universities with student admissions. The people who have had a positive impact on my life weren't necessarily the people with the most education. Rather they were the people who supported and encouraged me and believed in me.

That leads me to talk about the angels. Angels are the people who are there for you. They are there as a friend, they are supportive, they are kind, they respect your opinion, they treat you as a human being. They sit down with you and say, "OK, you have a problem, let's work this out, how can I assist you, what do you need?" Angels are not dominating, they are not taking over your rights, and are working along with you. And that's what an angel is for, to guide you, to help you where you cannot help yourself.

The last thing I'd like to share is my personal concept of recovery, a term we hear a lot about nowadays. I believe that recovery is an ongoing thing. I think, just like for a person who is addicted to alcohol or drugs, mental disabilities are a constant battle, something you struggle with on a daily basis. Anyone can tell you that. Struggling with a mental disability is a daily struggle and recovery is a daily process. I personally think that is easier for somebody that has had a mental disability and is doing well for a long period of time to slip and get ill again than a person that has recently been ill and is just out of hospital. Let me explain. Say a person has had a mental health problem, has been hospitalized or has gone through a process and recovered and has been healthy for several years. I believe, it is easier for that person to have another break down and slip back into a negative health situation than a person that just had a recent breakdown. My breakdowns now happen every 5 years or so, but when they do happen they are long term. I find that the time when I'm more prone to a breakdown is when I have been out of hospital for a number of years. I tend to become so energetic, so active in the community and in my work and I forget that I need to take care of myself and maintain myself. When I've just been out of hospital for 2 or 3 weeks I'd remind myself to look after myself, "You can't allow this thing to happen again."

Recovery really is a process. I think one of the main ingredients of recovery is knowing yourself. Once you know yourself, know what works for you, you are in touch with yourself, you can manage your recovery. For example, I know that I need my sleep, if I don't get enough sleep it's going to affect me mentally. I'll get burned out and once I get burned out I can't work and one thing leads to another. I also know that drinking a lot of coffee overwhelms me and deteriorates my mental health. Also, eating properly, I know that when I don't eat properly that affects me mentally. I noticed that most of the times when I had my breakdown I wasn't eating properly, I was eating a lot of junk food. I wasn't eating nutritious food. So what I know now is what affects me negatively, whether it's a lifestyle, drug, or behavior. So recovery to me means being in touch with myself, knowing what I need, and how to look after myself.

Since my decision to take control of my life, things have moved forward. Over the last few years I have been very active in the mental health community in Toronto. I am presently the President of the Board of Directors of Community Resources Consultants of Toronto (an agency that provides a variety of community-based services for people with serious mental health problems). As a board member of CRCT I have sat on a number of committees. One of my favorites was "Beyond Labels," a committee that provided an opportunity for people to come together to talk about how we can go "Beyond Labels," and what would help CRCT move forward to achieve its vision of fully integrating people into the life of the organization. It provided a lot of interpersonal and practical ways to interact with others. I thought that what we did was really significant.

I share my experience in other ways too. For example, I facilitate seminars on issues in a psychosocial rehabilitation program at a community college and also make presentations at other college and university classes.

At the time of writing this article, I have a job at an organization called Job Quest, I have a beautiful apartment, I have friends, I have mental health professionals who work with and for me, I have knowledge about what helps and what hinders my recovery process. I have hope.

Acknowledgments
I would like to acknowledge the assistance of Jennifer Pyke for help in putting down my story on paper, and Ewa Remowska for typing the manuscript.

Introduction to Chapter 5

LeRoy Spaniol

Throughout most of the past century, families were considered to be the cause of mental illnesses, and the illnesses themselves were seen as irreversible with a gradual downward course. The research presented in volume one clearly demonstrates otherwise. No evidence has been found that families cause mental illnesses, and recovery from mental illnesses is more common than it is rare. This chapter goes a step further by showing that families and supportive others can and have been an active resource and can play an important part in the recovery process.

Dixon, Adams, and Lucksted describe the benefits and limitations of a variety of family education models on families, including the family member with the disability. They describe how the provision of knowledge, coping skills, and support impact all members of the family—and are the key ingredients of any family education intervention. The goals of family education research have focused on education about mental illnesses, increasing coping skills, and reducing relapse rate. The authors address the need to assess a wider range of functional outcomes to better understand the impact of the various family intervention models. They also explore the barriers to successfully implementing family education and the need to more carefully personalize the interventions to the needs and readiness of family members.

While collaboration between professionals, family members, and people with mental illnesses has been shown to be effective in the recovery process and has been recommended by the American Psychiatric Association, often collaboration is not available to families. Confidentiality is one reason many professionals regard collaboration with caution. Bogart and Solomon address how to share treatment information while both respecting the confidentiality of the person with the disability and providing a trusting environment for collaboration. They discuss the value of collaboration in the recovery process and the need to educate professionals about its importance. The authors present a specific model for collaboration that includes procedures, a release form, and a process for integrating the procedures and form into routine clinical practice.

Robin Clark describes the importance of ongoing, day-to-day, concrete support from families in the clinical outcome of people with dual disorders. The author's long-term study involved multiple interviews with family and other caregivers over time. Significant relationships were found between economic assistance (providing for basic needs) and informal care giving and reduced substance abuse. Based on the robust findings for the value of family involvement, the author recommends that more research is needed to better understand the importance of non-clinical interventions in the recovery of people with dual disorders.

Cultural and ethnic variability is a given within the United States and many other countries. Laurene Finley describes how cultural forces need to be considered in understanding how family members interact with one another and with the systems that are established to support them. The author states that in more traditional cultures with extensive kinship networks, caretaking often is viewed as a valued role by both professionals and families. Also, patterns of caretaking and partaking in the recovery process are impacted by cultural differences. The author identifies several areas of potential differences such as problem solving, decision making, conflict resolution, role expectations, and help-seeking attitudes and values. Specific strategies for identifying and responding to cultural differences are discussed.

Kim Mueser and Lindy Fox describe how a significant number of people with mental illnesses abuse substances at some point during their life, and how substance abuse is associated with a wide variety of negative consequences. The authors describe the importance of family involvement in concurrently treating substance abuse and mental illnesses and suggest practical strategies that families can use to facilitate the recovery of their family member with a dual disorder.

McFarlane et al. describe how a combination of assertive community treatment (ACT), supported employment, and multiple family group therapy resulted in higher employment rates than conventional vocational rehabilitation for people with serious mental illnesses. The authors state that the effects are enhanced by close and continuous interaction between professionals, family members, and people with mental illnesses.

Spaniol, Zipple, and Lockwood describe the many roles that family members play in the rehabilitation and recovery process of their family member. All family members experience a recovery process from the traumatic onset of the illness, as well as from the prejudice and discrimination often associated it. The authors discuss the various roles family members perform, including dealing with their own loss and recovery process, their caregiving role, their role in supporting other families, their teaching and educational role, and their advocacy role. Specific strategies are suggested for how professionals can encourage collaboration with family members.

In the final article, Neugeboren describes his active involvement with his brother and the pain and pleasure that ensues. He feels at times heartbroken by his brother's struggles and crises while persistently loving and caring for him. He also describes his own, and his brother's, struggles with the mental health system and its, at times, bruising interventions.

The editors hope that this chapter will help readers understand the role of family members in the recovery process and the importance of the collaborative relationship between professionals, family members, and people with mental illnesses.

Update on Family Psychoeducation for Schizophrenia

Lisa Dixon, Curtis Adams, and Alicia Lucksted

At the time of original publication, Lisa Dixon, MD, MPH, was an associate professor of psychiatry at the University of Maryland School of Medicine, Baltimore, MD; Curtis Adams, MD, was an assistant professor of psychiatry at the University of Maryland School of Medicine; and Alicia Lucksted, PhD, was a senior research associate at the University of Maryland School of Medicine.

This article was published previously in the *Schizophrenia Bulletin*, 2000, 26(1), 5–20, and is reprinted with permission.

Abstract: The Schizophrenia Patient Outcomes Research Team and others have previously included family psychoeducation and family support in best practices guidelines and treatment recommendations for persons with schizophrenia. In this article we review in detail 15 new studies on family interventions to consider issues around the implementation of family interventions in current practice. The data supporting the efficacy of family psychoeducation remain compelling. Such programs should remain as part of best practices guidelines and treatment recommendations. However, assessment of the appropriateness of family psychoeducation for a particular patient and family should consider 1) the interest of the family and patient; 2) the extent and quality of family and patient involvement; 3) the presence of patient outcomes that clinicians, family members, and patients can identify as goals; and 4) whether the patient and family would choose family psychoeducation instead of alternatives available in the agency to achieve outcomes identified.

Families of people with schizophrenia often provide considerable support to their ill relatives and experience considerable burdens (and some benefits) as a result (Leff, 1994; Cochrane et al., 1997). Many people with schizophrenia rely on relatives for emotional support, instrumental and financial assistance, housing, and advocacy. Therefore, the quality of their relationships greatly influences family and client well-being and outcomes.

Psychosocial interventions for the families of persons with schizophrenia have been developed by mental health providers to offer information and support to optimize these outcomes. The rigor of randomized controlled trials of family psychoeducation and the consistency of their findings have formed the rationale for including family services in all current best practices treatment guidelines for persons with schizophrenia (Dixon, 1999).

Among these, the treatment recommendations developed by the Schizophrenia Patient Outcomes Research Team (PORT) strongly endorsed the value of family psychoeducation (Lehman et al., 1998a). The supporting evidence for the following PORT recommendations was outlined in a review of family psychoeducation prepared by PORT investigators (Dixon & Lehman, 1995). These recommendations include the following:

1. Patients who have ongoing contact with their families should be offered a family psychosocial intervention that spans at least 9 months and provides a combination of education about illness, family support, crisis intervention, and problem-solving skills training. Such interventions should also be offered to nonfamily caregivers. (Lehman et al., 1998a, p. 8)

2. Family interventions should not be restricted to patients whose families are identified as having high levels of "expressed emotion" (criticism, hostility, overinvolvement). (Lehman et al., 1998a, p. 8)

3. Family therapies based on the premise that family dysfunction is the etiology of the patient's schizophrenic disorder should not be used. (Lehman et al., 1998a, p. 8)

In spite of the PORT's endorsement of family psychoeducation, many questions remain unanswered. To what extent is family psychoeducation effective under usual practice conditions rather than just controlled research conditions? Who benefits most from family psychoeducation? Are there contraindications? This review will extend the original PORT appraisal, emphasizing studies published in the last 3 to 4 years. Because this recent research has also revealed the negligible extent to which these models have been implemented in actual practice, we will also summarize current knowledge about implementation and the other models that have arisen to address the unmet needs of families in the real world. We will conclude with a set of tentative observations or hypotheses about the role of family members in treatment planning.

EFFICACY OF FAMILY PSYCHOEDUCATION

Psychoeducation interventions offered to family members of people with schizophrenia have been developed with increasing sophistication over the past 20 years. Although the specific elements and construction of the various programs differ, successful programs share several characteristics:

1. They regard schizophrenia as an illness.

2. They are professionally created and led.

3. They are offered as part of an overall treatment package that includes medication.

4. They enlist family members as therapeutic agents, not "patients."

5. They focus on patient outcomes, although family outcomes are important.

6. They do *not* include traditional family therapies which presume that behavior and communication within the family play a key etiological role in the development of schizophrenia.

Family psychoeducation programs offer varying combinations of information about mental illness, practical and emotional support, skill development in problem solving, and crisis management. They may be conducted with individual families or multifamily groups and may take place in the home, in clinical settings, or in other locations. They also vary in length, timing with regard to phase of illness, and whether or not the person with schizophrenia is included in the family intervention.

The construct of "expressed emotion" (EE) has been important to the development of family psychoeducation interventions. Literature suggests that people with schizophrenia living with family members who exhibit high levels of EE (critical comments, hostility, and overinvolvement) are more likely to relapse (Koenigsberg & Handley, 1986; Scazufca & Kuipers, 1998). This association may be linked to the difficulty persons with schizophrenia have in processing complex emotions and in sustaining attention in emotionally charged environments. The concept itself has been criticized, and family members have expressed experiencing the EE literature as a resurrection of the family blaming theories of the 1950s (Lefley, 1992). Nonetheless, it is important to note that expressed emotion theory underlies many professionally created family psychoeducation programs. Many of these specifically target only "high EE" families.

The extensive 1995 schizophrenia PORT review of randomized clinical trials, in concert with other reviews of family psychoeducation, concluded that "there is a consistent and robust effect of family interventions in delaying, if not preventing, relapse" (Dixon & Lehman, 1995, p. 639). The relapse effect tended to vary according to the length and content of the programs. Other outcomes were supported by more modest evidence in the studies available when the PORT review was conducted: family psychoeducation may improve the patient's functioning—either directly or through fostering skill development—by delaying disruptive relapses (Falloon et al., 1982; Falloon & Pederson, 1985; Tarrier et al., 1988, 1989). The cost of family psychoeducation can be offset by reductions in hospitalization and other service use (McFarlane et al., 1995). The work of Falloon and of Zastowny et al. (1992) also indicated possible benefits of such programs to family well-being. The review also concluded that brief education alone shows inferior results compared to interventions that also incorporate engagement, support, and skill-building components.

LITERATURE UPDATE

Recent articles pertaining to family psychoeducation were located with a Medline search using the keywords "family and schizophrenia and (interventions or education)." The search encompassed articles published between 1994 and 1998 and identified 103 articles. After screening out those that did not have schizophrenia and family intervention as their primary focus, the subset of these articles that reported randomized controlled trials or other rigorous evaluations of family psychoeducation interventions ($n = 16$) are reported in Table 1. These studies do not merely attempt to replicate an already strong empirical data base supporting family psychoeducation. Rather, they build upon this previous work in a variety of ways: Family psychoeducation is tested with participants from a wider range of cultural groups than previously, and with the relatives of recent-onset patients as opposed to solely those of "chronic" patients. Family psychoeducation is compared with more sophisticated individual therapy models than previously available. Also, the recent studies focus on a wider range of outcomes, compare different family intervention strategies, and have more extended followup than previous studies.

Studies Conducted with Relatives from a Variety of Cultural Groups

Mingyuan et al. (1993) studied 3,092 patients diagnosed with schizophrenia and their family members from five cities in China: 2,076 were assigned the group psychoeducation condition; 1,016 were assigned to routine services and were controls. The intervention was provided in the context of primary-care-based mental health services. It consisted of ten standardized lectures and three discussions presented by psychiatrists in each community over the 12-month length of the program. Those in the intervention group fared significantly better than controls on a number of measures including relapse rate, positive and negative symptoms, functional disability, ability to work, and treatment compliance. Families experienced reduced burden and had increased knowledge.

Xiong et al. (1994) randomized 63 people with schizophrenia living with family in urban China to treatment as usual (control) or culturally specific family education that included the patient. In the intervention, biweekly meetings in the first 2 to 3 months provided families with information on schizophrenia and established a relationship between family and clinician. Phase 2 then involved monthly single-family meetings with the clinician, multifamily group sessions, home visits, and extended family outreach, all emphasizing problem-solving skills and illness management. After the patient's functioning and the family's coping strategies improved, the program moved into "maintenance" phase—attendance at monthly multifamily groups and briefer quarterly clinician meetings. At 12 and 18 months, patients in the intervention group had experienced significantly fewer and shorter hospitalizations, less social dysfunction, and longer employment tenure. Their family members reported significantly lower levels of burden than control families, and the intervention was less costly than standard treatment.

Xiang et al. (1994) conducted a 4-month family intervention in which 69 people with schizophrenia and 8 with affective psychoses in three rural communities in China were randomly divided into two conditions: family intervention plus drug treatment (intervention), and drug treatment only (control). The family intervention consisted of periodic workshops, family visits, discussions between health workers and family, local public informational broadcasts, and monthly supervision sessions for the facilitating doctors. The intervention group showed significant positive changes not found among the control group including enhanced treatment compliance; lessened neglect and abuse of the ill relative; and improved mental status, improved work functioning, and decreased disruptive behavior on the part of the ill relative.

Zhang et al. (1994) compared hospitalization rates between 39 first admission men with schizophrenia randomly assigned to a family intervention involving group and individual counseling sessions every 1 to 3 months and 39 similar patients randomly assigned to usual treatment in urban China. During the intervention, families facing similar issues were grouped together; home visits were occasionally used for families not attending the group meetings. After 18 months, patients in the intervention group were significantly less likely to have been hospitalized than controls. Regular medication use had significant independent and additive effects on outcome, so that people in the intervention group who also took medication regularly were 7.9 times less likely to be hospitalized over the duration of the study than controls who did not.

Telles et al. (1995) compared the effectiveness and cross-cultural applicability of behavioral family management (BFM) and standard case management (CM) in preventing exacerbation of symptoms and relapse among 40 low-income Spanish-speaking people diagnosed with schizophrenia, in Los Angeles, CA. Most participants were first generation immigrants. Patients were randomly assigned to the two conditions. BFM is a highly structured program comprising education about schizophrenia, communication skills, and problem-solving training. Its structure was not modified, although the sociocultural context was taken into account as this sample was different from those usually presented with BFM. For the total sample, BFM did not differ from CM in any outcomes. Among patients and families least assimilated to U.S. culture, BFM was significantly related to greater risk of symptom exacerbation. Among slightly more acculturated patients and families there was no effect across family treatment conditions. The authors emphasize the important influence of sociocultural factors in the effectiveness of various interventions.

Studies Involving Relatives of New-Onset Patients

Linszen et al. (1996) studied relapse among 76 young (15–26 years old) persons with recent-onset schizophrenia in the Netherlands. Subjects were randomized into two groups: individual psychosocial program (IPI, control group), or IPI plus a behavioral family intervention (IPFI, intervention group). During hospitalization, all family members attended three to four educational sessions. Groups were randomized at discharge and stratified by level of expressed emotion, after which patients in both groups met biweekly for 5 months, then monthly for 7 months, with clinicians in illness management sessions at the clinic (IPI). Family members of people assigned to the IPFI group also met with clinicians, following a similar schedule and a curriculum modeled on Falloon's BFM (psychoeducation, communications training, and problem-solving skills training). Twelve months after discharge, relapse rates were very low for both treatment groups. The overall relapse rate during the outpatient intervention was 16%. There was no positive effect from the addition of the family intervention. In the IPFI group, patients from "low EE" families relapsed slightly more often to a near significant extent. The authors speculate this may reflect the BFM program adding stress to such families by focusing on (unneeded, for them) communications training rather than (needed) emotional support.

Nugter et al. (1997) studied 52 individuals with recent-onset schizophrenic disorders and their families in the Netherlands. The same research group performed this study and the study by Linszen et al. (1996) already discussed. During hospitalization all patients received usual care, and all families were offered two psychoeducational meetings. At discharge they were randomly assigned to individual outpatient treatment (IT) or IT plus family treatment. The outpatient family treatment consisted of 18 sessions over 12 months of clinic-based BFM (Falloon & Pederson, 1985), focusing on education and communications and problem-solving skills training. The overall relapse rates were again low, ranging from 21% to 23% depending on criteria used. The addition of family psychoeducation to the IT did not affect family EE levels or patient relapse rates. The authors surmised that the BFM family treatment does not meet the needs of families of new-onset patients, as they may believe that the illness will not recur.

Table 1.a. Summary of Controlled Family Intervention Trials: Studies Conducted with Relatives from a Variety of Cultural Groups

Study	Participants	Intervention	Control Condition	Results
Mingyuan et al. 1993	3,092 people with schizophrenia and their families; 5 cities in China, randomly assigned	Group psychoeducation: 10 lectures and 3 group discussions, over 12 mos + usual services	Usual services provided by primary care clinic	Significantly better outcomes for relapse, symptoms, functional status, treatment compliance
Xiong et al. 1994	63 people with schizophrenia and cohabiting family in urban China, randomly assigned	Patient and family education, including 2–3 monthly meetings with clinician, then + multifamily group, home visits, tapering off at 12 mos as patient stabilizes	Usual services provided by primary care clinic	Fewer and shorter relapses, more employment at 12 and 18 mos, relatives report significantly less burden, less expensive
Xiang et al. 1994	69 people with schizophrenia + 8 people with affective psychoses and family in 3 rural communities in China, randomly assigned	Workshops, home visits, discussions, public information, mixed group, and single family over 4 mos medication + monitoring	Medication and monitoring only	Significantly improved mental status, work function, treatment compliance, and reduced disruptive behavior; reduced neglect and abuse of ill relative by family
Zhang et al. 1994	Relatives and 78 men with schizophrenia after first hospitalization in urban China, randomly assigned	Family group and individual family counseling monthly over 18 mos; families with similar problems grouped together + usual services	Usual services provided by primary care clinic	Significantly less likely to have been hospitalized, strong additive effect of consistent medication use
Telles et al. 1995	42 Spanish-speaking people with schizophrenia and families, very low income, 90% new immigrants to Los Angeles, randomly assigned	1 yr Falloon's BFM (a very structured education, communication skills, and problem-solving program, including patient) + standard case management	Standard case management	Patients with lowest acculturation score = more likely relapse (with BFM); no increased risk for patients with "higher" acculturation scores (all were quite low)

Table 1.b. Summary of Controlled Family Intervention Trials: Studies Involving Relatives of New-Onset Patients

Study	Participants	Intervention	Control Condition	Results
Linszen et al. 1996	76 adolescents with recent-onset schizophrenia from across the Netherlands and families, randomly assigned	Behavioral family intervention = family meetings with clinician + family education meetings during index hospitalization + biweekly to monthly individual illness management sessions for patients over 1 yr	Same family education meetings during index hospitalization, same individual illness management sessions	Low symptoms and hospitalization in both groups compared with usual rates, but in intervention condition, patients from "low EE" families had slightly higher relapse rate
Nugter et al. 1997	52 people with recent-onset schizophrenia and families in the Netherlands, randomly assigned	18 family sessions over 12 mos using Falloon's behavioral family model + 2 family education sessions while patient hospitalized + usual outpatient care	2 family education sessions while patient hospitalized + usual outpatient care	No difference between conditions for family EE levels or patient relapse
Rund et al. 1994	24 adolescents with schizophrenia and families in Norway; 12 intervention, 12 matched (not random) control	3-phase family treatment: engagement, problem solving, maintenance, over 2 yrs + usual care	Usual services provided by inpatient and outpatient facilities	Significantly lower number of patients with 2 relapses in family treatment; less expensive

Table 1.c. Summary of Controlled Family Intervention Trials: Comparison of Family Psychoeducation with Individual Therapy Developed for Schizophrenia

Study	Participants	Intervention	Control Condition	Results
Hogarty et al. 1997	151 people with schizophrenia and families in Pittsburgh, PA, across 4 conditions in 2 randomized trials	1. Personal relapse prevention therapy 2. Family psychoeducation 3. Personal relapse prevention + family psychoeducation	General supportive therapy	No positive, significant effects for family psychoeducation compared with #1 or #3

Table 1.d. Summary of Controlled Family Intervention Trials: Studies Testing Less Intensive or Briefer Family Education Models

Study	Participants	Intervention	Control Condition	Results
Schooler et al. 1997	313 people with schizophrenia or schizoaffective disorder and families from 5 sites across the US, randomly assigned to a 3x2 design; 3 medication conditions and 2 family conditions	Medication conditions (crossed with family conditions): Moderate dose, Low dose, Targeted early in symptom exacerbation	Family conditions: 1. Group family psychoeducation monthly 2. #1 + monthly home visits for communication, problem solving (not control)	Low relapse across both family conditions, comparable to other family intervention studies; moderate medication dose gave best results, across both family conditions; no significant interactions
Szmukler et al. 1996	"Principal caregiver" of 63 people with schizophrenia in Victoria, Australia, randomly assigned	6 individual weekly in-home counseling sessions w/o patient, focusing on schizophrenia education and problem solving	Single 2-hr informational presentation about schizophrenia	Significant reported improvement in relationship and understanding; no effects shown for better caregiving or reduced burden
Solomon et al. 1996, 1998	183 relatives of people with schizophrenia on the U.S. east coast, randomly assigned to 3 conditions	6–15 hrs individualized consultation over 3 mos; 10 2-hr weekly multifamily group psycho-educational meetings; Both included usual services	Wait list, usual services	No difference across conditions for extent of family contact with mental health staff; some significant increase of family member self-efficacy regarding ill relative
McFarlane et al. 1996	68 people with schizophrenia receiving ACT and families in Maine, randomly assigned	Ongoing multifamily psychoeducation groups + ACT, over 2 yrs	Intermittent, crisis-only family intervention + ACT	Low symptoms and hospitalization in both groups compared with usual rates, but no differences between conditions; ongoing intervention group had better employment outcomes
McFarlane et al. 2000	69 unemployed people with major psychiatric disorder receiving ACT and families in suburban and rural New York, randomly assigned	FACT including multifamily psychoeducation, over 18 mos	Conventional vocational rehabilitation	FACT condition showed significantly more competitive jobs and total earnings; no inpatient differences

Table 1.e. Summary of Controlled Family Intervention Trials: A Long Followup of an Original Family Psychoeducation Study

Study	Participants	Intervention	Control Condition	Results
Tarrier et al. 1994	40 people with schizophrenia and no relapse in 2 yrs in England, randomly assigned	5-and 8-yr followup of 9-mo behavioral family intervention designed to reduce EE and usual care	Usual services and 2 informational sessions about schizophrenia	Significantly fewer relapses 5 and 8 yrs after intervention; lower EE

Note.
ACT = assertive community treatment; BFM = behavioral family management; EE = expressed emotion; FACT = family-aided assertive community treatment.

Rund et al. (1994) provided families of 12 Norwegian adolescents (aged 13–18) diagnosed with early-onset schizophrenia spectrum disorders (9 with schizophrenia) with a three-part family intervention. The intervention began while the patient was hospitalized and lasted 2 to 3 years. During the inpatient phase, the families received bimonthly family sessions using a structured curriculum, and a day-long informational seminar about mental illness. After discharge, they received monthly family sessions in the home and one or more additional day-long seminars. When the patient was stabilized, family sessions were dropped back to every other month and were augmented by phone support as needed. Outcomes were compared with those for a matched (not random) comparison group of adolescent patients with schizophrenia. The authors found no differences between the two conditions in the number of patients who had one relapse over 2 years; however, only 8.3% of the intervention group patients relapsed twice over the 2-year interval compared with 58% of the control group. Psychosocial functioning was nearly significantly better in the experimental condition. The family condition was less expensive than treatment as usual because of nonsignificantly lower total weeks of hospitalization in the family treatment group.

Comparison of Family Psychoeducation with Individual Therapy Developed for Schizophrenia

Hogarty et al. (1997) compared four manualized treatment conditions: personal relapse-prevention therapy, family psychoeducation, personal relapse-prevention therapy plus family psychoeducation, and general supportive therapy in a total of 97 people diagnosed with schizophrenia who lived with their families. The therapies were delivered for 3 years postdischarge in Pittsburgh, PA, at the Western Psychiatric Institute and Clinic. Personal therapy was developed specifically for persons with schizophrenia. It was "designed to forestall the late (second-year) relapse common among modem psychosocial approaches...and to enhance personal and social adjustment through the identification and effective management of affect dysregulation that was believed to either precede a psychotic relapse or provoke inappropriate behavior that was possibly generated by underlying neuropsychological deficits" (Hogarty et al., 1997, p. 1506). The family therapy condition was similar to that previously evaluated by Hogarty et al. (1986). This study included 29 (27%) new onset patients and families with both high and low levels of EE. The overall relapse rate in this study was very low, with only 44 (29%) patients having a psychotic relapse over 3 years. Only 24 (16%) patients experienced a nonpsychotic affective relapse over 3 years. The study found no significant effects of personal therapy or family therapy in forestalling relapse, although personal therapy was nearly significantly superior in preventing psychotic relapse. The authors note that the remarkable survivorship of persons completing the study in the supportive therapy condition may account for the lack of personal therapy or family treatment effects. One-third of the supportive therapy patients had treatment-related terminations; supportive therapy patients who continued in the study had a 76% survivorship at 1 year, and 72% at 2 years. Authors also note that the supportive therapy condition in this study was very comprehensive and benefited from years of acquired knowledge in conducting research in schizophrenia at the Western Psychiatric Institute and Clinic.

Studies Testing Less Intensive or Briefer Family Education Models

Schooler et al. (1997) randomized 313 people with schizophrenia or schizoaffective disorder from five sites across the United States into one of three medication conditions (continuous moderate dose, continuous low dose, or targeted early intervention only during symptom exacerbation) and one of two family treatment strategies (supportive family management [SFM], or applied family management [AFM]). AFM was modeled on the behavioral family management program created by Ian Falloon. Over 2 years, SFM families attended monthly group meetings in which education and support were provided, while AFM families did the same and received monthly home visits focusing on communication and problem-solving skills. Both family conditions also had access to crisis intervention services from the research teams. There were no relapse differences across the family treatment strategies, although hospitalization rates under both conditions were similar to those reported in family treatment literature and lower than those for usual (no family intervention) treatment (25% over a 2-year period). The authors attribute the lack of difference to the high level of engagement attained in both conditions and to the enhanced staff and services availability built into the research protocol (compared with usual services).

Szmukler et al. (1996) randomly assigned the "principal caregiver" of 63 people with schizophrenia admitted to a psychiatric hospital in Victoria, Australia, to a single 1-hour informational presentation about schizophrenia (control) or to six counseling sessions (one per week) of education and assistance in problem solving. These sessions were conducted at home without the patient. Participants in the counseling sessions reported significant improvement in understanding their ill relative and having a more positive relationship at 3 and 6 months postintervention. However, there were no group differences on reports of the negative aspects of caregiving or in coping style.

Solomon et al. (1996) randomly assigned 183 family members of people with schizophrenia from a large east coast U.S. city to one of three conditions: 1) 6 to 15 hours of individualized consultation, 2) ten 2-hour weekly family psychoeducation group meetings, or 3) a 9-month wait-list control. Postintervention measures found that the consultation model increased participants' sense of self-efficacy regarding their ill relative(s) and that the psychoeducation group meetings had the same effect for relatives who had never before participated in a support or advocacy group for family members. There were no differences among conditions in the extent of family contact with mental health professionals (Solomon et al., 1998). The authors also speculated that other benefits would likely develop as family members used and practiced new skills.

McFarlane et al. (1996) examined outcome differences for 68 people with schizophrenia receiving assertive community treatment in Maine depending on whether their families were involved in family intervention only during crises (crisis family intervention) or more consistently and intensively in ongoing multifamily psychoeducation groups (ongoing family intervention). Participants were randomly assigned between groups and followed for 2 years. Patients in both conditions experienced hospitalization and symptom severity levels lower than expected with usual treatment. These did not significantly differ between the different family conditions. However, patients in the ongoing family intervention group had near-significant mean employment rates for the 2-year period (32% vs. 19%). During the period from 4 to 20 months, the ongoing family interaction group had significantly higher employment rates. Authors speculated that enhanced employment is tied to reduced family stress, enabling the identified patient to better tolerate work stress.

McFarlane et al. (2000) continued their examination of the combination of family psychoeducation and assertive community treatment on vocational outcomes. They compared the outcomes of 69 unemployed persons with a major psychiatric disorder (65% schizophrenia spectrum) randomly assigned to family-aided assertive community treatment (FACT) or to conventional vocational rehabilitation. Subjects were followed for 18 months. The study was conducted in an urban suburb of New York City and in a more rural area of New York State. The family condition consisted of multifamily psychoeducational groups as implemented in several other studies conducted by McFarlane, but embedded within an assertive community treatment team. Results indicate that FACT subjects had significantly more competitive jobs and more total earnings. For the schizophrenia subsample, there was significant treatment by time interactions for negative symptoms and general psychopathology favoring FACT. There were no differences between conditions for hospitalization. In this study, it is difficult to assess the differential impact of the assertive community treatment and the multifamily groups.

A Long Followup of an Original Family Psychoeducation Study

Tarrier et al. (1994) studied the effect on relapse of patients' relatives participating in psychoeducation as followup to a larger British study. They traced 40 people with schizophrenia who had not relapsed during 2 years after a randomized control trial of behavioral family intervention aimed at reducing EE and relapse risk. Those who had been in the 9-month family intervention condition showed significantly fewer relapses at 5 and 8 years than the "high EE" control group, and had profiles much more similar to the "low EE" control group. The authors interpret this as suggesting the intervention moved "high EE" families to "low EE" status.

ANALYSIS AND SYNTHESIS

How do these studies inform the recommended services to families of persons with schizophrenia? Taken as a group, these more recent studies confirm the potential advantages and benefits of services to families and family psychoeducation identified by the PORT and other reviews (Goldstein, 1994; Leff, 1994; Penn & Mueser, 1996). However, they raise important caveats as outlined below.

What Is the Control or Comparison Condition?

The four studies from China show a dramatic impact of family psychoeducation in reducing relapse and improving other outcomes. In contrast, family psychoeducation confers no benefit in relapse reduction in the two Dutch studies or in the 1997 study by Hogarty and colleagues of personal therapy in Pittsburgh. While these groups of studies differ in a variety of ways, one of the important differences is the nature of the comparison conditions. In the Dutch and Pittsburgh studies, family psychoeducation was compared to highly developed individual treatment models. Relapse rates were low for all groups. In China, the comparison conditions were bare bones individual services. Thus, individual therapy is not static but is itself changing and growing with research and changes in service systems such as managed care. The studies by McFarlane and colleagues were implemented within assertive community treatment teams, another type of service model that reduced relapse rates dramatically. The addition of multiple family groups did not reduce relapse but did improve employment outcomes. The point is that in predicting the added value of family psychoeducation for relapse reduction, it is important to consider the nature of the standard or comparison treatment. Enriched individual models or other innovative programs may be as effective as family psychoeducation for relapse reduction, especially in the context of improved medications. On the other hand, family psychoeducation is likely to show added benefit in terms of relapse reduction in settings with basic, unenriched services such as those common in the public sector during this era of cost containment.

What Are the Goals of Family Interventions?

The recovery paradigm for consumers and families has underlined the importance of looking beyond relapse when assessing program efficacy: Client and family functioning and quality of life must also be considered. The Chinese studies confirm the role of family psychoeducation in reducing patient functional disability and improving employment. They also suggest that the well-being of families improves with reduced burden and increased knowledge. McFarlane's work yields compelling data on the potential of multifamily groups to increase employment. The enhanced self-efficacy obtained in Solomon et al.'s study of family consultation and the family education program and the improvements in client-family relationships in the study by Szmukler et al. should not be dismissed. Unfortunately, even when they are measured, nonrelapse outcomes are usually secondarily reported.

Is There an Optimal or Best Type of Family Intervention?

A critical ingredient? The schizophrenia PORT recommendations specified that family interventions should be at least 9 months long. Indeed, Szmukler et al. and Solomon et al. both comment on intervention brevity (6 weeks and 3 months, respectively) as possible explanations for the limited impact of interventions they studied. However, the intervention reported in Xiang et al. was only 4 months long, with positive effect. The tension between the increased feasibility and possibly reduced efficacy of a shorter intervention program demands further research. The optimal intervention length may depend on program goals. Family programs intending to reduce patient relapse and improve patients' functional status must be at least 9 months, if not longer. Shorter programs may influence knowledge, attitudes, and the quality of relationships. Interestingly, the followup study by Tarrier et al. showed reduced hospitalization at 5 and 8 years after an only 9-month intervention, a testament to the durability of changes produced by the program.

The comparison between applied and supportive family management as investigated in the Treatment Strategies in Schizophrenia study (Schooler et al., 1997) is provocative. Both family interventions were equally effective for the reported outcomes. That is, the additional problem-solving techniques taught in the applied program did not add to the capacity of the model to reduce relapse. (There has also been some debate as to whether the family members actually acquired the skills taught in the applied condition [Liberman & Mintz, 1998]). However, it is critical to recognize that all the families in both models received extensive education, information, and support. Compared with studies of patients whose relatives received no family program, all families in Schooler et al.'s study appeared to derive benefit. It is also interesting to note that in the two Dutch studies, families in both the family treatment and the comparison conditions participated in educational groups during the inpatient phase. The extent to which families benefited from participating in this component of the program is unknown. More work is clearly necessary to delineate the critical components of family psychoeducation programs.

For Whom Does Family Psychoeducation Work Best?

The notion that one family program would meet the needs of all families and patients is counterintuitive. Phase of illness, family and patient life cycle stages, and cultural background are among the many participant factors that may influence the effectiveness of a given family program. Rund et al. (1994) found that the most symptomatic patients benefited most from the family intervention. Four studies (Rund et al., 1994; Zhang et al., 1994; Linszen et al., 1996; Nugter et al., 1997) focused on patients early in the course of schizophrenia. In two of these studies, relapse was reduced for clients in families that received the intervention. It is therefore difficult to draw conclusions about the differential merits of family psychoeducation for persons and families in early versus later phase of illness. At the very least, the qualitative nature of the intervention should be tailored somewhat for new-onset versus more chronic diagnoses. The reactions of "first break" families were noted to differ from families that have been dealing with the illness and an ill relative for a longer period of time (Linszen et al., 1996; Nugter et al., 1997; Solomon et al., 1996).

While none of the new studies reported here was restricted to families classified as being high in expressed emotion, Linszen et al. (1996) did stratify patients by levels of EE (low vs. high) before condition assignment. Nugter et al. (1997) measured expressed emotion and reported the relationship between patient outcome and change in EE ratings. Linszen et al. (1996) hypothesized that the near-significant increase in relapse observed in patients of "low EE" families receiving the family intervention may be due to the fact that the family model emphasizes communication and conflict skills training. They suggested that the intervention increased the stress levels of these families by implying something was wrong with their family interaction styles. While the data do not support offering family psychoeducation only to families who have first been assessed and classified as being high in expressed emotion, they do underscore the importance of families examining their own needs and understanding the goals and methods of a particular program before joining it.

The work by Telles et al. (1995) addressed the issue of adapting family psychoeducation along cultural (in addition to individual) lines. Their findings emphasized how differences in family "acculturation" influenced the efficacy of the behavioral family management model. However, the larger issue conveyed is that the program did not meet the needs of certain families because of their cultural background, even though technical aspects such as language were accommodated.

More positively, the Chinese programs spell out strategies the authors used to create family programs that fit with local practices and existing health care systems in rural and urban China (Mingyuan et al., 1993; Xiang et al., 1994; Xiong et al., 1994; Zhang et al., 1994). Other work (Shankar, 1994; Susser et al., 1996) has also suggested that individual as-needed consultation models may work better in communities where mental health is less professionalized, and so group psychoeducation or treatment programs are less accepted.

Is Family Psychoeducation Effective as Part of Usual Practice?

The first generation of research in family psychoeducation established positive outcomes in rarefied research settings with highly trained research staff and selected patients. However, truly effective interventions work under usual practice conditions. The conduct of research inevitably alters "usual practice" in a variety of ways, and the closer a study comes to approximating usual practice, the less methodologically rigorous it tends to be. Therefore, assessment of effectiveness requires some speculation. It appears that for the most part, the family interventions described in the studies reviewed here were creations of research and did not resemble usual practice. However, several studies with positive findings were carried out in clinical environments more representative of usual care (e.g., the studies in China; Rund et al., 1994; McFarlane et al., 1996; Solomon et al., 1996). A study of McFarlane's multifamily psychoeducation group is currently being conducted in the State of Washington by Dennis Dyck. This study modifies McFarlane's original study of this model by implementing the program in an outpatient managed care setting at sites with remote supervision and technical assistance. The early results from this study are promising (Dyck, personal communication), although it is premature to draw any conclusions.

The Current Status of Implementation of Family Interventions

The fact that so many of the family intervention studies use "usual treatment" as their control condition points out that access to family services is not the norm. The PORT study found that only 31% of a sample of persons who had family contact and who were receiving treatment for schizophrenia reported that their family received information about the illness (Lehman et al., 1998a, 1998b; Dixon et al., 1999a). Young et al. (1998) evaluated the quality of care for a cohort of persons with schizophrenia. They found that of the 68% of patients with close family contact, 39% received poor quality care as measured by the absence of any family contact. Family contact between clinicians and family members that does occur is likely to be informal rather than a part of a specific treatment program or model (Dixon et al., 1999a).

Barriers to implementation of family psychoeducation come from providers and payers, family members, and in some cases from consumers. Mental health professionals have expressed concern about the cost and length of structured family psychoeducation programs (9 months – 2 years), the interest of families in such programs, arid confidentiality (Dixon et al. 1997). A PORT-sponsored dissemination of McFarlane's multifamily psychoeducation group model found the following obstacles to implementation: lack of program leadership and conflict between the philosophy and principles of McFarlane's model and typical agency practices. Wright (1997) found that job and organizational factors were much more predictive of the frequency of mental health professionals' involvement with families than were professionals' attitudes. Bergmark (1994) noted the persistence of psychodynamic theory as a barrier in that some families perceive psychoeducation programs as family blaming, thereby inhibiting collaboration between professionals and families.

The World Schizophrenia Fellowship Strategy Development Group identified the following barriers to implementation of family programs (World Schizophrenia Fellowship, 1997): stigma against mental illness, psychoeducation treatments not seen as important, conflicted relationships between consumers and caregivers, varying models of family intervention, inadequate training of professional work force, costs, and structural problems in many mental health systems.

Family advocates have also expressed concern about the time commitment, the exclusion of families whose relative is not currently receiving treatment, psychoeducation's roots in EE theory, and the focus on patient relapse as the outcome of interest rather than family well-being (Solomon, 1996). Consumers also sometimes do not provide permission for providers to be in touch with family members.

WHAT HAS FILLED THE GAP? FAMILY EDUCATION BY FAMILIES

Despite the positive effects of professionally led family psychoeducation interventions that are documented by existing research, relatives of people with schizophrenia have experienced a paucity of services. Involved family members often report dissatisfaction with the mental health system and the professionals who compose it, especially around issues of information and support availability, access to clinicians, and inclusion in their ill relatives' treatment (Spaniol et al., 1987; Solomon & Marcenko, 1992; Hatfield et al., 1994; Greenberg et al., 1995; Struening et al., 1995). Families have created self-help groups and organizations to help fill these gaps and advocate for system reform. In this country, the National Alliance for the Mentally Ill (NAMI) is the best-known national group. Primarily, family members attend self-help and support groups to receive emotional support and accurate information about mental illness and mental health services (Heller et al., 1997a; Heller et al., 1997b).

In addition to ongoing support groups, the NAMI sponsored Family-to-Family Education Program as well as the Journey of Hope Program have enjoyed widespread support by state governments (Dixon et al., 1999b). These 12-week courses for family members combine information, skill building, and support—and so share many of the goals and strategies of family psychoeducation. However, while psychoeducation tends to be clinic based and delivered by mental health professionals, family-to-family education is community oriented, based on theories of stress, coping, and adaptation, and is delivered by trained peer family members (Solomon, 1996). It is also open to anyone with a family member who has serious and persistent mental illness; unlike most professionally led programs, the person with schizophrenia does not need to be receiving treatment in order for the family member to participate. These practices follow from the program's primary concern with *family* well-being, while professionally led family psychoeducation tends to emphasize *patient* outcomes. Their shorter length and volunteer leadership often mean family-to-family programs are less expensive than psychoeducation as well. Unfortunately, research on family-to-family education is not as extensive as research on family psychoeducation (Dixon & Lehman, 1995). Since no evaluations using comparison or control groups have been conducted, the efficacy of these programs cannot yet be evaluated.

The other alternative model of family intervention that has evolved is the more individualized "family consultation" model discussed in the work of Mingyuan et al. (1993), Xiang et al. (1994), and Zhang et al. (1994) in China, and Shankar's (1994) work in India. Consultation was also an arm of the study by Solomon et al. (1996, 1998). In this model, although education and groups may be available (or not), the primary focus is on private consultation between the family members and a trained clinician or family member consultant. The consultant's purpose is to provide whatever advice, support, and information is needed, tailored to the specific needs of the family as they articulate them. Consultations occur when the family, requests them and may lead to other referrals, simultaneous involvement in other programs, or termination or restart at any time. As with the family-to-family education model, the efficacy of consultation cannot be assessed because virtually no research has been conducted.

CONCLUSIONS AND RECOMMENDATIONS

The data supporting the efficacy of family psychoeducation remain compelling. Such programs should remain as part of best practices guidelines and treatment recommendations. The recent literature suggests that assessing the appropriateness of family psychoeducation for a particular patient and family should consider the following questions, to which affirmative answers would increase the appropriateness of family psychoeducation for an individual patient and his or her family:

- Are the family and patient interested in participating in family psychoeducation?

- To what extent is the patient involved with the family and what is the quality of that relationship?

- Are there clear patient-related outcomes that clinicians, family members, and patients can identify as goals, such as decreased relapse or increased employment?

- Would the patient and family choose family psychoeducation instead of alternatives available in the agency or community to achieve outcomes identified?

The role of other family intervention models might include a consultation to assist the family and patient in coming to a decision about participation in family psychoeducation. Peer-led family education programs conducted outside of the service system clearly have a role when the patient is not in treatment or is unwilling to give permission for the family to participate in it, making relatives ineligible for professionally led family psychoeducation. Although again there is little research on the peer models, they may also serve certain needs psychoeducation does not or have particular strengths because they are peer led and emphasize family well-being. Support of family-to-family models by mental health professionals will be valuable in addressing these unknowns. At this point, however, professionally led family psychoeducation models that at least have support, information, and crisis intervention components appear to be the only ones documented as useful in achieving patient improvement.

This review also highlights the incompleteness of our knowledge, the widespread lack of dissemination and implementation of family psychoeducation, and the potential existence of other effective service models. Research must address the following issues:

- We need to better understand the state of affairs regarding services for relatives of people with serious mental illnesses. Currently available information is inadequate to accurately describe what services and support family members are or are not getting, and from what sources. Rectifying this will require addressing multiple issues: patients, families, providers, finances, and service organizations. In some cases, the details of family needs are not even well understood.

- We need to devise more sophisticated evaluations of family interventions to better discern what works for whom at what cost. These evaluations need to identify key critically effective "ingredients" and best practices in general and consider the differing needs of diverse family members.

- To make an actual contribution to family members' and consumers' lives, such research must be applied to developing even more beneficial models of family intervention. This may mean creating programs (or components of programs) that address the differential issues of parents versus siblings of adults with schizophrenia, or family members of people whose illness is of recent onset versus those who have been dealing with the illness for years, for example. Research may also consider optimal combinations of models: structured group and consultation; peer and professional.

- Other work must address the systems-level problems. We have some clues as to why family services, even proven low-cost ones, are unavailable in most places. However, the dynamics of these obstacles, and their dismantling, have not been addressed. The many political and economic issues of doing so in the current and future mental health system must be taken into consideration, as must questions about successful family services shifting responsibilities and costs of care onto families. Disseminating and implementing successful models requires simultaneous top-down and bottom-up efforts in the mental health system-gaining the support of managing institutions and companies as well as the involvement of front-line providers, family members, and consumers.

- Underpinning these various research directions is also a need to better understand the role of family members in the illness management; coping, course of illness, and recovery of the individual with schizophrenia. Inquiry in this area, as others, must be driven by appreciation for the full biopsychosocial model, rigorous research, and the strengths and stresses of all parties.

When this work is done, we hope family psychoeducation and family-to-family programs will be much more accessible to family members who want them. In the meantime, family-provider interactions will continue to take place most often in the daily course of the consumer's receiving services. Providers, consumers, and families will continue to work in their local communities to find and create the relationships and resources that can address consumer and family-member needs in the absence of proven and prepackaged intervention programs.

The literature regarding family-member services contains many suggestions for doing this with optimal effectiveness. Family members invariably express needs for information, skills, and support. Commonalties among the interventions reviewed in this paper directly address these needs and can be adapted for provider use outside of formal psychoeducation programs. First, providers can offer family members information about schizophrenia and other mental illnesses, illness management, navigating the mental health system, and community resources they might find helpful. Such information should not be offered only once, but consistently. Many consumers and family members will want more detailed and sophisticated information as time and their knowledge base increase—providers can and do anticipate this and offer both conversation and written materials that are tailored to current needs.

Second, providers can assist family members in learning communication and problem-solving skills. Mental illness brings many disruptions and fears into a family, often causing considerable conflict. While information can create understanding, effective communication, negotiation, and problem solving can make difficult and emotional conversations constructive. Some providers may decide to see a client and his or her involved family members together to discuss tenets of good communication, methods of conflict resolution, and how to use them. Others may want to frame such interventions as family therapy, or facilitate families' taking part in community-based workshops. Ongoing assistance to identify and resolve conflicts as they arise can both support the family and teach skills in vivo.

Third, family members need support. Good relationships with mental health providers and enhanced ability for family members to support each other are both helpful. Additionally, consumers and family members may need help understanding and responding to reactions others in their support system may have to mental illness, especially stigma. Moreover, they may desire contact with people who have schizophrenia or a relative with it, to share experiences and information. Self-help and support groups for family members, and for consumers, are increasingly common in community mental health centers, self-help organizations, and other facilities. Providers may want to know about those in their area, as well as state or national organizations that might have such information.

The three provider actions summarized above assume competencies that some providers may not have. Providers wishing to serve families and consumers better may first have to teach themselves about surrounding community resources. They may have to examine their own abilities to conduct family therapy, or to teach communications and coping skills. If these abilities are found wanting, providers may need to invest in increasing their capacities before offering such services, or refer consumers and families to other providers for these services. They may need to take a lead in creating community resources as well.

Underlying all of these components are the relationships among family members, consumers, and providers. The actions outlined above require investments of time and interaction. The most successful formal programs list building rapport and trust as important ingredients. Both are perhaps even more important when working to meet family and consumer needs without the structure of formal family psychoeducation programs.

REFERENCES

Bergmark, T. (1994). Models of family support in Sweden: From mistreatment to understanding. *New Directions in Mental Health Services, 62,* 71–77.

Cochrane, J. J., Goering, P. N., & Rogers, J. M. (1997). The mental health of informal caregivers in Ontario: An epidemiological survey. *American Journal of Public Health, 87,* 2002–2008.

Dixon, L. (1999). Providing services to families of persons with schizophrenia: Present and future. *Journal of Mental Health Policy and Economics, 2,* 3–8.

Dixon, L., & Lehman, A. (1995). Family interventions for schizophrenia. *Schizophrenia Bulletin, 21*(4), 631–643.

Dixon L., Lyles, A., Scott, J., Lehman, A. L., Postrado, L., Goldman, H., & McGlynn, E. (1999a). Services to families of adults with schizophrenia: From treatment recommendations to dissemination. *Psychiatric Services, 50,* 233–238.

Dixon, L., Goldman, H. H., & Hirad, A. (1999b). State policy and funding of services to families of adults with serious and persistent mental illness. *Psychiatric Services, 50,* 551–553.

Dixon, L., Scott, J., Lyles, A., Fahey, M., Skinner, A., & Shore, A. (1997). Adherence to schizophrenia PORT family treatment recommendations. *Schizophrenia Research, 24,* 220.

Falloon, I. R. H., Boyd, J. L., McGill, C.W., Razani, J., Moss, H. B., & Gilderman, A.M. (1982). Family management in the prevention of exacerbations of schizophrenia: A controlled study. *The New England Journal of Medicine, 306,* 1437–1440.

Falloon, I. R. H., & Pederson, J. (1985). Family management in the prevention of morbidity of schizophrenia: The adjustment family unit. *British Journal of Psychiatry, 147,* 156–163.

Goldstein, M. J. (1994). Psychoeducational and family therapy in relapse prevention. *Acta Psychiatrica Scandinavica, 382*(Suppl), 54–57.

Greenberg, J. S., Greenley, J. R., & Kim, H. W. (1995). The provision of mental health services to families of persons with serious mental illness. *Research in Community and Mental Health, 8,* 181–204.

Hatfield, A., Coursey, R. D., & Slaughter, J. (1994). Family responses to behavior manifestations of mental illness. *Innovations & Research, 3,* 41–49.

Heller, T., Roccoforte, J. A., & Cook, J. A. (1997a). Predictors of support group participation among families of persons with mental illness. *Family Relations, 46,* 437–442.

Heller, T., Roccoforte, J. A., Hsieh, K., Cook, J. A., & Pickett, S. A. (1997b). Benefits of support groups for families of adults with serious mental illnesses. *American Journal of Orthopsychiatry, 67,* 187–198.

Hogarty, G. E., Anderson, C. M., Reiss, D. J., Kornblith, S. J., Greenwald, D. P., Javana, C. D., Madonia, M. J., & the Environmental/Personal Indicators in the Course of Schizophrenia Research Group. (1986). Family psychoeducation, social skills training, and maintenance chemotherapy in the aftercare treatment of schizophrenia: I. One year effects of a controlled study on relapse and expressed emotion. *Archives of General Psychiatry, 43,* 633–642.

Hogarty, G. E., Kornblith, S. J., Greenwald, D., DiBarry, A. L., Cooley, S., Ulrich, R. F., Carter, M., & Flesher, S. (1997). Three-year trials of personal therapy among schizophrenic patients living with or independent of family: I. Description of study and effects on relapse rates. *American Journal of Psychiatry, 154,* 1504–1513.

Koenigsberg, H. A., & Handley, R. (1986). Expressed emotion: From predictive index to clinical construct. *American Journal of Psychiatry, 143,* 1361–1373.

Leff, J. (1994). Working with the families of schizophrenic patients. *British Journal of Psychiatry, 164*(Suppl 23), 71–76.

Lefley, H. P. (1992). Expressed emotion: Conceptual, clinical and social policy issues. *Hospital and Community Psychology, 43,* 591–598.

Lehman, A. F., Steinwachs, D. M., & PORT coinvestigators. (1998a). At Issue: Translating research into practice: The Schizophrenia Patient Outcomes Research Team (PORT) treatment recommendations. *Schizophrenia Bulletin, 24*(1), 1–10.

Lehman, A. F., Steinwachs, D. M., & PORT coinvestigators. (1998b). Patterns of usual care for schizophrenia: Initial results from the Schizophrenia PORT Client Survey. *Schizophrenia Bulletin, 24*(l), 11–19.

Liberman, R. P., & Mintz, J. (1998). Reviving applied family intervention. *Archives of General Psychiatry, 55,* 1047–1048.

Linszen, D., Dingemans, P., van der Does, J. W., Nugter, A, Scholte, P., Lenoir, R., & Goldstein, M.J. (1996). Treatment, expressed emotion, and relapse in recent onset schizophrenic disorders. *Psychological Medicine, 26,* 333–342.

McFarlane, W. R., Lukens, E., Link, B., Dushay, R., Deakins, S., Newmark, M., Dunne, E. J., Horen, B., & Toran, J. (1995). Multiple-family groups and psychoeducation in the treatment of schizophrenia. *Archives of General Psychiatry, 52,* 679–687.

McFarlane, W. R., Dushay, R., Statsny, P., Deakins, S., & Link, B. (1996). A comparison of two levels of family-aided assertive community treatment. *Psychiatric Services, 47,* 744–750.

McFarlane, W. R., Dushay, R. A., Deakins, S., Lukens, E.P., Toran, J., & Link, B. (2000). Employment outcomes in family-aided assertive community treatment. *Journal of Orthopsychiatric Association, 70,* 203–214.

Mingyuan, Z., Heqin, Y., Chengde, Y., Jianlin, Y, Qingfeng, Y., Peijun, C., Lianfang, G., Jizhong, Y., Guangya, Q., Zhen, W., Jianhua, C., Minghua, S., Jushan, H., Longlin, W., Yi, Z., Buoying, Z., Orley, J., & Gittelman, M. (1993). Effectiveness of psychoeducation of relatives of schizophrenic patients: A prospective cohort study in five cities of China. *International Journal of Mental Health, 22,*47–59.

Nugter, A., Dingemans, P., van der Does, J. W., Linszen, D., & Gersons, B. (1997). Family treatment, expressed emotion and relapse in recent onset schizophrenia. *Psychiatry Research, 72,* 23–31.

Penn, L. D., & Mueser, K. T. (1996). Research update on the psychosocial treatment of schizophrenia. *American Journal of Psychiatry, 153,* 607–617.

Rund, B. R., Moe, L., Sollien, T., Fjell, A., Borchgrevink, T., Hallert, M., & Naess, P. O. (1994). The psychosis project: Outcome and cost-effectiveness of a psychoeducational treatment program for schizophrenic adolescents. *Acta Psychiatrica Scandinavica, 89,* 211–218.

Scazufca, M., & Kuipers, E. (1998). Stability of expressed emotion in relatives of those with schizophrenia and its relationship with burden of care and perception of patients' social functioning. *Psychological Medicine, 28,* 453–461.

Schooler, N. R., Keith, S. J., Severe, J. B., Matthews, S. M., Bellack, A. S., Glick, I. S., Hargreaves, W. A., Kane, J. M., Ninan, P. T., Frances, A., Jacobs, M., Lieberman, J. A., Mance, R., Simpson, G. M., & Woerner, M. G. (1997). Relapse and rehospitalization during maintenance treatment of schizophrenia—The effects of dose reduction and family treatment. *Archives of General Psychiatry, 54,* 453–463.

Shankar, R. (1994). Interventions with families of people with schizophrenia in India. *New Directions for Mental Health Services, 62,* 79–88.

Solomon, P. (1996). Moving from psychoeducation to family education for families of adults with serious mental illness. *Psychiatric Services, 47,* 1364–1370.

Solomon, P., Draine, J., Mannion, E., & Meisel, M. (1996). Impact of brief family psychoeducation on self-efficacy. *Schizophrenia Bulletin, 22*(l), 41–50.

Solomon, P., Draine, J., Mannion, E., & Meisel, M. (1998). Increased contact with community mental health resources as a potential benefit of family education. *Psychiatric Services, 49,* 333–339.

Solomon, P., & Marcenko, M. (1992). Families of adults with severe mental illness: Their satisfaction with inpatient and outpatient treatment. *Psychosocial Rehabilitation Journal, 16,* 121–134.

Spaniol, L., Jung, H., & Zipple, A. (1987). Families as a resource in the rehabilitation of the severely psychiatrically disabled. In A. B. Hatfield, & H. Lefley (Eds.), *Families of the mentally ill: Coping and adaptation,* (pp. 167–190). New York, NY: Guilford Press.

Struening, E. L., Stueve, A., Vine, P., Kreisman, D. E., Link, B. H., & Herman, D. B. (1995). Factors associated with grief and depressive symptoms in caregivers of people with mental illness. *Research in Community and Mental Health, 8,* 91–124.

Susser, E., Collins, P., Schanzer, B., Varma, V .K., & Gittelman, M. (1996). Can we learn from the care of persons with mental illness in developing countries? *American Journal of Public Health, 86,* 926–928.

Szmukler, G. I., Herrman, H., Colusa, S., Benson, A., & Bloch, S. (1996). A controlled trial of a counseling intervention for caregivers of relatives with schizophrenia. *Social Psychiatry and Psychiatric Epidemiology, 31,* 149–155.

Tarrier, N., Barrowclough, C, Porceddu, K, & Fitzpatrick, E. (1994). The Salford Family Intervention project—Relapse rates of schizophrenia at 5 and 8 years. *British Journal of Psychiatry, 165,* 829–832.

Tarrier, N., Barrowclough, C., Vaughy, C., Bamrah, J. S., Porceddu, K., Watts, S., & Freeman, H.L. (1988). The community management of schizophrenia: A controlled trial of a behavioural intervention with families to reduce relapse. *British Journal of Psychiatry, 153,* 532–542.

Tarrier, N., Barrowclough, C., Vaughy, C., Bamrah, J. S., Porceddu, K., Watts, S., & Freeman, H. L. (1989). Community management of schizophrenia: A two-year follow-up of a behavioural intervention with families. *British Journal of Psychiatry, 154,* 625–628.

Telles, C., Karno, M., Mintz, J., Paz, G., Arias, M., Tucker, D., & Lopes, S. (1995). Immigrant families coping with schizophrenia: Behavioral family intervention v. case management with a low-income Spanish-speaking population. *British Journal of Psychiatry, 167,* 473–479.

World Schizophrenia Fellowship. (September, 4–5, 1997). *Strategy development: Family interventions work: Putting research findings into practice.* Report of the World Schizophrenia Fellowship, following discussions at the Christchurch Convention Center, New Zealand.

Wright, E. R. (1997). The impact of organizational factors on mental health professionals' involvement with families. *Psychiatric Services, 48,* 921–927.

Xiang, M. G., Ran, M. S., & Li, S. G. (1994). A controlled evaluation of psychoeducational family intervention in a rural Chinese community. *British Journal of Psychiatry, 165,* 544–548.

Xiong, W., Phillips, M. R., Hu, X., Wang, R., Dai, Q., Kleinman, J., & Kleinman, A. (1994). Family-based intervention for schizophrenic patients in China: A randomized controlled trial. *British Journal of Psychiatry, 165,* 239–247.

Young, A. S., Sullivan, G., Burnam, M.A., & Brook, R. H. (1998). Measuring the quality of outpatient treatment for schizophrenia. *Archives of General Psychiatry, 55,* 611–617.

Zastowny, T. R., Lehman, A. F., Cole, R. E., & Kane, C. (1992). Family management of schizophrenia: A comparison of behavioral and supportive family treatment. *Psychiatric Quarterly, 63,* 159–186.

Zhang, M., Wang, M., Li, J., & Phillips, M. R. (1994). Randomized-control trial of family intervention for 78 first-episode male schizophrenic patients: An 18-month study in Suzhou, Jiangsu. *British Journal of Psychiatry, 165*(Suppl 24), 96–102.

Procedures to Share Treatment Information among Mental Health Providers, Consumers, and Families

Tina Bogart and Phyllis Solomon

At the time of original publication, Tina Bogart, MSW, was a predoctoral fellow at the Center for Mental Health Policy and Services Research at the University of Pennsylvania; and Phyllis Solomon, PhD, was a professor in the School of Social Work at the University of Pennsylvania.

This article was published previously in *Psychiatric Services*, 50, 1321–1329, October 1999, and is reprinted with permission.

Abstract: Although practice guidelines for the treatment of persons with severe mental illness recommend involving family members in all phases of the treatment process, in many states unclear confidentiality statutes and regulations may present a barrier. This paper describes approaches used by a few locales to clarify confidentiality procedures for releasing information to families. It presents a model of steps that regional systems or local agencies may take to manage this barrier to provider-family collaboration. Policy guidelines must clearly state that release of information to family members requires client consent. A specific form for release of information to families indicating the types of information that may be released is then developed. Verbal release of information and a 1-year time limit on release are recommended. The form, which should comply with state statutes and regulations, can then be integrated into routine clinical practice. Providers should be trained to discuss and explore issues about the release of information with both consumers and family members.

INTRODUCTION

Significant evidence exists that providing information to families about their relatives' illness decreases the frequency of relapse and thereby reduces rehospitalization (Anderson, Reiss, Hogarty, 1986; Falloon, Boyd, & McGill, 1985; Leff, Kuipers, Berkowitz et al., 1982). Practice guidelines for the treatment of severe mental illness have integrated these findings and other evidence and now recommend involving families in all phases of routine care (Dixon & Lehman, 1995; Frances, Docherty, & Kahn, 1996; "Practice Guidelines for the Treatment of Patients with Schizophrenia," 1997).

Although the guidelines call for families to be involved in a collaborative treatment process to the greatest extent possible, few strategies for implementing provider-family collaboration have been developed. As a result, many families are not involved in the treatment process or given any information about their relatives' illness (Herz, 1985; Holden & Lewine, 1982;

Bernheim, 1989; Biegel, Song & Milligan, 1995; Hanson, 1995; Solomon & Marcenko, 1992; Wright, 1997).

A number of factors have been examined as potential barriers to implementing provider-family collaboration (Holden & Lewine, 1982; Bernheim, 1989; Biegel, Song, & Milligan, 1995; Hanson, 1995; Solomon & Marcenko, 1992; Wright, 1997). However, one potential barrier that has not been fully explored is unspecified or unclear statutes and regulations related to confidentiality (Petrila & Sadoff, 1992; Zipple, Langle, & Spaniol et al., 1990; Marsh & Magee, 1997; Biegel, Johnsen, & Shafran, 1997). This paper discusses the dilemma faced by consumers, families, and mental health care providers in balancing consumers' right to confidentiality and families' need for information. Issues involved in clarifying confidentiality as it relates to the release of information to families are outlined, and innovative approaches developed by two counties in response to these issues are presented. Finally, based on a review of the current approaches, a model for clarifying confidentiality is proposed.

THE DILEMMA OF CONSUMERS, FAMILIES, AND PROVIDERS

Symptoms of mental illness such as confusion, cognitive deficits, isolation, and withdrawal make it difficult for consumers to recognize signs of relapse and to seek help. Consequently, families are frequently the first to recognize warning signs and symptoms (Herz, 1985). For this reason, families' role in their relatives' support network is often an integral component of effective treatment (Solomon, 1996).

To fulfill this role, families must have, at a minimum, ongoing contact with providers and information about their relatives' diagnosis and treatment. Without such information, families may not be able to distinguish between warning signs of relapse and medication effects (Petrila & Sadoff, 1992) or to support treatment goals and promote recovery (Marsh & Magee, 1997, Solomon, Draine, Mannion, et al., 1998). Without ongoing contact with providers, families may observe signs of relapse but have no means to share this information with providers who may intercede to prevent a crisis (Leazenby, 1997).

Providers are increasingly aware that families can be a vital resource in the treatment process, and providers recognize the need to share information with involved and supportive family members. However, in most states providers are presented with confidentiality statutes and regulations that do not mention the release of information to families. Therefore, under the letter of the law, providing even the most basic information about a client's condition without written consent, such as informing family members that their relative is improving, is technically a breach of confidentiality (Ulan H,

Pennsylvania Department of Public Welfare, personal communication, Sept ember, 1998).

A preliminary review of state statutes revealed that some states, such as New Hampshire, Iowa, Maine, New York, Maryland, Massachusetts, and Rhode Island, have included language about the release of information to families (NH Mental Health Services System: Access to Information, 1992; IA Disclosure of Mental Health Information, 1986; ME Disclosure of Information Pertaining to Mentally Disabled Clients, 1994; NY Clinical Records: Confidentiality, 1987; MD Confidentiality and Disclosure Generally, 1997; MA Departmental Records of Persons Admitted to Its Facilities, 1986; RI Disclosure by Mental Health Professional, 1993). Each of these states permits exceptions to obtaining client consent before release of information to families. According to the New Hampshire and Iowa statutes, for example, providers who receive written requests from a family are permitted to disclose specific information without the consumer's consent under certain conditions. First, the attending provider must verify that the family member is directly involved in providing care or monitoring the treatment of the ill relative. Second, the information disclosed must be necessary for the provision of care and monitoring of treatment. Although such exceptions to client consent are permitted, most state statutes strongly encourage obtaining consent whenever possible.

Requiring client consent is vital for a number of reasons. First, it safeguards consumers' trust, which is essential in the therapeutic relationship. Providers build trust by ensuring that information is not disclosed without clients' permission (Petrila & Sadoff, 1992). Trust is a crucial component of successful treatment. Disclosing information, even to families, without explicit consent of the client is a violation of trust. Second, obtaining consent empowers consumers to develop their own support network, promoting both independence and the acceptance of mental illness as a chronic illness, like diabetes, that can be monitored and managed. Third, by discussing with clients the options for releasing information to families, providers communicate respect and validation of consumers' ability to make decisions in their own best interest.

As providers attempt to fulfill the statutory requirement to obtain client consent, they often discover that forms and procedures specifically for releasing information to families do not exist. Instead, the only option available is to use general agency release forms. Because these general forms are typically created for interagency use, the release is often limited to 30, 60, or 90 days, or the form specifies that the information may be released one time only. Because mental illnesses are chronic and recurrent, these restrictions make the forms cumbersome and impractical to use for families who need to receive information on an ongoing, long-term basis. In addition, the short time limit is difficult to keep updated and often impedes communication at times when it is most needed, such as during a crisis.

The lack of specific forms and procedures creates a real dilemma for providers, and this dilemma is further complicated by unclear definitions of confidential and nonconfidential information. Nonconfidential information includes basic information about mental illnesses, including etiology, warning signs and symptoms, general prognoses, and basic treatment options. In reality, much of the information families seek may be disclosed in a manner that does not breach confidentiality (Solomon & Marcenko, 1992, Zipple et al., 1990).

For example, consumers often tell family members their diagnosis and where they are receiving treatment. Families may call the agency requesting information with the sole purpose of learning more about the illness to provide more effective support to their ill relative. Providers may believe that responding to the request is a breach of confidentiality when, in fact, many of the questions may be answered without disclosing any identifying (confidential) information. However, in the face of legal and ethical obligations, providers often respond cautiously and may mistakenly withhold even general information from families (Zipple et al., 1990, Marsh & Magee, 1997).

Zipple and colleagues (1990) outlined methods of providing general information to families without violating client confidentiality. For example, providers may simply state that they cannot verify whether the individual receives services at the agency, but that they can share basic information about mental illnesses, the services provided by the agency, and other community resources. When contacted, providers may also listen to families and receive information about clients without breaching confidentiality. General information and contact with providers is crucial for families attempting to understand and support their ill relative (Zipple et al., 1990).

INNOVATIVE LOCAL APPROACHES

Local efforts have been directed at filling in gaps when confidentiality statutes are not specific and developing clear procedures to guide the disclosure of information to families. The first issue involved in establishing procedures is deciding who is responsible for initiating the consent process. Many agencies require that consumers or families request information. Two counties, Riverside County, California, and Allegheny County, Pennsylvania, have taken a proactive stance by developing procedures that place the responsibility for initiating the consent process in the hands of providers (CA Mental Health Department: Confidentiality Guidelines for Family/Social Support

Network, June 1997; Holder B, Alliance for the Mentally Ill of Southwestern Pennsylvania, personal communication, 1998).

This approach is reasonable and effective for a variety of reasons. First, substantial evidence about consumers' and families' experience with mental illness suggests that leaving the responsibility to consumers or families is likely to be extremely burdensome. One reason is that both consumers and families battle with the stigma and shame of mental illness (Abosh & Collins, 1996; Hatfield & Lefley, 1987; Marsh & Johnson, 1997; Terkelsen, 1986). It is natural for both consumers and families to minimize or doubt symptoms, blame themselves, and become isolated from friends and other supports. Consequently, requesting information and initiating the consent process may be difficult for them.

Furthermore, current practice guidelines recommend that providers involve families in the treatment process. Providers' initiation of the consent process is a concrete strategy for fulfilling this recommendation. Moreover, it affords a means to engage consumers in a dialogue about the benefits of involving their family in the treatment process.

Not designating providers as initiators of the consent process has some potentially negative effects. For example, families and consumers who do not understand that information from the clinical record is confidential may attribute providers' silence to a belief that mental illness is shameful. When providers fail to raise the issue of releasing information to families, outdated beliefs that mental illness should not be discussed are reinforced. By initiating honest discussions with consumers about disclosing information about their illness to their families, providers are taking the first step in breaking the secrecy that maintains the shame and stigma of mental illness.

Riverside County's procedures also contain several elements integral to promoting collaboration. The procedures raise awareness of the importance of support networks and encourage a team approach with an open dialogue between providers, consumers, and families. Providers are responsible for discussing with clients options such as releasing limited or specific information to a designated family member. Once a client chooses to sign such a release form, providers are responsible for encouraging the family member to become involved. For family members who are hesitant to participate in the treatment process, providers are instructed to respectfully explore the reasons for their reluctance.

Riverside County's procedures are an important first step in alleviating misunderstandings between families, consumers, and providers about confidentiality, but the impact of the county's educational effort has been limited. Riverside County has relied on brochures to educate both providers and families about the procedures. Although the brochures were widely distributed, many providers are unaware of the procedures, which were developed in 1997. Moreover, the lack of countywide training for providers has resulted in inconsistent implementation of the procedures. Therefore, the potential effectiveness of the effort has been reduced (C. Callahan, County of Riverside Mental Health Department, personal communication, September, 1998).

Riverside County's procedures clarify confidentiality on the provider level, whereas Allegheny County implemented a systemwide policy clarification. Allegheny County's efforts began about 8 years ago when public mental health officials, families, consumers, and county legal staff convened and, over a period of 2 years, introduced a form specifically for releasing information to families. They also developed procedures for disclosing information to families and implemented systemwide provider training.

The release form developed by Allegheny County includes several key components that address issues arising from the use of general consent forms. First, consumers choose the family member or significant other to whom information will be verbally released. Verbal release of information promotes flexible communication by allowing providers to update families with a brief phone call rather than requiring formal written correspondence. In addition, verbal release can protect clients from the chance of written correspondence ending up in the wrong hands.

Second, consumers choose the types of information they wish to release, such as the provider's name, the name of the treatment program, the treatment plan, medications, and the dates of scheduled appointments. General forms often require the categorical release of all information in the clients' medical record. Consumers who refuse to sign a categorical release may be willing to release specific types of information. Therefore, these provisions enhance the likelihood that consumers will benefit from family involvement and support.

A third key component in the Allegheny County approach is that clients who are physically unable to give written consent may verbally authorize release of information with the signature of two witnesses. Fourth, Allegheny County addressed the problematic issues associated with short time limits on information release by adopting a non-time-limited form and allowing clients to revoke the release form at any time by submitting a written request.

Besides the creation of a specific release form, procedures were established to integrate the release form into routine clinical practice. The form is presented to clients at intake into the county mental health system. The medical records department of the central intake agency in each of Allegheny County's catchment areas is responsible for retaining the original release form, notifying all involved agencies, and maintaining records of which agencies are notified. A notice is also sent to the designated family member to inform him or her of the type of confidential information that may be released on an ongoing basis. The centralized process ensures that the information that consumers and families receive is uniform across all agencies.

All staff in Allegheny County's mental health system, including intake workers, psychiatric nurses, therapists, and receptionists, were required to attend a training session to help providers integrate the form into routine clinical practice. Allegheny County's experience has indicated that given the option of releasing specific information to families, 90% of clients agreed to sign the form (Marsh & Johnson, 1997). If a consumer chooses not to sign the form, it is the treating therapist's responsibility to discuss the policy with the client. Treating therapists are instructed to keep in mind clients' right to refuse while exploring their hesitations. If a client is too ill to provide consent, then the treating therapist is instructed to reintroduce the form when the client is stabilized. The mandatory training helped providers in Allegheny County discuss these issues as well as procedures for implementing the policy consistently across agencies.

Although no formal evaluation of the implementation of these procedures has been conducted, anecdotal information suggests that the efforts have been quite successful. According to members of the local Alliance for the Mentally Ill, it has been many years since complaints have been received from families feeling disengaged from the treatment process (B. Holder, Alliance for the Mentally Ill of Southwestern Pennsylvania, personal communication, 1998).

STEPS FOR DEVELOPING A POLICY AND A FORM TO RELEASE INFORMATION TO CLIENTS' FAMILIES

1. Clearly state in the policy guidelines that release of information from the client's clinical record to family members requires client consent.

2. Develop a form specifically for the release of information to family members. Create categories for the types of information that may be released that are applicable to the local agency or system. Consider an appropriate time limit for the release form. Indicate how information will be released (a verbal or a written release, or both). Review state statutes and regulations to ensure that the form is in compliance with the law.

3. Establish procedures for the form to be integrated into routine clinical practice. Present the release form to clients at intake to the agency or mental health system. If a client is too ill to provide consent, determine the procedure for reintroducing the release form once the client

is stabilized. Develop procedures for updating the release form (if applicable)

4. Develop training for providers. Train providers in ways to discuss and explore issues about the release of information with both consumers and family members. Include information about the release of general information to family members when consent is not provided. Develop procedures for integrating training into the orientation for new employees

STEPS FOR CLARIFYING CONFIDENTIALITY AT THE LOCAL LEVEL

Although guidelines for clarifying confidentiality policies may be developed on the federal, state, or local levels, the model proposed here integrates the strengths of current approaches and outlines steps that may be taken by regional mental health systems or local agencies.

Step 1: Clarifying the Need for Client Consent

The proposed model places a high priority on the protection of clients' rights by requiring consent for the release of any confidential information to families. Therefore, the proposed model is in accord with the most conservative interpretations of confidentiality statutes and may feasibly be implemented in any state.

Step 2: Developing a Release Form

Several factors need to be considered when developing a form specifically for releasing information to families. The first consideration concerns the categories of information that may be released. Although the categories developed in Allegheny County may be used as a model, they may need to be adjusted to meet local needs or to accurately describe services. If the form is to be used system wide, the categories on the form should represent all types of information that may be released from the various agencies in the system.

The second factor to consider is the use of a time limit. For mental health systems or agencies that decide to institute a time-limited form, a 1-year limit is recommended. Selection of this time frame is based on balancing tradeoffs between the extreme options of release forms with very short time limits to those with no time limits.

Although forms with no time limits ensure that continuity is not disrupted by the formality of updating forms, the inclusion of a reasonable time limit offers important protections for the consumer. For example, when properly implemented, time limits compel providers to update the form, thereby accommodating changes in consumers' social networks. Updating the form reminds both providers and consumers of the importance of involving families in the treatment process. Moreover, the inclusion of a time limit fulfills statutory requirements for states that require beginning and end dates on all release forms.

A third factor to consider in developing a release form is the manner in which the information will be released. Based on the advantages discussed above, the proposed model recommends a verbal release of information.

Step 3: Integrating the Release Form into Routine Clinical Practice

In the proposed model, providers are responsible for initiating the consent process. The release form may be presented to clients at intake into the agency or mental health system. If the client is too ill to consent at that time, a designated provider may reintroduce the form once the client is stabilized. The designated provider should be selected from the client's treatment team and offered training on how to discuss and explore the options for releasing information with the client. The designated provider is the likely choice for being responsible for updating the release form if the form includes a time limit.

If the release form is integrated system wide, the coordinating procedures used in Allegheny County offer a feasible model. In this model, the original forms are stored in a central location, and copies are dispersed to all appropriate mental health agencies. The designated provider forwards all updates to the central record-keeping location, which then notifies all appropriate agencies and the designated family member of updates about the status of the release form.

In mental health systems in which efforts cannot be feasibly coordinated on a systemwide basis, agencies may independently integrate the release form into routine clinical practice. The agency would then be responsible for notifying designated family members that the release has been signed. Furthermore, families would need to be informed that the form is specific to one agency only and that a new release form must be signed in order to receive information from any other agency.

Step 4: Developing Training for Providers

The proposed model recommends mandatory training for all providers. The purpose of the training is to review the newly developed procedures and offer providers skills for addressing issues about the release of information to families. Procedures developed in Riverside and Allegheny Counties offer a model for others to adopt. The training should emphasize that families are entitled to receive general information, regardless of whether they have been designated by their ill relative to receive confidential information.

To maintain consistency across agencies in the implementation of the confidentiality policy, it is necessary to develop procedures for training incoming staff after the initial implementation training. Mental health systems may consider integrating the training into orientations for new employees. Other options include developing a manual for new employees or designating trainers within each agency.

CONCLUSIONS

The intent of confidentiality statutes and regulations is to provide clients with the choice of releasing information from their clinical record to individuals they deem appropriate and trustworthy. However, procedures to make this choice a reality are frequently not available. With significant evidence mounting about the benefits of involving families in the treatment process, it is vital for local mental health systems to reconsider current procedures for releasing information to families. The model outlined here can help bridge the gap between recommended standards for working with persons with severe mental illness and the current mode of routine clinical practice.

REFERENCES

Abosh, B. & Collins, A. (1996). *Mental illness in the family: Issues and trends.* Toronto: University of Toronto Press.

Anderson, C., Reiss, D., & Hogarty, G. (1986). *Schizophrenia and the family.* New York: Guilford.

Bernheim, K. F. (1989). Psychologists and families of the severely mentally ill. *American Psychologist, 44,* 561–564.

Biegel, D. E., Johnsen, J. A., & Shafran, R. (1997). Overcoming barriers faced by African American families with a family member with mental illness. *Family Relations, 46*(2), 163–178.

Biegel, D. E., Song, L., & Milligan, S. E. (1995). A comparative analysis of family caregivers' perceived relationships with mental health professionals. *Psychiatric Services, 46,* 477–482.

County of Riverside, (CA) Mental Health Department. *Confidentiality guidelines for Family/Social Support Network, Policy no 206,* effective June 1997.

Dixon, L. & Lehman, A. F. (1995) Family intervention for schizophrenia. *Schizophrenia Bulletin, 21,* 631–643.

Falloon, I., Boyd, J., & McGill, C. (1985). *Family care of schizophrenia.* New York: Guilford.

Frances, A., Docherty, J. P., & Kahn, D. A. (1996). Expert consensus guideline series: Treatment of schizophrenia. *Journal of Clinical Psychiatry, 57,* 1–58.

Hanson, J. G. (1995). Families' perceptions of psychiatric hospitalization of relatives with a severe mental illness. *Administration and Policy in Mental Health, 22,* 531–541.

Hatfield, A. B., & Lefley, H. P. (1987) *Families of the mentally ill: Coping and adaptation.* New York: Guilford.

Herz, M.I. (1985). Prodromal symptoms and prevention of relapse in schizophrenia. *Journal of Clinical Psychiatry, 46,* 22–25.

Holden, D. F., & Lewine, R. R. J. (1982). How families evaluate mental health professionals, resources, and effects of illness. *Schizophrenia Bulletin 8,* 626–633.

Iowa Code Chapter 228, Disclosure of Mental Health Information. (1986).

Leazenby, L. (1997): Confidentiality as a barrier to treatment (ltr). *Psychiatric Services 48,* 1467–1468.

Leff, J., Kuipers, L., Berkowitz, R., et al. (1982). Controlled trial of social interventions in the families of schizophrenic patients. *British Journal of Psychiatry 141,* 121–134.

Maine Sec 1.34–B MRSA §1207, sub-§5, Disclosure of Information Pertaining to Mentally Disabled Clients (1994).

Marsh, D. T., & Johnson, D. (1997). The family experience of mental illness: implications for intervention. *Professional Psychology: Research and Practice 28,* 229–237.

Marsh, D. T., Magee, R. D. (1997). *Ethical and legal issues in professional practice with families.* New York: Wiley.

Maryland §4–302, Confidentiality and Disclosure Generally, suppl. (1997).

Massachusetts Chapter 123 §36, Departmental Records of Persons Admitted to Its Facilities. (1986).

New Hampshire RSA 135–C:19-a, Mental Health Services System: Access to Information. (1992).

New York MHL §33.13, Clinical Records: Confidentiality. (1987).

Petrila, J. P., & Sadoff, R. L. (1992). Confidentiality and the family as caregiver. *Hospital and Community Psychiatry, 43,* 136–139.

Practice Guidelines for the Treatment of Patients with Schizophrenia. American *Journal of Psychiatry 154*(Apr suppl):1–63, 1997

Rhode Island §40.1–5-27.1, Disclosure by mental health professional. (1993).

Solomon, P., Draine, J., Mannion, M., et al. (1998). Increased contact with community mental health resources as a potential benefit of family education. *Psychiatric Services, 49,* 333–339.

Solomon, P., & Marcenko, M. (1992). Families of adults with severe mental illness: Their satisfaction with inpatient and outpatient treatment. *Psychosocial Rehabilitation Journal 16*(1), 121–134.

Solomon, P. (1996). Moving from psychoeducation to family education for families of adults with serious mental illness. *Psychiatric Services, 47,* 1364–1370.

Terkelsen, K. (1986). A historical perspective on family-provider relationships, In H Lefley & D.L. Johnson (Eds.), *Families as allies in treatment of the mentally ill.* Washington, DC: American Psychiatric Press.

Wright, E. R. (1997). The impact of organizational factors on mental health professionals' involvement with families. *Psychiatric Services, 48,* 921–927.

Zipple, A. M., Langle, S., Spaniol. L., et al. (1990). Client confidentiality and the family's need to know: Strategies for resolving the conflict. *Community Mental Health Journal, 26,* 533–545.

Family Support and Substance Use Outcomes for Persons with Mental Illness and Substance Use Disorders

Robin E. Clark

At the time of original publication, Robin Clark, PhD, was associate professor of Community and Family Medicine and of Psychiatry at Dartmouth Medical School, Hanover, NH.

This article was published previously in the *Schizophrenia Bulletin*, 2001, 27(1), 93–101, and is reprinted with permission.

Abstract: This article explores the relationship between direct support from family members and friends and substance use outcomes for people with co-occurring severe mental illness and substance use disorders. Data are from a 3-year randomized trial of 203 patients in treatment for dual disorders. Informal (family) caregivers for 174 participants were asked about economic assistance and direct care that they provided to participants. Associations between family support and substance use outcomes were examined with bivariate comparisons of abstainers and nonabstainers and with regression models using change in substance use and cumulative substance use as dependent measures. Family economic support was associated with substance abuse recovery in bivariate and regression analyses. Caregiving hours were significantly associated with substance use reduction but not with cumulative substance use. Informal support was not associated with changes in psychiatric symptoms. The findings suggest that direct family support may help people with dual disorders to reduce or eliminate their substance use. Further research is needed to confirm this connection and to establish the mechanisms by which support is useful.

Family caregivers for people with severe mental illnesses (SMIs) such as schizophrenia are an increasingly important focus of treatment and research. Several studies demonstrate how family interventions can improve the course of illness (e.g., Hogarty et al., 1986; McFarlane et al., 1994). Others explore the general stress (Tessler & Gamache, 1994; Solomon & Draine, 1995) and the financial burden (Hoenig & Hamilton, 1966; Stevens, 1972) that family caregivers feel. Surprisingly, few researchers have examined the role that instrumental support, such as financial contributions or direct caregiving by families, plays in the well-being of people with mental disorders.

Economic assistance from families could make an important difference in the lives of people with SMI, who are often poor and unemployed (Rice & Miller, 1996). A significant percentage of those enrolled in income support programs, such as Supplemental Security Income (SSI) and Social Security Disability Insurance (SSDI), have mental disorders (Kochar & Scott, 1995).

Though vital, these publicly funded programs offer meager financial support, allowing some beneficiaries to remain below federal poverty guidelines. Unemployment and inadequate income support often leave people with SMI few resources to meet basic living expenses. Fortunately, many get financial assistance from their families or friends.

Direct assistance with the tasks of daily living is another valuable resource. Many people with SMI receive health care through Medicaid, Medicare, or both, but even the best formal service providers rarely duplicate the concrete, practical, and consistent help that families and friends can provide. Although the significance of families as caregivers for people with SMI is well documented (Franks, 1990; Carpentier et al., 1992; Clark & Drake, 1994), we know little about how informal care affects mental health and substance abuse. This knowledge gap is particularly apparent for people with co-occurring SMI and substance use disorders.

CO-OCCURRING SUBSTANCE USE DISORDERS

Substance abuse is a common problem among people with SMI. Lifetime prevalence of substance use disorders for those with schizophrenia is approximately 50% (Regier et al., 1990). Alcohol and other drugs are associated with a wide range of negative outcomes, including increased hospitalization (Kivlahan et al., 1991), higher treatment costs (Dickey & Azeni, 1996), poor treatment compliance (Owen et al., 1996), higher rates of arrest and violence (Stedman et al., 1998; Clark et al., 1999), victimization (Mueser et al., 1998), homelessness (Caton et al., 1994, 1995), and increased risk of HIV infection (Cournos et al., 1991). Reducing or eliminating substance use could significantly improve the lives of many people with SMI.

Several approaches to treatment of comorbid mental and substance use disorders have been proposed and evaluated (Blankertz & Cnann, 1994; Jerrell et al., 1994; Drake et al., 1998a; Drake et al., 1998b) but almost no attention has been given to the role that nontreatment supports play in recovery. This omission is especially troubling because people with co-occurring disorders tend to be marginally engaged in treatment. Families can easily become the primary source of continuous care. When treatment fails, they may be the providers of last resort.

Still, the consequences of family support are not clear. At least one study suggests that people with comorbid substance use disorders are significantly less satisfied with their family relationships than are those with SMI alone (Dixon et al., 1995). Dissatisfaction could mean that family contact is undesirable or even detrimental. Stressful family relationships are associated with high relapse rates (Kashner et al., 1991; Kavanagh, 1992). Relying on family support might exacerbate problems by increasing conflict, by supplying additional money to purchase drugs or alcohol, or by insulating people with dual disorders from the negative consequences of their substance use. On the other hand, informal economic assistance and caregiving could be a vital resource for meeting basic food, shelter, and safety needs.

Several factors have impeded our understanding of informal support: the difficulty of measuring family contributions, the impracticality of developing randomized studies of informal assistance, and a failure of researchers and funding sources to recognize its potential importance. Inattention to family support leaves a large gap in our knowledge about factors that may contribute to or detract from the quality of life for people with co-occurring disorders.

In this article, we use data collected in a randomized trial of formal treatments for persons with co-occurring disorders to explore the relationship between family support—economic assistance and direct care—and substance use outcomes.

METHODS

Sample

Data used in this study are from a 3-year randomized trial of treatment for co-occurring SMI and substance use disorders. The study was conducted at seven community mental health centers in New Hampshire between 1989 and 1995. Participants were randomly assigned either to standard case management with enhanced substance use treatment services or to assertive community treatment with integrated mental health and substance abuse treatment. Mental health center clients were eligible for the study if they met the following criteria: 1) *DSM-III-R* diagnosis of schizophrenia, schizoaffective, or bipolar disorder (American Psychiatric Association, 1987); 2) an active *DSM-III-R* substance use disorder within the past 6 months; 3) 18 to 60 years of age; 4) absence of additional severe medical conditions or mental retardation; and 5) willingness to provide well-informed written consent to participate in the study. Of the original 223 persons who enrolled, 203 completed the study. Completers were not significantly different from those who did not remain in the study. For results of the trial and a detailed discussion of sample selection and attrition, see Drake et al. (1998a). The study did not find statistically significant differences between the two treatments in the number of persons who achieved abstinence or in the amount of change in substance use during the study.

Study participants were predominantly male (74%), nonminority white (96%), unemployed (82%), never married (61%), and educated at least through high school (63%). Average age at study entry was 34 years (standard deviation [*SD*] = 8.5). Slightly more than half (53.6%) had schizophrenia,

22.7% had schizoaffective disorder, and 23.6% had bipolar disorder. All had a substance use disorder as defined by *DSM-III-R* criteria; 72.6% had an alcohol use disorder and 41.8% had a drug use disorder. Other than alcohol, the primary drugs of abuse at study entry were cannabis (38.9%) and cocaine (14.8%). Participants lived in a mix of small urban and rural areas. At study entry, 76% were receiving SSI or SSDI; 91% received these benefits by the end of the study.

Participants were asked to nominate for study participation the family member or friend who gave them the most assistance. Over the course of the study, trained research staff interviewed caregivers for 174 of the 203 participants at least once. The structured interview asked detailed questions about the type and amount of care and economic support provided. Caregivers were interviewed at 6-month intervals. One primary caregiver per participant reported amounts of time and money spent on behalf of the study participant by all family members. Because of a limited study budget and because most patients identified only one caregiver, comparisons of reports across caregivers for the same patient were not conducted. In all but three cases (cases in which primary caregivers changed), the same caregiver was interviewed throughout the study. The number of family interviews completed in each time period was as follows: 66 at study entry, 111 at 6 months, 141 at 12 months, 151 at 18 months, 142 at 24 months, 140 at 30 months, and 134 at 36 months. Missing data in early periods were due primarily to limited interviewer time rather than to client refusal. Families completed an average of 5.37 interviews, and 45 caregivers completed all seven interviews.

Due to the large amount of missing caregiver data for the study entry period, our analysis focused on the six periods after enrollment. Comparison of families who completed all interviews with those who completed fewer interviews showed no significant differences in average family expenditures or in average number of caregiving hours per month. Client-reported family contact was no different in periods of missing and nonmissing family reports. However, those with at least one, but fewer than four, interviews received lower amounts of direct care (Wilcoxon Rank Sum, $z = 7.9$, $p < 0.01$) and less economic support ($z = 2.5$, $p = 0.02$) from their families. Average family caregiving time and economic assistance, rather than total time and assistance, were used in subsequent analyses to address the potential bias associated with this difference.

The majority of caregivers (67%) were parents; 17% were siblings. Another 11.5% were grandparents, spouses, children, or other relatives; 4.5% were not related to the study participants. Caregivers ranged in age from 25 to 88 years ($M = 56$, $SD = 12$); 82% were women. In 18% of the cases, caregivers and study participants lived together. This percentage is similar to those reported for community-based studies in which family participation was not a criterion for selection (17–21%: Creer et al., 1982; Tessler & Gamache, 1994) but much lower than some hospital-based studies (40–65%: Goldman, 1982; Mueser et al., 2000) and others where membership in a family support group was required for study admission (30–45%: Franks, 1990, Mannion et al., 1996).

Family Expenditures and Caregiving Hours

Caregivers reported time they spent on behalf of the client in the previous 2 weeks on the following tasks: money management; transportation; speaking with mental health or law enforcement personnel; general care like cooking, cleaning, and assistance with grooming; illness related care such as assisting with medication compliance or responding to crises; participating in structured leisure activities; shopping; speaking with the client by telephone; and all other care. Family expenditures on behalf of the client were classified in the following categories: food and clothing; client's rent and utilities if client did not live with the family; client's share of family household expenses if the client lived with family; mental health, medical, and dental care; transportation; leisure activities; fines and property damage; and other family expenses. In-kind gifts such as food or clothing were assigned a monetary value and treated as family expenditures. For purposes of this analysis, average monthly family expenditures and average monthly caregiving hours during the study period (i.e., after enrollment) were computed for all valid data points. Reports for 2-week periods were multiplied by 2.16 to estimate monthly expenditures. Average expenditures and caregiving time for the various categories are reported in Tables 1 and 2.

Table 1. Hours of Caregiver Activities

Type of Activity	Caregiving Hours, Monthly Mean [1] *(SD)*	
Money management	1.00	(1.82)
Transportation	3.51	(4.96)
Talking with health service personnel	0.90	(1.82)
Talking with law enforcement personnel	0.23	(0.97)
General care	9.01	(18.52)
Illness care	6.71	(11.65)
Structured leisure activities	9.90	(13.80)
Shopping	1.47	(2.64)
Telephone conversations	2.90	(7.10)
Other contact	18.32	(23.83)

Note. *SD* = standard deviation.
[1] For all post enrollment study periods.

Table 2. Caregiver Expenditures and Client Contributions

Type of Expenditure	Monthly Mean,[1] 1995 US$	(SD)
Mental health care	2.13	(8.49)
Medical and dental care	12.42	(36.72)
Food and clothing	67.77	(86.98)
Rent, utilities, and telephone	27.07	(72.08)
Pocket money	32.34	(52.12)
Other	122.34	(260.75)
Transportation	39.28	(44.58)
Fines and property damage	6.33	(30.61)
Leisure activities	22.67	(36.83)
Family household expenses	32.58	(64.97)
Client's contribution to family	32.46	(101.52)

Note. *SD* = standard deviation.

[1] For all post enrollment study periods.

Substance Use Measures

Substance use outcomes were measured by combining information obtained from self-reports, case manager ratings of substance use, clinical records, and laboratory tests. Drug and alcohol use were rated separately on the following 5-point scale: 1 = abstinence, 2 = use without impairment, 3 = abuse, 4 = dependence, and 5 = severe dependence (Mueser et al., 1995). Interrater reliability, measured with intraclass correlations, was 0.94 for the alcohol use scale and 0.94 for the drug use scale.

Each participant was also given a Substance Abuse Treatment Scale (SATS) rating (McHugo et al., 1996) for each measurement period. Trained research staff who were blind to the treatment condition assigned SATS ratings. Ratings are based on Osher and Kofoed's (1989) model of treatment and recovery, in which 1 = early engagement, 2 = late engagement, 3 = early persuasion, 4 = late persuasion, 5 = early active treatment, 6 = late active treatment, 7 = early relapse prevention, and 8 = late relapse prevention. This rating combined alcohol and drug use outcomes in a single measure. Intraclass correlation for the SATS was 0.93.

Other Measures

Other explanatory variables used in the analyses included diagnosis as determined with the Structured Clinical Interview for the *DSM-III-R* (Spitzer et al., 1988); psychiatric symptoms as measured with the Expanded Brief Psychiatric Rating Scale (BPRS; Lukoff et al., 1986); gender; mental health outpatient costs as determined from provider records (Clark et al., 1998); average family income across all reporting periods, based on caregiver reports; participants' self-reported monthly income averaged across all study periods; and the Family Relations Scale from Lehman's Quality of Life Interview (QLI; Lehman, 1988). This scale is based on participant interviews and combines the following four questions concerning the participant's feelings about his or her family, each question beginning with "How do you feel about": Your family in general? How often you have contact with your family? The way you and your family act toward each other? The way things are in general between you and your family? Finally, we examined client reports of cash income received from family members in each study period.

Variables related to clients' demographic or psychiatric status were added to the analysis to account for factors other than family support that might affect substance use. Self-reported family income was included to differentiate the direct effects of family support from those that might be associated with family wealth. Adding outpatient treatment allowed us to examine the independent effects of formal treatment and family support on substance use.

Analysis Plan

For descriptive purposes, we used simple nonparametric statistics and *t* tests to compare characteristics of those who were abstinent at the end of the study with those who were not. To examine associations between the factors described above and recovery from substance use disorder, we constructed four regression equations. The first two models used ordinary least-squares (OLS) to predict change in treatment stage between study entry and the final measurement period. The second pair used OLS to predict the cumulative treatment score. Cumulative scores were computed by calculating the number of months a participant spent in each treatment stage, weighting months by the stage ranking, and summing these scores for the 3 years following study entry. In comparison to change scores, which emphasize the difference between beginning points and endpoints, cumulative scores give greater weight to participants who reduced substance use earlier in the study and sustained these reductions.

Because family expenses and hours of care were collinear, each of these variables was entered in a separate equation. Expenditures are included in models 1 and 3; caregiving hours are in models 2 and 4. The remaining explanatory variables were the same in all four models.

RESULTS

Participants advanced an average of 2.17 (*SD* = 1.85) treatment stages during the study, from a mean of 2.79 (engagement) to one of 4.95 (late persuasion or early active treatment). After 3 years of treatment, 15.9% of study participants (36) had been abstinent for at least 6 months.

Those who achieved abstinence were no more likely than others to report receiving SSI or SSDI ($\chi^2 = 0.82$, $df = 1$, ns) or to have a legally designated representative payee who managed their money ($\chi^2 = 1.15$, $df = 1$, ns). There were no differences in the percentage of clients who reported receiving any cash contributions from a family member ($\chi^2 = 0.59$, $df = 1$, ns). Exploration of the types of services used did not reveal significant differences between those who were abstinent and those who were not. Participants who achieved abstinence did not receive more assertive community treatment or case management services than nonabstainers ($t = 0.64$, df = 192, ns), nor did their families ($t = 0.13$, $df = 192$, ns). Scores on the QLI family relations scale and on its individual components were remarkably similar, with no differences between the groups at any of the seven measurement periods or across all periods ($t = 0.40$, $df = 192$, ns). Psychiatric symptom (BPRS) scores for abstainers and nonabstainers (44.2 [$SD = 13.5$] vs. 45.6 [$SD = 13.38$]) were not different at study entry (ns), but mean symptom scores were significantly different for the entire study period (38.9 [$SD = 8.35$] vs. 42.9 [$SD = 9.35$]; $t = 2.37$, $df = 198$, $p = 0.02$).

Family caregivers for abstainers were not significantly different from those of nonabstainers in age, income, co-residence, or relationship to the study participant.

All patients received at least some minimal care from a relative during the study. Most (97.5%) also received economic assistance. The percentage receiving financial help from family members within a given 6-month period ranged from 81% to 85%.

Families of those who had achieved abstinence at the 3-year mark consistently reported giving more financial assistance than did families of nonabstainers ($t = 2.34$, $df = 71.7$, $p = 0.02$; $z = 2.15$, $p = 0.03$). Mean expenses and mean caregiving hours for the study period were highly correlated (Spearman rank $r = 0.74$, $p = 0.001$). Other comparisons are shown in Table 3.

Regression results in Table 4 show that, taking initial treatment stage into account, clients who were women, who used more outpatient services, who had higher personal income, or who received more assistance from caregivers showed greater change in stage of treatment ratings (models 1 and 2) than did others. Negative coefficients for baseline stage of treatment indicate that those in higher stages at study entry changed significantly less than those in lower stages. In this equation, higher average family expenses on behalf of the study participant were associated with reductions in substance use ($p = 0.003$). More caregiving hours in model 2 were also significantly associated with substance use reduction ($p = 0.03$).

Findings were similar in models 3 and 4, which examined the association between cumulative treatment scores and the same independent variables used in models 1 and 2. When baseline substance use, the amount (cost) of outpatient services used during the study, and participant income were taken into account, family expenditures ($p = 0.02$) were significantly associated with better substance use outcomes. Direct family caregiving ($p = 0.16$) was not associated with cumulative change in substance use.

Standardized coefficients (betas) for family expenditures and treatment costs were, respectively, 0.23 and 0.17 in model 1 and 0.18 and 0.20 in model 2. This suggests that the comparative strength of association with substance use recovery was quite similar for family economic support and for treatment.

To demonstrate the robustness of findings, models 1 through 4 were repeated using logged versions of the dependent variables. These analyses explained a slightly lower percentage of the total variance; otherwise, results were very similar to those in the unlogged versions.

Table 3. Characteristics of Study Participants Abstinent and Nonabstinent at 36 Months [1]

Characteristic	Abstinent (SD)		Nonabstinent (SD)	
	(n = 31)		(n = 129)	
Age at study entry (yrs)	34.1	(8.94)	33.7	(8.02)
% male	63.8		76.4	
Diagnosis (% with schizophrenia spectrum disorders)*	63.8		77.6	
% assigned to assertive community treatment	52.8		50.9	
Average monthly income of client at study entry (1995 US$)	$790	($547)	$660	($355)
Average income of family during study period (1995 US$)	$26,719	($20,374)	$24,311	($19,210)
Beginning score on OLI family relations scale	4.26	(1.72)	4.42	(1.45)
Average family caregiving expenses per month** (1995 US$)	$398	($417)	$362	($482)
Average hours of family caregiving per month	51.36	(48.90)	49.68	(55.64)
Average BPRS score during study period*	38.9	(8.35)	42.9	(9.35)
Beginning stage of treatment[2]*	3.19	(1.19)	2.70	(0.78)
Beginning consensus alcohol rating[3]*	2.94	(1.20)	3.36	(0.98)
Beginning consensus drug rating[3]*	1.94	(1.23)	2.42	(1.26)

Note. BPRS = Expanded Brief Psychiatric Rating Scale; OLI = Quality of Life Interview; SD = standard deviation.

[1] Original study n = 203; table n is lower due to missing data for family caregiving and/or psychiatric symptoms.

[2] A higher score means less substance use.

[3] A higher score means more alcohol or drug use.

* Significantly different, $p < 0.05$;

** Significantly different, $p < 0.05$, after natural log transformation and with Mann-Whitney U Test.

Table 4. Substance Use Outcomes at 3 Years for Persons with Severe Mental Illness
$(n = 151)$[1]

Explanatory Variables	Change in Treatment Stage		Cumulative Treatment Score	
	(1) Expenditures	(2) Hours	(3) Expenditures	(4) Hours
Diagnosis (0 = schizophrenia spectrum, 1 = bipolar)	0.641	0.715*	25.548**	27.171**
Gender (0 = male, 1 = female)	0.612*	0.455	11.768	8.514
Baseline treatment stage rating	-0.601 **	-0.613**	17.763**	17.617**
Mental health outpatient costs (log)	0.349*	0.405*	11.139*	11.895**
Average monthly family expenditures (log)	0.318**	—	6.977*	—
Average monthly family caregiving hours (log)	—	0.006*		0.102
Family income ($1,000s)	0.003	0.008	-0.007	0.083
Participant income ($1,000s)	0.172*	0. 162*	5.211**	5.033**
Adjusted R²	0.169	0.142	0.255	0.232

[1] Original study $n = 203$; table n is lower due to missing data for family caregiving and/or psychiatric symptoms. Family expenses and family caregiving hours are entered separately to avoid co-linearity. Regression coefficients are unstandardized.
* $p < 0.05$; ** $p < 0.01$

The same set of explanatory variables employed in the regression models were used to predict BPRS scores. These models, which are not shown, were poor predictors of symptom change, accounting for a small amount of variance. They did not show significant associations between family support and psychiatric symptoms.

The largest expense categories were food and clothing in second place and in first, a general category that was composed of relatively large and infrequent expenditures, such as car repairs. Transportation was the third largest category, followed by family household expenses attributable to the client; pocket money; rent, utilities, and telephone; and leisure activities. Mental health care was the lowest category of expenditure.

The categories in which caregivers spent the most time were "other contact" (which often included unstructured leisure activities) and structured leisure activities, followed closely by general caregiving (providing meals, cleaning, assisting with personal hygiene), caregiving related to illness (e.g., assisting with medications or with crises), transportation, and telephone conversations.

Relatively few clients (36.9%) reported receiving cash assistance from family members. The number reporting such assistance declined slightly, from 72 at study entry to 64 at the end of 3 years. Less than 10% of the financial assistance given by families was described as "pocket money," defined as small cash gifts for general purposes.

DISCUSSION

Assistance from family and other informal caregivers was associated with reduced substance use in people with dual disorders. Direct financial assistance was a stronger and more consistent predictor of change than was the average amount of informal care given. Greater amounts of family economic assistance and higher outpatient treatment costs during the study period were related to reduction in substance use and to lower cumulative substance use over 3 years.

Although family expenses and caregiving hours are highly correlated, the former were more consistently associated with reductions in substance use than the latter. Assistance in securing basic necessities, primarily through in-kind contributions, may have a greater impact on substance use than does nonpecuniary help from family and friends. The implication is that clients with dual disorders can address substance use problems more effectively when their basic economic needs are met.

An alternate interpretation of the abstinence findings might be that families are more willing to support a relative who is engaged in substance abuse treatment. However, the effects of family support remained strong when baseline stage of treatment ratings were taken into account in the analyses of change and cumulative substance abuse treatment scores. This suggests that family support is not simply a function of how well the client is doing in treatment.

The positive association between substance use reduction and economic assistance is particularly interesting in light of concerns among treatment providers that clients will use such contributions to purchase alcohol or other drugs. Abstainers were no more likely to have a representative payee than were nonabstainers, but families may have played an informal role as resource managers. Although the data do not allow a definitive analysis of family-reported cash versus in-kind contributions, the low frequency of cash assistance reported by clients and the relatively small amount of pocket money reported by families suggest that most family economic assistance took the form of in-kind contributions, which would be more difficult to convert to substances of abuse.

Formal treatment providers may have helped families manage clients' substance abuse more effectively. It is difficult to determine how much treatment providers influenced family caregivers. Treatment teams were trained to help clients and families manage money, and some families attended psychoeducation groups that included information on substance abuse. This assistance may have helped families manage their involvement with clients more effectively and avoid "enabling" behaviors.

It is important to note that the amount of family expenditures, not family income, was a significant predictor of outcomes. Many of the families had relatively low incomes but spent a high proportion of them in support of a relative with dual disorders (Clark, 1994). While spending is certainly limited by total income, family income did not appear to be an important factor at the levels of support observed in this sample. Higher personal income for clients was associated with greater reductions in substance use.

There were no clear differences in families of abstainers and nonabstainers. The two family groups were quite similar in age, kinship, gender, and baseline measures of family relations.

Although it was associated with less substance use, direct family support appeared to be unrelated to improvement in psychiatric symptoms. One interpretation is that psychiatric symptoms are more intractable than substance use in a sample that is receiving adequate treatment.

Participants with schizophrenia appeared to have lower rates of abstinence and improvement on substance use measures than those with bipolar disorders. These results suggest that we need more research on how specific psychiatric diagnoses, and the associated symptoms, affect response to substance abuse treatment. Such studies should include a larger number of people with bipolar disorder than was available in this sample.

The data have some limitations. Even though we focused on post-baseline periods where higher percentages of family caregivers were interviewed, missing data on family caregiving may have affected results. We cannot completely rule out the presence of undetected bias.

A number of analyses were conducted, particularly in analyzing the effects of abstinence. It is possible that some statistically significant relationships were due to chance. However, the association between family economic assistance and substance use reduction appears to be robust.

All study participants received significant amounts of high quality, publicly funded mental health treatment. Results may be different in areas where access to formal care is more restricted. Homogeneity of ethnicity and the mix of urban and rural settings could also affect the generalizability of these findings to groups with different characteristics. Additional research is certainly needed to replicate these findings in other locations with different populations before firm conclusions can be drawn.

CONCLUSIONS

The findings suggest that both direct family economic support and engagement in targeted treatment play an important role in helping people with dual disorders reduce substance use. The results highlight the often ignored fact that access to economic resources and informal assistance can have a significant impact on clinical outcomes. People without family support are at a significant disadvantage and may require more formal treatment services and public assistance than those whose relatives give such support.

More research on how family support affects the long-term recovery and well-being of people with SMI is clearly needed. If the effects observed in this study are substantiated in others, then a critical re-examination of treatment policies and practices may be in order. Current practices, at best, tend to view involvement of family caregivers as an adjunct to clinical improvement. At worst, family involvement may be seen as a barrier to achieving independence. These findings suggest that concrete family support is far from a barrier to improvement. In fact, it may be an important contributor to recovery from substance use disorders. Helping to support and sustain family caregivers could be one of the most important functions that formal treatment providers can serve.

REFERENCES

American Psychiatric Association. (1987). *DSM-III-R: Diagnostic and statistical manual of mental disorders. 3rd ed., revised.* Washington, DC: APA.

Blankertz, L. E., & Cnann, R. A. (1994). Assessing the impact of two residential programs for dually diagnosed homeless individuals. *Social Services Review, 68,* 536–560.

Carpentier, N., Lesage, A., Goulet, I., Lalonde, P., & Renaud, M. (1992). Burden of care of families not living with young schizophrenic relatives. *Hospital and Community Psychiatry, 43,* 38–43.

Caton, C. L. M., Shrout, P. E., Eagle, P. F., Opler, L. A., Felix, A., & Dominguez, B. (1994). Risk factors for homelessness among schizophrenic men: A case-control study. *American Journal of Public Health, 84*(2), 265–270.

Caton, C. L. M., Shrout, P. E., Eagle, R. E., Opler, L. A., Felix A., & Dominguez, B. (1995). Risk factors for homelessness among women with schizophrenia. *American Journal of Public Health, 85,* 1153–1156.

Clark, R. E. (1994). Family costs associated with severe mental illness and substance use. *Hospital and Community Psychiatry, 45*(8), 808–813.

Clark, R. E., & Drake, R. E. (1994). Expenditures of time and money by families of people with severe mental illness and substance use disorders. *Community Mental Health Journal, 30*(2), 145–163.

Clark, R. E., Ricketts, S. K., & McHugo, G. J. (1999). Legal system involvement and costs for persons in treatment for severe mental illness and substance use disorders. *Psychiatric Services, 50*(5), 641–647.

Clark, R. E., Teague, G. B., Ricketts, S. K., Bush, P. W., Xie, H., McGuire, T. G., Drake, R. E., McHugo, G. J., Keller, A. M., & Zubkoff, M. (1998). Cost-effectiveness of assertive community treatment versus standard case management for persons with co-occurring severe mental illness and substance use disorders. *Health Services Research, 33*(5), 1283–1306.

Cournos, F., Empfield, M., Horwath, E., McKinnon, K., Meyet, I., Schrage, H., Currie, C., & Agosin, B. (1991). HIV seroprevalence among patients admitted to two psychiatric hospitals. *American Journal of Psychiatry, 148,* 1225–1230.

Creer, C., Sturt, E., & Wykes, T. (1982). The role of relatives. In Wing, J.K., (Ed.) Long term community care: Experience in a London Borough. [Monograph]. *Psychological Medicine (Suppl 2), 29*–39.

Dickey, B., & Azeni, H. (1996). Persons with dual diagnosis of substance abuse and major mental illness: Their excess costs of psychiatric care. *American Journal of Public Health, 86*(7), 973–977.

Dixon, L., McNary, S., & Lehman, A. (1995). Substance abuse and family relationships of persons with severe mental illness. *American Journal of Psychiatry, 152,* 456–458.

Drake, R. E., McHugo, G. J., Clark, R. E., Teague, G. B., Xie, H., Miles, K., & Ackerson, T. H. (1998a). A clinical trial of assertive community treatment for patients with co-occurring severe mental illness and substance use disorder. *American Journal of Orthopsychiatry, 64*(2), 201–215.

Drake, R. E., Mercer-McFadden, C., Mueser, K. T., McHugo, G. J., & Bond, G. R. (1998b). A review of integrated mental health and substance abuse treatment for patients with dual disorders. *Schizophrenia Bulletin, 24*(4), 589–608.

Franks, D. D. (1990). Economic contribution of families caring for persons with severe and persistent mental illness. *Administration and Policy in Mental Health, 18,* 9–18.

Goldman, H. H. (1982). Mental illness and family burden: A public health perspective. *Hospital and Community Psychiatry, 33*(7), 557–560.

Hoenig, J., & Hamilton, M. W. (1966). The schizophrenic patient in the community and his effect on the household. *International Journal of Social Psychiatry, 12*(3), 165–176.

Hogarty, G. E., Anderson, C. M., Reiss, D. J., Kornblith, S. J., Greenwald, D. R, Javna, C. D., & Madonia, M. J. (1986). Family psychoeducation, social skills training, and maintenance chemotherapy in the aftercare treatment of schizophrenia. *Archives of General Psychiatry, 43,* 633–642.

Jerrell, J. M., Hu, T., & Ridgely, M. S. (1994). Cost-effectiveness of substance disorder interventions for people with severe mental illness. *Journal of Mental Health Administration, 21*(3), 283–297.

Kashner, T. M., Rader, L. E., Rodell, D. E., Beck, C. M., Rodell, L. R., & Muller, K. (1991). Family characteristics, substance abuse, and hospitalization patterns of patients with schizophrenia. *Hospital and Community Psychiatry, 42,* 195–197.

Kavanagh, D. J. (1992). Recent developments in expressed emotion and schizophrenia. *British Journal of Psychiatry, 160,* 601–620.

Kivlahan, D. R., Heiman, J. R., Wright, R. C., Mundt, J. W., & Shupe, J. A. (1991). Treatment cost and rehospitalization rate in schizophrenic outpatients with a history of substance abuse. *Hospital and Community Psychiatry, 42,* 609–614.

Kochar, S., & Scott, C. G. (1995). Disability patterns among SSI recipients. *Social Security Bulletin, 58,* 3–14.

Lehman, A. F. (1988). A quality of life interview for the chronically mentally ill. *Evaluation and Program Planning, 11,* 51–62.

Lukoff, K., Liberman, R. P., & Nuechterlein, K. H. (1986). Symptom monitoring in the rehabilitation of schizophrenic patients. *Schizophrenia Bulletin, 12*(4), 578–602.

Mannion, E., Meisel, M., Solomon, P., & Draine, J. (1996). A comparative analysis of families with mentally ill adult relatives: Support group members versus non-members. *Psychiatric Rehabilitation Journal, 20*(1), 43–50.

McFarlane, W., Lukens, E., Link, B., Dushay, R., Deakins, S.A., Newmark, M., Dunne, E.J., Horen, B., & Toran, J. (1994). Multiple-family groups and psychoeducation in the treatment of schizophrenia. *Archives of General Psychiatry, 52,* 679–687.

McHugo, G. J., Drake, R. E., Burton, H. L., & Ackerson, H. (1996). A scale for assessing the stage of substance abuse treatment in persons with severe mental illness. *Journal of Nervous and Mental Disease, 183,* 762–767.

Mueser, K. T., Drake, R. E., Clark, R. E., McHugo, G. J., Mercer-McFadden, C., & Ackerson, T. H. (1995). *Evaluating substance abuse in persons with severe mental illness.* Cambridge, MA: Human Services Research Institute.

Mueser, K. T., Goodman, L. B., Trumbetta, S. L., Rosenbert, S. D., Osher, F. C., Vidaver, R., Auciello, P., & Foy, D. W. (1998). Trauma and posttraumatic stress disorder in severe mental illness. *Journal of Consulting and Clinical Psychology, 66,* 493–499.

Mueser, K. T., Yartiold, P. R., Rosenbert, S. D., Swett, C. Miles, K. M., & Hill, D. (2000). Substance use disorder in hospitalized severely mentally ill psychiatric patients: Prevalence, correlates and subgroups. *Schizophrenia Bulletin, 26*(1), 179–192.

Osher, F. C., & Kofoed, L. L. (1989). Treatment of patients with psychiatric and psychoactive substance abuse disorders. *Hospital and Community Psychiatry, 40,* 1025–1030.

Owen, R. R., Fischer, E. P., Booth, B. M., & Cuffel, B. J. (1996). Medication non-compliance and substance abuse among patients with schizophrenia. *Psychiatric Services, 47,* 853–858.

Regier, D. A., Farmer, M. E., Rae, D. S., Locke, B. Z., Keith, S. J., Judd, L. L., & Goodwin, F. K. (1990). Comorbidity of mental disorders with alcohol and other drug abuse: Results from the Epidemiologic Catchment Area (ECA) Study. *Journal of the American Medical Association, 264,* 2511–2518.

Rice, D. P., & Miller, L. S. (1996). The economic burden of schizophrenia: Conceptual and methodological issues, and cost estimates. In M. Moscarelli, A. Rupp & N. Sartorius (Eds.), *Schizophrenia: Volume I in the handbook of mental health economics and health policy.* West Sussex, Great Britain: John Wiley and Sons.

Solomon, P., & Draine, J. (1995). Subjective burden among family members of mentally ill adults: Relation to stress, coping, and adaptation. *American Journal of Orthopsychiatry, 65,* 419–427.

Spitzer, R. L., Williams, J. B., & Gibbon, M. (1988). *Structured Clinical Interview for DSM-III-R-Patient Version (SCID-P).* New York: Biometric Research Department, New York State Psychiatric Institute.

Steadman, H. J., Mulvey, E. P., Monahan, J., Robbins, P. C., Appelbaum, P. S., Grisso, T., Roth, L. H., & Silver, E. (1998). Violence by people discharged from acute psychiatric inpatient facilities and by others in the same neighborhoods. *Archives of General Psychiatry, 55,* 393–404.

Stevens, B. C. (1972). Dependence of schizophrenic patients on elderly relatives. *Psychological Medicine, 21*(1), 17–32.

Tessler, R., & Gamache, G. (1994). Continuity of care, residence, and family burden in Ohio. *Milbank Quarterly, 72,* 149–169.

Acknowledgments
This project was supported by grants MH-00839, MH-46072, and MH-47567 from the National Institute of Mental Health and AA-08341 from the National Institute on Alcohol Abuse and Alcoholism, and by the New Hampshire Division of Mental Health and Developmental Services. Special thanks to study participants with dual disorders and their families.

The Cultural Context: Families Coping with Severe Mental Illness

Laurene Y. Finley

At the time of original publication, Laurene Y. Finley, PhD, was an assistant professor in the Department of Psychiatry, Division of Behavioral Healthcare Sciences at Allegheny University of the Health Sciences, Philadelphia, Pennsylvania.

This article was published previously in the *Psychiatric Rehabilitation Journal*, 1998, 21(3), 230–240, and is reprinted with permission.

Abstract: The unique needs of families from different ethnic and cultural backgrounds coping with a member with severe mental illness are often neglected. All families must be recognized, understood, and supported within their sociocultural context. This article provides an overview of research on coping mastery among ethnic caregivers. Obstacles encountered by these families that may affect their participation in current family support group models are discussed. Practical family and provider self assessment guidelines are recommended to facilitate mutual understanding of value similarities, and differences. Examples of alternative, and innovative culturally compatible approaches to enhance partnership, and support of families are described.

INTRODUCTION

Families throughout the world must adjust to the onset of a psychiatric disability and its resulting complications and challenges (Lefley, 1985). In over two thirds of the world's countries, families are an essential resource to members who have either a physical or a mental illness, providing general social and psychological support in ways perceived as alien in western service delivery (Bell, 1982; Lefley, 1985). Family members may be perceived as allies and integral to the treatment process. They may travel long distances and live in close proximity to the hospital in order to "wait out" the hospitalization of a family member. They may also participate in the feeding, nursing, and medication monitoring of the mentally ill family member (Bell, 1982). In the Philippines, persons who stay with their relatives while in the hospital are called "watchers" (Higginbotham, 1979). The "watcher" family role has been emulated in more traditional psychiatric systems as a model for conducting discussion and education with families.

There is supportive evidence that the prognosis for severe and persistent mental illness may be better in more traditional cultures with extensive kinship systems as compared to cultures with more nuclear family structures (Kleinman & Good, 1985; Sartorius, Joblensky, & Korten, 1986; Waxler, 1979). A critical factor contributing to the intercultural differences could well be the view extended family members have towards the caretaking role.

Caretaking is often perceived as a valued involvement providing psychological, emotional, and economic buffers that differ from the western, nuclear family experience (Lefley, 1987; 1990).

Over the last 15 to 20 years, the family therapy literature has promulgated the importance of applying a "multicultural lens" to the study of all families (Ho, 1987; McGoldrick, Pearce, & Giordano, 1982; McGoldrick, Giordano, & Pearce, 1996). Within a contextualist theoretical framework we understand that behavior *cannot* be understood outside of the context in which it occurs (Szapocznik & Kurtines, 1993). Consumers, therefore, are best understood within the context of their families; families are understood within their cultural context; the culture within the broader, diverse, complex, pluralistic society (Szapocznik & Kurtines, 1993). Cultural forces are always impacting on the way in which family members interact with one another and with other systems at large.

The definition of "family support" and the design of innovative support models, therefore, must occur within the context of the family's culture (Alston & Turner, 1994) and are specifically mediated by factors such as family background, ethnicity, ethnic identity, cultural affiliation, socioeconomic status, and acculturation. Views towards mental health, attitudes about mental health services, preferences concerning interventions, types of medications, and providers may all be culturally determined. Examples of variations in worldview that may influence not only family perception of formal and informal support but provides perceptions of families are:

- *Family structure.* Who is considered family? Family structures differ cross-culturally. Extended family and kinship networks may include a variety of persons both related and nonrelated. "Play aunts," "play uncles," godparents, neighbors, boyfriends, and members of the church family may all be part of an ethnic family's kinship system. Members of this system may be available for support of the family coping with a member with severe and persistent mental illness.

- *Communication and presentation styles.* Culturally determined presentation styles often affect the manner in which family issues and psychological distress may be presented. Some families may be more verbally expressive, open, and self-disclosing; others more closed. Cultures also dictate different norms about nonverbal behaviors, such as eye contact and distances in personal space. Often incorrect motives and behavioral assessments are attributed to presentation styles which differ from those of the provider.

  Studies have examined the significance of expressed emotion (EE) in the communication among family members, to relapse prevention and rehospitalization of the person with severe mental illness (Brown, Birley, & Wing, 1972; Leff & Vaughn, 1985; Vaughn & Leff, 1976; Lefley, 1992). Family members have been particularly critical of these studies, feeling that they are being held responsible for the relapse of their family member and that other powerful, environmental factors, not accounted for by these studies, may contribute to a consumer's relapse. Additional caution must be exercised in applying these outcome studies to ethnic families because they do not seem to reflect the cultural and communication styles which exist in many family structures (Lefley, 1992).

- *Problem solving, decision making, and conflict resolution.* Some ethnic groups, such as African-Americans, Italian-Americans, and Latinos, tend to emphasize cooperation among the family and community group in times of distress (Randall-David, 1989). Family members may be highly involved in the decision-making process, conferring with other members and sanctioning or not sanctioning recommended forms of treatment. Learning more about the family's processes and identifying these lay members who are most involved are critical to any development of a family-professional partnership.

- *Role expectations.* Functions and responsibilities of family members may or may not be traditionally ascribed according to gender and/or age of family members. In less acculturated Latinos, for example, the male may be the key decision maker in matters outside of the home. Females may be primarily responsible for childrearing and education, functioning as mediators between fathers and children (Guarnaccia, et al., 1992). In African-American families, one might expect to find flexibility of roles within the family. Decision making may rest with either the male or female head of household. In families in which several generations often reside in the same household, the seniors or elders may hold great influence in family decision making.

- *Help-seeking attitudes and behavior.* Strong religious and spiritual beliefs may affect conceptions about illness and health. Mental illnesses may be perceived as the "devil's work," possession by evil spirits, caused by witchcraft, or punishment for disobeying God. Ethnic family members may not make clear demarcations between physical illness, emotional illness, and spiritual complaints.

"Si Dios quiere" (if God wishes) or "Que dios nos bendiga"(may God bless us) are common responses heard among Latino families, for example, caring for a member with persistent mental illness

(Guarnaccia, Parra, Deschamps, Milstein, & Argiles, 1992). These refrains reflect the hopes, frustrations, and religious beliefs that may be experienced in dealing with a deeply troubling illness that frequently defies explanation.

Home remedies, folk medicine and/or folk healers, dependence on religious leaders, and prayer are different types of approaches ethnic family members may utilize either singly or collectively alongside biomedicine. The following basic assumptions underscore our learning about ethnic families (Alston & Turner, 1994; Szapocznik & Kurtines, 1993):

- Families are embedded in a systemic context;

- Ethnicity and culture are powerful determinants of family norms and patterns;

- Embedded within cultures are potential sources of strength, which can be used by families as resources for recovery and a sense of well-being (Finley, 1997);

- Engagement and involvement of ethnic families requires the successful acknowledgement and utilization of these strengths;

- Every family has a cultural context to be valued, understood, and explored.

UNDERSTANDING FAMILIES IN A MULTICULTURAL CONTEXT

Group membership for many ethnic families may be a source of pride, cohesion, safety, and a buffer against psychological stressors in times of crisis, loss, stress, or disability. Families will rely upon these strengths, coping skills, and solutions learned from the familial, cultural context (Devore & Schlesinger, 1981). On the other hand, the family's interaction with the broader, pluralistic, societal context may, at times, contribute to tension and confusion.

At least five struggles, either singly or in combination, may be faced by these families:

1. economic survival;

2. overcoming negative societal, group stereotypes;

3. development of a clear sense of ethnic identity and heritage;

4. reconciliation of tensions stemming from acculturation of the values and behaviors of the mainstream culture; and

5. continual adaptations and responses to a circular feedback process, that is, the "victim-system" (Boyd-Franklin, 1989; Chestang, 1972; Pierce, 1970; Pinderhughes, 1982).

A by-product of racism, poverty, and oppression, the victim-system strongly limits access to the opportunity structure, which in turn limits achievement and skill attainment by members of the ethnic group. These limitations in turn produce poverty. Poverty places undue stress on familial relationships such that, over time, the family's capacity to perform social roles adequately and to support their communities may become restricted. Families may be challenged by the multiplicative effects of stigma, resulting from one or more co-occurring illnesses of a family member and a devalued "minority" status within the broader society.

All families that come for mental health services bring their unique sociocultural histories. Though not all ethnic families are trapped in the victim system, those that are may also bring with them an additional worldview in which the surrounding environment and its institutions are perceived as hostile, dangerous, and unpredictable. This "cultural paranoia" (Mirowsky, 1985), which is a protective survival mechanism, may present itself as a family being overly sensitive, too racially or ethnically conscious or sensitive, or unduly suspicious of providers and the systems which they represent. These families are frequently wary of receiving help from outsiders. Perceiving these outsiders as intrusive or fearing that providers may perceive them as weak may explain the reluctance of many ethnic families to work with persons outside the nuclear and extended family. Neighbors and Jackson (1984), for example, found that a majority of African-American respondents were more likely to make contact with their informal social network than with more formal mainstream institutions.

ETHNIC CAREGIVERS AND COPING MASTERY

Ethnic groups in the United States vary widely in cultural heritage. Values in these groups, however, seem to be closer to those of the more traditional cultures found in developing countries. These cultures tend to be more group and family oriented, interdependent, and less individualistic than members of the American mainstream (Lefley, 1990).

Research on the role of family involvement in mental health is emerging in the United States, though few studies have examined the specific needs of ethnic families, the ways in which they cope with a member who has a severe mental illness, differential perceptions of caregiving duties and caregiving burden, and the patterns or differences in use of informal supports (Adebimpe, 1994; Cook, Pickett, & Cohler, 1997; Pickett, Damian, Vraniak, Cook, & Cohler, 1993). The research that exists focuses on families caring for relatives with long standing illnesses such as severe and persistent mental illness and dementia among older adults.

The limited research has also included comparisons between African-American and white caregivers. In a couple of instances, attempts have been made to include Latino families; either sample size limitations or no significant differences were found in the perceived burden between Latino and white caregivers in these studies (Stueve, Vine, & Struening, 1997).

Investigations of the differential self-perceptions of blacks and whites caring for a relative with severe and persistent mental illness found that black parents challenged the stereotype that they were more likely to cope poorly and have lower self-esteem (Pickett et al., 1993; Ulbrich, Warheit, & Zimmerman, 1989). Generally, black parents, in comparison with white parents, seemed to have an ability to cope and feel better about themselves; this seemed to correlate with the number of resources and amount of experience they had in dealing with their child's mental illness. Though black families may live with greater life strains than whites, in general a more pragmatic attitude seemed to allow them to maintain an outlook whereby mental illness may be seen as just another life challenge to which they must adjust.

There has been some support for ethnically bound differences in the prevalence of depression among caregivers, though research participants were caregivers of elderly persons with dementia (Mintzer & Macera, 1992). It does appear, however, that different kinds of attributions and expectations may be made by ethnic caregivers regarding care of relatives with long-term illnesses.

Ethnic differences have also been noted in systematic studies of what caretakers do and how burdensome the family members may find their roles. White and African-American parents report equivalent caregiving obligations and responsibilities. The basically equivalent duties, however, are perceived as a generally less stressful burden for blacks than for whites (Horwitz & Reinhard, 1995; Stueve et al., 1997). Perhaps the greater involvement of African-Americans in their extended kinship system may make caring for an adult child with severe mental illness more normative and less stressful (Angel & Angel, 1993).

In a study that also considered differences in caregiving among siblings of persons with severe mental illness, important differences between blacks and whites were also noted. Blacks reported more caregiving duties and yet also viewed these responsibilities as less burdensome (Horwitz & Reinhard, 1995). The higher levels of perceived stigma regarding mental illness existing among white parents could have exacerbated their experience of stress and sense of burden (Horwitz & Reinhard, 1995).

These findings are perplexing in light of the systemic and institutional sociocultural conditions that daily impinge upon caregivers of non-majority groups (e.g., discrimination, a greater degree of poverty). The following is a summary of several explanations that might account for these differential results (Horwitz & Reinhard, 1985; Lefley, 1985, 1990; Picket et al., 1993; Stueve et al., 1997):

- Attributions about illness, religious involvement, and social support may provide protective mechanisms;

- Members of some ethnic groups may be more practiced in attending to the needs of the extended family network, such that helping kin is highly valued. This normative context may help to diminish the emotional costs of caregiving;

- Ethnic caregivers may have greater access to their social support networks;

- Reliance on strong religious or spiritual beliefs such as prayer, the minister, folk healers, or the congregation may provide familial supports in a context which is more culturally congruent (Delgado & Humm-Delgado, 1982; Griffith, Young, & Smith, 1984). Pickett and colleagues, (1993) point out, however, that simply having more numbers in one's familial and church network may not always mitigate against stress for some ethnic group members. The reciprocal nature of the relationships may sometimes create additional problems contributing a to reluctance to utilize these informal supports;

- Members of different ethnic subgroups may offer alternative interpretations of psychiatric symptoms that are less stigmatizing and emphasize more normal social roles, demonstrating a capacity to integrate the person with the disability into family life (Lefley, 1990).

In summary, caregiving is shaped by multiple factors, with different groups experiencing different consequences or differences in how distress is handled. Ethnic families who are caregivers do have a story to tell that fairly consistently differs from families from the majority culture. Application of innovative methods to explore the unique strengths of ethnic families should provide a greater understanding of how culturally adaptive styles might be used effectively in working with different ethnic groups (Pickett et al., 1993). It should not be inferred, however, that members of different ethnic groups are necessarily more resilient or less distressed with caregiving demands (Stueve et al., 1997). There may be multiple ways in which a family caregiver's psychological well-being may be affected. Finding differences between any set of ethnic groups on one outcome does not assure that similar differences will be found on other measures (Stueve et al., 1997).

BARRIERS TO THE PARTICIPATION OF ETHNIC FAMILIES IN MAINSTREAM SUPPORT GROUPS

It is likely that if families from the dominant culture experience difficulties with the mental health system, ethnic and culturally diverse family needs are neglected as well (Solomon, 1988; Spaniol & Zipple, 1988). Though family support programs have been increasing, many mutual support or self-help groups have been less successful in the recruitment of families who are not middle-class, Anglo-American, or not just female participants (Borkman, 1990; Guarnaccia, et al., 1992). It is possible that underutilization of these programs stems from their incompatibility with the values and characteristics of various ethnic families. Pernell-Arnold and Finley (1992) suggest potential barriers to those programs wanting to incorporate ethnic group membership.

1. The expectation that some ethnic family members may want or feel that they need currently existing family support models may be incorrect. It is possible that these families may be quite content with the level of support derived from their kinship system. Research suggests that contact with the informal social network is more likely and that some families may utilize the network either first or in combination with professional supports (Neighbors & Jackson, 1984). We need to find out more about how the social network functions as a referral system, the types of problems taken to the network, and how informal helpers attempt to resolve these problems (Neighbors & Jackson, 1984).

2. Current family support models may not adequately simulate the cultural patterns of support with which ethnic families may be familiar. Programs may be held in settings outside of ethnic neighborhoods or communities in places where people either feel uncomfortable and therefore either avoid attending or attend infrequently. For example, holding meetings in a mental health agency setting may be stigmatizing for some families.

3. Organizational structure and leadership styles may not be compatible with those experienced in more community settings. For example, some groups may be accustomed to formal structures; others with a more informal, relational style. If Arab family members attended a family support group, for example, in which a woman presided, where children were excluded, food was not served, or prayer not initiated

either at the start of or close of the meeting, cultural dissonance might be experienced by these family members. Club Sociales, as another example, are home town clubs in Puerto Rican communities where the organizational structure fulfills multiple functions such as recreation, orientation for individuals new to the community, social services, and employment (Delgado & Humm-Delgado, 1982). The extent to which the family group is perceived as compatible or incompatible with these functions and needs, may affect Latino participation.

4. The content of meetings may not address the needs of ethnic members. Perceived lack of practicality, type of presentation styles, and a business focus rather than a relationship orientation may all be impediments to members from different ethnic communities.

5. Social activities sponsored by a mainstream support group may not always be appreciated by members of a different class or cultural background. For example, a support group fund-raising event featuring cocktails and a night out at the symphony may not appeal to some African-American participants with different food and music preferences.

6. Member composition at meetings in which only one or two ethnic family members may be present may contribute to feelings of alienation, intimidation, and isolation. Environments may not be perceived as safe or welcoming to the sharing of the family member's experiences. Perceptions of any incompatibility based on socioeconomic status, life style, or family organization may result in decreased comfortability.

7. Not unlike numerous other institutions within the mainstream culture (e.g., churches, schools, mental health programs, country clubs, and corporations) family support group leaders and members are frequently uncertain and uncomfortable with diversity. They may not have the knowledge or information required to address issues of cultural competence in their group sessions and programs. Training in these areas has been infrequent, if occurring at all. Programs desirous of change, with little preparation, are often faced with the task, perceived as insurmountable, of creating a milieu supportive of diversity with few existing prototypes or internal/external supports.

8. Ethnic group members may, indeed, be interested in family supports but find themselves in situations with competing survival demands, such as child care, transportation needs, and/or working two or more

jobs. Any or all of these may present potential obstacles not addressed by many family support program models.

9.   Some ethnic group members may be sensitive to either direct or indirect forms of perceived oppression and discrimination, that is, acts or institutional procedures that may help to create or perpetuate continued advantages of the majority group. There may be a level of mistrust that emanates from prior negative experiences with social systems that is easily projected onto new situations where either intentional or unintentional slights may occur.

10. Mainstream groups may fail to reach out aggressively and innovatively to ethnic families. Many programs do not really know how to access ethnic communities and sometimes are without the time and resources to do so.

BRIDGING CULTURAL GAPS WITH ETHNIC FAMILIES: A MULTIDIMENSIONAL APPROACH

Normative transactions in ethnic families are frequently subject to negative misinterpretation by providers from different cultures (Lefley, 1985). A multidimensional approach to culture is required, which outlines the various contexts that can influence value formation and that can provide a framework for assessment of both shared and different world views between the provider and family members. Such an approach can assist providers in synthesizing family value orientations into a "cultural snapshot" of each family that can then be contrasted with the provider's own "snapshot" (Karrer, 1993). Clarified commonalties can be used as "bridge builders"; differences can be used as opportunities to challenge and help expand views and ways in which to conceptualize cross-cultural impact.

The following multidimensional approach outlines eight separate dimensions. Though each one is important, it may or may not be salient for a given ethnic family (Karrer, 1993). For example, for some families religious values may be more salient; for others, acculturation issues may be predominant. Variations may exist not only across these dimensions but also within each.

Socio-environmental context. This dimension includes identification of the family's nationality; appraisal of external socioeconomic stressors, barriers, and obstacles to achievement; and the family's relationship and familiarity with mainstream cultural norms useful for accessing required goods and resources.

Kinship network. Identification of both biologically related kin as well as "fictive" kinship relationships (i.e., close friends, babysitters, neighbors, boarding home operators, stepfathers, boyfriends, and grandparents, in addition to members of the "church family," such as ministers and deacons) begins to answer the question, "who is family?" Essentially these kin relationships are potentially each family member's social network system, which can be relied upon for mutual aid or support in times of need or crises. These persons may live either within the household, the neighborhood, the country of origin, or throughout the United States.

Gathering information on the family's perceptions of their problems, and assessing how decisions are made and problems solved facilitates the engagement process. Randall-David (1989) recommends asking the following questions in order to learn more about family perceptions: "What do you think is your problem?" "What do you think caused your problem?" "What do you think that your sickness does to your body?" "What type of treatment do you think you should receive?"

Perceived gender role responsibilities and expectations must be understood. It should be determined if the gender roles are more traditional or contemporary.

Cultural values and beliefs. The provider attempts to gather information about the attitudes, values, norms, and beliefs that guide the family. Examples are beliefs about illness and wellness; help-seeking values and behaviors (i.e., who the family seeks out when there is an illness); gender roles; attitudes towards caregiving roles and responsibilities; communication styles; and problem-solving and decision-making styles. Interdependence as a family value (i.e., the extent the family holds allegiance to one another and the group) is weighed against the value of individual, personal liberties (Karrer, 1993). Description of religious beliefs, and rites or rituals that may affect family attitudes should also be identified.

Cultural transitions and acculturation. It is important to understand the history of the family, and its key transitions from one culture to the next (Jacobson, 1988; Karrer, 1993). Determining factors precipitating these transitions, length of time in this country, and past and present socioeconomic status are all critical in learning more about the family's adaptational and survival styles in adjusting to the mainstream culture.

Language. Linguistic patterns are closely related to ethnicity and culture. Language provides not only a means of communication but also a cognitive structuring of the world that is linked to one's worldview, identity, self-concept, and self-esteem. What language does the family utilize in formal and informal situations? Families may be proficient in using a language for less formal, interpersonal encounters, for example, but not in formal family conferences with multiple service providers present. Do family members "conveniently" code switch, that is, possess differential skills in two languages but alternate between them, even within a single sentence? Code switching might occur when family members are under emotional stress and easily revert back to their native language.

Ethnic identity development. How do family members see themselves as members of their own ethnic group? What attitudes about their group membership are manifested? What are the attitudes about self, members from other ethnic groups, as well as members of the mainstream culture? What behaviors are exhibited as a result of how family members define themselves? Do these behaviors allow the family to interact comfortably in different cultural settings? Ethnic identity attitudes may influence the extent to which family members may be comfortable with providers from either the mainstream or other cultures (Helmes, 1990). These attitudes may also affect the extent to which members may be able to incorporate themselves into family support groups in which they may be the only representatives of their cultural group.

Mistrust and discriminatory experiences. What has been the family's history and experience with discriminatory events? What are their coping styles? How do they handle their interface with institutions both within and outside of their community? Racism, for example, is a daily social stressor and unless the provider can acknowledge these experiences, he or she may be perceived as a part of just another abusive societal institution.

Regional background. Within cultures, there are wide variations based on geographical regions, living environments, and climate. These variations often affect family lifestyle patterns and values. For example, in comparison with urban environments, rural settings may tend to be slow-paced and sanction more interpersonal proximity (Karrer, 1993).

APPLYING A MULTICULTURAL LENS: GUIDELINES AND APPROACHES

1.   Apply a "cultural lens" to each family. Assume that each family is a unique representation of its culture and be able to describe each family's worldview and perceptions.

2.   Partner with families. Demonstrate comfort with differences by raising racial or ethnic differences, when appropriate. Ask family members directly how they may feel about working with providers from another cultural background.

3.   Demonstrate genuineness and concrete support. Genuine interest in and support of one or more family members will garner respect from other family members.

4. Identify and describe one's own worldview and values. Own and share them respectfully and directly with the family, when applicable.

5. Identify the family group's perception of mental illness and help-seeking/coping traditions. Attend to the cultural explanations which the family may provide about the mental illness and their experiences in managing the illness. Use the family members' explanations as the framework for engaging them.

6. Use the multidimensional approach previously described to assess points of similarity and differences between one's own worldview and that of the family. Use points of contact and similarities to bridge the differences.

7. Assess and support the extended family and social network. Determine the degree to which external provider or agency support may be required or acceptable to the family.

8. Develop a support model for the family that is consistent with its ethnic/cultural style and strengths (Lefley, 1990). An educational, problem-solving model, for example, may be congruent for some Latino families because it does not override the Latino family's authority or undermine the intricate pattern of Hispanic interpersonal relationships (Rivera, 1988). Members of the family system are mobilized to meet their own, self-defined needs (Rivera, 1988). At the same time, using egalitarian problem-solving models, not attending to spiritual and religious needs, misinterpreting spiritual beliefs, and assessing the family as "over-involved" with one of its members with mental illness would be culturally incompatible.

9. One of the most widely studied family intervention models, that is, Behavioral Family Therapy (BFT), may be particularly applicable to ethnic families (Falloon, Boyd, & McGill, 1984; Penn & Mueser, 1996). Originally provided on an individual basis, directly in the home, it can easily involve the kinship system, that is, parents, siblings, spouses, other relatives, neighbors, or close friends and the consumer (Mueser, 1996). Family strengths are assessed and the members' understanding of the psychiatric illness is evaluated.

A combination of home-based and clinic-based sessions have also been found to be successful. The home-based sessions, particularly when offered at the beginning of the intervention sequence, may be optimal in facilitating the engagement of ethnic families who might otherwise be labeled as "resistant" (Mueser, 1996). Some ethnic families may view the family home as the appropriate place to care for their member (Guarnaccia et al., 1992).

BFT is both family and individually goal oriented, with goals tailored to each family and each member. Family members are cast as experts, which could help to reduce potential provider threat. Communication skills training and problem-solving methods are concrete, structured approaches taught to families using didactic, experiential, participatory, and/or discussion formats (Mueser, 1996). Disenfranchised, often disempowered families are empowered by the ability to attain goals and solve problems on their own through problem-solving meetings, which might be chaired by a family member with another member playing the role of the secretary.

10. It is frequently assumed that families coping with mental illness are isolated from their support networks so that a new network of families must be created. Building upon the strengths of the social and cultural matrix within the ethnic community by developing supportive family networks within the family kinship system is another viable alternative.

Family network approaches (Speck & Attneave, 1973), as opposed to building a group of unrelated individuals, builds upon larger family networks that share kinship ties or membership in key community institutions. These networks may serve as innovative strategies for collective problem solving and conflict resolution for rural, Italian-American, African-American, Latino, Native-American as well as numerous other ethnocultural extended family systems (Speck & Attneave, 1973). Families with more ruptured networks could be integrated with other kinship systems and community institutions with more resources for providing support (Guarnaccia et al., 1992). Alternative settings for these meetings would be needed, such as the home, the church, or a well-regarded, neighborhood community center or facility.

DEVELOPING A CULTURALLY SPECIFIC FAMILY SUPPORT GROUP
Providing family support to ethnic families may require different models and approaches, ranging from the offer of no support based on lack of need or family preference to enhancement of an already existing kinship network, outreach and incorporation of ethnic family members into already existing, mainstream programs; or culturally specific homogeneous, multiple family groups where ethnic family members are recruited and assisted in the development of mutual self-help and support. There has been some anecdotal support for the efficacy of such ethnically or culturally specific psychoeducational consumer groups, where members are all from the same cultural

group, that is, gender, race, or sexual orientation (Finley, 1978; Merta, 1995; Primm, 1990; Simoni & Perez, 1995). Culturally specific groups may offer participants several advantages: 1) perception of having less conflict; 2) the use of positive cultural identification as the means for facilitating cohesion; 3) providing more support; 4) being better attended; 5) the creation of an environment of safety and protection as a buffer to a perceived hostile environment; and 6) providing more rapid symptom relief than heterogeneous groups (Finley, 1978; Merta, 1995; Simoni & Perez, 1995).

Strategies to be considered in the formation of a "same culture" or culturally-specific family support group model, for African-Americans or Latino families, for example, might include the following:

- Develop a clear strategy. An example might be to form a partnership with one or more ethnic family members either from an agency or from a mainstream family support group. These persons may be cultural guides or "cultural brokers" to assist in the same-culture group formation.

- Be patient and persist in your efforts. Building trust between provider, institutional systems, and ethnic family members may take time to develop. Structured, active, and directive interventions and greater self-disclosure can assist in the creation of more reciprocal relationships with family members (Simoni & Perez, 1995).

- Identify and assess the ethnic/neighborhood network system (e.g., ethnic organizations, botanicas, churches, Club Sociales, sororities, fraternities). Be knowledgeable about the language abilities, acculturation levels, and adherence to traditional ethnic values. Support from community leaders can be instrumental in the successful development of a culturally specific support group model.

- Give talks on mental illness and the needs of persons with severe and persistent mental illness at churches and local community groups. Continue this process for a period of time and then try to establish a long-term relationship with the organization (Pernell-Arnold & Finley, 1992).

- Have a festive open house. Invite members of the community. Integrate culturally relevant celebratory activities, food, and music. Provide games and activities for the entire family.

- Begin a group designed to help families relate to and help their family member in the neighborhood, the church, or the family home (Pernell-Arnold & Finley, 1992). The group focus should be very pragmatic, that is, helping to solve immediate problems of behavior involving the consumer. Off-site consultation would be invaluable. Demonstrate usefulness to the family group, first and foremost. Groups should meet at times most conducive to their members. Language considerations must also be incorporated.

- Be aggressive in outreach to ethnic families. Personally contact family members of consumers served in the agency. Outreach is welcoming. Personal contacts should be made using multiple methods: 1) written contact using official letterhead; 2) culturally sensitive and "catchy" flyers; 3) by phone; and 4) by personal invitation from persons who have rapport with the family (for example, a case manager). Personal invitations should be extended to fathers, mothers, or other adults in the extended kinship system (Boyd-Franklin, 1989; Pernell-Arnold & Finley, 1992; Simoni & Perez, 1995).

- Contact or a friendly "check-in" may be required between each and every meeting. Such contact conveys personal interest and concern, and provides helpfulness with ongoing stressors while also serving as meeting reminders. Engagement of ethnic families may be intensive in its initial stages. Do not be discouraged if initial groups have a lower attendance than desired. If participants enjoy their experiences, if they find the outcomes useful, they will become the nucleus that promotes further development of the group.

- Family needs and obstacles should be anticipated. Tangible assistance may be required, for example, transportation, child care arrangements, clothing for recent immigrants.

- Give out certificates for almost everything (Pernell-Arnold & Finley, 1992), for example, attendance, volunteer activities, and participation in meetings. Family support programs for ethnic members may require built-in achievement mechanisms and recognition opportunities in order to facilitate empowerment. Provide ancillary supports and opportunities for further achievement such as adult basic education or G.E.D. classes, assistance in attending a community college and job training or placement.

- Eventually, ask for volunteers to help staff member lead other groups, speak to church groups, and/or speak with professionals (Pernell-Arnold & Finley, 1992).

- Ask participants if staff member may speak at their church or community organizations (Pernell-Arnold & Finley, 1992).

- Attempt to get a church or community organization to adopt a program; for example, a family day picnic, a talent show, an art show, or a trip to a play, museum, ball game, or park. The organization may either send volunteers or provide financial assistance (Pernell-Arnold & Finley, 1992).

- Train some of the group participants to be group leaders; conduct leadership training sessions. Consider different leadership structures, for example, rotating leadership or election of officers. Be prepared to maintain a coaching or mentoring relationship with the newly emerging leadership.

- Initially, expect greater discretion in disclosure than what might be expected in support groups of middle-class Anglo-Americans (Simoni & Perez, 1995). Shame and issues of confidentiality may be major concerns for ethnic participants. Also expect differential participation by members. Persons who do not prefer to engage in discussion should be allowed this option.

- Stress harmonious social relationships. It is advisable to warn family group members that differences of opinion are inevitable and encourage the participants to devise ways to manage them (Simoni & Perez, 1995).

- Survey families. Find out what questions and concerns they may have. Expert guest speakers may come and discuss these topics of interest. The preference for outside "experts," among Latinos, for example, is consistent with cultural emphasis on power differential and value of lineality (Delgado, 1981). Consideration should be given to the cultural diversity of invited speakers.

- Provide information to families regarding how to handle not only situations of discrimination as they interface with the mental health system, but other forms of ethnic or cultural discrimination as well. What have been their experiences? What strategies or advocacy are needed to combat this additional factor?

REFERENCES

Adebimpe, V. R. (1994). Race, racism and epidemiological surveys. *Hospital and Community Psychiatry, 45,* 27–31.

Alston, R., & Turner, W. (1994). A family strengths model of adjustment to disability for African-American clients. *Journal of Counseling and Development, 72,* 378–382.

Angel, R. J., & Angel, J. (1993). *Painful inheritance: Health and the new generation of fatherless families*. Madison, WI: The University of Wisconsin Press.

Bell, J. (1982). The family in the hospital: Experiences in other countries. In H. Harbin (Ed.), *The psychiatric hospital and the family*. (pp. 120–129). New York: Spectrum.

Borkman, T. (1990). Self-help groups at the turning point: Emerging egalitarian alliances with the formal health care system. *American Journal of Community Psychology, 18,* 332.

Boyd-Franklin, N. (1989). *Black families in therapy: A multidisciplinary approach*. New York. Guilford Press.

Brown, G. W., Birley, J. L. T., & Wing, J. K. (1972). Influence of family life on the course of schizophrenic disorders: A replication. *British Journal of Psychiatry, 121,* 241–258.

Chestang, L. (1972). *Character development in a hostile environment (occasional paper No. 3)*. Chicago: University of Chicago School of Social Administration.

Cook, J., Pickett, S., & Cohler, B. (1997). Families of adults with severe mental illness—The next generation of research: Introduction. *American Journal of Orthopsychiatry, 67*(2), 172–176.

Delgado, M. (1981). Hispanic cultural values: Implications for groups. *Small Group Behavior, 12,* 69–80.

Delgado, M., & Humm-Delgado, D. (1982). Natural support systems: Sourcing strength in Hispanic communities. *Social Work,* 83–89.

Devore, W., & Schlesinger, E. (1981). *Ethnic sensitive social work and practice*. St. Louis, MO: C. W. Mosley Company.

Falloon, I. R. H., Boyd, J. L., & McGill, C. W. (1984). *Family care of schizophrenia: A problem-solving approach to the treatment of mental illness*. New York: Guilford Press.

Finley, L. (1978). The black experience group: A therapeutic activity model for the black schizophrenic. In American Personnel & Guidance Association (Ed.), *Innovations in counseling services* (pp 165-171), Washington, D.C.: American Personnel and Guidance Association.

Finley, L. (1997). The multiple effects of culture and ethnicity on psychiatric disability. In L. Spaniol, C. Gagne, & M. Koehler (Eds.) *Psychological and social aspects of psychiatric disability* (pp. 497–510). Boston: Center for Psychiatric Rehabilitation, Sargent College of Health and Rehabilitation Sciences.

Griffith, E. E. H., Young, J. L., & Smith, D. L. (1984). An analyses of the therapeutic elements in a black church service. *Hospital and Community Psychiatry, 35,* 464–469.

Guarnaccia, P., Parra, P., Deschamps, A., Milstein, G., & Argiles, N. (1992). Si Dios queiere: Hispanic families' experiences of caring for a seriously mentally ill family member. *Culture, Medicine and Psychiatry, 16,* 187-215.

Helms, J. E. (1990). *Black and white racial identity: Theory, research and practice*. Westport, CT: Greenwood Press.

Higginbotham, H. N. (1979). *Delivery of mental health services in three developing Asian nations: Feasibility and cultural sensitivity of "modern psychiatry."* Unpublished doctoral dissertation, University of Hawaii.

Ho, M. K. (1987). *Family therapy with ethnic minorities.* Beverly Hills, CA: SAGE Publications.

Horwitz, A., & Reinhard, S. (1995). Ethnic differences in caregiving duties and burdens among parents and siblings of persons with severe mental illnesses. *Journal of Health and Social Behavior, 36,* 138–150.

Jacobson, F. M. (1988). Ethnocultural assessment. In L. Comas-Diaz, & E. E. H. Griffith, (Eds.), *Clinical guidelines in cross cultural mental health,* (pp. 135–147). New York: John Wiley.

Karrer, B. M. (1993). The importance of understanding the cultural dimensions when treating adolescents and their families. In W. Snyder & T. Osmond (Eds.), *Empowering families: Helping adolescents.* (pp. 59–70). Publication developed by contract from the Office of Treatment Improvement of the Alcohol, Drug Abuse and Mental Health Administration, Rochelle, Minn.

Kleinman, A., & Good, B. (Eds.) (1985). *Culture and depression.* Berkley, CA: University of California Press.

Leff, J., & Vaughn, C. (1985). *Expressed emotion in families: Its significance for mental illness.* New York: Guilford Press.

Lefley, H. P. (1985). Families of the mentally ill in cross-cultural perspective. *Psychosocial Rehabilitation Journal, 8,* 57–75.

Lefley, H. P. (1987). Culture and mental illness: The family role. In A. B. Hatfield and H. P. Lefley (Eds.), *Families of the mentally ill: Coping and adaptation,* (pp. 30–59). New York: Guilford Press.

Lefley, H. P. (1990). Culture and chronic mental illness. *Hospital and Community Psychiatry, 41*(3), 277–286.

Lefley, H. P. (1992) Expressed emotion; conceptual, clinical and social policy issues. *Hospital and Community Psychiatry, 43*(6), 591–598.

McGoldrick, M., Pearce, J., & Giordano, J. (Eds.) (1982). *Ethnicity and family therapy.* New York: Guilford Press.

McGoldrick, M., Giordano, J., & Pearce, J. (Eds.) (1996). *Ethnicity and family therapy, (2nd edition).* New York: Guilford Press.

Merta, R. (1995). Groupwork. In J. Ponterotto, J. Casas, L. Suzuki, & C. Alexander, (Eds.), *Handbook of multicultural counseling,* (pp. 567–585). Thousand Oaks, CA: SAGE.

Mintzer, J. E., & Macera, C. A. (1992). Prevalence of depressive symptoms among white and African-American caregivers of demented patients. *American Journal of Psychiatry, 149*(4), 575–576.

Mirowsky, J. (1985). Disorder and its context: Paranoid beliefs as thematic elements of thought problems, hallucinations and delusions under threatening social conditions. *Research in Community and Mental Health, 5,* 185–204.

Mueser, K. (1996). Helping families manage severe mental illness. *Psychiatric Rehabilitation Skills, 1*(2), 21–42.

Neighbors, H., & Jackson, J. (1984). The use of informal and formal help: Four patterns of illness behavior in the black community. *American Journal of Community Psychology, 12*(6), 629–644.

Penn, D. L., & Mueser, K. T. (1996). Research update on the psychosocial treatment of schizophrenia. *American Journal of Psychiatry, 15,* 607–617.

Pernell-Arnold, A., & Finley, L. (1992). *Psychosocial rehabilitation services in action: Principles and strategies that result in rehabilitation* (Contract Bid # P09-07-09-92-DP). Columbia, S.C.: South Carolina Department of Mental Health.

Pickett, S., Damian, A., Vraniak, D., Cook, J., & Cohler, J. (1993). Strength in adversity: Blacks bear burden better than whites. *Professional Psychology: Research and Practice, 24*(4), 460–467.

Pierce, C. (1970). Offensive mechanisms. In F. Barbour (Ed.), *The black seventies.* (pp.265–282). Boston, MA: Sargent.

Pinderhughes, E. (1982). Afro-American families and the victim system. In M. McGoldrick, J. Pearce, & J. Giordano (Eds.), *Ethnicity and family therapy,* (pp. 108–122). New York: Guilford Press.

Primm, A. M. (1990, February). Group psychotherapy can raise self-esteem in mentally ill black men. *The Psychiatric Times: Medicine and Behavior, 24–25.*

Randall-David, E. (1989). *Strategies for working with culturally diverse communities and clients* (Report No. MCH 113793). Washington, DC: The Association for the Case of Children's Health.

Rivera, C. (1988). Culturally sensitive aftercare services for chronically mentally ill. Hispanics: The case of the pychoeducational treatment model. *Fordham University Hispanic Research Center Research Bulletin, 11,* 16–25.

Sartorius, N., Jablensky, A., & Korten, A. (1986). Early manifestations and first contact incidence of schizophrenia in different cultures. *Psychological Medicine, 16,* 909–928.

Simoni, J., & Perez, L. (1995). Latinos and mutual support groups: A case for considering culture. *American Journal of Orthopsychiatry, 65*(3), 440–445.

Solomon, P. (1988). Racial factors in mental health service utilization. *Psychosocial Rehabilitation Journal, 11,* 3–12.

Spaniol, L., & Zipple, A. (1988). Family and professional perceptions of family needs and coping strengths. *Rehabilitation Psychology, 33,* 37–45.

Speck, R., & Attneave, C. (1973). Family Networks. New York: Vintage Books.

Stevenson, H., & Renard, G. (1993). Toasting ole' wise owls: Therapeutic use of cultural strengths in African-American families. *Professional Psychology: Research and Practice, 24*(4), 433–442.

Stueve, A., Vine, P., & Struening, E. (1997). Perceived burden among caregivers of adults with serious mental illness: Comparison of black, Hispanic and white families. *American Journal of Orthopsychiatry, 67*(2), 199–209.

Szapocznik, J., & Kurtines, W. (1993). Family psychology and cultural diversity: Opportunities for theory, research and application. *Journal of the American Psychological Association, 48*(4), 400–407.

Ulbrich, P., Warheit, G., & Zimmerman, R. (1989). Race, socio-economic status and psychological distress: An examination of differential vulnerability. *Journal of Heath and Social Behavior, 30,* 131–146.

Vaughn, C., & Leff, J. (1976). The measurement of expressed emotion in families of psychiatric patients. *British Journal of Social Clinical Psychology, 15,* 157–165.

Waxler, N. E. (1979). Is outcome for schizophrenia better in non-industrial societies? The case of Sri Lanka. *Journal of Nervous and Mental Diseases, 167,* 144–158.

Dual Diagnosis: How Families Can Help

Kim T. Mueser and Lindy Fox

At the time of original publication, Kim T. Mueser, PhD, was a professor of psychiatry at Dartmouth Medical School and Associate Director of the New Hampshire Dartmouth Psychiatric Research Center; and Lindy Fox, MA, was a research associate for New Hampshire-Dartmouth Psychiatric Research Center.

This article was published previously in the *Journal of the California Alliance for the Mentally Ill,* 1998, 9, 53–55, and is reprinted with permission.

In addition to being a clinician, I am a consumer with a dual diagnosis. When I was first diagnosed with bipolar disorder I was using alcohol to self-medicate the symptoms of my mental illness. For 2 years I used alcohol without any questions about substance use from my treatment providers. My illness was very unstable, and I had many hospitalizations. Finally one clinician recognized my alcohol abuse and I began getting some treatment for my drinking problem. The treatment for my mental illness was not coordinated with my substance abuse treatment, so it took me another 2 years to stop my drinking. When I did stop using alcohol to medicate symptoms, my bipolar disorder became much more stable and I stopped going in and out of hospitals. I believe this would have happened sooner if my family and I had been educated about dual disorders, and I had received integrated treatment.—Lindy Fox

In recent years there has been a growing awareness that persons with severe psychiatric disorders such as schizophrenia and major affective disorders are at increased risk for developing substance use disorders (alcohol and drug abuse or dependence) compared to the general population. Individuals with both psychiatric and substance use disorders (i.e., *dually diagnosed* persons) pose special challenges to mental health professionals and families alike, and require interventions designed to treat both disorders. Families can play a critical role in helping dually diagnosed relatives by becoming knowledgeable about the treatment of these disorders and collaborating actively with professionals.

A FEW BASIC FACTS ABOUT WHEN MENTAL ILLNESS AND SUBSTANCE USE DISORDERS OCCUR TOGETHER

Many studies have shown that persons with severe mental illness also have high rates of substance use disorders. In general, between 50 and 60% of persons with severe mental illness experience a substance use problem at some time during their lives, and between 25 and 35% of clients have a current substance use disorder. The most commonly abused type of substance is alcohol, followed by either cannabis or cocaine, depending on where the person lives. Among persons with severe mental illness, substance abuse is more common in men, individuals who are younger, have lower levels of education, and have never married. For many dually diagnosed individuals, substance use problems are either chronic or episodic, with the severity of abuse varying over time.

Many theories have been proposed to explain the high rate of substance abuse in persons with severe mental illness. For example, it has been hypothesized that some persons with severe mental illness use substances in an effort to cope with their psychiatric symptoms. Another explanation for the high rate of substance abuse in this population involves their vulnerability to small doses of alcohol and drugs. People with severe mental illness are believed to have a psychobiological vulnerability to a psychiatric disorder that can be decreased by medication and increased by stress or substance use. This psychobiological vulnerability makes persons with severe mental illnesses more sensitive to the effects of even small amounts of alcohol and drugs. In line with this hypothesis, research studies show that individuals with severe mental illness are more sensitive to small doses of substances such as stimulants. Furthermore, patients with dual diagnoses tend to abuse lower quantities of substances than persons with a primary substance use disorder. Thus, dually diagnosed individuals may be different from the general population because they are more likely to experience negative consequences of even moderate to low amounts of substance use, not because they use more alcohol and drugs.

Substance abuse in psychiatric clients is associated with a wide range of negative consequences. Particularly common consequences include symptom relapses and rehospitalization, money problems, estranged relationships with family and friends, housing instability, suicidality, violence, and poor health. These negative consequences result in a lower overall quality of life for dually diagnosed persons and threaten the viability of social supports such as family relationships.

HOW FAMILIES CAN HELP

When families recognize that alcohol and drugs, even in small amounts, can have a negative effect on their family member's mental illness, they can play a key role in helping that member to reduce or eliminate their use. The first step families can take is to begin to talk about and try to understand their relative's substance abuse. It is important for relatives to express their concerns, but to be as nonjudgmental as possible in order to keep the stress and tension to a minimum. When family members attempt to understand why the person is using substances, and what needs are being met by this behavior, they begin an important dialogue.

Once the ill family member is willing to discuss his or her use of substances, it may be helpful to take a problem solving approach to helping the person reduce use or work towards abstinence. Families are often aware of the negative consequences of the member's substance abuse, but in order to develop an effective plan they must also be aware of the positive consequences. For example, the client may drink to fit in and socialize with others, even though it increases the symptoms of mental illness. The family might help the client identify the problem of needing a sober peer group, and develop a plan for their ill member to engage in new, substance-free activities where he or she could make some new friends.

As families gain a better understanding of their relative's substance use problem they may be able to work collaboratively with the member's treatment team. Families have important and valuable information to share with professionals. As they become part of the treatment team they can play a major role in monitoring substance use, providing support, and developing strategies for reducing substance use, promoting abstinence, or guarding against relapses of substance abuse. Families often are in key positions to increase the positive consequences of abstinence and to identify and reduce high risk situations for using substances.

Families need to remember to take care of themselves in these situations. Participating in self-help organizations such as the Alliance for the Mentally Ill can provide the additional support families need. We also encourage family members to attend to other needs, including their personal goals, leisure activities, and getting together with friends. When relatives attend to their needs, they are in a better position to care for an ill member.

HOW PROFESSIONALS CAN HELP

Until recently, there were few mental health services specifically tailored to meet the unique needs of persons with a dual diagnosis. Over the past decade, however, treatment programs have been developed that provide integrated mental health and substance abuse treatments for dually diagnosed clients.

An integrated treatment program can be defined as a program in which both mental health and substance abuse treatment services are provided by the same clinician (or team of clinicians) at the same time. The treatment provider, not the client, assumes the responsibility for integrating the mental health and substance abuse interventions in a seamless manner. Research indicates that these integrated treatment programs are successful at both engaging dually diagnosed clients and improving their long-term outcomes, including reducing substance abuse.

Many dually diagnosed clients are not active participants in mental health treatment. If these clients are to be engaged in treatment, clinicians must reach out to them and meet with them in their own natural environments in the community, rather than providing only clinic-based service. In addition, once a therapeutic relationship has been established, assertive outreach can help the clinician monitor the course of the dual diagnosis more effectively and evaluate the possible role the environment plays in maintaining ongoing substance abuse or threatening relapses.

Integrated treatment programs for persons with a dual diagnosis recognize that many such individuals are not motivated to address their substance use problems. In order to engage and work with these clients towards the eventual goal of reducing substance abuse, integrated programs employ motivation-based interventions that are tailored to help clients make gradual progress towards improvement or recovery based on their own personal goals, rather than those of the clinician or program. One particularly useful approach to helping clinicians use interventions that are appropriate to a client's current motivational level has been the concept of stages of treatment.

Stages of Treatment

The stages of treatment are based on the observation that clients with a dual diagnosis progress through a series of stages as they improve and recover from substance abuse. Each stage is defined in terms of the client's level of awareness and motivation to address substance use related problems.

- At the *engagement stage,* the client does not have a working relationship with a clinician who can address dual diagnosis problems. The most important goal of this stage is to establish a therapeutic relationship with the client, so that substance abuse can be addressed at a later time.

- In the next stage of treatment, the *persuasion stage,* the client has a working relationship with the clinician, but he or she is not motivated to address substance abuse. The goal of this stage is to help the client see that substance abuse has significant negative consequences that interfere with achieving personal goals.

- During the *active stage* of treatment the client recognizes substance abuse as a problem and has begun to reduce substance use. The goal of this stage is to help the client further reduce substance use and, if possible, to achieve abstinence.

- During the *relapse prevention stage,* the client has successfully reduced substance use and has not experienced substance use related problems for at least 6 months. The goal of this stage is to help the client remain aware that relapse is possible and to begin working on other important areas of functioning, such as social relationships and work.

Substance Abuse in Severe Mental Illness

What Families Need To Know

- Persons with severe mental illness often have substance abuse problems: 50% of clients have a substance use disorder at some time during their lives.

- Persons with severe mental illness are highly sensitive to low doses of alcohol and drugs.

- Common consequences of substance abuse include relapses and rehospitalizations, money problems, legal problems, and conflicts with friends and family.

How Families Can Help

- Recognize the signs of substance abuse (e.g., relapses, money problems, conflict with others non compliance).

- Begin a dialogue with the client about his or her use of substances.

- Collaborate with mental health professionals.

- Problem-solve with the client about substance abuse, its consequences, and how to address them.

- Get help and support for yourself.

How Mental Health Professionals Can Help

- Provide integrated mental health and substance abuse treatments.

- Use assertive outreach to work with clients in their natural environments.

- Employ motivation-based interventions to help clients address concerns important to them.

- Provide comprehensive programming that addresses multiple areas of functioning, including substance abuse, work, social relationships, and health.

- Take a long-term perspective towards improving dual disorders.

Important Features of Effective Treatment Programs

One important feature of integrated treatment programs is their focus on substance abuse. However, this is not the exclusive focus of effective programs. Dually diagnosed clients, like other people with a severe mental illness, have a wide range of treatment and rehabilitation needs. Therefore, integrated treatment programs are most effective when they are comprehensive and address the broad range of client's functioning, including work, social relationships, housing, skills for independent living, symptom management, and family relationships.

Research on integrated treatment indicates that dually diagnosed clients improve more rapidly than when treated with more traditional approaches that separate substance abuse and mental health services. However, the rate of improvement of dual disorders is relatively slow.

In research conducted at the New Hampshire–Dartmouth Psychiatric Research Center we have found that 10 to 15% of dually diagnosed clients achieve stable remission of their symptoms per year. While this rate of improvement is encouraging, it also means that in order for integrated treatment programs to be effective, they need to be provided over a long-term basis for many years. Therefore, short-term programs for dually diagnosed clients tend to produce only short-term benefits.

SUMMARY AND CONCLUSIONS

Mental health professionals and families have improved their understanding of the problem of dual diagnosis. If untreated, the outcome of substance abuse and severe mental illness is often tragic, including frequent rehospitalizations, legal problems, and damaged family relationships. However, by working side-by-side, mental health professionals and families can improve the long-term course of dual diagnosis clients, resulting in a better quality of life for these persons and their families.

Employment Outcomes in Family-Aided Assertive Community Treatment

William R. McFarlane, Robert A. Dushay, Susan M. Deakins,
Peter Stastny, Ellen P. Lukens, Joanne Toran, and Bruce Link

At the time of original publication, the authors' affiliations were listed as follows: William R. McFarlane, MD, Maine Medical Center, Portland, ME; Robert A. Dushay, PhD, Institute for Community Research, Hartford, CT; Susan M. Deakins, MD, and Bruce Link, PhD, New York State Psychiatric Institute, New York; Peter Stastny, MD, New York State Office of Mental Health, New York; and Ellen P. Lukens, PhD, MSW, and Joanne Toran, MPA, Columbia University, New York.

This article was published previously in the *American Journal of Orthopsychiatry*, 2000, 70(2), 203–214, is reprinted with permission.

The work was supported by grant R18 SM 47642 from the National Institute of Mental Health.

Abstract: Family-aided assertive community treatment (FACT) was enhanced by adding vocational specialists to help persons with severe mental illness obtain competitive employment. Results were then tested against those of conventional vocational rehabilitation (CVR). The FACT cohort demonstrated significantly better employment rates than did the CVR, while negative symptoms declined in the former and increased in the latter. No evidence was found that competitive work presented a significant risk for relapse.

The present situation for persons with severe mental disorders is a study in contrasts. Most of this population now lives in the community, supported by increasingly useful treatment systems. More effective pharmacological and psychosocial interventions provide many with a stability and freedom from psychotic symptoms that was only a dream a decade ago. Consequently, those patients fortunate enough to be treated in a state-of-the-art program may experience years, rather than months, of remission from acute episodes (Bellack & Mueser, 1993; Lehman, Carpenter, Goldman, & Steinwachs, 1995; Okin, Borus, Baer, & Jones, 1996).

The contrasts lie in the realm of vocational rehabilitation. Recent reviews of the literature (Bond, 1992; Bond & Boyer, 1988; Lehman, 1995) have disclosed improvement in rates of placement and retention in sheltered workshops, transitional employment, hospital work programs, work enclaves, and some supported employment programs. However, until recently, no single study of a vocational rehabilitation approach had reported a significant effect for competitive employment (Bond, 1992), which remains the stated goal for most of the affected population and their families (Bachrach, 1991). For at least the last two decades, only about 10% have been successfully employed in mainstream jobs and occupations (Anthony, Cohen, & Vitalo, 1978; Bond, 1992).

In conventional approaches to vocational rehabilitation, patients have been referred to relatively large, specialized sheltered workshops or vocational training programs. In them, staff tend to assume that many of the mentally ill persons, like some of those with developmental disabilities, will be unable to meet the demands of competitive jobs. An unintended effect of this approach is to group recipients of rehabilitation together and thereby segregate them from normal workplaces. Although a goal of many such programs is to prepare clients for competitive job placement, their demonstrated efficacy has continued to be unsatisfactory (Bond, 1992; Lehman, 1995).

Newer approaches, including assertive community treatment (ACT) (Stein & Test, 1980; Test, Knoedler, & Allness, 1985), family psychoeducation (Anderson, Reiss, & Hogarty, 1986; Falloon, Boyd, & McGill, 1984; McFarlane, 1990), and individual support and placement (Becker & Drake, 1994), attempt to provide jobs in competitive, integrated settings. They undertake whatever steps are necessary to help clients find and retain normative employment, and their methods focus on skill training in job interviewing, providing guarantees of reliable work activity to employers, and on-site job coaching, as well as development of jobs suited to people with mental illness. Integration and close coordination of clinical treatment, ongoing family support, and rehabilitation services are inherent and routine in these programs. Their methods are individualized and do not involve grouping or segregating participants. Recent studies have supported their efficacy (Chandler, Meisel, Hu, McGowen, & Madison, 1997; Drake et al., 1994; Drake, McHugo, Becker, Anthony, & Clark, 1996; Falloon et al., 1985; Hogarty et al., 1991; McFarlane, Dushay, Stastny, Deakins & Link, 1996; Test, 1995). On the negative side, these community-integration approaches, because of their greater expense, can only achieve cost effectiveness by reducing service utilization and raising the ultimate earning power of the individuals served.

A rehabilitation approach, Training in Community Living, was developed by Stein and Test, with a later variant, the Program for Assertive Community Treatment (PACT) (Knoedler, 1979; Stein & Test, 1980; Test, 1995; Test et al., 1985). Drake, Becker and their colleagues have also shown that when employment specialists are integrated with clinical and case management services, promising employment outcomes ensue (Drake et al., 1994; Drake, Becker, Biesanz, Wyzik, & Torrey, 1996; Drake, McHugo, Becker, Anthony, & Clark, 1996).

Another treatment and rehabilitation approach spurred by deinstitutionalization has been to educate and provide ongoing guidance and support to the family of the person with severe mental illness. Family intervention

(Anderson et al., 1986; Falloon et al., 1985; Goldstein, Rodnick, Evans, May, & Steinberg, 1978; Leff, Kuipers, Berkowitz & Sturgeon, 1984; McFarlane, Link, Dushay, Marchal & Crilly, 1995; McFarlane, Lukens et al., 1995) has consistently yielded 2-year relapse rates in the 10% to 30% range, compared to 60% to 90% from individual supportive treatment. Family intervention also promotes functional adaptation (Falloon & Pederson, 1985; Hogarty et al., 1991; Kopeikin, Marshall & Goldstein, 1983; McFarlane, Link et al., 1995; McFarlane, Lukens et al., 1995), with higher employment rates and school participation reported during or after family intervention, and trends favoring multifamily groups.

A previous study (McFarlane et al., 1996) concluded that when ACT and psychoeducational multifamily groups (MFGs) were combined into family-aided assertive community treatment (FACT), the deficiencies of each of these approaches were addressed, while their advantages were retained. In that trial, which compared ACT with ongoing FACT, twice as many FACT patients were employed during the study. The same approach to rehabilitation has been used in the present study: clinical and rehabilitative intervention in the patient's natural environment were combined with family education, guidance, and collaboration with the FACT team, and implemented in multifamily groups (MFGs). This amalgam was designed to provide focused support and training in work-related problem-solving skills, carried out in the context of an expanded and rehabilitation oriented family and social support system. The goal of this combined treatment and rehabilitation approach was meaningful, competitive employment.

METHOD

The study was designed for direct comparison of vocational and clinical outcomes in FACT and conventional vocational rehabilitation (CVR), and to assess clinical outcomes and their relationship to work outcomes in both experimental conditions. It was hypothesized that FACT would be similar to CVR in clinical outcomes but superior in vocational outcomes, and that clinical outcomes would be predictive of vocational outcomes.

Two New York state community mental health centers (CMHCs), one in Ulster County the other in Westchester County, were the sites for the study.

Rehabilitation Intervention

Assertive Community Training. ACT is by now well known and empirically tested (Olfson, 1990; Test et al., 1985) (treatment manuals are available from the senior author). Each family-aided ACT (FACT) team in the current study consisted of three primary staff: two social workers or psychiatric nurses with prior experience treating the study population, and one vocational specialist (VS), together with a senior clinician team leader and a psychiatrist.

The staff to patient ratio was 1:8. However, the teams were somewhat smaller than recommended by ACT fidelity criteria.

The addition of a VS to the FACT team originated with Frey and Test and their colleagues (Russert & Frey, 1991) and has been adapted by Becker, Drake, and their colleagues (Becker & Drake, 1994). The VSs in the study reported here, trained by Becker, consisted of a vocational rehabilitation counselor on one team and a social worker with special training and experience in vocational rehabilitation on the other. Their specific tasks were to:

1. Lead 9-session goal-setting groups, using a format developed by Miller and Wilder (1990) that established individualized vocational plans for all FACT participants.

2. Work with each individual to identify and contact potential employers.

3. Work on job development for the entire cohort, to find cooperative potential employers.

4. Coach participants on and off the job site in the initial month or two of employment.

5. Provide technical assistance to their teammates in job-coaching.

6. Develop methods for assessing work readiness, preparing resumes, and practicing interviewing skills.

Psychoeducational Multifamily Group Treatment. As applied in FACT, the MFG treatment approach emphasized vocational rehabilitation, stepwise functional progression, early crisis intervention, and relapse prevention. For families, ingroup, cross-family social support and problem solving, as well as out-of-group socializing, were encouraged. The psychoeducational multiple family group treatment is described elsewhere (McFarlane, 1990; 1994; McFarlane et al., 1996).

An MFG problem-solving method was consistently applied with a view to the gradual, step-wise resumption of work by each participant and to developing specially suited employment opportunities. Families in the MFGs were involved in developing a consensus about goals for employment that were established in the group goal-setting process, and went on to provide support and encouragement in finding and keeping employment. The clinicians' role was to implement solutions developed in the MFG, especially those that might find a job or avoid losing one. That is, the MFGs operated integrally with the team as an auxiliary to the in-vivo vocational rehabilitation effort. The groups included seven or eight cases, met biweekly for 90 minutes, and were led by two members of the FACT team. The cost of the family intervention was negligible relative to the overall costs of the team, because this intervention simply displaced effort that otherwise would have been devoted to work with individual participants.

Once the MFG had become a cohesive network, its members and their extended kin were polled as a source of job leads; this garnered jobs that, in general, were potentially less stressful, since they involved social connections and thus carried a degree of familiarity for the participants. To a large degree, this approach was modeled after the usual modes—networks and personal connections—by which a mentally healthy individual obtains a job or job leads (Granovetter, 1973). Some clients, who otherwise met the study's inclusion criteria (see below), did not have family members available to join the MFG. The protocol was therefore changed so that up to one third of the cases in a given MFG could be nonfamily subjects. No differences were evident in outcome measures for nonfamily clients and family-member clients.

Conventional Vocational Rehabilitation. The comparison CVR model was implemented by master's-level clinicians working in the same mental health centers as the FACT teams. With caseloads varying from 1:23 at the Ulster County site to 1:13 at the Westchester County site, the clinicians oversaw the CVR referral, followed up when crises or drop-outs occurred (arranging to place CVR drop-outs in other rehabilitation programs), and consulted on all decisions about rehabilitation program changes and job placement. They carried out family crisis support, research assessment, and tracking procedures; made referrals to the state-operated vocational rehabilitation service; and assisted subjects in following through on assessment, training, and placement phases. Each center was affiliated with a rehabilitation agency to which the state agency referred CVR subjects, and these were typical in orientation, and unusually well-managed and competent. Many CVR cases were placed in sheltered workshops, and the clinicians provided support at entry and during their stay. For clients who declined to use the state service or workshops, clinicians held regular sessions to review their job plans and provide vocational counseling. They did not, however, provide supported employment services outside the usual office setting.

Thus, the principal differences between CVR and FACT experimental conditions were that in CVR:

1. All vocational rehabilitation was initiated by referral to the state Office of Vocational Rehabilitation.

2. Vocational rehabilitation staff, even if employed at site-affiliated rehabilitation services, worked on the basis of referral from the CVR clinicians and case managers.

3. No MFGs or vocational specialists worked closely with the clinicians.

4. Case loads were heavier.

Medication. Staff psychiatrists at the sites administered medication as indicated, using the lowest dose that effectively controlled symptoms.

Sample

The study was conducted at two typical community mental health centers (CMHCs) that had close ties to excellent vocational rehabilitation services. To enhance generalizability, one of the two service sites was located in an increasingly urbanized suburb of New York City (New Rochelle, Westchester County) and the other in rural New York state (Kingston, Ulster County), thus representing a broad cross-section of the U.S. population. In 1984, Ulster County had a population of 168,000 that included few minorities, low population density, and an average per-capita income of $12,445; at the start of the study in 1990, it had a 7.6% unemployment rate. Westchester County, with a population of 872,000 and a per-capita income of $21,130 (thanks to a few very wealthy towns), is largely working- and middle-class; in 1990 it had an unemployment rate under 8%, and an average proportion (15.4%) of minorities.

Two major setbacks to the program's employment effort were the recession of the early 1990s and the closing of Ulster County's principal employer mid-way through the study. The latter removed the economic backbone of the region and eliminated over 6,000 jobs, sending the unemployment rate from under 5% in 1990 to over 11% by the end of 1993.

Subjects were recruited from case rolls and community referrals at Ulster County CMHC and the Guidance Center of New Rochelle. The sites involved in this project had large, long-standing, state-funded community support service programs in which potential subjects were invited to participate.

Study eligibility criteria were: age 18 to 55 years, a diagnosis in either the schizophrenia (e.g., schizophrenia, schizoaffective, schizophreniform) or the mood disorder (e.g., major depressive disorder, bipolar disorder) spectrum, not employed competitively for the past 6 months, an available family member, and an explicit wish to work.

Of the 112 cases first considered for inclusion, 69 were admitted. Those excluded were primarily individuals who did not meet entry criteria or refused to give informed consent. Fewer women than men met the inclusion criteria; otherwise there were no differences in demographic characteristics between those included and excluded. Baseline demographic, clinical, and employment history characteristics of the sample are presented in Table 1. The modal patient was male, unemployed for over a year, with a schizophrenic disorder of a long and chronic course, was not living with family, and had a lower level of acuity and substance abuse than in many samples in other clinical trials. To control for potential bias, prior job counts were entered as a covariate in all analyses of employment outcomes.

Table 1. Demographic, Clinical, and Employment Characteristics of Sample

CHARACTERISTIC		FACT N = 37	CVR N = 32	TOTAL N = 69
Demographic				
Age (years)	Mean	34.4	31.3	33.0
	Standard Deviation	8.3	8.8	8.6
Sex (%)	Female	35.0	25.0	30.0
	Male	65.0	75.0	70.0
Ethnicity (%)	White	86.0	88.0	87.0
	Hispanic-American	3.0	3.0	3.0
	Other	8.0	3.0	6.0
Marital Status (%)	Never married	65.0	84.0	74.0
	Separated/divorced	19.0	6.0	13.0
	Married	16.0	10.0	13.0
Education (%)	Not high school graduate	14.0	29.0	21.0
	High school graduate	46.0	19.0	34.0
	Some college	30.0	42.0	35.0
	College grad/postgrad	10.0	10.0	10.0
Residence (%)	With family member	33.0	41.0	36.0
	Nonfamily	67.0	59.0	64.0
Government Aid (%)	SSA	6.0	3.0	4.0
	SSD	43.0	56.0	49.0
	SSI	68.0	59.0	64.0
Patient SES	Mean	4.1	3.9	4.0
	Standard Deviation	1.0	1.0	1.0
Parent SES	Mean	2.7	2.1	2.5
	Standard Deviation	1.3	1.1	1.2
Clinical				
Diagnosis (%)	Schizophrenia spectrum	73.0	56.0	65.0
	Mood spectrum	27.0	44.0	35.0
Age of Symptom Onset (yrs)	Mean	19.0	19.3	19.2
	Standard Deviation	8.4	8.8	8.5
Hospitalizations (past 3 yrs)	Mean	1.2	1.7	1.4
	Standard Deviation	1.4	1.5	1.5
Prior Hospitalizations	Mean	5.6	4.4	5.1
	Standard Deviation	6.1	3.9	5.2
Alcohol Use (%)	None/rare	91.0	86.0	89.0
	Regular light/moderate	9.0	14.0	11.0
Other Substance Use (%)	Never/rare	94.0	91.0	92.0
	Regular light/moderate	6.0	9.0	8.0
Employment				
Prior Jobs (number)	Mean	6.5	5.2	5.9
	Standard Deviation	3.4	4.7	4.0
Prior Jobs (duration/mos)	Mean	20.0	22.6	21.2
	Standard Deviation	24.2	22.4	23.2
Last Job (months since)	Mean	14.5	16.3	15.3
	Standard Deviation	18.7	35.2	27.2
Duration (mos)	Mean	15.2	31.8	22.5
	Standard Deviation	22.2	56.0	41.3

In both FACT and CVR cases, the participants' primary clinician engaged their family. Once baseline data had been collected and family engagement secured, subjects were randomly assigned to FACT or CVR. After this, ACT and the MFGs began in the FACT-assigned cohort, thus removing the initial family engagement component as a variable affecting outcome and leaving ACT, an educational workshop, and the ongoing MFG as the experimental treatment elements.

Measures

The primary outcome measures were subjects' employment and clinical status during 18 months of treatment and rehabilitation. This status was assessed every 3 months after the start of the study.

Clinical Status. Clinical status was assessed by measuring participant symptomatology and tracking psychiatric hospitalizations. Symptomatology was measured by independent interviewers, using the Positive and Negative Syndrome Scale (PANSS) (Kay, Fiszbein, & Opler, 1987), a standard instrument, with an additional affective subscale added from the Schedule for Affective Disorders (SADS-C) (Endicott & Spitzer, 1978). Rater reliability for the PANSS, measured by ratings against standardized videotaped interviews, was adequate. Scores were expressed as the per-item mean score for each symptom subscale: positive, negative, general psychopathology, and affective. Thus, subscale and full-scale scores ranged from 1 (no symptoms) to 7 (extremely symptomatic).

Pre-project hospitalization rates were obtained by taking the mean of subject and family member recollection, which were highly correlated ($r = +0.93$). In-treatment rehospitalizations were reported by therapist and site directors. Although truly accurate measures of medication compliance are all but impossible to obtain without direct measurement of blood levels, psychiatrists' estimates of medication compliance were obtained every 6 months, using all available data from clinicians, subjects, and family members. Compliance was scored on a 3-point ordinal scale (less than 50%, 50–99%, and 100% compliant). Psychiatrists' estimates of the accuracy of patients' reports were also obtained. Diagnoses were established at baseline with the Structured Clinical Interview for *DSM-III-R* (American Psychiatric Association, 1987; Spitzer et al., 1985).

Employment Status

Employment outcome was documented using a checklist developed for this study, the Employment Tracking Form (ETF). Clinicians completed an ETF for each subject every 3 months, recording employment activity over the prior month. The ETF provided a checklist of the most likely types of employment activity: student, homemaker, volunteer, sheltered workshop, supported employment, job coaching, non-tax-reported (paid "under the table," but not actual criminal activity) employment, competitive employment, and vocational training. It also recorded specific job titles and responsibilities, providing a check on job categories, number of weeks employed in the past month, and income earned by the subject. For analytic purposes, employment was collapsed into four categories: unemployed, sheltered work, unpaid work (including homemaking), and competitive work (including non-tax-reported employment).

RESULTS

Employment Outcomes

The primary outcome of the study was employment. Reported here are the number of people employed at any time in each job category over the 18 months of the project, i.e., the cumulative employment rate (see Table 2). Since subjects often had different types of jobs during the study, the cumulative data is reported in two ways. The first notes only the "highest level" job, ranked in the following order: unemployment, sheltered work, volunteer and unpaid work, and competitive work. The second reports all the jobs held by each participant. Both methods demonstrated that FACT and CVR were similar in sheltered and unpaid work, but that FACT had dramatically fewer unemployed subjects: 16.2% compared to 43.3% in CVR. Averaged across the 18 months, more FACT subjects held competitive jobs: 27.8% compared to 9.8% in CVR. FACT subjects were significantly more likely to be employed than CVR subjects (ANCOVA: $F_{(1,54)} = 7.72$, $p < .01$). Competitive employment in FACT peaked at 12 months, at 37.1%, with a nonsignificant decline to 26.5% at 18 months (see Figure 1). Competitive employment in CVR remained consistently lower: 7.7% at 12 months, and 8% at 18 months (slightly below CVR baseline level). FACT was found significantly better than CVR at 12 and 18 months (univariate ANCOVA, 12 months: $F_{(1,56)} = 9.21$, $p < .01$; 18 months: $F_{(1,54)} = 5.11$, $p < .05$).

The difference in amount of employment was not due to a "revolving door" effect, with continual firing and hiring. The duration of competitive jobs was highly variable. In CVR the range was 1 to 18 months, with a median of 4.5 months; in FACT it was 3 to 15 months, with a median of 12 months (Mann Whitney $U = 31.5$, $z = 1.39$, NS). Of the 37 FACT subjects, 17 held 26 jobs; of the 32 CVR subjects, 6 held 8 jobs. Total time employed during the study was greater (though nonsignificantly) for FACT subjects: 10.4 months compared to 7 months ($N = 23$). Site effects (employment was lower at baseline and throughout the study in Westchester) were negligible.

Mean total earnings over the 18 months of the study were strongly in FACT's favor. For the whole sample, PACT cases earned $755, compared to $214 for CVR (Mann-Whitney $z_{(69)} = 2.35$, $p = 0.019$). For subjects with any competitive employment, FACT earnings averaged $1,448, compared to $320 for CVR (Mann-Whitney $z_{(22)} = 2.08$, $p = 0.038$), while hourly wages averaged $6.34 and $3.64, respectively (Mann-Whitney $z_{(22)} = 1.92$, $p = .055$). At a mean of over $6 per hour, these were not just minimum-wage positions.

Employment data were available for some individuals who continued in treatment after the formal study ended. At 24 months, of a total sample of 35, 27.3% of the FACT cohort were competitively employed and 40.9% unemployed; of the CVR cohort, the comparable figures were 7.7% and 69.2%. Among the 22 cases with available data at 30 months, 29.4% of FACT cases were in competitive employment, and only 35.4% were unemployed— a fairly low rate compared to CVR cases, none of whom was employed. Although employment rates in the general population were declining rapidly while these data were being gathered (1993–1995), FACT employment rates declined no further after the formal study period.

Table 2. Cumulative Employment Rates and Jobs in Each Type Over 18 Months

Job Type	Highest Level Job				Number of Jobs Held	
	Fact		CVR*		Fact	CVR
	N	%	N	%		
Unemployed	6	16.2	11	43.3		
Sheltered	6	16.2	7	21.8	10	10
Volunteer	8	21.6	8	25.0	13	9
Competitive	17	45.9	6	18.8	17	6

*$F_{(1,54)} = 7.72$, $p < 0.01$.

Symptom Outcomes

As hypothesized in the study design, outcomes on symptoms, rehospitalizations, and medication compliance showed FACT and CVR to have been equally effective clinical treatments.

For the schizophrenic subsample, significant treatment x time interactions were evident for negative symptoms (MANCOVA, controlling for baseline symptoms and site: $F_{(1,38)} = 6.03$, $p < .05$) and general psychopathology ($F_{(1,38)} = 5.69$, $p < .05$), indicating improvement or no change, respectively, for FACT, and worsening for CVR. Posthoc t-tests found the only significant change over time was a .6 increase in negative symptoms for cases assigned to CVR ($t_{(14)} = 2.24$, $p < .05$). No differences between treatments were evident for the mood disorder subsample.

Over 18 months, the total sample showed improvements in positive symptoms (0.4 points; $F_{(1,14)} = 5.94$, $p < .05$), general psychopathology (0.4 points; $F_{(1,4)} = 5.40$, $p < .05$), and affective symptoms (0.5 points; $F_{(1,13)} = 6.42$, $p < .05$).

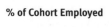

Figure 1. Competitive Employment Outcome

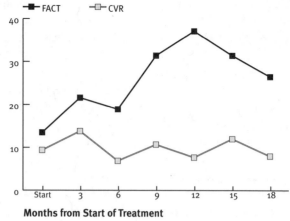

Months from Start of Treatment
12 months: $F_{(1,56)} = 9.21$, $p = .004$
18 months: $F_{(1,56)} = 5.11$, $p = .028$

Medication Compliance

No differences were found on medication compliance. Most subjects were scored at 50% to 100% compliance, regardless of diagnosis or treatment assignment. Roughly one third of the schizophrenic subsample and one quarter of the mood disorder subsample had 100% compliance. Data were analyzed using four chi-square models, analyzing baseline and 18-month data for each diagnostic group. As noted, no differences were evident at baseline, nor were any found at 18 months. Further, compliance did not change over the duration of the study.

These findings are consistent with earlier trials of MFGs and ACT; in both approaches, medication compliance reached high levels, and the additional incentive of staying employed appeared to bolster subjects' resolve to remain compliant.

Hospitalization Outcomes

Rehospitalizations were tracked during the study and no differences were found between the two treatments (ANOVA: $F_{(1,65)} = 0.11$, NS). Subjects in both treatments had significantly fewer hospitalizations during the study period than in the 18 months prior to treatment. In fact, there were only 23 hospitalizations for 69 subjects over the study's 18 months, yielding a pre-treatment rate of 0.48 hospitalizations per year, compared to an in-treatment rate of 0.32. This represented a reduction of .16 hospitalization (95% confidence interval: -.31 to -.01; $t_{(62)} = 2.19$, $p < .05$).

As subjects became employed, hospitalization rates did not rise (during months 0 to 9 and 10 to 18 they were .20 and .19, respectively).

Clinical and Vocational Outcome Interactions

In the integration of clinical and vocational rehabilitation, three sets of findings were of interest. Looked at more closely than in most previous research, they also shed light on the long-standing controversy about the effects of clinical condition on ability to find and keep a competitive job (Anthony & Jansen, 1984; Bell & Lysaker, 1995; Lysaker & Bell, 1995; Strauss & Carpenter, 1977). As in those prior studies, the best predictor of employment at any given time in the present study was prior employment (multiple regression $\beta = .47$, $SE = 0.14$, $t = 3.35$, $p = 0.0016$).

Large, though nonsignificant, differences were evident in rates of hospitalization in different types of employment. At 18 months, only 9% of participants competitively employed had had at least one hospitalization during the study, compared to 52% of those unemployed. For subjects in voluntary employment and sheltered employment, the figures were 56% and 70%, respectively.

Timing of rehabilitation was associated with a provocative finding about job loss. The rate of job loss in FACT declined dramatically during the study: of jobs held at the 3- or 6-month points in the study, 69.6% were lost; of jobs held at 9 months, none were lost; and the average job-loss rate for the 12- and 15-month points was 33.5%. Of 11 subjects who started competitive employment before 9 months, 8 (72%) had lost them by the 9-month assessment, leaving only 3 (27%) employed through that point. Of 12 who started employment after the 9-month point, 7 (58%) still had their jobs at 18 months; and 1 more had obtained another job and was employed at 18 months. That is, 67% of those obtaining any job between 9 and 15 months were employed at 18 months. For the 13 subjects with at least 6 months of continuous employment, only 4 (30.7%) began those jobs before the 9-month point.

The relationship between continuity of competitive employment and symptom levels across the time span of the study was examined for the whole sample. Diagnosis-specific symptoms (the mean of positive and negative symptoms for schizophrenia spectrum on the PANSS, and the mean of affective symptoms for those with mood disorders on the SADS-C) were divided into high- and low-symptom categories, using a mean per-item score cutoff of 2.5. Employment status was categorized as either unemployed (not working at any time point 3 months prior to, at, or following the assessment points of 0, 9, and 18 months), or employed (having competitive employment at any of the assessment points).

The results are striking (as can be seen in Figure 2): over each of the time periods, only those subjects who had low symptom levels were employed, with the exception of one case in the last time period. Only two people with high symptom levels had any competitive employment at all. Of those with any employment, 85.7% were all but asymptomatic, while those unemployed were 65% asymptomatic and 35% symptomatic, about the same ratio as in the entire sample (74% versus 26%) at study termination. Caution is indicated in the interpretation, in that these associations did not reach statistical significance, probably because of the small subsample sizes.

Study Limitations

This study contains two primary threats to validity. First, the data are likely to underestimate earned income and number of jobs. At least one subject who had unreported employment was not willing to disclose the amount of money he earned, lest he encounter tax or disability payment difficulties. Other "under the table" employment may not have been reported at all. Further, it is possible that the few clinicians in the CVR cell who were less connected to the FACT team may have underreported their clients' outside employment activity, despite efforts to the contrary. However, because the Westchester County CVR clinicians worked very closely with their FACT counterparts, and the Ulster CVR clinicians reported administratively to the FACT team leader, plus the lack of difference in CVR employment rates before and during the study, biased underreporting seems unlikely. The other threat to validity is the possible Hawthorne effect, to which all clinical studies are prey: participants may have been motivated by the extra attention they got as research subjects and by the fact that the treatment was new. Clinicians may have been similarly encouraged by the support provided by the research supervision.

The economic recession and unexpected loss of potential jobs caused by the sudden disappearance of the major employer at the Ulster site may also have constituted contrary threats to validity. They reduced the likelihood of study participants obtaining employment during (roughly) the second half of the study. However, FACT competitive employment levels at the Ulster site still remained higher than those of the CVR cohorts, or even than those of the FACT cohort at the Westchester site, where the decrease in general employment was less.

DISCUSSION

Because subjects entered the study either directly from acute episodes (at one extreme) or from long-term sheltered work (at the other), this study was a test of FACT's ability both to achieve any competitive employment among the unemployed and to raise the level of employment among those unsatisfactorily employed. The results were encouraging: 84% of the FACT sample achieved some form of employment, and 46% held a competitive position at some time during the 18-month observation period. With a mean job retention interval of over 6 months, accumulated time competitively

Figure 2. Competitive Employment by Symptom Level

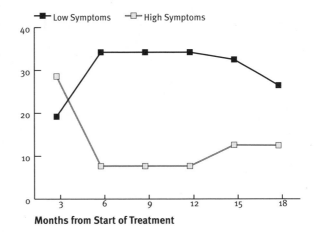

% of Cohort Employed

Note.
Percentages are
proportion of each
symptom group that
was employed, both
cohorts combined.
Sample size reduced
by missing assess-
ments of usable
symptoms.

employed and total earnings were markedly greater in the FACT group than in the CVR comparison group. Among those who had any competitive job, the FACT cohort's earnings were four times greater than the CVRs. Given that both cohorts were all but unemployed at baseline, these outcomes represent a significant advance for a population often assumed incapable of working at any level in the mainstream job market. They resulted both from obtaining employment for FACT subjects initially (often for a long time), and from helping them find another job if they lost one. This ability to place subjects in successive jobs contrasts starkly with the experience in CVR, where, only two people obtained a second competitive job. The FACT approach was designed for continuous and flexible work with individuals, specifically compensating for more difficult, symptomatic periods by providing increased clinical and rehabilitative support. Families were asked to assist by extending team members a degree of protection from stress during these periods and by being patient if their ill member chose to leave employment for a time.

FACT used ACT, psychoeducational MFGs, and team-integrated employment specialists, according to the needs of individual and situation; i.e., in some cases, much of the employment effort focused on problem-solving in the MFGs whereas, in others, it was on job coaching by members of the team. The team decided which elements to apply in a given case, in consultation with the research team's supervisors (PS, SMD, and WRM).

Earnings were less than would be expected for nondisabled workers in the same job market. The mean weekly salary was just over $50, not enough to allow subjects to support themselves or drop Social Security benefits. This is partly an effect of the short time frame for the study, plus the extensive use of part-time employment as the first step. The protocol recommended that subjects be stabilized over an average of 6 months before job placement.

Given the variability in the rate at which stability was achieved, some individuals did not enter the job market until 12 or more months into the study period. As a result, at the 18-month point some who could have obtained a job with further effort, especially in a better economy, were unemployed. This was the price of having clients progress gradually to higher levels of responsibility, rather than make abrupt entry into full-time jobs whose demands might be overwhelming. Some subjects left one job and took another, a few at higher levels, as do most members of the general population. However, the progression that marks most careers occurs more slowly than can be contained in the time frame of this study. Furthermore, many subjects, usually with the support of the VS, actively avoided earning more than was allowed under their respective SSI/SSDI benefits. Clearly' this phenomenon depressed earnings (it is now the subject of corrective Congressional legislation).

Impact of the Local Economy

In contrast to the first 12 months of the intervention, the proportion of the sample competitively employed declined, nonsignificantly, between 12 and 18 months, while volunteer employment increased and sheltered employment rates remained almost the same throughout. The impression from the data is that subjects moved from competitive to unpaid positions after 12 months. However, the job-loss rate fell over the course of the study, from 70% of jobs held during the first 6 months to less than 35% of those held in the last 6. The decline in competitive employment was the combined result of a small but continuing job-loss rate, the near cessation of job acquisition, and some movement from competitive to volunteer employment. The unemployment rate in Ulster County, which had the preponderance of the sample, peaked at nearly 12%, considered an indicator of economic depression by many economists. At both sites, it was difficult for the team or the study subjects to find available positions, while the job leads from MFGs were all but nil, as more of the relatives became unemployed themselves. A continuing long-term increase in the proportion employed at these sites has been reported by Test and her colleagues (1995); it had reached nearly 70% by 7 years, a period that spanned a full economic cycle.

Types and Sequences of Employment

Not all of the jobs the subjects obtained were the mid-level positions they had hoped for. The most common were odd jobs, indoors and out, frequently lawn work or snow-shoveling. They obtained jobs as maintenance workers or cashiers in the service industry. Occasionally, they held these types of jobs at their treatment, vocational, or drop-in centers, but also at the local library or restaurants. Of the competitive jobs they obtained, about one quarter could be classified as "informal," such as lawn maintenance. The remainder were generally unskilled but fully competitive, and included janitor, hot-dog cart vendor, home health aide, clerk, cashier, and cab driver.

Little evidence supported the notion of sheltered work as preparation for competitive work; it was markedly difficult to persuade individuals with sheltered jobs that it was worth chancing an entry into the competitive arena, particularly in light of a major economic recession. Sheltered work is unusually secure and reliable for people who are highly vulnerable to lay-offs during difficult economic times. It may also be of value in fully developed supported employment systems as the employer of last resort for those who have repeated failures, even using the best rehabilitative practices and most reasonable accommodations in competitive settings.

Clinical Status and Employment

The findings relating to the interaction of the clinical and vocational rehabilitation efforts suggest a model that has face value and also reflects the experience of the clinicians in this project. That is, employment success is enhanced by optimal response to optimal treatment provided during the preparation for entry into the competitive job market, and success in gaining and retaining employment appears to enhance clinical stability if clinical supports are continued. More precise statistical confirmation of the direction of the observed relationships in this study was difficult because the rehabilitation model itself stipulated that symptom improvement should both precede and result from entry into employment. Thus, the modest delay in initiating employment was deliberate but also effective. While seemingly at odds with a literal interpretation of the rapid placement approach, the average delay amounted to only a few months, probably the time necessary to compensate for the stress engendered by the new consumer-professional relationships, assessments, and job preparation activities inherent in all supported employment approaches. Moreover, some of the delay was at the choice of participants, many of whom wanted their first job during the study to suit their longer-term career aspirations, which took longer for some to achieve.

An appropriate caveat is that conclusive proof that symptom improvement enhances the likelihood of later employment would require finer grained measurement than was undertaken in this study. That employment may lead to improvement in clinical status has been claimed by many practitioners in the psychosocial literature, and one other study to date has empirically demonstrated such an effect (Bell & Lysaker, 1995). On the other hand, the present study offered no evidence that competitive employment carries risk of relapse.

These findings appear to support a brief delay in competitive job placement until a solid treatment relationship is established and the maximum possible symptom remission has been achieved. The finding that negative symptoms improved in FACT and became worse in CVR suggests that work improved the deficit syndrome, while inactivity worsened it. Thus, prolonged delay in initiating employment may be as great a risk as premature placement.

CONCLUSION

The principle implication of this study is that for those with severe mental illness, a combination of MFG treatment, ACT, and supported employment can achieve levels of competitive employment higher than those gained by a typical publicly operated CVR service system. Coordination of treatment and rehabilitation efforts is markedly more effective if the expert staff, family members, and/or caretaking friends are in close and continuous communication. The implications for state vocational rehabilitation services are less promising. The combination of higher attrition rates and poor competitive employment outcomes for CVR, in spite of its state-of-the-art clinical treatment, is a serious challenge to the effectiveness of some state-operated CVR services. The results of the current study mimic those of Drake and colleagues' study (Drake, McHugo et al., 1996), which used a similar comparison intervention. The best approach may be to establish mechanisms for reimbursing employment specialists to work on clinical teams.

REFERENCES

American Psychiatric Association. (1987). *Diagnostic and statistical manual of mental disorders (3rd ed., rev.).* Washington, DC: Author.

Anderson, C., Reiss, D., & Hogarty, G. (1986). *Schizophrenia and the family: A practitioner's guide to psychoeducation and management.* New York: Guilford Press.

Anthony, W. A., Cohen, M. R., & Vitalo, R. (1978). The measurement of rehabilitation outcome. *Schizophrenia Bulletin, 4,* 365–383.

Anthony, W. A., & Jansen, M. A. (1984). Predicting the vocational capacity of the chronically mentally ill. *American Psychologist, 39,* 537–544.

Bachrach, L. L. (1991). Service planning for chronic mental patients: Some principles. *International Journal of Group Psychotherapy, 41*(1), 23–31.

Becker, D. R., & Drake, R. E. (1994). Individual placement and support: A community mental health center approach to vocational rehabilitation. *Community Mental Health Journal, 30,* 519–532.

Bell, M. D., & Lysaker, P. H. (1995). Psychiatric symptoms and work performance among persons with severe mental illness. *Psychiatric Services, 46,* 508–510.

Bellack, A. S., & Mueser, K. T. (1993). Psychosocial treatment for schizophrenia. *Schizophrenia Bulletin, 19,* 317–36,

Bond, G. R. (1992). Vocational rehabilitation. In R.P. Liberman (Ed.), *Handbook of psychiatric rehabilitation* (pp. 244–263). New York: MacMillan.

Bond, G. R., & Boyer, S. L. (Eds.). (1988). *Rehabilitation programs and outcomes.* Baltimore: Johns Hopkins Press.

Chandler, D., Meisel, J., Hu, T., McGowen, M., & Madison, K. (1997b). A capitated model for a cross-section of severely mentally ill clients: Employment outcomes. *Community Mental Health Journal, 33,* 501–516.

Drake, R.E., Becker, D. R., Biesanz, J.C., Torrey, W. C., McHugo, G. J., & Wyzik, P. F. (1994). Rehabilitative day treatment vs supported employment: I. Vocational outcomes. *Community Mental Health Journal, 30,* 519–532.

Drake, R. E., Becker, D. R., Biesanz, J. C., Wyzik, P. F., & Torrey, W. C. (1996). Day treatment versus supported employment for persons with severe mental illness: A replication study. *Psychiatric Services, 47,* 1125–1127.

Drake, R. E., McHugo, G. J., Becker, D. R., Anthony, W. A., & Clark, R. E. (1996b). The New Hampshire study of supported employment for people with severe mental illness. *Journal of Consulting and Clinical Psychology, 64,* 391–399.

Endicott, J., & Spitzer, R. (1978). A diagnostic interview: The schedule for affective disorders and schizophrenia. *Archives of General Psychiatry, 35,* 837–844.

Falloon, I., Boyd, J., McGill, C., Williamson, M., Razani, J., Moss, H., Gilderman, A., & Simpson, G. (1985). Family management in the prevention of morbidity of schizophrenia. *Archives of General Psychiatry, 42,* 887–896.

Falloon, I. R. H., Boyd, I., & McGill, C. (1984). *Family care of schizophrenia.* New York: Guilford Press.

Falloon, I. R. H., & Pederson, J. (1985). Family management in the prevention of morbidity of schizophrenia: The adjustment of the family unit. *British Journal Psychiatry, 147,* 156–163.

Goldstein, M. J., Rodnick, E. H., Evans, J. R., May, P. R. A., & Steinberg, M. R. (1978). Drug and family therapy in the aftercare of acute schizophrenics. *Archives of General Psychiatry, 35,* 1169–1177.

Granovetter, M. (1973). The strength of weak ties. *American Journal of Sociology, 78,* 1360–1380.

Hogarty, G. E., Anderson, C. M., Reiss, D. J., Kornblith, S. J., Greenwald, D. P., Ulrich, R. F., & Carter, M. (199 1). Family psychoeducation, social skills training, and maintenance chemotherapy in the aftercare treatment of schizophrenia: II. Two-year effects of a controlled study on relapse and adjustment. *Archives of General Psychiatry, 48,* 340–347.

Kay, S., Fiszbein, A., & Opler, L. (1987). The positive and negative syndrome scale (PANSS) for schizophrenia. *Schizophrenia Bulletin, 13,* 261–276.

Knoedler, W. H. (1979). How the Training in Community Living Program helps patients work. *New Directions for Mental Health Services, 2,* 57–66.

Kopeikin, H., Marshall, V., & Goldstein, M. (1983). Stages and impact of crisis-oriented family therapy in the aftercare of acute schizophrenia. In W.R. McFarlane (Ed.), *Family therapy in schizophrenia* (pp. 69–98). New York: Guilford Press.

Leff, J. P., Kuipers, L., Berkowitz, R., & Sturgeon, D. (1984). A controlled trial of social intervention in the families of schizophrenic patients: Two year follow-up. *British Journal of Psychiatry, 146,* 594–600.

Lehman, A. F. (1995). Vocational rehabilitation in schizophrenia. *Schizophrenia Bulletin, 21,* 645–656.

Lehman, A. F., Carpenter, W. T., Jr., Goldman, H. H., & Steinwachs, D. M. (1995). Treatment outcomes in schizophrenia: Implications for practice, policy, and research. *Schizophrenia Bulletin, 21,* 669–675.

Lysaker, P., & Bell, M. (1995). Work rehabilitation and improvements in insight in schizophrenia. *Journal of Nervous and Mental Disease, 183,* 103–106.

McFarlane, W. (1990). Multiple family groups in the treatment of schizophrenia. In H. Nasrallah (Ed.), *Handbook of schizophrenia (Vol. 4),* pp. 167–189). Amsterdam: Elsevier.

McFarlane, W. R. (1994). Multiple-family groups and psychoeducation in the treatment of schizophrenia. *New Directions in Mental Health Services, 62,* 13–22.

McFarlane, W. R., Dushay, R. A., Stastny, P., Deakins, S. M., & Link, B. (1996). A comparison of two levels of Family-aided Assertive Community Treatment. *Psychiatric Services, 47,* 744–750.

McFarlane, W. R., Link, B., Dushay, R., Marchal, J., & Crilly, J. (1995a). Psychoeducational multiple family groups: Four-year relapse outcome in schizophrenia. *Family Process, 34*(2), 127–144.

McFarlane, W. R., Lukens, E., Link, B., Dushay, R., Deakins, S. A., Newmark, M., Dunne, E. J. , Horen, B., & Toran, J. (1995). Multiple-family groups and psychoeducation in the treatment of schizophrenia. *Archives of General Psychiatry, 52,*679–687.

Miller, S., & Wilden J. (1990). *Psychiatric rehabilitation manual.* Bronx, NY: Albert Einstein College of Medicine.

Okin, R.L., Borus, J. F., Baer, L., & Jones, A.L. (1996). Research update on the psychosocial treatment of schizophrenia. *American Journal of Psychiatry, 153,* 607–617.

Olfson, M. (1990). Assertive community treatment: An evaluation of the experimental evidence. *Hospital and Community Psychiatry, 41,* 634–641.

Russert, M. G., & Frey, J. L. (1991). The PACT vocational model: A step into the future. *Psychosocial Rehabilitation Journal, 14*(4), 7–18.

Spitzer, R. L., Williams, J. B. L., Gibbon, M., Burke, J., Keith, S. J., & Schooler, N. (1985). *Structured clinical interview for DSM-III-R: Psychotic disorders version.* New York: Biometric Research Unit, New York State Psychiatric Institute.

Stein, L. I., & Test, M. A. (1980). Alternative to mental hospital treatment: 1. Conceptual model, treatment program and clinical evaluation. *Archives of General Psychiatry, 37,* 392–397.

Strauss, J. S., & Carpenter, W. T. (1977). Prediction of outcome in schizophrenia. *Archives of General Psychiatry, 34,* 159–163.

Test, M. A. (1995, October). *Long-term employment outcome in the Program for Assertive Community Treatment.* Paper presented at the American Psychiatric Association Institute on Psychiatric Services, Boston.

Test, M. A., Knoedler, W. H., & Allness, D. J. (1985). The long-term treatment of young schizophrenics in a community support program. *New Directions for Mental Health Services, 26,* 17–27.

The Role of the Family in Psychiatric Rehabilitation

LeRoy Spaniol, Anthony M. Zipple, and Doris Lockwood

At the time of original publication, the authors' affiliations were as follows: LeRoy Spaniol, PhD, Senior Director for Publications, Center for Psychiatric Rehabilitation, Boston University; Executive Publisher of the *Psychiatric Rehabilitation Journal*; Anthony M. Zipple, ScD, Executive Director of Thresholds in Chicago; Doris Lockwood, PhD, (deceased), was Assistant Professor, Emmanuel College, Boston, MA, a member of the Massachusetts NAMI, and a psychologist in private practice.

This article was published previously in the *Schizophrenia Bulletin*, 1992, 18(3), 341–348, and is reprinted with permission.

Abstract: This article describes the multiple roles that families can play in the psychiatric rehabilitation process and suggests ways for professionals to collaborate with them. The authors discuss the family's experience of loss and their process of recovery; their caregiving role; their role in supporting other families; their teaching and educational role; their advocacy role; their role as researchers and research subjects; and some suggestions for supporting family roles.

During the past decade, the literature on helping families of persons with mental illness has broadened considerably. Reported approaches include psychoeducational groups (Hatfield & Lefley, 1987), emotional support mechanisms (Byalin et al., 1982), and models for training professionals to be more responsive to the needs of these families (Zipple & Spaniol, 1987).

One key to improving clinical collaboration between families who have a family member with a mental illness and mental health professionals is to help professionals understand the family's initial experience and their subsequent role in psychiatric rehabilitation. The onset of mental illness triggers major role changes in families that are not dissimilar to the role changes experienced by families of persons with other disabilities (Power & Dell Orto, 1980). Few families are prepared to deal with such traumatic role changes, especially when these changes are precipitously forced upon them (Hatfield, 1987; Spaniol, 1987; Terkelsen, 1987; Tessler et al., 1987).

Interestingly enough, professionals are often as unprepared as families to respond appropriately to this kind of profound crisis. In fact, we frequently see a parallel process in the emotional and cognitive responses of the mental health professional and the family: both feel helpless, angry, despairing, and anxious. The scarcity of useful helping models and the relative lack of solid scientific data about mental illness leave the psychiatrist, the psychologist, the social worker, or the mental health practitioner with little confi-

dence to help families. Most professionals have been taught about mental illness and some have been taught about families, but many professionals do
not understand families who have experienced mental illness. Indeed,
numerous studies have shown a dramatic difference between professionals'
perceptions of what families need and the families' own perceptions of their
needs (Hatfield et al., 1982; Spaniol & Zipple, 1988a).

The training that professionals receive often fails to provide the skills,
supervision, peer support, and validation necessary to assist families with
coping and adaptation skills (Wasow, 1982; Bernheim & Lehman, 1985;
Minkoff, 1987). On the contrary, professionals are frequently still taught that
families both cause and perpetuate the illness and decompensation of their
family member. These professional beliefs and attitudes, and the lack of
appropriate helping skills, coupled with a real sense of inadequacy due to lack
of knowledge and a "cure," often lay an extra burden of guilt on the newly
traumatized families (Terkelsen, 1983).

The Task Force on Families and Mental Illnesses of the California
Alliance for the Mentally Ill conducted a survey of California graduate training programs in the core mental health disciplines. They found that 53% of
all training programs surveyed still teach a theory of family causation for serious mental illness (NAMI Training Matters, 1991). Further, 82% of the programs reported that they prepare their students only "somewhat" or "not at
all" to work with families of people with mental illness. This is in spite of the
enormous interest during the last decade in educational and supportive
approaches for families with mentally ill members (Beels & McFarlane, 1982;
Leff et al., 1982; Falloon et al., 1984; Bernheim & Lehman, 1985; Anderson et
al., 1986). Unfortunately, the training received by professionals does not consistently reflect the value of these educational and supportive interventions.

It is little wonder that professionals fail to understand and value the role
of the family in psychiatric rehabilitation. Understanding of the family's
complex and highly charged emotional experience can give professionals a
basis on which to develop new techniques more helpful to the family.
Professionals can help families to see their experience as a natural result of a
traumatic crisis, one which requires new coping and adaptation skills. This
article describes the multiple roles that families can play in the psychiatric
rehabilitation process and suggests ways for professionals to collaborate with
them. We will discuss the family's experience of loss and their process of
recovery, their caregiving role, their role in supporting other families, their
teaching and educational role, their advocacy role, and their role as
researchers and research subjects.

COPING WITH TRAUMA: LOSS AND RECOVERY

The families of persons with mental illness experience a very difficult adjustment and recovery process that is likely to last for many years (Terkelsen, 1987; Tessler et al., 1987). They go through the normal shock, denial, depression, anger, acceptance, coping, and final affirmation of any person confronted with a traumatic illness (Power & Dell Orto, 1980; van der Kolk, 1987). In addition to the typical stages and tasks of adjustment, we are beginning to discover unique aspects of their adjustment process. For example, the lack of clarity around the process and outcome of mental illness results in many families regularly cycling through hope and then despair. While these shifts in feelings and the resultant behavior may at times seem quite extreme, painful, and confusing to families, the experience is quite normal. Professionals who do not understand the adjustment process of families frequently view these reactions as evidence of pathology.

During the early stages of their recovery process, families often experience severe guilt, embarrassment, and self-blame. Contact with caring and knowledgeable professionals is critical at this time because these feelings and beliefs may be intensified by contact with professionals who continue to believe that the family is the source of the problem. Families initially exhibit strong reliance on professionals, believing they will provide answers. As the persistence of the illness becomes apparent, pessimism and despair replace the unquestioning faith in the doctor and the mental health system. Professionals may experience angry and assertive families as negative and intrusive, misinterpreting their increasing alliance with other families as resistance to therapy. At this point, however, other families who have been through the same experience often have more to offer than professionals. When families begin to accept the limitations of what can be done, they focus more on the management of symptoms and improving the functioning of the family member with the mental illness. The professional's response at this point is crucial. Professionals often reject the family as its members become more assertive because they fear that this involvement will lead to a breach of confidentiality (Zipple et al., 1990).

As families experience less self-blame and more assertiveness, they show an increased interest in working more closely with knowledgeable and caring professionals. Family members also frequently find that they have changed, that they are no longer the people they were when the initial trauma occurred. They are more confident in the value of persistence and united action over time.

Professionals have dealt with losses just as families have. Understanding the families' experience as a loss experience requiring support, coping, and adaptive skills can lead to greater compassion and new competencies.

Parent and Caregiver

In typical families, parents serve a crucial caregiving role for other family members. While this is particularly evident in the case of supporting young, dependent children, this caregiving role often extends to adult family members who need special support. The special needs of a family member with a mental illness, coupled with a service system that can often be unresponsive, place many families into the role of primary caregiver (Thurer, 1983). This is usually not a role families freely choose for themselves. Further, they frequently lack the knowledge, skills, and support system required to provide specialized mental health care (Bernheim et al., 1982). In addition, not all families are equally well equipped to support their family member with a disability. Families who have a member with a mental illness include a broad range from families who are sophisticated and have extensive resources to families who may be struggling with other problems and are less able to offer significant assistance without personal support for themselves.

While families are eager to assist their family member with the disability, they believe that professionals should assume the role of primary caregiver (Fisher et al., 1989). Unfortunately, for many reasons, the mental health system has been unable and sometimes unwilling to provide the necessary services, and these gaps in service delivery have forced families to assume this responsibility themselves (Hatfield, 1981).

As professionals begin to assume their role of primary caregivers, families can still provide coaching around daily living and problem solving skills. Families can assist in administering medication and monitoring its side effects. Family gatherings provide social opportunities and families are also in a position to encourage and support friendships. Families can also support their disabled member's vocational and educational initiatives. Many of these suggestions are simply extensions of the normal parenting/caregiving role of families with any family member. However, they often assume a new level of importance and become more difficult to implement because of the disability.

There are some problems in caregiving that are particularly difficult for families that include a person with a mental illness. These include management of medication, bizarre and abnormal behavior, antisocial and aggressive behavior, social withdrawal and isolation, educational and career deficits, hygiene and appearance problems, and self-destructive and suicidal behavior. These problems require specialized and additional coping strategies, and families often find themselves alone and tormented in coping on a day-to-day basis (Spaniol, 1987; Spaniol & Zipple, 1988b). Professionals frequently lack the practical experience or training to adequately assist families. It is no wonder then that families who have achieved some stability in these areas quickly become primary resources for other families facing these same issues.

It is difficult and often frightening for families to manage the delicate balance between independence and age-appropriate behavior, such as living away from home, and the functional limitations imposed by the disability. Also, although most families struggle to separate from their caregiving role, they do not trust that their family member will be supported as he or she should be because of the current mental health structure and the financial climate of our times. Most families prefer to have the day-to-day caregiving provided and managed by an ongoing community support system (Lefley, 1990). The family's role should not be abused because of lack of community facilities. Professionals and family members need to find solutions together. Families do not want to take over the mental health system, but they do want to radically change it.

Supporting Other Families

Gartner and Riessman (1982) have written about the profound importance of self-help and mutual aid groups in supporting individuals with special needs. Families of persons with mental illness have organized their own mutual aid groups and have become an essential source of support for each other. The National Alliance for the Mentally Ill is the largest and best known of these groups in the United States; it has grown from a few hundred family members in 1979 to over 130,000 in 1991. These groups nurture and support their members and also promote the roles of family members as advocates and teachers. No one can understand the pain of these families as well as other families in the same situation. Professionals can help families in many ways, but not with the kind of healing that one family member gives to another.

One of the primary functions of peer support is to provide families a place to share their stories about coping with mental illness. Because it is such a profoundly distressing experience, one that leaves them feeling helpless, bruised, alone, and vulnerable, families need to be heard in a non-blaming atmosphere such as their peer group. Through these groups, families can develop more effective coping mechanisms. They can mourn their loss and feel validated in their experience, and from this their ability to cope begins to grow. Even when there are no answers, families can learn to live better with what they cannot change. Families are the most important resource for one another in developing strategies for successful coping (Spaniol, 1987).

A final function of the peer support system is to highlight the limitations of the current service system and delineate the family's role in the psychiatric rehabilitation process. Families are keenly aware of the limitations of the service their family member is receiving and they know what techniques, community services, and professional help are required. Peer support and effort are clearly important in implementing any changes that need to be made. As families move into a more active role, they need less support for their own adjustment and more for their outside activities as advocates and teachers.

Teacher and Educator

As families experience less self-blame and become more assertive, they develop an increased interest in working more closely with knowledgeable and caring professionals. In some cases families have become especially knowledgeable and may even know more than many professionals, particularly about some aspects of their own relative's illness. This knowledge is an important resource in the rehabilitation process. For example, they know their family member's reaction to life stresses, strengths and weaknesses, and reactions to the illness and to the interventions of the mental health system. This family knowledge is an important addition to the knowledge professionals gain from their experience with their client.

Families also need to educate professionals about how they experience the mental illness of their family member and to confront the negative beliefs some professionals hold toward families. Professionals need to see the family's experience as valid and normal. One way in which families can educate professionals is by helping to train professionals to work with other families and with persons who have a mental illness (Zipple & Spaniol, 1987).

Families are also important educators for providers of mental health services. They can monitor and provide feedback to programs on how they are functioning and on how well clients are being served (McElroy, 1987). They can also be an important source of imaginative ideas about program changes and innovations and encourage providers to maintain their commitment to the most severely disabled.

Advocate

Families have begun to realize that even sensitive professionals and sympathetic legislators have their own interests to protect and cannot adequately speak for them. Families have therefore assumed a much more direct role in changing the mental health system. Advocacy is a healthy response to the hopelessness that families often feel. When families learn to be more helpful to themselves and to their family member with mental illness, when they begin to feel their impact on the mental health system, when they see laws, policies, and legislative practices change because of their influence, then they feel empowered, confident, and truly hopeful about their ability to affect their own lives and those of their family member who has a disability. Advocacy is also a natural and a necessary stage in the adjustment and recovery process of families.

Advocating for services for individual family members is one aspect of family advocacy. Families are advocating for a balanced service system, including accredited hospitals, improved medications, more enlightened rehabilitation programs, supported housing, supported work, supported education, and other programs which support community integration. Families are also in the vanguard of those advocating for the adoption of new treatment methodologies. They support programs that treat their family members as individuals and prepare them with useful skills that they can present to society.

Because families know that gains for their family member mean gains for other people who have a mental illness, their concern goes beyond their own situation. They have a shared sense of effort and advocacy with one another. Advocacy brings families out of the shadows, making the inherent strengths of families more available to the greater community and building the families' sense of confidence in their ability to make a difference for their family member and for others. Advocacy strengthens the potential for healing within families and within society.

Families want to be seen as partners in the psychiatric rehabilitation process and advocacy is a way to shift the balance of power between families and professionals (Bernheim, 1987). This requires a change in the way professionals relate to families (Spaniol & Zipple, 1984). Advocacy is fostered primarily by the support process within the family movement, but it is difficult for some professionals to support family advocacy when they are often its primary target. Also, some professionals are not prepared to deal with intact and assertive families. The family's shift toward advocacy is why professional support begins to have diminishing returns as families move further on in their own recovery process. It is also one reason why family support groups led by professionals have only limited usefulness (Zipple & Spaniol, 1991). As families get better at coping, they need the support of other families to move into personal, organizational, and legislative advocacy.

Professionals can also benefit from family advocacy. Families can bring pressure to bear on the mental health system and its funding sources that professionals alone could never bring about. Families are determined to make major changes in the way clients are served by changing how professionals are trained, how programs are operated, and how systems are funded, planned, and managed. Many professionals have also wanted these changes, but they have not felt sufficiently empowered to bring them about.

Researcher and Research Subject

In spite of the tremendous advances that have been made in the past 20 years, the profession's knowledge of the experience of families coping with mental illness is still in its infancy. Recently, families have been able to recognize the importance of their participation in research projects and have conceived and implemented their own research (Johnson, 1992). They have also filled out questionnaires and have been interviewed, both of which take time and often raise painful memories and issues. Even though families have good reason to be somewhat cautious about participating in research projects because of the risk that some forms of research might simply continue the many myths about families and mental illness (Hatfield et al., 1987), many families are highly committed to having their experience validated. They want to influence the mental health profession's perception of them and thus be involved in making an exceptional contribution to the field. This collaboration requires great humility on the part of professionals because the role of helper often gets reversed. It also forces professionals to come closer to sharing the grief, pain, discouragement, and anger that families often experience.

SUGGESTIONS FOR SUPPORTING FAMILY ROLES

Professionals play a crucial role in supporting families in these new roles. This is not always a comfortable position. Previous training (Minkoff, 1987), concerns about confidentiality (Zipple et al., 1990), and their own feelings of frustration as they attempt to assist their clients can interfere with the professional's ability to be helpful. While each professional will want to develop his or her own ways to support families in their roles, the following are some general guidelines (Spaniol et al., 1984):

- *Clarify roles.* Professionals can be open to negotiating and clarifying with families the varied roles that they play. These roles can change over time for the same family. Professionals can be observant of the changing needs, abilities, and willingness of families and assertive in suggesting and encouraging their assumption of new roles.

- *Work as a team.* Consider developing a team approach to working with families. Utilize families as collaborative adjuncts to a professional practice. Most families want to work cooperatively, and both the professional and the disabled family member will discover valuable benefits from such a collaborative relationship (Lefley & Johnson, 1990).

- *Use educational approaches.* Families often feel comfortable in the role of "learner" and are anxious to assimilate all of the information and advice professionals have to offer them. They can then go on to act as educators for peers, professionals, and their own family member with a mental illness.

- *Include families in planning and system monitoring groups.* Family members can provide input into program evaluation, system planning, human rights issues, and monitoring. Inviting family members to assume these positions and supporting their roles at this level will be very helpful to both the family and the mental health system.

- *Learn to respond to intense feelings.* Families often report a long history of frustration and even abuse by mental health professionals. Their feelings are deeply felt and may be expressed at unexpected times or with great intensity. Families need professionals to listen with understanding and compassion, rather than defensiveness, to what they are saying.

- *Meet local support groups.* Professionals can get to know families in their area by visiting their meetings and finding out what their concerns and strengths are. These groups are a great resource for recruiting family members who are interested in new roles. Some professionals have compiled lists of family groups in their area and distributed them to other professionals. If you are part of an agency, consider an agency liaison for the family groups. This person can help to update other professionals in the agency on the needs, concerns, and availability of family members. Make yourself available as a resource to a local family group. Volunteer to share information through formal presentations or group discussion. Ask family members in to talk to your staff. Invite their comments on your program and how it might better serve their needs. Join the National Alliance for the Mentally Ill as a professional member.

- *Acknowledge diverse beliefs.* Learn to acknowledge that there is a wide variety of beliefs and needs in the mental health field. Families may often disagree with you just as other mental health professionals often do! The professional's learned assumptions, allegiances, and loyalties may be regularly challenged as he or she begins to get more involved with families. Learning to accept these challenges is an important part of supporting families in new roles.

- *Point out family strengths.* A major part of supporting families in new roles is letting them know that they have a great deal to offer. Be specific in acknowledging their abilities and in describing how these competencies will support them in new roles.

- *Develop your own supports.* Because of new stresses and challenges that they will likely encounter working in new ways with families, it is important for professionals to develop their own support network.

Working with families in their varied roles will not come easily, and professionals will need their own support resources to debrief their experiences, share successes and failures, gain new knowledge, and learn new skills.

- *Be clear about your limitations.* Be clear with families about the complexity of the disability and the limitations of current knowledge and resources to treat it. Let families know that you are also struggling to help their family member. This awareness will help families come to terms with their own hopes, fears, and limitations. Awareness will also prepare them to be partners in developing workable expectations and plans for programs, the mental health system, and their own family member's rehabilitation,

CONCLUSION

Families play a crucial role in the vital area of psychiatric rehabilitation, and professionals can learn to work more cooperatively with them. The different roles of families in the psychiatric rehabilitation process have the potential to benefit the family member with the disability, the family itself, and the mental health system.

REFERENCES

Anderson, C. M., Reiss, D. J., & Hogarty, G. E. (1986). *Schizophrenia and the family: a practitioner's guide to psychoeducation and management.* New York: Guilford Press.

Beels, C. C., & McFarlane, W. R. (1982). Family treatments of schizophrenia: Background and state of the art. *Hospital and Community Psychiatry, 33,* 541–550.

Bernheim, K. F. (1987). Family consumerism: Coping with the winds of change. In A. B. Hatfield and H. D. Lefley (Eds.), *Families of the mentally ill: Coping and adaptation,* (pp. 244–260). New York: Guilford Press.

Bernheim, K. F., & Lehman, A. F. (1985). *Working with families of the mentally ill. New York: W.W. Norton & Company.*

Bernheim, K. F., Lewine, R. R. J., & Beale, C. T. (1982). *The caring family: Living with chronic mental illness.* New York: Random House.

Byalin, K., Jed, J., & Lehman, S. (September, 1982). *Family intervention with treatment-refractory chronic schizophrenics.* Presented at the 20th International Congress of Applied Psychology, Edinburgh, Scotland.

Falloon, I. R. H., Boyd, J. L., & McGill, C. W. (1984). *Family care of schizophrenia.* New York: Guilford Press.

Fisher, H., Spaniol, L., Zipple, A. M., & Corapi, A. (1989). The family and psychiatric rehabilitation: A family/professional perspective. In M. Farkas and W. Anthony, (Eds.), *Psychiatric rehabilitation program services: Putting theory into practice*, (pp. 216–225). Baltimore, MD: Johns Hopkins University Press.

Gartner, A. J., & Riessman, F. (1982). Self-help and mental health. *Hospital and Community Psychiatry, 33*, 631–635.

Hatfield, A. B. (1981). Self-help groups for families of the mentally ill. *Social Work, 26*, 408–413.

Hatfield, A. B. (1987). Systems resistance to effective family coping. In A.T. Meyerson (Ed.), Barriers to treating the chronic mentally ill, *New Directions for Mental Health Services, No. 33*, (pp. 51–62). San Francisco: Jossey-Bass.

Hatfield, A. B., Fierstein, R., & Johnson, D. (1982). Meeting the needs of families of the psychiatrically disabled. *Psychosocial Rehabilitation Journal, 6*, 27–40.

Hatfield, A. B., & Lefley, H. P., (1987). *Families of the mentally ill: Coping and adaptation*. New York: Guilford Press.

Hatfield, A. B., Spaniol, L., & Zipple, A. M. (1987). Expressed emotion: A family perspective. *Schizophrenia Bulletin, 13*, 221–226.

Johnson, D. (1992). Training psychologists to work with people with serious mental illness: A survey of directors of clinical psychology training programs. *Innovations and Research, 1*(2), 25–30..

Leff, J. P., Kuipers, L.,.Berkowitz, R., Eberbein-Vries, R., & Sturgeon, D. A. (1982). A controlled trial of social intervention in the families of schizophrenic patients. *British Journal of Psychiatry, 141*, 121–134.

Lefley, H. (1990). Rehabilitation in mental illness: Insights from other cultures. *Psychosocial Rehabilitation Journal, 14*, 5–12.

Lefley, H., & Johnson, D. L. (1990). *Families as allies in the treatment of the mentally ill: New directions for mental health professionals*. Washington, DC: American Psychiatric Press.

McElroy, E. M. (1987). Sources of distress among families of the hospitalized mentally ill. In A. B. Hatfield (Ed.), Families of the mentally ill: meeting the challenges. *New Directions for Mental Health Services, No. 34*, (pp. 61–72). San Francisco: Jossey-Bass.

Minkoff, K. (1987). Resistance of mental health professionals to working with the chronic mentally ill. In A. B. Hatfield (Ed.), Barriers to treating the chronic mentally ill. *New Directions for Mental Health Services, No. 33*, (pp. 3–20). San Francisco: Jossey-Bass.

NAMI Training Matters. (1991). Newsletter of the NAMI Curriculum and Training Network, *1*, 2–3.

Power, P., & Dell Orto, A., (Eds.) (1980). *The role of the family in the rehabilitation of the physically disabled*. Austin, TX: PRO-ED.

Spaniol, L. (1987). Coping strategies of family caregivers. In A. B. Hatfield and H. Lefley (Eds.), *Families of the mentally ill: Coping and adaptation*, (pp. 208–224). New York: Guilford Press.

Spaniol, L., & Zipple, A. M. (1984). How professionals can share power with families: A practical approach to working with families of the mentally ill. *Psychosocial Rehabilitation Journal, 8,* 77–84.

Spaniol, L., & Zipple, A. M. (1988a). Family and professional perceptions of family needs and coping strengths. *Rehabilitation Psychology, 33,* 37–45.

Spaniol, L., & Zipple, A. M. (1988b). *Coping strategies for families of people who are psychiatrically disabled.* Unpublished manuscript. Boston, MA: Center for Psychiatric Rehabilitation, Boston University.

Spaniol, L., Zipple, A. M., & FitzGerald, S. (1984). How professionals can share power with families: Practical approaches to working with families of the mentally ill. *Psychosocial Rehabilitation Journal, 8,* 77–84.

Terkelsen, K. G. (1983). Schizophrenia and the family, II: Adverse effects of family therapy. *Family Process, 22,* 191–200.

Terkelsen, K. G. (1987). The evolution of family responses to mental illness through time. In A. B. Hatfield and H. D. Lefley, (Eds.), *Families of the mentally ill: Coping and adaptation,* (pp. 151–166). New York: Guilford Press.

Tessler, R. C., Killian, L. M., & Gubman, G. (1987). Stages in family response to mental illness: An ideal type. *Psychosocial Rehabilitation Journal, 10,* 3–17.

Thurer, S. (1983). Deinstitutionalization and women: Where the buck stops. *Hospital and Community Psychiatry 34,* 1162–1163.

van der Kolk, B. (1987). *Psychological trauma.* Washington, DC: American Psychiatric Press.

Wasow, M. (1982). *Coping with schizophrenia: A survival manual for parents, relatives, and friends.* Palo Alto, CA: Science and Behavior Books.

Zipple, A. M., Langle, S., & Spaniol, L. (1990). Confidentiality and the family. *Community Mental Health Journal, 26,* 533–545.

Zipple, A. M., & Spaniol, L. (1987). *Families that include a mental illness: What they need and how to provide it.* (A trainer's manual). Boston, MA: Center for Psychiatric Rehabilitation Boston University.

Zipple, A. M., & Spaniol, L. (1991). *Guidelines for professionals for developing family support and educational programs.* Unpublished manuscript. Boston, MA: Center for Psychiatric Rehabilitation Boston University.

Meanwhile, Back on the Ward . . .

Jay Neugeboren

Jay Neugeboren is the author of a number of nonfiction and fiction works, including: *Transforming Madness: New Lives for People Living with Mental Illness, Imagining Robert, Open Heart: A Patient's Story of Life Saving Medicine and Life Giving Friendship, The Stolen Jew,* and *Before My Life Began.*

This essay was published previously in *American Scholar,* Summer 1994, and in the *Psychiatric Rehabilitation Journal,* 1995, 19/2, 75–81, and is reprinted with permission.

At 3:00 A.M., on a cool summer night—a few hours after my youngest son has graduated from high school—I find myself cruising the deserted streets of Northampton, Massachusetts searching for the 50-year-old man who is my brother. I have considered calling the police, but I know that, if a policeman actually finds my brother and approaches him, Robert might, as in the past, panic and become violent.

My brother Robert has spent most of his life, since the age of 19, in mental hospitals and psychiatric wards in and around New York City. The list is long: Hillside, Creedmoor, Elmhurst, Gracie Square, Mid-Hudson, Bellevue, Kings County, Rikers Island, South Beach, and others.

Robert had, until the time of his first breakdown in 1962, been a delightful, popular and gifted boy and young man—talented at dancing, acting, and singing, invariably winning the lead in school and camp plays and skits. He'd had a love and talent for tennis, writing, and chess (he was in a chess club with Bobby Fischer at Erasmus Hall High School in Brooklyn, but Fischer refused to play with him; 'With you, Neugeboren, I don't play,' he always said to me," Robert says. Why not? "Because," Robert says, smiling, "I played crazy"). He was a good if erratic student in high school, won a New York State Regents Scholarship to college, and successfully completed his freshman year at CCNY. He was, in short, a bright and idiosyncratic young man with a sense of life and humor all his own, a person who, until his first breakdown, showed no signs (except for those that, looking back, any of us might find in ourselves) that such a breakdown was at all likely, much less inevitable.

Robert's diagnosis has changed frequently in the past 30 years, depending largely upon which drugs have been successful in keeping him calm, stable, or compliant. He was schizophrenic when enormous doses of Thorazine and Stelazine calmed him; he was manic depressive (bipolar) when lithium worked; he was manic-depressive-with-psychotic-symptoms or hypomanic when Tegretol or Depakote (anti-convulsants), or some new anti-psychotic or anti-depressant—Trilafon, Adapin, Mellaril, Haldol—promised to make him cooperative; and he was schizophrenic (again) when various doctors promised cures through insulin coma therapy or megadose vitamin therapy or gas therapy. At the same time, often in an attempt to minimize side effects, other drugs were poured into him: Artane, Benadryl, Cogentin, Kemadrin, Symmetrel, Prolixin, Pamelor, Navane....

During these years, Robert also participated in a long menu of therapies: group therapy, family therapy, multi-group family therapy, Marxist therapy, Gestalt therapy, psychoanalytically-oriented psychotherapy, goal-oriented therapy, art therapy, milieu therapy, et al. Most often, though—the more chronic his condition, the truer this became—he received no therapy at all. It is as if, I often think, the very history of the ways in which our century has dealt with those it calls mentally ill has, for more than 30 years now, been passing through my brother's mind and body.

Robert and I talk with each other almost every day and see each other often, sometimes in New York, sometimes in Massachusetts, and though our visits are not without their difficulties (why should we be different from other brothers?), visits in my home, with my children, have invariably been without incident.

"I've never seen Uncle Robert this way," each of my children said to me, the day before and the day after my son Eli's graduation. "Is he going to be all right? Can I help?" And then: "And what about you, Pop? Are you going to be all right?"

My son Eli returned home from his all-night (supervised) graduation party at the local county fairgrounds at about 6:00 A.M., and Robert arrived not long after that and ordered me to put him on a bus for New York immediately. He looked ghastly (he had—inexpertly—given himself a haircut and shaved off his mustache) and seemed altogether disoriented: his hands and arms were flapping uncontrollably, his body was hunched over, his eyeglasses were covered with a milk-white sticky substance ("Scum!" he declared, when I asked), his movements were jagged, and he kept turning on me and screaming things that made no obvious sense. Whether I did or did not reply, he became more and more enraged, telling me again and again that I wasn't listening to him, that I never listened to him, and that if I didn't do what he said, he didn't know what he might do.

At the bus stop he scurried around wildly, virtually on all fours, picking up cigarette butts and looking for money. Then he went to each of a half-dozen sidewalk newspaper kiosks and began putting quarters in them, taking out papers, and either stacking them on top of the kiosks, or putting them in a mailbox. He went back and forth to a pay phone, dialing for information about people on Staten Island and yelling at the operator; he walked across the street to a parking lot and shouted questions at me.

I had been in situations like this with Robert before—dozens of times through the past 30 years—and though, as I said to my children, seeing Robert like this was not new for me, each time it happened it took me by surprise, and each time it happened, it seemed unutterably sad and heartbreaking.

How could it be that somebody who was so warm and loving, so charming and happy one moment—one day, one hour—could become so angry and lost moments later? And how could it be that each time it happened—no matter the years gone by—it felt as if it were happening for the first time?

With the years, I've learned to cope with these situations—to be able to help me and Robert get through. Though with the years Robert has actually reversed the path his life had been on (despite the dreadful prognostications, he had come, in recent years, to be able to spend more time out of hospitals than in them, to have made more of a life for himself than most people had dreamt possible), I still found myself going through litanies of familiar questions and doubts: Should I call the local police and have them take him to a hospital and deal with getting him back to New York City? Should I ask Robert where he had been all night, and if he had been drinking, and if he thought he could get back to the city by himself? Should I leave my children and try to drive Robert the 200 miles back to Staten Island?

What could I do that might ease his pain and confusion—that might minimize damage? If he were in free fall, as it were, was there anything I could do to help buffer the fall, so that, instead of plummeting downwards ten stories before he crashed, he could bounce down gently after, say, only falling a few steps? Should I say anything at all, and was there a right thing or wrong thing to say, and was there anyone I could call on who could help get us through? Or, was it better to say nothing and to just leave him be?

How much of what was going on with Robert was frightening my children or taking away from their celebration and reunion? Was it best to shield them from the worst of Robert's troubles? Or should I inform them more fully of what was happening—of my fears, and of my intentions? In a situation like this, despite the many times I'd been here before, and despite all that I thought I knew about myself and Robert and about how to handle these situations, what I felt most of all was an overwhelming sadness and helplessness. Who knew if there was anything at all that might ease things, or make them less awful? Who knew, really, what to do?

What I did finally—what I found myself doing—was what I've been doing more and more through the years: simply trusting my instincts, and Robert's. I found myself acting on my belief that, despite all, Robert still knew himself, even at a time like this, better than anyone else did, and that if he was determined to get back to Staten Island by himself, he would.

Robert had stayed far away from my children most of the time during his three days with us, and—his innate kindness, as ever, at work—had kept both his anger and his confusion hidden, for the most part, when in their presence. Still, each of them noticed what a hard time he was having, and each came to me and offered sympathy and help.

When, while changing from cap and gown into casual clothes for his graduation party, Eli asked if he could do anything to help with Robert, I told him the best thing he could do was to go off and enjoy the party, that Robert was my responsibility, not his. Eli had replied, "But he's mine, too, Pop."

I smiled. "Maybe, I said. But today is your day. This one's on me, okay?"

My sense of the fear and humiliation (along with the logistical problems) that would result from having local agencies deal with getting Robert from Massachusetts to New York, or my trying to deal with him in a locked car for 4 or 5 hours (a week before his first breakdown in 1962, he had, while we were going 70 miles an hour on a highway, opened the car door and threatened to jump), reinforced my instincts to believe that the best immediate solution was the simplest one: to let Robert get back to his home by himself and as quickly as he could.

So I did what I usually do when things get bad for Robert. I tried, gently and firmly, to be as patient and direct with him as I could. I told him, for example, that I would call ahead to his halfway house to let them know he was on his way and asked him if he wanted me to drive him to Staten Island. When he came near to me—and when he walked off and seemed especially lost—I put my arms around him and talked to him and told him I loved him.

While people waiting for the bus stared, or tried not to stare, or moved away, Robert stayed close to me and seemed to be listening. I was glad he'd been able to visit, I said, and I wished he wasn't having such a hard time again, and we'd talk on the phone that evening after he was back at his halfway house, and I was very glad he'd been able to be here for Eli's graduation, and we would see one another again soon.

Robert navigated the long trip home—bus, subway, ferry, and bus—successfully. We spoke that night—he cried a lot, said he hoped he hadn't embarrassed my children, and then he was off on flights of words that, because I knew the reference points (events and people from our childhood, jokes we loved, experiences we'd been through together), seemed more poignant than strange. The following morning, for the first time in a year, and for at least the fiftieth time in his life, he was hospitalized.

When I called the doctor in charge of Robert's ward, he asked what I thought had precipitated Robert's break. I answered by saying that there were some immediate causes that seemed obvious, but that the real precipitant, it seemed to me, was simply the fact of Robert's life—of the last 31 years of his life. If you'd been where Robert had been, and had suffered all the drugs and abuse and incompetence and pain he had suffered, the wonder, it seemed to me, wasn't why he'd broken again, but why he hadn't, like so many others he'd known, died or killed himself or deteriorated completely.

But after I said this, I did name some of the things that had been going on in Robert's life that might have precipitated this break. There was the graduation and being with family (but Robert had been in this situation dozens of times before and had had no difficulties). There were his desires and fantasies about living with me in Massachusetts, now intensified because Eli would be going off to college and I would be living alone. (But I've been the single full-time parent of three for many years, and though Robert had often asked about moving in with me, I'd never encouraged him, and he himself had been saying he didn't think it a good idea.) There was the fact that, a few weeks before, Robert's best friend had been moved out of the home in which he and Robert had lived together for 2 years and to which Robert had been hoping to return soon (so where would he live now?). There was also the fact that he had been out of the hospital for 11 months, and the better he became—the more alert, the more himself—the less the make-work activities of the hospital's day center interested him, and the more bored he became.

Though I could, as ever, talk about what I thought had caused Robert's condition, long-term and short-term, the more important question, it seemed to me, wasn't what had caused this breakdown, or any of the others, but what, given his life, had enabled him to survive, and to do more than survive—to retain his generosity, his warmth, his humor, and his sense of self. This, it seemed to me, was the true miracle and mystery.

I had, not long before, asked Robert the same questions the doctor asked me. Did he ever have any sense of what made him go off the way he did sometimes—of what the difference was, of what made things change for him, or in him? He had been silent for a long time and then had said, "No answer."

These were, I said at once, afraid that my questions might have hurt him, questions for which nobody seemed to have the answers.

"So why should I know?" Robert said then. "Am I different from anybody else?"

The doctor concluded that Robert's breakdown had been precipitated by alcohol and substance abuse. Robert had admitted that, on the way up to visit me, he had had a few beers and had inhaled amyl nitrite. The alcohol and substance abuse, the doctor said, had destabilized the parts of Robert's brain that his medications—lithium and Depakote—had stabilized. The problem, therefore, was non-compliance.

I had heard this from doctors many times before, and I responded with the obvious question: Okay, but what was it that had caused the noncompliance? If mental illness was as debilitating and awful a condition as it seemed to be (as surely it had been for Robert), and if the medications alleviated that condition, why would anyone ever stop taking the medications, or do anything to interfere with their beneficial effects? As my father had once put it, to a doctor who refused to continue treating Robert because Robert had stopped taking his pills. "So where, Doctor, is the pill to make him want to take the pills?"

When I visited Robert after his breakdown, on a locked unit at South Beach Psychiatric Center on Staten Island, he was, as he had been before, on isolation: living, day after day, 24-hours a day, in a bare room in which there was nothing but a bed and a dresser. This was called "reduced stimulation."

When I had previously questioned, as gently as I could, whether being on isolation, and on heavy doses of Thorazine (which Robert hated above all drugs), and not being permitted to make or receive calls or visitors, might not feel to Robert like punishment instead of therapy, the staff psychologist had replied that this might temporarily be the case. "But our experience," he said, "is that in retrospect patients come to appreciate the reduction of stimulation—the limits and boundaries that have been set for them."

He had also assured me that Robert was not just locked away in a, room—that every hour on the half hour, for 5 minutes, he was taken to the bathroom and for a walk down the hallway. When I asked if Robert had or would be receiving any therapy, the therapist's reply was abrupt: "Robert cannot tolerate therapy."

This seemed to me an absurd statement—Robert couldn't tolerate therapy? You mean you can't tolerate trying to work with him, I wanted to scream. Why are you a therapist if you don't want to work with patients, to listen to them? And when will Robert be able to "tolerate" therapy—when he's well?

But it was the same old story, and I was in the same old quandary: if I complained too much, or confronted the hospital's staff with their inadequacies, or sent off the letters I composed in my head, I feared they would only talk with me less, care for Robert less.

Robert had been here, in this ward and ones like it, and in even worse places more than once before. (One time at Mid-Hudson, I remembered him telling me, when they had him in a straitjacket for a long period of time, he asked for a smoke so he could let the ashes fall on the jacket and set himself on fire. He succeeded. After the aides got him out of the straitjacket, one of them took him to the basement, beat him up, warned him never to do what he had done again.)

Now, because of my visit, Robert has been granted courtyard privileges, and we sit by ourselves in the small courtyard at a picnic table. He opens the bag of food I've brought for him for lunch, but his hands are shaking so badly that when he tries to eat an egg salad sandwich, the egg salad sprays everywhere. He is apologetic and embarrassed. I talk with him easily, we joke back and forth, and after a short while I scoop up pieces of egg, tomato, lettuce, and bread, he takes his false teeth out, and I feed him with my fingers, placing the food directly into his mouth.

When he cannot stand the shaking, he walks away. He calls to me, and I sit next to him on a bench, and we talk about the ward, and the doctors, and my trip down, about Eli's graduation, and the floods in the Midwest, and our cousins. Suddenly Robert turns, leans down, and, with great gentleness, kisses the back of my hand several times, after which he begins weeping.

"Oh, Jay, Jay" he cries softly. "They're barbarians here. Barbarians, barbarians! Pavlovians...."

He presses his mouth to the back of my hand, and I take him to me, hold him close. A few minutes later, we walk around the courtyard. Then he tells me that he likes to walk back and forth, in a diagonal, between two trees—they are about 10 yards apart—and count the number of times. So we walk back and forth together, and I sing to him, and then he joins in—putting his arm around my waist, leaning on my shoulder—and we go back and forth again and again, loudly singing old camp songs we remember from our childhood.

He eats some more, and then we walk again, side by side, our hands clasped behind us, mimicking two diplomats, trading stories and news. He clutches his dentures in one hand, a piece of bread locked in their bite, and when he puts the top bridge back in his mouth, I say something about his being on uppers.

He starts giggling, inserts the lower bridge.

"And now you're on lowers," I say, and add that I don't understand why, since he's on uppers and lowers, which probably balance one another, the hospital has to give him any other medications.

"It's how they make their profit," he says.

When I call Robert from Massachusetts after our visit, he is flying—repeating everything he says twice, rambling on about people living and dead as if they are there with him on the ward, thanking me for visiting him and for the things I brought him, giving me lists of all the foods he has eaten and all the things he wants me to send him, mixing these lists with references to scenes in movies and scenes from our childhood, talking about Adlai Stevenson and Bill Clinton (who is, he says, his son) and how the whole country is in a very big depression—and all the while he keeps telling me he has to hang up, he has to hang up. When he finally takes a breath, and I tell him I love him, his voice suddenly drops and slows down, and he talks to me in a way that is entirely natural. "Oh Jay," he says, "don't you see? There's nothing better in my life than what's happening! You don't know. You don't know, Jay. You don't want to know." He weeps freely, keeps talking. "This life of working here and there in hospitals, or as a volunteer, and being here now, and doing nothing—isn't there ever going to be anything better for me? Please get me out of here, Jay. Please, please...."

When, later in our conversation, I tell him that I called him the day before but nobody could find him, he asks me what I called him, and when I say, "I called you my brother," he laughs, says, "That's an old one, Jay. That's an old one—but listen, I'm going to switch the phone to my good ear, all right?"

"There," he says, a few seconds later. "Now can you hear me better?"

Moved as I am by Robert's situation and his life—and his plea for a life different from the one he has —I find, after our visit and our talk, that I am feeling relieved, and, even, mildly exhilarated. Because the truth (I shrug when I realize this, as if to say, to myself: What can I do? That's the way it is.) is that when we're together, whether in my home or on his ward, whether on the West Side of Manhattan (where we lived next door to one another during his first year out of Creedmoor) or in Atlantic City (where, 6 weeks before Eli's graduation, we went together for 2 days at his request to celebrate his fiftieth birthday), we're happy. Not always, and not without a pervasive sense of loss and sadness, but happy to be with each other, no matter the context, because it seems good, simply, in an often frightening and miserable life, to be known and to be able to be near the person who knows you and is known by you.

During the weeks that follow Robert's hospitalization, we talk regularly. I visit him and send notes and gifts, and whenever we talk, Robert asks about each of my children, his niece and two nephews. Though our talks sometimes last for less than a minute, and though sometimes he is angry (at doctors, at me, at life) and sometimes sad, and sometimes high—and though sometimes I am nearly swept away by grief, from my sense of all that he senses his life has become and has not become—I find, strangely enough, real pleasure, as ever, in our time spent together.

This happens not only because I know Robert's patterns, if patterns they are, fairly well, but because I know that once his sense of humor returns (and once he begins opening up to me in direct ways about his feelings and needs), his recovery will follow and that he will be back before long in the real world most of us live in. It happens simply because, that is, for better or worse, our lives, in a crucial time for each of us, have once again been joined.

In a few months, Robert will probably, as in the past, get out of his ward and return to his halfway house. If things go well there, he will move from the halfway house into an apartment, and we'll probable go to Atlantic City together again, and we'll see each other more frequently than ever. We'll talk and laugh and trade jokes, argue and complain and become irritable with one another, reminisce and make plans, and go on trips. And he'll gradually tell me, without my asking (as he has already begun to do), about what he did and where he went on the night of Eli's graduation, and that too will become part of the history we share.

The more I know about him, the more I'll wonder about how he came to be who he is. What continues to surprise—but why?—is that the more I know Robert and know about him, the more I'll want to know. And this will only increase, not the sadness of his life, but its wonder.

Several weeks after Eli's graduation, while Robert is still on isolation in his ward at South Beach, I come across a full-page advertisement in the *New York Times* sponsored by NARSAD (the National Alliance for Research on Schizophrenia and Depression), an organization founded by the four most prominent mental health groups in the United States, that talks about the many urgent scientific projects that are paving the way for better treatments and the cure we all hope for. The cure? I want to scream. "New hope of a breakthrough cure is on the horizon," the ad proclaims, "as we start to iden-tify the genetic markers that cause depression."

The ad sets forth the current and conventional wisdom about depres-sion and mental illness: its symptoms, the suffering it brings, the numbers of people afflicted. What the ad says echoes what I've read in most literature put out by mental health professionals and agencies: that mental illness is a "bio-chemical illness" and a "no-fault biologically based brain disease."

Surely, thinking of mental illness in this way—believing that biology causes mental illness (as it causes diabetes or heart disease, illnesses to which it is compared) and that nobody's to blame—does enormous good: it reduces stigma and guilt, it inspires hope, it allows for increased coverage under insurance plans, it enables useful legislation and research, and so on.

What it does not do, however, is deal directly with the major fact of mental illness for those who suffer its larger devastations: its generally long-term, chronic character and how this is experienced, as on Eli's graduation night, by the mentally ill and by those who care for them.

Robert and I have been hearing talk about "breakthrough cures" for more than thirty years now. First it was electroshock, and then it was insulin coma therapy, and then it was family therapy, and then it was the new range of anti-psychotic drugs, and then it was megadose vitamin therapy, and then it was lithium therapy, and then it was anticonvulsant therapy, and then it was Prozac, and then it was clozapine.

What upset me in the *Times* ad—what upsets me whenever I hear language about breakthrough cures and genetic markers and brain disease—is not the possibility that Robert's condition is chemical, but the belief so many people have in its corollary: that if the condition is chemical, it can be corrected with chemicals. Oh how easy it would be for everybody if there were chemical causes and chemical cures! How free of responsibility we might all be then!

But even if we find cause and cure, what then do we do with the life lived, and the history—and fear, and shame, and doubt, and despair, and sheer misery—that have accompanied that life? If behavior and feelings can change the chemistry and patterns of the brain (compare the feelings and physiological changes in athletes, musicians, stockbrokers, writers, artists, and others when in intensely productive periods), just as chemicals can change behavior and feelings, how can we know which is cause and which effect?

The instant I see the words about breakthrough cures, and read about how NARSAD has provided financial support to 315 doctors and scientists in 78 leading universities, medical schools, and research institutions, what I also see, but more vividly, is my brother, in a room by himself, lying in bed hour after hour and day after day, trembling from medications and fear and loneliness.

In a realm where the relation of mind to body remains so complex and mysterious, why, I wonder yet again, is so much time and money spent in the search for chemical and organic causes and cures, while back on the ward patients languish and die for the simple lack of human attention to their ordinary, daily needs?

For even if we do one day separate out the gene or the neuron that proves to be the cause of what we decide is this or that species of mental illness, what, then, will we do about the life that has come before and will continue after the moment of diagnosis and medication, and of how the fact of having this condition has affected an individual's history?

Hope and research are fine, and genuine gains have been made. But meanwhile, back on the ward, Robert has to sneak out of his room to telephone me, and his doctors never call me to inform or consult or confer, and the only link to the outside world for thirty or so acutely psychotic patients is a single pay phone. Meanwhile, back on the ward, important messages don't get through. (When Robert, for the first time in his life, threatened suicide, and I informed one of the nurses, and I called back a few days later to speak with Robert's doctor, I discovered that the doctor had never been informed of Robert's threat.) Meanwhile, back on the ward, the major activities are TV and Bingo, the staff is outnumbered and overworked, the refrigerator is padlocked, and the only time patients can get snacks is when an aide unlocks it twice a day at "refrigerator time."

As it was, for the most part, 30 years ago, so it is now: the little that passes for therapy is simply reward and punishment done up, if at all, in the guise of crude behavior modification programs whose aim is not enhancement, but containment and neutralization. In the world Robert too often lives in, ordinary habits and idiosyncrasies (sloppiness about clothing, loud talking) become psychological deficits for which one receives demerits, and worse. In the world Robert has been living in for too many years, model patients are not very different from model prisoners.

At least, I say to Robert, during one conversation, they don't use straitjackets anymore. When I say this, we both laugh and talk about the time he asked a friend visiting him at Creedmoor if she could take his dirty clothes home for him and get them washed. The friend took Robert's laundry bag to a Chinese laundry, started removing the clothes, only to find that mixed in with the dirty socks and underwear was Robert's straitjacket.

"In the old days it was straitjackets and wet sheets and electricity," Robert says, "and now, I guess, it's isolation and injections."

A few weeks before Eli's graduation, I had asked Robert why he thought it was that he had survived when so many others he knew, from Creedmoor and Mid-Hudson and South Beach and Hillside, never got out, or killed themselves, or deteriorated to the point of no return. Had it ever occurred to him to wonder why, despite all he had been through and all the drugs and therapies that had been poured into him, he had not gone under? Why was he able, more than three decades after his first breakdown (when he tried to kill our father; when he hallucinated extravagantly; when he believed he was being taken, by ambulance, to my funeral; when he tried to chew his tongue out of his mouth; when he was straitjacketed and shot up with large doses of Thorazine; when he had catatonic seizures), to make a life for himself that was so much better than often, during these decades, seemed likely?

"Well," he exclaimed, I had wonderful parents!" He laughed, then was silent for a while. When he spoke again, his voice was warm, thoughtful. "I just wanted to survive and persist," he said. "That's all. And—I don't know— but it's like Faulkner said in the speech he made, for the Nobel, remember?— I wanted to endure somehow. I never really wanted to stay on the wards, but I'd get there and then the minute they locked the door on me, I would think, 'Oh my God—I've got to get out of here!' But then I'd throw fits and stuff."

"And also," he added, smiling, "because my brother didn't want to keep visiting me in hospitals."

Introduction to Chapter 6

Larry Davidson

That this chapter addresses the question "How can mental health systems evolve into recovery-oriented systems of care?" offers one encouraging indication of how far the field has come over the last 30 years. While we began the preface to these volumes bemoaning the fact that many researchers and practitioners in the field have yet to embrace the reality of recovery in the lives of people with serious mental illnesses, we can bring this anthology to a close celebrating the fact that the world of mental health policy, in contrast, has evolved in the direction of implementing a recovery vision on a scope and to a degree that many of us would have considerable unrealistic, if not impossible, as recently as a decade ago. Veterans of psychiatric rehabilitation may suggest that policy is finally catching up to the kinds of research we have highlighted in our first five chapters. Others, however, will suggest that developments in policy have actually outstripped this research base and are encouraging the field to now move into relatively unexplored, not to mention unstudied, territory. Regardless of one's position on this issue, it is very clear, and very encouraging, that the vision of recovery, which was once held dear by only a small minority of dedicated individuals on the periphery of the broader field of community mental health, has since found its way into the mainstream.

As we noted in our preface when identifying the recent impetus for pulling together and publishing this recovery anthology, the arrival of recovery as the overarching aim of mental health care was first signaled in the U.S. by the 1961 report *Action for Mental Health* (Joint Commission on Mental Illness and Health, 1961). It has been repeatedly reaffirmed and stated more emphatically both through the President's New Freedom Commission Report, *Achieving the Promise: Transforming Mental Health Care in America* (DHHS, 2003), and in the resulting *Federal Action Agenda* released by the Substance Abuse and Mental Health Services Administration (DHHS, 2005). Both of these landmark policy statements assert that all mental health services and systems need to be re-oriented to promoting the recovery of persons with serious mental illnesses, recognizing that such a re-orientation will require dramatic, even "revolutionary" (DHHS, 2005), changes in practice. Some of the seeds for these changes are included in this section, including Anthony's 2000 article on setting standards for recovery-oriented service systems. A truly ground-breaking and visionary piece, this article was several years ahead of its time and is therefore even more relevant today, as systems embark on their own transformation process, than it was when originally published. Some of the basic assumptions about recovery that Anthony mentions as providing the foundation for system change, such as the assumption that "recovery can occur without professional intervention," remain as controversial today as they were when this article was first published. Others of these assumptions, however—such as the key roles of supportive others and personal choice in the recovery process—have become well-accepted cornerstones of the vision of recovery-oriented care being promoted by federal, state, and local authorities. System leaders are well-advised to consult Anthony's descriptions of the essential services and characteristics of recovery-oriented systems as they go about addressing the challenges inherent to making this vision a reality.

Jacobson and Curtis' review of the strategies adopted by state authorities early in their efforts to implement a recovery vision likewise remains relevant to current efforts. The confusion regarding different meanings of recovery they describe continues to plague reform efforts, as does the tendency of over-burdened and entrenched systems to simply want to repackage old wine in new, recovery-oriented bottles rather than make the considerable investments of time and resources required to struggle through the process of making substantive and enduring change (i.e., "transformation"). Of the several strategies they describe, consumer and family involvement, as originally envisioned by the Mental Health Planning Act, remains both the most crucial and yet the most elusive to achieve.

The following three articles all grapple with the challenges involved in implementing evidence-based practices. A policy direction that has evolved somewhat in parallel to the introduction and elaboration of the recovery vision, this focus on evidence-based practices has become a defining criterion of contemporary psychiatry and will guide innovations and resource allocation in clinical and rehabilitative practice for the foreseeable future. The first piece, by Frese and colleagues, tackles the thorny issue of how a focus on evidence-based practices can be reconciled with a recovery vision that emphasizes client choice and self-determination. As Frese and colleagues capably demonstrate, these two directions are not contradictory or mutually exclusive but rather can each make their respective contributions to improving the quality of care offered to people in recovery and their families. The two remaining articles by Torrey and his colleagues and Essock and her colleagues address different contextual and systemic issues and concerns encountered in the wide-scale adoption of evidence-based practices and offer system managers practical strategies and advice for ways to overcome these challenges. As both of these contributions make clear, educated and engaged stakeholders are a necessary ingredient for any system reform efforts to succeed; it therefore becomes incumbent upon leaders to articulate the ways in which stakeholders will benefit from the goals of such reform efforts—whether based on the values of recovery, scientific evidence, or both.

We next turn to Chamberlin's and Roger's perspectives on the State Comprehensive Mental Health Plan Act (Public Law 99-660) (1986). Coinciding with passage of the American's with Disabilities Act, these legislative initiatives were watershed events in establishing the rights of individuals with psychiatric disabilities to take control of their own lives and their own care, and to exert leadership in system reform; issues which continue to lie at the heart of what is currently being pursued under the banner of "transformation."

The final article in this section, a first-person recovery narrative by Gwen Davis, reminds us both of what any and all system reform efforts need to have as their primary aim—i.e., each person's reclaiming his or her life from the horrors of mental illness—and that one of the major impediments to these efforts remains the stigma, ignorance, and lack of understanding of serious mental illnesses in our popular culture. As Davis eloquently concludes: "mental illness does not turn humans into non-humans who may be ignored or ridiculed, but...is just as much a part of life as anything else." Perhaps we can add this insight to our list of indicators of how we will know when the transformation to a recovery-oriented system of care has been achieved; when having a mental illness means just having a mental illness, and not the whole lot more that currently inhibits people from seeking care, further adds to the burden of the disease by making recovery more protracted and difficult, and finally complicates their return to and reintegration into community life. When people can access effective care in a timely way and continue on with their lives, rather than become de-integrated from their community to begin with, then everyone's work, and lives, will be considerably easier and more gratifying. We look forward to this day, and offer these articles as useful tools in moving toward this destination.

Joint Commission on Mental Illness and Health. (1961). *Action for mental health: Final report*. New York: Science Editions.

President's New Freedom Commission on Mental Health. (2003). *Achieving the promise: Transforming mental health care in America, final report* (No. Pub. No. SMA-03-3832.). Rockville, MD: U.S. Department of Health and Human Services.

State Comprehensive Mental Health Plan Act of 1986, Public Law 99-660, Title V. (1986).

U.S. Department of Health and Human Services. (2005). *Transforming mental health care in America—The Federal Action Agenda: First steps*. Rockville, MD: U.S. Department of Health and Human Services, Substance Abuse and Mental Health Services Administration.

A Recovery-Oriented Service System: Setting Some System-Level Standards

William A. Anthony

William A. Anthony, PhD, is Executive Director of the Center for Psychiatric Rehabilitation at Boston University.

This article was published previously in the *Psychiatric Rehabilitation Journal,* 2000, 23(4), 159–168, and is reprinted with permission.

Abstract: In the 1990s a number of state mental health systems, behavioral managed care entities, and county systems of care declared that their service delivery systems were based on the vision of recovery. A recovery vision of service is grounded in the idea that people can recover from mental illness, and that the service delivery system must be constructed based on this knowledge. In the past, mental health systems were based on the belief that people with severe mental illness did not recover, and that the course of their illness was essentially a deteriorative course, or at best, a maintenance course. As systems strive to create new initiatives consistent with this new vision of recovery, new system standards are needed to guide the development of recovery-oriented mental health systems. Based on research on previous system initiatives and current consensus around accepted recovery practices and principles, a set of system standards that are recovery focused are suggested to guide future system developments.

The 1990s has been called the "decade of recovery" (Anthony, 1991). Two seminal events of the preceding decade paved the way for the concept of recovery from mental illness to take hold in the 1990s. One factor was the writing of consumers (e.g., Anonymous, 1989; Deegan, 1988; Houghton, 1982; Leete, 1989; McDermott, 1990; Unzicker, 1989). For the preceding decades, and culminating in the decade of the 1980s, consumers had been writing about their own and their colleagues' recovery. The consumer literature suggests that recovery is a deeply personal, unique process of changing one's attitudes, values, feelings, goals, skills, and/or roles. It is a way of living a satisfying, hopeful, and contributing life. Recovery involves the development of new meaning and purpose in one's life as one grows beyond the catastrophic effects of psychiatric disability (Anthony, 1993). Conceptual and empirical studies on the recovery process have begun to appear (Spaniol, Gagne, & Koehler, 1999; 2003). Based on the writings of consumers, Table 1 identifies several assumptions about the recovery process that can be used to guide service system development.

Table 1. Assumptions about Recovery

Factors/Items	Reasons
1. Recovery can occur without professional intervention.	Professionals do not hold the key to recovery; consumers do. The task of professionals is to facilitate recovery; the task of consumers is to recover. Recovery may be facilitated by the consumer's natural support system.
2. A common denominator of recovery is the presence of people who believe in and stand by the person in need of recovery.	Seemingly universal in the recovery concept is the notion that critical to one's recovery is a person or persons in whom one can trust to "be there" in times of need.
3. A recovery vision is not a function of one's theory about the causes of mental illness.	Recovery may occur whether one views the illness as biological or not. The key element is understanding that there is hope for the future, rather than understanding the cause in the past.
4. Recovery can occur even though symptoms reoccur.	The episodic nature of severe mental illness does not prevent recovery. As one recovers, symptoms interfere with functioning less often and for briefer periods of time. More of one's life is lived symptom-free.
5. Recovery is a unique process.	There is no one path to recovery, nor one outcome. It is a highly personal process.
6. Recovery demands that a person has choices.	The notion that one has options from which to choose is often more important than the particular option one initially selects.
7. Recovery from the consequences of the illness is sometimes more difficult than recovering from the illness itself.	These consequences include discrimination, poverty, segregation, stigma, and iatrogenic effects of treatment.

Adapted from Anthony (1993).

In addition to the conceptual work of consumers, the other major factor precipitating the acceptance of the recovery vision was the empirical work of Harding and her associates, whose research and analytic work initially impacted the field in the 1980s. Over the years Harding (1994) and her colleagues have reviewed a number of long-term research studies, including their own (Harding, Brooks, Ashekaga, Strauss, & Breier, 1987a; 1987b), that suggested that a deteriorating course for severe mental illness is not the norm. "The possible causes of chronicity may be viewed as having less to do with the disorder and more to do with a myriad of environmental and other social factors interacting with the person and the illness" (Harding, Zubin, &

Strauss, 1987, p. 483). It was the ongoing analysis of long-term outcome studies by Harding and associates that provided the empirical basis for the recovery vision.

In contrast to Harding's research and the emerging consumer literature, throughout most of the 1980s, and officially until the appearance of *DSM III-R,* the belief was that severe mental illness, particularly schizophrenia, was a deteriorative disease (American Psychiatric Association, 1980). This seemingly definitive diagnostic conclusion turned out to be ill-conceived, and inhibited acceptance of the recovery vision. Antithetical to the concept of gradual deterioration due to mental illness over time is the concept of recovering over time from mental illness. Harding's later work (Desisto, Harding, McCormick, Ashikaga, & Brooks, 1995a, 1995b) involved a comparison of the long-term outcome of people with psychiatric disabilities in two different states. This masterfully designed, three decade long follow-up examined what might account for system wide differences in consumers' recovery, and once again confirmed, as consumers had been saying, that recovery from mental illness was happening.

SYSTEM PLANNING AND THE RECOVERY VISION

During the 1990s increasing numbers of states and counties adopted a recovery vision as the overriding vision for their system planning. The Community Support System (CSS) perspective as to the critical services needed to be helpful to people with psychiatric disabilities became a part of the thinking of many system planners and administrators. Most comprehensive mental health system initiatives in the 1980s and 1990s can be traced to the CSS conceptualization of basic services (National Institute of Mental Health, 1987). Anthony (1993) used the CSS model as a basis for describing the essential services of a recovery-oriented system. Based on the CSS framework, the Center for Psychiatric Rehabilitation has identified the quintessential outcome of each service intervention and the description of the process each service uses to achieve that outcome (Anthony, Cohen, Farkas, & Gagne, 2002. (See Table 2.)

The Boston University Center for Psychiatric Rehabilitation, along with its organizational consultation affiliate, BCPR, is directly aware of recovery initiatives in selected states in which they have been consulting, including such states as California, Iowa, New York, Ohio, and Washington. The Center is currently collaborating with the National Association of State Mental Health Directors (NASMHPD), the National Association of Consumer/ Survivor Mental Health Administrators (NAC/SMHA) and the Consumer Organization Networking and Technical Assistance Center (CONTAC) to describe and evaluate the extent to which state mental health systems have implemented policies and practices that promote recovery.

Table 2. Essential Services in a Recovery-Oriented System

Service Category	Description	Consumer Outcome
Treatment	Alleviating symptoms and distress	Symptom relief
Crisis intervention	Controlling and resolving critical or dangerous problems	Personal safety assured
Case management	Obtaining the services client needs and wants	Services accessed
Rehabilitation	Developing clients' skills and supports related to clients' goals	Role functioning
Enrichment	Engaging clients in fulfilling and satisfying activities	Self-development
Rights protection	Advocating to uphold one's rights	Equal opportunity
Basic support	Providing the people, places, and things clients need to survive (e.g., shelter, meals, health care)	Personal survival assured
Self-help	Exercising a voice and a choice in one's life	Empowerment
Wellness/prevention	Promoting healthy lifestyles	Health status improved

In Anthony, Cohen, Farkas, & Gagne (2002). Adapted from: Cohen, M., Nemec, P., Farkas, M., & Forbess, R. (1988). *Training technology: Case management*. Boston, MA: Center for Psychiatric Rehabilitation.

Jacobson & Curtis (2000) have already examined several states' recovery-based planning, focusing on how states are using specific strategies to work toward a recovery vision. These strategies include: developing recovery vision statements; educating personnel about recovery; increasing the involvement of consumers and family in planning and service delivery; and implementing "user-controlled" services.

RELEVANT SYSTEMS-LEVEL RESEARCH

Perhaps the most straightforward definition of a system—and a definition most relevant to today's mental health service system in particular—is that a service system is a combination of services organized to meet the needs of a particular population (Sauber, 1983). A difficulty in creating a mental health service system stems from the varied, multiple needs of the client population. Since deinstitutionalization, many different service systems have been designated as responsible for meeting one or more of the individual needs of persons with long-term psychiatric disabilities (e.g., mental health, health, substance abuse, vocational rehabilitation, social security). The diverse needs of persons with severe psychiatric disabilities for housing, health care, economic, educational, vocational, and social supports dictates coordination between multiple service providers. The mental health service system has become the primary system responsible for preventing individuals who need services from being ignored or falling through the cracks. The challenge to the mental health field has been to develop a mental health service system that could consistently meet the diverse needs of all clients (Reinke & Greenley, 1986). In essence, not only must effective and relevant services be available, but they must also be well-coordinated so that they are easily accessible and efficient, without controlling the consumer to the point of simply replicating the state mental hospital in the community. No doubt the most pressing, obvious national example of service system fragmentation is the system of services for people who have been labeled dually diagnosed, i.e., people with psychiatric disabilities and substance abuse problems (Drake, McLaughlin, Pepper, & Minkoff, 1991; Ridgely, Goldman, & Willenbring, 1990; Ridgely & Dixon, 1995).

Although many studies have noted that multiple, fragmented service systems can interfere with effective service delivery to persons with psychiatric disabilities, until the 1980s little systems-level research was undertaken (Anthony & Blanch, 1989). In 1977, Armstrong reported that 135 federal programs in 11 major departments and agencies had direct impact on people with mental illness. He reported that many of the failures of deinstitutionalization could be attributed to funding disincentives and lack of coordination among these programs (Armstrong, 1977). Other early evidence of the need for system development and integration included the interrelationship of health and mental health as demonstrated by the frequent conflict between services rendered by primary care physicians and mental health professionals (Burns, Burke, & Kessler, 1981). Currently, the integration of behavioral managed care and physical health care is a major concern of those planning managed care systems. Also making system development difficult is the fact that existing funding streams have conflicting regulations and eligibility criteria (Dickey & Goldman, 1986).

Moreover, the lack of coordination directly affects clients. Tessler (1987) found that when clients do not connect with resources after discharge from inpatient care, their overall community adjustment is poorer and there are more complaints about them. On the other hand, poor coordination is sometimes blamed for failures actually due to insufficient resources or inappropriate services (Solomon, Gordon, & Davis, 1983). At some point, the sheer quantity of services (or lack thereof) does affect quality. Research has not yet clarified the relationship between the numbers, types, or coordination of services and client outcome.

Anthony and Blanch (1989) categorized various attempts at ensuring the integration of services into four types, according to whether they emphasized a) legislated relationships and program models, b) financing mechanisms, c) strategies for improving interagency linkages, and/or d) assignment of responsibility. Many initiatives have, of course, incorporated several of these elements.

Within the last several decades, data collection on systems-level interventions has occurred sporadically. One example is the previously mentioned work of Harding (Desisto, et al., 1995a, 1995b) that involved comparing the long-term outcome of people with psychiatric disabilities served by two different systems in two separate states. This study concluded that differences in recovery outcome were probably due to system-wide differences in psychiatric rehabilitation programming. Another example is the ongoing research investigating various Community Support System (CSS) services. In the 1990s the National Institute of Mental Health and later the Center for Mental Health Services (CMHS) initiated nationwide a number of research demonstrations of essential CSS service components, including vocational rehabilitation, case management, crisis response services, and other supportive services (Jacobs, 1998). An analysis of the results of 29 projects found that the majority of the studies reported positive findings on one or more of the following outcomes: symptomatology, consumer outcomes (e.g., competitive employment), satisfaction with services, and service utilization. More recently, ongoing CMHS demonstrations should inform system planners and policymakers into the next decade.

Another CMHS sponsored research initiative examined the impact of service integration on housing outcomes for persons who were homeless and mentally ill using data from the Access to Community Care and Effective Services and Supports (ACCESS) program (Cocozza, Steadman, & Dennis, 1997; Rosenheck et al., 1998). Results showed a significant relationship between measures of service system integration and independent housing outcomes.

A final example of systems-level research is the effort launched by the Robert Wood Johnson (RWJ) foundation in the late 1980s. The RWJ initiative was based on the fundamental assumption that a central authority would enhance continuity of care, and that such improvements would lead to improved client outcomes. Nine cities were selected on a competitive basis to develop community-wide systems of care (Shore & Cohen, 1990). Within the 5-year demonstration period each city was expected to create a local mental health authority that would assume central responsibility for developing and coordinating public sector services. For the most part the RWJ system initiative did not attempt to improve practitioner competencies and program standards; rather, RWJ focused almost exclusively on organization and financing.

Little significant consumer impact was found (Lehman, Postrado, Roth, McNary, & Goldman, 1994; Shern, et al., 1994).

ORIGIN OF THE RECOVERY-ORIENTED SYSTEM STANDARDS

Unlike the development of standards for particular program models, there are no standards for recovery-oriented systems. Typically, standards have been most often considered in the development of model programs, such as Assertive Community Treatment (ACT), (Teague, Drake, & Ackerson, 1995), IPS (Becker & Drake, 1993; Drake, 1998), Clubhouse (Beard, Propst, & Malamud, 1982), and Choose-Get Keep (Anthony, Howell, & Danley, 1984; Anthony, Cohen, Farkas, & Gagne, 2002). A comparable set of standards has not been advanced for a recovery-oriented mental health system. Furthermore, there is no model of a recovery-oriented mental health system currently operating, although as pointed out previously, a number of systems are declaring the development of a recovery-oriented system to be their intent. Direction and guidelines are needed to stimulate and reinforce the development of a recovery-oriented system. The system that existed for most of the last century was based on the notion that people with severe mental illness do not recover, and that maintenance and care of people with severe mental illness should be the goal.

Lacking a currently functioning model system for guidance, it becomes necessary to suggest the system-level standards that might be helpful for system designers. The recovery-oriented system standards outlined in Table 3 are meant to serve as a starting point of reference and as a guide for system development. Furthermore, the identification of system standards on which each system is based allow for system-level research to be more meaningful. In addition, technical assistance for system development can use the standards as a jumping off point.

The particular standards identified in Table 3 are derived from several sources. First, they are consistent with the systems-level research that has so far occurred. Secondly, they are compatible with the aforementioned recovery principles. Lastly, the system-level consultants of the Boston University Center for Psychiatric Rehabilitation and its affiliate BCPR reviewed each standard and made changes to the standards based on their consultative experience. Standards were not included unless there was consensus. Over the last 17 years consultants from these organizations have on average provided technical assistance and training in about 17 states and 3 countries per year.

RECOVERY SYSTEM STANDARD DIMENSIONS

The standards have been grouped according to the system-level dimensions which best describes the focus of the standard. However, this categorization of standards is done for ease of presentation and not as part of a deliberate attempt to characterize how system standards must be organized. As the standards are used, modified, and refined, new ways to organize and name the system dimensions will no doubt occur.

Design

The mission and outcomes of the system incorporate the language of recovery. Consumers and their families are integrally important in the design process. The identified mission and consumer outcomes include such dimensions as improvements in role functioning, empowerment, consumer satisfaction, and quality of life. The mission is achieved through a set of identified services (see Table 2) which, when combined together, contribute to the achievement of the recovery outcomes (Anthony, 1993). A specific *service* (e.g., crisis intervention services, case management services) is defined by its unique process and outcomes. A *setting* is defined by its location (e.g., inpatient, community mental health center). A *program* is defined by certain administrative, staffing, and service standards (e.g., intensive case management program, clubhouse program). The system is designed around the CSS configuration of services and is *not* designed around a specific set of programs or settings; rather programs and settings must indicate which of the services they provide and on what consumer outcomes they will be held accountable. For example, a PACT program may indicate that they provide treatment, rehabilitation, crisis intervention, and case management services, and that they are accountable for implementing the process associated with each of those services.

Evaluation

Each program providing services in the system must identify the unique consumer outcomes they will achieve. For example, in rehabilitation services, no matter what the rehabilitation program is called (e.g., IPS, Clubhouse) and no matter what the setting (e.g., psychosocial rehabilitation center, mental health center), the service must achieve improvements in the consumers' role functioning (see Table 2). Treatment services must achieve symptom alleviation, and so on. Outcomes assessments must always include the perspectives of consumers and family members.

Leadership

The vision of recovery must be present in most all of the leadership's written and public statements. Recovery is such a paradigm-shifting notion (Anthony, 1991), that its fundamental assumptions and principles must constantly be reinforced. Recovery is a vision incompatible with the mission of the mental health system of the past century. The leadership must demon-

Table 3. Characteristics of a Recovery-Oriented System

System Dimension	Recovery System Standard	Example of Current Nonrecovery Standard
Design	Mission includes recovery vision as driving the system	Mission includes description of service principles (e.g., continuity of care)
	Mission implies recovery measures as overall outcome for system (e.g., empowerment, role functioning)	Mission implies no measures of recovery outcome (e.g., comprehensive range of services)
	Core set of needed services are identified for system (e.g., treatment, rehabilitation)	Core set of programs or settings are identified for system (e.g., day treatment programs and inpatient settings)
Evaluation	Primary consumer outcomes identified for each service are measurable and observable (e.g., number of crises, percentage of people employed)	Outcomes for each service are process measures or program quality measures only (e.g., number of people seen in service; time before first appointment)
	Consumer and family measures of satisfaction included in system evaluation	Consumer and family perspectives are not actively sought for system evaluation
Leadership	Leadership constantly reinforces recovery vision and recovery system standards	Leadership vision is focused on developing specific programs or settings
Management	Policies insure that a core set of processes (i.e., protocols) are described for each identified service	Policies do not insure that service protocols guide service delivery
	Policies expect programs within each service to have policies and procedures directly related to implementing the service process	Policies and procedures are about staffing, physical setting, and so forth, and not about service process
	Policies insure that MIS system collects information on service process and outcomes	Policies focus MIS on collecting information on types of clients served and costs, but not on service processes and outcomes
	Policies insure that supervisors provide feedback to supervisees on service process protocols as well as on progress toward consumer goals	Policies on supervision do not focus on supervisors providing feedback on protocols and consumer goals; primarily on symptomatology and medication

Table 3. Characteristics of a Recovery-Oriented System *(continued)*

System Dimension	Recovery System Standard	Example of Current Nonrecovery Standard
Management (cont.)	Policies encourage service programs to be recovery friendly (i.e, procedures are compatible with recovery values)	Policies encourage service programs to value compliance and professional authority
	Policies encourage the assignment of service staff, to greatest extent possible, to be based on competencies and preferences	Policies direct service staff to be assigned primarily by credentials
Integration	Function of case management is expected to be performed for each consumer who wants or needs it	Case management function is not expected to be provided to all who want or need it
	Standardized planning process across services that is guided by consumer outcomes	Planning process varies between services, and is not guided by consumer outcomes
	Policies encourage the development and implementation of system integration strategies to achieve specific consumer outcomes	Policies on system integration strategies do not address development, implementation, and evaluation of such strategies
	Referrals between services include consumer outcomes expected of service provider	Service referrals include consumer descriptions rather than consumer outcomes
Comprehensiveness	Consumer goals include functioning in living, learning, working, and/or social environments	Consumer goals do not include functioning in living, learning, working, and social environments (typically only residential environment)
	Consumer goals include functioning in nonmental health environments, not controlled by the mental health settings (e.g., YMCA, religious organizations	Consumer goals emphasize adjustment in mental health environments

Table 3. Characteristics of a Recovery-Oriented System *(continued)*

System Dimension	Recovery System Standard	Example of Current Nonrecovery Standard
Comprehensiveness (cont.)	Consumer goals include outcomes from any of the identified services	Consumer goals include outcomes for only a few of identified services
	Policies insure that programs provide an array of settings and a variety of levels of supports within a setting	Policies allow programs to provide a limited array of settings and supports within settings
Consumer involvement	Consumers are actively sought for employment at all levels of organization	Consumers are not actively sought for employment at all levels of employment
	User-controlled, self-help services are available in all geographic areas	User-controlled, self-help services are not available or available in only a few geographic areas
	Consumers and families integrally involved in system design and evaluation	Consumers and families are involved in a token way in system design and evaluation—if at all
Cultural Relevance	Policies insure that assessments, planning, and services interventions are provided in a culturally competent manner	Policies with respect to assessments, planning, and services intervention do not take cultural diversity into consideration
	Policies insure that the knowledge, skills, and attitudes of personnel enable them to provide effective care for the culturally diverse populations that might wish to use the system	Policies related to personnel do not attend to issues of cultural diversity
	Policies insure that settings and programs and the access to them reflect the culture of their current and potential consumers	Policies only insure that settings and programs are compatible with the predominant culture
Advocacy	Advocates for a holistic understanding of people served	Advocates primarily for particular programs, settings, or disciplines
	Advocates for consumers to have the opportunity to participate in community roles	Advocates for consumers to have the opportunity to participate in mental health programs

Table 3. Characteristics of a Recovery-Oriented System *(continued)*

System Dimension	Recovery System Standard	Example of Current Nonrecovery Standard
Advocacy (cont.)	Advocates for an understanding of recovery potential of people served	Advocacy for understanding of recovery potential of people served is lacking
Training	Policies insure that all levels of staff understand recovery vision and its implications within service categories	Policies make no mention of recovery vision nor its implications for services
	Policies encourage selection and training methods designed to improve knowledge, attitudes, and skills necessary to conduct particular service that staff is implementing	Policies on selection and training based on interests of staff or training coordinator
	Policies insure that all levels of staff understand recovery vision and its implications within service categories	Policies make no mention of recovery vision nor its implications for services
	Policies encourage selection and training methods designed to improve knowledge, attitudes, and skills necessary to conduct particular service that staff is implementing	Policies on selection and training based on interests of staff or training coordinator
Funding	Dollars across services are expended based on consumers' expressed needs	Dollars across services are expended based on information other than consumer needs
	Dollars across services are expended based on expected process and outcomes of services	Dollars across services are expended based on historical, traditional funding
Access	Access to service environments is by consumer preference rather than professional preference	Access to environments is based primarily on professional decisions
	Access to service environments is not contingent upon using a particular mental health service	Access to service environments is contingent on participation in certain mental health services
	Access to living, learning, working, and social environments outside mental health system is expected	Access to living, learning, working, and social environments outside mental health system is not encouraged

strate through their words and actions that they and everyone else in the system need to "buy in" to this dramatically new direction.

Management

System management, through system-level policies and procedures, must ensure that each individual service define itself by the unique process they use. Service protocols are developed and implemented so that the basic service processes are possible to monitor (Anthony, 1998). An MIS system exists for each service. For example, the basic protocol for case management might include process components such as setting a service goal, planning, linking, and negotiating for service access. The protocol for rehabilitation might include setting the overall rehabilitation goal, functional assessment, resource assessment, planning, skill development, and resource development. Supervisory sessions revolve around effective ways to implement the protocol. System management looks for "recovery-oriented" values in the programs they fund, and staff assignment to programs is based, to the greatest extent possible, on competencies and preferences, rather than credentials.

Integration

The system polices include the provision of case management for all who need and want it. Each service, within the array of services offered by the system, has a standardized planning process that shares some common process elements across services, that is, each service contains the major process elements that are standard across services. Common process elements might be: an *assessment* of the consumer's goal(s), a *plan* to reach the goal(s), and specific *interventions* to achieve the goal(s). For example, enrichment services might perform an assessment to determine which enrichment activities the consumer prefers, *plan* how to access that activity, and *intervene* by providing or arranging the preferred recreational, social, and so forth activity according to the plan. Case management services might *assess* the person's service goal, *plan* for accessing those services, and *intervene* through linking and/or negotiating for those services. In addition, when referrals occur between different service programs, the referral includes a specific description of the consumer outcomes the receiving service is expected to achieve.

Comprehensiveness

All the possible residential, work, educational, and social environments in which a consumer might potentially function are included as a consumer goal(s) and measurable consumer outcome(s). Functioning in nonmental health environments (e.g., schools, social clubs) is included as goals. It is the policy of the system that consumer supports that facilitate a consumer's functioning are provided in a wide variety of environments. A particular support exists in more than one environment. For example, intensive residential support may be provided in group residences, but also in an individual's own apartment.

Consumer Involvement

Selection and recruitment materials for staff throughout the system target consumers and family members for employment, as well as voluntary service on boards. User-controlled services are available in all the designated catchment areas served by the system.

Cultural Relevance

The system promulgates policies designed to increase the possibility that the system reflects the culture of the consumers served. Specifically, policies on cultural competence address the training and experience of practitioners, the assessment, planning, and intervention process, and culturally relevant programs and procedures to access them.

Advocacy

System advocacy occurs for the recovery vision, for a holistic understanding of the persons served, and for consumers to have the opportunity to participate fully in community roles.

Training

System-level policies on training are designed so that delivery of specific services is improved; training is grounded in the vision of recovery, and not just in the interest of certain staff.

Funding

Funding from the system is based on the consumers' recovery goals. Funding directly supports the processes and outcomes that the system is designed to achieve.

Access

Policies encourage access to services based on the consumers' goals rather than professional preference. Access is not contingent upon the consumer attending certain mental health services. For example, access to housing is not contingent on taking medication. Access to nonmental health environments is expected.

CONCLUSIONS

As system planners use all or some of these standards they will undoubtedly modify, refine, and/or add to these standards. This first attempt at providing recovery-oriented system standards should prove useful in a number of ways. First of all, it can provide direction to system planners as they develop proposals for their system. It can provide a basis for consumer and family advocacy and monitoring at the system level. The standards can be used in system-level research and evaluation of recovery-oriented systems, and as a framework to make comparisons across systems. Lastly, as these standards outlined in Table 3 are put into use, it will further encourage the operationalization of these standards.

These recovery-oriented system standards are a first step in moving a system with no recovery vision to a system that believes that consumers can develop meaningful and purposeful lives, despite having experienced the catastrophe of severe mental illness. A mental health system guided by a recovery vision must have policies and procedures in place to increase the possibility of recovery occurring—for the system itself as well as for those it serves.

REFERENCES

American Psychiatric Association (1980). *Diagnostic and statistical manual of mental disorders (3rd ed.).* Washington, DC: Author.

Anonymous (1989). How I've managed chronic mental illness. *Schizophrenia Bulletin, 15,* 635–640.

Anthony, W. A. (1991). Researching the unresearchable! *Psychosocial Rehabilitation Journal, 14*(3), 1.

Anthony, W. A. (1993). Recovery from mental illness: The guiding vision of the mental health service system in the 1990s. *Psychosocial Rehabilitation Journal, 16*(4), 11–23.

Anthony, W. A. (1998). Psychiatric rehabilitation technology: Operationalizing the "black box" of the psychiatric rehabilitation process. *New Directions for Mental Health Services, 79,* 79–87.

Anthony, W. A., & Blanch, A. K. (1989). Research on community support services: What have we learned? *Psychosocial Rehabilitation Journal, 12* (3), 55–81.

Anthony, W. A., Cohen, M. R., Farkas, M., & Gagne, C. (2002). *Psychiatric rehabilitation (2nd ed.).* Boston: Boston University, Center for Psychiatric Rehabilitation.

Anthony, W. A., Howell, J., & Danley, K. S. (1984). Vocational rehabilitation of the psychiatrically disabled. In M. Mirabi (Ed.), *The chronically mentally ill: Research and services* (pp. 215–237). Jamaica, NY: Spectrum Publications.

Armstrong, B. (1977) A federal study of deinstitutionalization: How the government impedes its goal. *Hospital and Community Psychiatry, 28,* 417, 425.

Beard, J. H., Propst, R. N., & Malamud, T. J. (1982). The Fountain House model of psychiatric rehabilitation. *Psychosocial Rehabilitation Journal, 5*(l), 47–53.

Becker, D. R., & Drake, R. E. (1993). *A working life: The individual placement and support (IPS) program.* Concord, NH: Dartmouth Psychiatric Research Center.

Burns, B. J., Burke, J. D., & Kessler, L. G. (1981). Promoting health-mental health coordination: Federal efforts. In A. Broskowski, E. Marks, & S. H. Budman (Eds.), *Linking health and mental health.* Beverly Hills, CA: Sage Publications.

Coccozza, J. J., Steadman. H. J., & Dennis, D. (1997). *Implementing system integration strategies: Lessons from the ACCESS program.* New York: Policy Research Associates.

Cohen, M. R., Nemec, P. B., Farkas, M. D., & Forbess, R. (1988). *Psychiatric rehabilitation training technology: Case management* (Trainer package). Boston: Boston University, Center for Psychiatric Rehabilitation.

Deegan, P. E. (1988). Recovery: The lived experience of rehabilitation. *Psychosocial Rehabilitation Journal, 11*(4), 11–19.

DeSisto, M. J., Harding, C. M., McCormick, R. V., Ashikaga, T., & Brooks, G. W. (1995a). The Maine and Vermont three-decade studies of serious mental illness: I. Matched comparison of cross-sectional outcome. *British Journal of Psychiatry 167,* 331–338.

DeSisto, M. J., Harding, C. M., McCormick, R. V., Ashikaga, T., & Brooks, G. W. (1995b). The Maine and Vermont three-decade studies of serious mental illness: II. Longitudinal course comparisons. *British Journal of Psychiatry, 167,* 338–341.

Dickey, B., & Goldman, H. H. (1986). Public health care for the chronically mentally ill: Financing operation costs: Issues and options for local leadership. *Administration in Mental Health, 14,* 63–77.

Drake, R. E. (1998). A brief history of the individual placement and support model. *Psychiatric Rehabilitation Journal, 22*(1), 3–7.

Drake, R., McLaughlin, P., Pepper, B., & Minkoff, K. (1991). Dual diagnosis of major mental illness and substance disorder. In K. Minkoff (Ed.), Dual diagnosis of major mental illness and mental disorder, 3–12. *New Directions for Mental Health Services, No. 50.* San Francisco: Jossey-Bass, Inc.

Harding, C. M. (1994). An examination of the complexities in the measurement of recovery in severe psychiatric disorders. In R.J. Ancill, S. Holliday, & G.W. MacEwan (Eds.), *Schizophrenia: Exploring the spectrum of psychosis* (pp. 153–169). Chichester: J. Wiley & Sons.

Harding, C. M., Brooks, G. W., Ashikaga, T., Strauss, J. S., & Breier, A. (1987a). The Vermont longitudinal study of persons with severe mental illness: I. Methodology, study sample, and overall status 32 years later. *American Journal of Psychiatry, 144,* 718–726.

Harding, C. M., Brooks, G. W., Ashikaga, T., Strauss, T. S., & Breier, A. (1987b). The Vermont longitudinal study of persons with severe mental illness: 11. Long-term outcome of subjects who retrospectively met DSM-III criteria for schizophrenia. *American Journal of Psychiatry, 144,* 727–735.

Harding, C. M., Zubin, J., & Strauss, J. S. (1987). Chronicity in schizophrenia: Fact, partial fact, or artifact? *Hospital and Community Psychiatry, 38,* 477–486.

Houghton, J. F. (1982). Maintaining mental health in a turbulent world. *Schizophrenia Bulletin, 8,* 548–552.

Jacobs, J. (Ed.) (1998). *Community support research demonstration grants, 1989–1996: Major findings and lessons learned.* Rockville, MD: Center for Mental Health Services.

Jacobson, N. & Curtis, L. (2000). Recovery as policy in mental health services: Strategies emerging from the states. *Psychiatric Rehabilitation Journal, 23*(4), 333–341.

Leete, E. (1989). How I perceive and manage my illness. *Schizophrenia Bulletin, 15,* 197–200.

Lehman, A., Postrado, L., Roth, D; McNary, S., & Goldman, H. (1994). Continuing of care and client outcomes in the Robert Wood Johnson Foundation Program on chronic mental illness. *Milbank Quarterly, 72*(1), 105–122.

McDermott, B. (1990). Transforming depression. *The Journal, 1*(4), 13–14.

National Institute of Mental Health (1987). *Toward a model plan for a comprehensive, community-based mental health system.* Rockville, MD: Division of Education and Service Systems Liaison.

Reinke, B., & Greenley, J. R. (1986). Organizational analysis of three community support program models. *Hospital and Community Psychiatry, 37,* 624–629.

Ridgely, M., & Dixon, L. (1995). Policy and financing issues in the care of people with chronic mental illness and substance abuse disorders. In A.F. Lehman & L.B. Dixon (Eds.), *Double jeopardy: Chronic mental illness and substance abuse.* (pp. 277–295). New York: Harwood Academic Publishers.

Ridgely, M., Goldman, H., & Willenbring, M. (1990). Barriers to the care of persons with dual diagnoses: Organizational and financial issues. *Schizophrenia Bulletin, 16,* 123–132.

Rosenheck, R., Morrissey, J., Lam, J., Calloway, M., Johnson, M., Goldman, H., Randolph, F., Blasinsky, M., Fontana, A., Calysn, R., & Teague, G. (1998). Service system integration, access to services, and housing outcomes in a program for homeless persons with severe mental illness. *American Journal of Public Health, 88*(11), 1610–1615.

Sauber, S. R. (1983). *The human services delivery system.* New York: Columbia University Press.

Shern, D., Wilson, N., Coen, A. S., Patrick, D., Foster, M., Bartsch, D., & Demmler, J. (1994). Client outcomes II: Longitudinal client data from the Colorado treatment outcome study. *Milbank Quarterly, 72*(1), 123–148.

Shore, M., & Cohen, M. D. (1990). The Robert Wood Johnson Foundation program on chronic mental illness: An overview. *Hospital and Community Psychiatry, 41*(11), 1212–1216.

Solomon, P., Gordon, B., & Davis, J. M. (1983). An assessment of aftercare services within a community mental health system. *Psychosocial Rehabilitation Journal, 7*(2), 33–39.

Spaniol, L., Gagne, C., & Koehler, M. (1999). Recovery from serious mental illness: What it is and how to support people in their recovery. In R. P. Marinelli, & A. E. Dell Orto (Eds.), *The psychological and social impact of disability (4th Ed.).* New York: Springer.

Spaniol, L., Gagne, C., & Koehler, M. (2003). The recovery framework in rehabilitation: Concepts and practices from the field of serious mental illness. In J. R. Finch & D. P. Moxley (Eds.), *Sourcebook of rehabilitation and mental health services.* New York: Kluwer Academic Publishers.

Teague, G. B., Drake, R. E., & Ackerson, T. H. (1995). Evaluating use of continuous treatment teams for persons with mental illness and substance abuse. *Psychiatric Services, 46*(7), 689–695.

Tessler, R. C. (1987). Continuity of care and client outcome. *Psychosocial Rehabilitation Journal, 1*(1), 39–53.

Unzicker, R. (1989). On my own: A personal journey through madness and re emergence. *Psychosocial Rehabilitation Journal, 13*(1), 71–77.

Recovery as Policy in Mental Health Services: Strategies Emerging from the States

Nora Jacobson and Laurie Curtis

At the time of original publication, Nora Jacobson, PhD, was a researcher at the University of Wisconsin School of Nursing, Madison, Wisconsin; and Laurie Curtis, MA, was identified as an independent consultant and educator specializing in recovery-oriented policies, practices, and lifestyles and an associate clinical professor for the Graduate Program in Community Mental Health, Trinity College of Vermont, Middlesex, Vermont.

This article was published previously in the *Psychiatric Rehabilitation Journal*, 2000, 23(4) and is reprinted with permission.

Abstract: The concept of recovery has emerged as a significant paradigm in the field of public mental health services. This article outlines how the concept is being implemented in the policies and practices of mental health systems in the United States. After a brief overview of the historical background of recovery and a description of the common themes that have emerged across the range of its definitions, the article describes the specific strategies being used by the states to implement recovery principles. The authors conclude by raising key questions about the implications of adopting recovery as system policy.

CONCEPTUALIZING RECOVERY

Medical professionals have long recognized that people can recover from physical illnesses. Treatments for diseases commonly take recovery—defined as return to the pre-morbid state—as their goal. Most people have had the experience of coming to terms with traumatic or stressful life events. In common parlance, this experience is also called recovery. As alcoholism and other addictions have been reconceptualized as diseases (rather than failings of character), the word recovery has been applied to the process of learning to live a full life without alcohol or drugs. The meaning of "recovery" has different nuances: restoration of normal health and functioning; a strength of character born of surviving tough times; the challenge of wresting control of one's life away from a chronic illness. Conceptualizing recovery as a possibility leads to the development of specific interventions and practices to promote it. Thus, the possibility of recovery becomes an expectation.

Application of recovery concepts to psychiatric disorders is comparatively recent and stems largely from two interrelated sources: the consumer/survivor/ex-patient movement, a grassroots self-help and advocacy initiative with overtly political goals (Brown, 1981; Chamberlin, 1984, 1990; Everett 1994); and psychiatric rehabilitation, a professional approach to mental health services provision (Anthony, 1991, 1993).

Like many other social movements that emerged in the 1960s and 1970s, the consumer/survivor/ex-patient movement[1] began with a claim for a unique group identity and desire for broad acknowledgment of the lack of civil and human rights granted to members of the group. Activists demanded that society recognize the oppression and marginalization of psychiatric patients and called for liberation. The liberatory goals of the movement were encapsulated in the notion of empowerment, understood both systemically—as a redistribution of the power held by the state and the institution of psychiatry, and individually—as the consumer taking control and responsibility for his or her own life.

Psychiatric rehabilitation initiatives, on the other hand, have been primarily the work of professionals and mental health advocates. These initiatives have helped to shape the emergence of community resources and best practices in treatment for persons with psychiatric disabilities by: a) recognizing the value of community and work in the lives of persons diagnosed with mental illness, and b) demonstrating that functional ability is dependent on more than diagnosed pathology or the intensity of symptoms. It is the product of interactions between the individual and the environment (Anthony, Cohen, & Farkas, 1990).

The conceptualizations of recovery that come from these two sources reflect their different orientations. For many consumer/survivor activists, "recovery" has a political as well as personal implication: to recover is to reclaim one's life, to validate one's self in order that one may be validated as an autonomous, competent individual in the world. Recovery is a manifestation of empowerment. In psychiatric rehabilitation terms, recovery refers in large part to functional ability. To recover is to improve and maintain functioning in one or more of the major domains of life—work, housing, relationships, recreation—and by so doing to "[live] a satisfying, hopeful, and contributing life even with limitations caused by illness...[and to develop] new meaning and purpose in one's life" (Anthony 1993, p. 15).[2] Recovery is the desired outcome of a mental health services system that has fully incorporated psychiatric rehabilitation and community support principles and practices.

1   The phrase "consumer/survivor/ex-patient movement" is, we realize, a simplification. As several authors have pointed out, there are ideological distinctions between people who identify themselves as consumers and those who call themselves survivors or ex-patients. Barbara Everett (1994) writes that "people who call themselves survivors feel that consumers are dupes for believing that the mental health system has any value at all while survivors are tough freedom fighters...consumers believe that there is no shame in working for change from within the mental health system and that, in fact, the survivor brand of loud, rude criticism only delays reform." (p. 63)
2   That Anthony credits this description of recovery to the writings of consumer/survivors is one example of the interrelatedness of the consumer/survivor/ex-patient and psychiatric rehabilitation movements.

The contrast between these notions was explored in an article by Patricia Deegan, (1988) a clinical psychologist and an activist who identifies herself as having a psychiatric disability. Drawing from her own experience and from the disability rights movement, Deegan made a crucial distinction between rehabilitation and recovery:

> Disabled persons are not passive recipients of rehabilitation services. Rather, they experience themselves as *recovering* a new sense of self and of purpose within and beyond the limits of the disability…Rehabilitation refers to the services and technologies that are made available to disabled persons so that they may learn to adapt to their world. Recovery refers to the lived or real life experience of persons as they accept and overcome the challenge of the disability (Deegan, 1988, p. 11).

Deegan further described that "lived experience" as "a process, a way of life, an attitude, and a way of approaching the day's challenges" (p. 15) and, paraphrasing the poet Roethke, as "the urge, the wrestle, and the resurrection" (p. 15).

The different conceptualizations of recovery have been supported by evidence from both research and anecdote. Long-term studies of the impact of serious mental illness on individuals have shown that mental illness does not necessarily take a course of inevitable deterioration and that, for a significant number of people, a return to full functioning is possible (Harding, Brooks, Ashikaga, Strauss, & Brier, 1987). Further research (e.g., Campbell & Schraiber, 1989; Copeland, 1992, 1994) and first-person narratives of consumer/survivor/ex-patients (e.g., Unzicker, 1989; Leete, 1989) have illustrated the practical resilience of persons diagnosed with severe mental illness, identified various pathways of healing, and articulated factors which enhance or detract from this healing process. Increasingly, recovery has become both a subject of mental health services research (e.g., Hatfield, & Lefley 1993; Sullivan, 1997 [1994]; Ralph, 1996) and a term that is emblematic of many of the goals of the consumer/survivor/ex-patient movement (Fisher, 1994).

Several themes have emerged as particularly salient across the different conceptualizations of recovery:

- Recovery is generally seen as a *process*. That is, it represents not a cure-like endpoint, but a state of being and becoming, a path rather than a destination.

- The course of that path is understood to be highly *singular* or *unique;* no two people will have identical paths or use the same benchmarks to measure their journeys.

- In contrast to the passivity of being a patient or a voiceless recipient of services, recovery is *active* and requires that an individual take personal responsibility for his or her own recovery, often in collaboration with friends, family, supporters, and professionals.

- A recovery orientation includes an emphasis on *choice,* a concept that encompasses support for autonomous action, the requirement that the individual have a range of opportunities from which to choose and full information about those choices, and increasing personal responsibility for the consequences of choice.

- The emotional essence of recovery is *hope,* a promise that things can and do change, that today is not the way it will always be.

- A key theme is that of *meaning,* or the discovery of purpose and direction in one's life. The search for meaning is highly personal. For some people meaning may be reflected through work or social relationships. Others derive meaning from advocacy and political action. For others, the pursuit of meaning takes on strongly spiritual elements.

POLICY AND PROGRAMMING: STRATEGIES FOR IMPLEMENTING RECOVERY CONCEPTS

Prompted by advocacy groups, the emerging literature, and concurrent demands to improve the effectiveness of public mental health services, a few state mental health systems have introduced recovery into the public policy lexicon (Beale & Lambric, 1995; Legislative Summer Study Committee of the Vermont Division of Mental Health, 1996; State of Wisconsin Blue Ribbon Commission on Mental Health, 1997; State of Nebraska Recovery Workteam, 1997; Barton, 1998). In many states, the introduction of recovery concepts into mental health policy has coincided with a shift towards a managed care approach to services financing and system accountability. In this context, recovery is envisioned as a set of guiding principles whose application can result in cost effective behavioral healthcare and that suggest measurable treatment outcomes.

How are state and regional mental health authorities incorporating recovery into policy and practice?[3] As with any important system change ini-

3   The research on which this paper is based was conducted by the first author during the first 6 months of 1998. Information was gathered using semi-structured telephone interviews of key informants at states identified as having an interest in recovery. Initially, this identification was made through the visibility of the state in the national recovery movement. As the study continued, however, more informants were identified—in the manner of a snowball sample—through referral. A second source of data was the collection, by both authors, of state-level policy documents. References to specific states are given for the purpose of example only. The aim of the paper is to provide a comprehensive overview of *strategies*, not of the states that are implementing them.

tiative, the first steps include understanding the concept and ascertaining its viability and value within clinical and financial contexts. Many states are beginning by developing recovery vision statements, written statements meant both to explain recovery and to demonstrate a real commitment to it (Schmook [undated document]). In order to develop such vision statements, mental health authorities typically establish a work group or task force comprised of a diverse set of stakeholders. The group studies the literature and solicits advice from many sources and experts–including first-person testimonials from consumers. It then develops a document that provides a working definition of recovery and makes recommendations for implementing its principles.

With vision statements in hand, some states simply rename their existing programs. The actual services offered remain the same. Community support services, vocational rehabilitation, or housing support are now described as "recovery-oriented" services. This renaming process demonstrates a lack of understanding of recovery: in particular, a failure to acknowledge the necessity for a fundamental shift toward sharing both power and responsibility. States that have moved beyond such cosmetic efforts tend to focus on several specific strategies for operationalizing and implementing recovery. These strategies include education, consumer and family involvement, support for consumer-operated services, emphasis on relapse prevention and management, incorporation of crisis planning and advance directives, innovations in contracting and financing mechanisms, definition and measurement of outcomes, review and revision of key policies, and stigma reduction initiatives. Examples of state efforts in each of these approaches are presented below.

EDUCATION

A number of states are stimulating discussion and understanding about recovery through structured education initiatives, conferences, newsletters, and changes to academic curricula. Recovery education may be designed for consumers, family members, service providers, or administrators. States are developing their own educational programs, or are using one or more of the emerging curricula (e.g., Copeland, 1992, 1994, 1997; Center for Community Change, 1996; Spaniol, Koehler, & Hutchinson 1994). The content of the educational programs varies depending on the intended audience. Recovery education for consumers and family members emphasizes basic information about mental illness and the mental health system, strategies for self-management of symptoms and self-advocacy, and the development of peer support (Hatfield & Lefley, 1993; Muser & Gingerich, 1994; McFarlane et al., 1995). Education for providers and administrators focuses on exploring the concept of recovery, challenging assumptions, and presenting information about the role of workers in stimulating and facilitating the process. Several states (e.g., Massachusetts, New York) have incorporated modules on recovery into their statewide core curricula.

Recovery education and training sessions are often conducted by consumers trained as recovery educators, who work either independently or with a mental health worker as a co-trainer. The content of these programs is enhanced by the role modeling and inspiration provided by consumer trainers. Curtis (1999a), the Center for Community Change (1996), as well as the State of Vermont (undated) have developed a variety of training-of-trainers programs for consumer/survivors and mental health professionals.

A key component of many recovery education initiatives is cross-training. Workers with different disciplinary backgrounds, consumers, family members, and administrators join together as learners with a shared investment in understanding more about recovery. Each group is encouraged to contribute its unique expertise and knowledge. One innovative educational strategy developed in New York in the early 1990s is the recovery dialogue, in which groups of providers and service recipients meet as equals on neutral ground to discuss recovery (Blanch, Fisher, Tucker, & Chassman, 1993; New York State Office of Mental Health [undated]). States may use recovery dialogues as one-time events, or they may become part of an on-going process of consciousness raising, education, and change. Bluebird (2000) has developed a format for facilitating these dialogues among diverse groups of stakeholders.

Another source of recovery education is the increasing number of state, regional, and national conferences on recovery. Such meetings have been held in Nebraska, New Hampshire, Pennsylvania, and Vermont. Early in 1998, the National Technical Assistance Center for State Mental Health Planning (NTAC) and the Nebraska Mental Health Planning and Evaluation Council co-sponsored a regional training conference on recovery (NTAC, 1998). The National Empowerment Center (NEC) has presented a series of "Learning From Us" conferences that bring people together and help to stimulate awareness and dialogue about recovery (1997). The Alternatives conferences sponsored by the Center for Mental Health Services (CMHS) has a long tradition of providing consumers/survivors/ex-patients with a forum for exploring various pathways to recovery, consumer leadership, and political action.

CONSUMER AND FAMILY INVOLVEMENT

One success of the consumer and survivor movement and of the family movement has been to increase recognition that these groups are critical stakeholders and must be key players in mental health system design and service delivery. At no other point in the history of mental health system reform have consumers and family members played such an active and valued role in influencing the direction of reform.

Organizations and systems are seeking to increase the involvement of consumer and family representatives in most aspects of policy planning and service delivery. Consumers are being hired to design and conduct mental health services research (Campbell & Schraiber, 1989; Scott, 1993), including evaluations of service effectiveness (Srebnick, Robinson, & Tanzman, 1990; Ferry, 1996; Campbell, 1997). Consumers are also being recruited to serve on the boards of service organizations. Some states now require consumer and family participation on agency boards of directors and other decision-making bodies (e.g., California, Nebraska, New Hampshire, Rhode Island, Vermont). Many states are establishing state-level offices of consumer affairs that are led and staffed by consumers or they are creating consumer liaison positions within existing departments (e.g., Arkansas, Connecticut, Nebraska, New Hampshire, New York, South Carolina, Wisconsin). Elsewhere states are contracting with existing consumer organizations to provide technical assistance and advisory functions (e.g., Illinois, Oregon, Vermont). Many consumers have found that political action is an important component of personal recovery as well as a strategy for system change (Carling, 1997; Deegan, 1992; Friere, 1997).

Many service providers are hiring consumers to work as staff members (e.g., Curtis, 1999b; Mowbray, Moxley, Jasper, Hawell, Abbot, Wolf, & Diksa, 1997; Abbot, 1995). The move to hire consumers or survivors is grounded in assumptions about their unique value: for example, consumer advocates assert that because they have life experiences that are unlike that of traditional professionals, they can bring special expertise to the work. They contend that for many the very presence of consumer staff can stimulate hope and images of successful recovery. Research into the efficacy of consumer staff members in case management services has demonstrated enhanced service outcomes (Soloman & Draine, 1995; Felton et al., 1996).

Increasingly, it is being recognized that the recruitment and involvement of consumers, without adequate and parallel capacity building, runs the risk of being reduced to tokenism. Organizations and consultants have jumped into the gap, providing technical education and leadership training to ensure that consumer participation has value beyond the symbolic (Nichols & Palmer, 1997). Additionally, some states are recognizing the need for accommodations that allow consumers and families to participate fully in policy-making activities, such as scheduling meetings for weekends or evenings so that people who cannot take time away from their jobs may attend (Anderson & Deegan, 1999; Curtis, 1991; Valentine & Capponi, 1989).

Consumer-Run Services

These services, also described as "user-controlled alternatives," are one manifestation of the self-help ideology of the consumer/survivor/ex-patients movement (Chamberlin, 1990). Their specific offerings may include peer-support and self-help networks, drop-in centers, wellness programs, crisis and respite care, and hospitalization alternatives. Founded, governed, and run by consumers (although some have a degree of nonconsumer involvement as well), they are typically organized nonhierarchically and emphasize mutual aid and support (Gartner & Reissman, 1997). Proponents argue that, because of their ideological heritage, such programs are the only truly "recovery-oriented" services available (Chamberlin, 1984; Fisher, 1994). With the current emphasis on recovery, several states (Missouri, Nebraska, New Hampshire, Ohio, Rhode Island, Vermont) are looking to consumer-run and self-help services as essential elements of the array of core services and are considering mechanisms by which consumer-operated services may be reimbursable through Medicaid.

As with consumer involvement, there is a growing awareness that support for consumer-run services requires more than just lip service (Solomon, Jonikas, Cook, & Keroac, 1998). Several states are exploring how to support these services through adequate funding, leadership and management training, mentoring, and accountability mechanisms that reflect the spirit of a self-help orientation (e.g., Nebraska, New Hampshire, Ohio, West Virginia). Bringing consumer-run services into the mainstream of mental health services can be problematic. For example, accepting public funding means finding a way to balance "from the heart" mutual aid and professionalized services with mandates for accountability, demonstrable outcomes, and adequate staff credentials.

RELAPSE PREVENTION AND MANAGEMENT

In several states (e.g., California, Maine, New Hampshire, Vermont) the education and self-help strategies for promoting recovery are prompting growing attention to preventive self-care and relapse prevention. Recovery education curricula directed at consumers emphasize techniques for recognition and management of symptoms and relapse triggers (Spaniol, Koehler, & Hutchinson, 1994; Copeland, 1992, 1994, 1997). In many places, support for recovery means providing financial support for the dissemination of such information and techniques among the consumer and family population. Some academic curricula train professionals to help individuals to develop effective relapse management and crisis prevention plans (e.g., Program in Community Mental Health at Trinity College of Vermont; Center for Psychiatric Rehabilitation, Boston University).

CRISIS PLANNING AND ADVANCE DIRECTIVES

Crisis planning is premised on the argument that proactive and prudent decision-making can mitigate the negative consequences of crisis situations and diminish the use of coercive interventions such as involuntary commitment, use of restraints and seclusion, and forced medication. While they are doing reasonably well, consumers develop plans for managing future crises. Building upon the recognition of triggers and the self-management skills emphasized in relapse prevention, crisis plans usually specify the signs and symptoms that the individual typically exhibits when in crisis and the individual's preference for disposition at that point—including preferred treatment facility and medication. The consumers may appoint a representative to advocate for their interests and wishes and to look after their daily affairs, e.g., call employer, pay rent, and other bills (Collier, 1994; Copeland, 1997). Such crisis plans may serve as guidelines, or they may be formalized as legal documents, for example as advance directives or for establishing a durable power of attorney for healthcare. States are promoting crisis planning either by encouraging consumers to formulate plans or by making such planning a requirement in certain treatment programs (e.g., California, Missouri, New Hampshire, Vermont). Vermont recently passed a state law that states that legally established advance directives can be overridden by court orders for involuntary treatment only after the plan outlined in the advance directive has been given an opportunity to work. Although the idea of crisis planning has gained considerable support from many consumer advocates and providers, the use of advance directives and durable power of attorney to direct psychiatric healthcare preferences, particularly in emergency situations, will likely come under judicial review in most states.

CONTRACTING AND FINANCING MECHANISMS

In many areas the shift to a recovery orientation has coincided with initiatives to move public mental health services into a managed care model (Mechanic, 1998). There is some trepidation about the fit between managed care (often perceived only as a cost control and service access mechanism) and the needs of the people with severe and persistent mental illness for quality care. Some advocates have asserted that the adoption of a managed care model, with its emphasis on rationalizing each level of care in order to ensure effective service delivery and improved outcomes, in fact represents the best chance for real mental health reform (Fisher, undated document). Certainly there is congruence between the managed care principle of minimizing high-cost, maintenance-oriented services, and the recovery principle of helping people to have "real lives" rather than subsisting in custodial programs. However, many of the elements that consumers describe as fundamental to establishing and maintaining recovery (such as work, good relationships, pets, spiritual connections) are not typically considered medically necessary. Capitation can give healthcare authorities increased flexibility to offer individuals such recovery-oriented supports, but an overly narrow conceptualization of recovery may provide latitude for managed care organizations to restrict access or to terminate services prematurely.

States and regional mental health authorities are seeking, quite literally, to write recovery principles into their contracts with managed care organizations (e.g., California, Massachusetts, New York, Ohio, Washington). Contracts may specify that the organizations must demonstrate a recovery orientation: for example, by requiring that the organizations maintain a certain level of consumer representation on their advisory boards, or that a certain proportion of their funding is devoted to consumer-run services.

The lynch pin of any contract is the phrase "medical necessity." Recovery advocates seek to expand the definition of "medical necessity" to encompass recovery-oriented psychiatric services such as housing, employment and educational support, wellness programs, recreational and spiritual opportunities, and other interventions and activities that can diminish the need for high cost services like hospitalization (e.g., California, Ohio, Rhode Island). New Hampshire has drafted a preliminary set of clinical practice guidelines for adults in community support programs that include standards for facilitating recovery and maintaining and extending gains (Torrey & Wyzik, 1997).

OUTCOMES

Managed care initiatives and new Federal requirements emphasize the measurement of outcomes as a strategy for ensuring the accountability of mental health providers to the purchasers and funders of behavioral healthcare and to regulatory bodies. The emerging emphasis on recovery principles in mental health services suggests that recovery should be seen as a measurable outcome. Across the country, health services researchers and medical information systems experts are trying to turn the concept of recovery from an abstraction into an instrument (e.g., New Hampshire, Ohio, Rhode Island, Vermont, Wisconsin). The process of developing such measures involves first specifying the dimensions of recovery, often through the use of qualitative or participatory action research methods, then finding ways to operationalize and measure them reliably and validly across time. The challenge is to find variables that appropriately capture the unique "lived experience" of recovery in ways that can satisfy the demands for system accountability. Harding (1994) identifies inherent complexities in this effort. She suggests that viewing recovery as an outcome or endpoint defies its highly individual and fluid character and often overlooks cultural and developmental aspects of its course. Such outcomes should be reframed as benchmarks or "markers of course" (Harding, 1994, p. 164).

POLICY REVISION

As recovery comes into the mainstream, it is stimulating a process of reflection and appraisal at the systems level as well as reassessment of "what works" on a program and personal level. Policymakers are looking at such issues as informed consent, confidentiality, involuntary commitment, and risk sharing, seeking ways to make actual practices congruent with the philosophy embedded in recovery (e.g., Maine, Massachusetts, Ohio, Vermont). Similarly, at the level of service provision, providers are reviewing treatment practices, identifying best practices, and developing guidelines that make manifest the principles of recovery (Curtis, 1997). For example, Jennings (1994), Rose (1991), and others are helping service systems to understand the prevalence of trauma histories among persons with mental illness, and how many existing policies and practices can be very injurious to service recipients. For those who are survivors of trauma, experiences in the service system are, in effect, perpetuating the trauma and the exact symptoms or problems the services are intended to ameliorate.

STIGMA REDUCTION

There is an increasing recognition of the deep level of stigma against persons with mental illness within the system (Reidy, 1994). For many consumers, this stigma is internalized, and contributes to the debilitating process of becoming a "mental patient" (Deegan, 1990). Recovery advocates suggest that such external and internal stigma can be reduced through the strategic application of recovery principles. For example, they argue, respect for the strengths of consumer-run services will follow the legitimization implied by making them eligible for Medicaid reimbursement. Respect for persons with mental illness will increase as their expertise is recognized and they become not "patients" or "clients," but co-workers and equal participants in the policy and service arenas (Mowbray et al., 1997; Solomon et al., 1998).

Finally, the concept of recovery looks beyond the service provider and the mental health system, construing a society that stigmatizes and discriminates against persons with mental illness as one that is itself in need of recovery. Stigma reduction, conceptualized as an application of recovery to the broader community, involves increasing awareness of the negative stereotypes of persons with psychiatric disabilities, denouncing such images as destructive, and then moving forward through such measures as community education and media campaigns.

KEY QUESTIONS

The current transformation of mental health services is fraught with both dangers and opportunities. The states' efforts to operationalize and implement recovery reflect both extremes. Some critics view the recent initiatives as a co-optation, an attempt to force the sometimes ineffable magic of recovery into a standardized and measurable model of traditional services. Consumer advocates have expressed concern that the movement to bring a recovery orientation to mental health policy is little more than a fad, a passing fashion. As state-level policymakers become enamored with recovery, they warn, recovery will become little more than a new label on an old bottle, simply another name for professionally driven rehabilitation programs. Their message is that without fundamentally re-conceptualizing the relationship between individual consumers and the system, we risk promulgating a cosmetic initiative that maintains the dependence of individuals on the system.

The possibilities reside in the strategies that are being used to integrate recovery-oriented principles into service system design. So far, these policies and programs are seen as in good faith, but preliminary efforts in moving toward recovery as a guiding principle for behavioral healthcare. Much remains to be learned about recovery. Among the questions that must be answered:

1. How can we deepen our understanding of recovery as an individual process? What stimulates and sustains that process? What hinders or smothers it? What are the best methods for answering such questions?

2. Can recovery be measured? Should it be measured? What are the risks of doing so? Of not doing so?

3. How can we transfer our knowledge about recovery as an individual process to our policymaking and service planning activities? How do specific policies and services affect individual recovery?

4. How will we know we are creating a recovery-oriented system? By what criteria should the system be judged? Should we measure individual gains? Aggregate outcomes? System-level change? Over what period of time?

5. How can we balance recovery as an individual, singular process, with the system's need for standardization? Can we formulate a generalized concept of recovery and still respect the process as unique?

6. For what should we hold the system accountable? Are we willing to trade off some system liability for the increased self-determination and personal responsibility that seem to be the hallmark of recovery?

7. What barriers stand in the way of implementing a recovery orienta-
    tion? What forces sustain the status quo?

8. *Should* recovery be the foundational principle of the mental health
    system?

These questions start with problems of epistemology—how best to
study and measure recovery. But they end in problems of politics and values—what is to be our society's approach to helping persons with psychiatric
disabilities? For recovery to herald a real change in our assumptions and practices, and to make a difference in the lives of people living with severe and
persistent mental illness, it is vital that all of these questions be engaged.
How we chose to answer them will shape mental health services in the coming decades.

REFERENCES

Abbot, B., Wolf, R. & Diksa, E. (1995). *Hiring mental health consumers to work within
county mental health programs: Survey results.* Sacramento, CA: California
Institute for Mental Health.

Anderson, D., & Deegan, P. (1994). *Overcoming barriers to effective consumer/survivor
participation on boards and committees.* (unpublished document)

Anthony, W. (1991). Recovery from mental illness: The new vision of service
researchers. *Innovations & Research 1*(1), 13–14.

Anthony, W. (1993). Recovery from mental illness: The guiding vision of the mental health service system in the 1990s. *Psychosocial Rehabilitation Journal
16*(4), 11–23.

Anthony, W., Cohen, M., & Farkas, M. (1990). *Psychiatric rehabilitation.* Boston:
Center for Psychiatric Rehabilitation, Boston University.

Barton, R. (1998). The rehabilitation-recovery paradigm: A statement of philosophy
for a public mental health system. *Psychiatric Rehabilitation Skills, 2*(2),
171–187.

Beale, V., & Lambric, T. (1995). *The recovery concept: Implementation in the mental
health system.* Columbus, OH: Ohio Department of Mental Health.

Blanch, A., Fisher, D., Tucker, W., & Chassman, J. (1993). Consumer-practitioners
and psychiatrists share insights about recovery and coping. *Disability Studies
Quarterly 13*(2), 17–20.

Bluebird, G. (2000). *Participatory dialogs: A how-to manual.* Rockville, MD: Center
for Mental Health Services.

Brown, P. (1981). The Mental Health Patients' Rights Movement and mental health
institutional change. *International Journal of Health Services, 11*(4), 523–540.

Campbell, J. (1997). How consumers are evaluating the quality of psychiatric care.
Evaluation Quarterly 21(3), 357–363.

Campbell, J., & Schraiber, R. (1989). *The well-being project: Mental health clients speak for themselves.* Sacramento, CA: California Department of Mental Health.

Carling, P. J. (1997). *Recovery as the core of our work: The challenge to mental health systems and professionals.* Keynote Presentation to the New Hampshire Partners for Change Conference on Recovery, Nashua, NH, September 5, 1997. Burlington, VT: Center for Community Change through Housing and Support, Trinity College of Vermont.

Center for Community Change through Housing and Support (1996). *Recovery Institute: Knowing and practicing recovery skills.* Burlington, VT: Center for Community Change Through Housing and Support, Trinity College of Vermont.

Chamberlin, J. (1984). Speaking for ourselves: An overview of the ex-psychiatric inmates' movement. *Psychosocial Rehabilitation Journal, 8*(2), 56–64.

Chamberlin, J. (1990). The ex-patients' movement: Where we've been and where we're going. *The Journal of Mind and Behavior, 11*(3&4), 323–336.

Collier, D. (1994). Recovery. In *Recovery: The New Force in Mental Health.* Columbus, OH: Ohio Department of Mental Health.

Copeland, M. E. (1992). *The depression workbook: A guide to living with depression and manic depression.* Oakland, CA: New Harbinger Press.

Copeland, M. E. (1994). *Living without depression and manic depression: A workbook for maintaining mood stability.* Oakland, CA: New Harbinger Press.

Copeland, M. E. (1997). *WRAP-Wellness Recovery Action Plan.* Brattleboro, VT: Peach Press.

Curtis, L. C. (1997). *New directions: International overview of best practices in recovery and rehabilitation for people with serious mental illness.* A discussion paper prepared for the New Zealand Mental Health Commission. Burlington, VT: Center for Community Change.

Curtis, L. C., McCabe, S. S,. & Montague, W. (1991). *Strategies for increasing and supporting consumer involvement in mental health policy/planning, management and service delivery.* Burlington, VT: Center for Community Change through Housing and Support, Trinity College of Vermont.

Deegan, P. E. (1988). Recovery: The lived experience of rehabilitation. *Psychosocial Rehabilitation Journal, 11*(4), 11–19.

Deegan, P. E. (1990). *How recovery begins.* Paper presented at the Eighth Annual Education Conference of the Alliance for the Mentally Ill of New York State, Binghamton, NY.

Deegan, P. E. (1992). The independent living movement and people with disabilities: Taking back control over our own lives. *Psychosocial Rehabilitation Journal, 15*(3), 3–9.

Everett, B. (1994). Something is happening: The contemporary consumer and psychiatric survivor movement in historical context. *The Journal of Mind and Behavior, 15*(1 & 2), 55–70.

Felton, C .J., Stastny, P., Shern, D. L., Blanch, A., Donahue, S. A., Knight, E., Brown, C. (1995). Consumers as peer specialists on intensive case management teams impact on outcomes. *Psychiatric Services, 46*(10) 1037–1044.

Ferry, L. (1996). Ensuring consumer satisfaction. *Behavioral Health Management,* Nov/Dec, 15–16.

Fisher, D. B. (undated). *Self-managed care: Ways that managed care organizations and their partners can promote the participation of consumers in their recovery.* Lawrence, MA: National Empowerment Center.

Fisher, D. B. (1994). Health care reform based on an empowerment model of recovery by people with psychiatric disabilities. *Hospital and Community Psychiatry, 45*(9), 913–915.

Friere, P. (1997). *Pedagogy of the oppressed.* New York: Continuum.

Gartner, A. J. & Riessman, F. (1997). Self-help and mental health. In L. Spaniol, C. Gagne, & M. Koehler(Eds.), *Psychological and social aspects of psychiatric disability*, pp.390–397. Boston: Center for Psychiatric Rehabilitation, Boston University. Reprinted from *Hospital and Community Psychiatry, 33*(8), (1982), 631–635.

Harding, C. M. (1994). An examination of the complexities in the measurement of recovery in severe psychiatric disorders. In R. Aneill (Ed.) *Schizophrenia: Exploring the spectrum of psychosis.* New York: John Wiley and Sons.

Harding, C. M., Brooks, G. W., Ashikaga, T., Strauss, J. S., Brier, A. (1987). The Vermont longitudinal study of persons with severe mental illness II: Long-term outcome of subjects who retrospectively met *DSM-III* criteria for schizophrenia. *American Journal of Psychiatry, 144*(6), 727–735.

Hatfield, A .B., & Lefley, H. P. (1993). *Surviving mental illness: Stress, coping, and adaptation.* New York: The Guilford Press.

Jennings, A. (1994). On being invisible in the mental health system. *Journal of Mental Health Administration, 21*(4), 374–387.

Leete, E. (1989). How I perceive and manage my illness. *Schizophrenia Bulletin, 15*(2), 197–200.

Legislative Summer Study Committee of the State of Vermont Division of Mental Health. (1996). *A position paper on recovery and psychiatric disability.* Waterbury, VT: Vermont Developmental Disability & Mental Health Services.

McFarlane, W. R., Lukens, E., Link, B., Dushay, R., Deakins, S. A., Newmark, M., Dunne, E. J., Horn, B., & Torah, J. (1995). Multiple-family groups and psychoeducation in the treatment of schizophrenia. *Archives of General Psychiatry, 52*, 679–687.

Mechanic, D. (1998). Emerging trends in mental health policy and practice. *Health Affairs, 17*(6), 82–98.

Mowbray, C. T., Moxley, D. P., Jasper, C. A., & Howell, L. L. (Eds.) (1997). *Consumers as providers in psychiatric rehabilitation.* Columbia, MD: International Association of Psychosocial Rehabilitation Services.

Muser, K T., & Gingerich, S. (1994). *Coping with schizophrenia: A guide for families.* Oakland, CA: New Harbinger Publications.

National Technical Assistance Center for State Mental Health Planning (1998). *Regional Training Conference: Recovery: A guiding vision for mental health services.* Summary of a conference held in Omaha, NE, April 1998.

New York State Office of Mental Health (undated). *A dialogue on recovery: Tips for structuring a recipient dialogue and a dialogue on recovery: An experiment in progress.* Albany, NY.

Nichols, N., & Palmer, H. (1997). *Developing consumer leadership: An annotated bibliography.* Burlington, VT: Center for Community Change through Housing and Support, Trinity College of Vermont.

Ralph, R.O. (1996). *Recovery.* Plenary presentation at the 38th Annual Southern Regional Conference on Mental Health Statistics. New Orleans, LA.

Reidy, D. (1994). The mental health system as agent of stigma. *Resources, 6*(3), 3–10.

Rose, S. (1991). Acknowledging abuse backgrounds of intensive case management clients. *Community Mental Health Journal, 27*(4), 255–263.

Schmook, A. (undated). *Creating a recovery vision statement.* Distributed by the National Association for State Mental Health Program Directors.

Scott, A. (1993). Consumer/survivors reform the system, bringing a 'human face' to research. *Resources, 5*(1), 3–6.

Soloman, P. & Draine, J. (1995). The impact of case management and the efficacy of a consumer case management team: One year outcomes of a randomized trial. *Evaluation and Program Planning, 18*(2), 117–127.

Solomon, M. L., Jonikas, J. A, Cook, J. A., & Keroac, J. (1998). *Positive partnerships: How consumers and non-consumers can work together as service providers (2nd Ed.).* Chicago, IL: University of Illinois at Chicago, National Research and Training Center on Psychiatric Disability.

Spaniol, L., Koehler, M., & Hutchinson, D. (1994). *The recovery workbook: Practical coping and empowerment strategies for people with psychiatric disability.* Boston: Center for Psychiatric Rehabilitation, Boston University.

Srebnick, D., Robinson, M., & Tanzman, B. H. (1990). *Participation of mental health consumers in research: Empowerment in practice.* Burlington, VT: Center for Community Change through housing and support, Trinity College of Vermont.

State of Nebraska Recovery Workteam. (1997). *Recovery: A guiding vision for consumers and providers of mental health services in Nebraska. Lincoln, NE.*

State of Vermont (undated). *Vermont recovery education project.* Waterbury, VT: Vermont Division of Developmental and Mental Health Services.

State of Wisconsin Blue Ribbon Commission on Mental Health. (1997). *Final report.* Madison, WI: Department of Health and Family Services.

Sullivan, W. P. (1997). A long and winding road: The process of recovery from severe mental illness. In L. Spaniol, C. Gagne, & M. Koehler (Eds.), *Psychological and social aspects of psychiatric disability* (pp 14–24). Boston: Center for Psychiatric Rehabilitation, Boston University. Reprinted from *Innovations and Research, 3*(3), (1994), 19–27.

Torrey, W. C., & Wyzik, P. F. (1997). *New Hampshire clinical practice guidelines for adults in community support programs (version 1).* Lebanon, NH: West Central Services.

Unzicker, R. (1989). On my own: A personal journey through madness and re-emergence. *Psychosocial Rehabilitation Journal, 13*(1), 71–77.

Valentine, M. B., & Capponi, P. (1989). Mental health consumer participation on boards and committees: Barriers and strategies. *Canada's Mental Health,* June, 8–12.

Acknowledgments

Nora Jacobson's work on this project was supported by a training grant from the National Institute of Mental Health (Grant No. 5T32MH14641) and by the State of Wisconsin Bureau of Community Mental Health and the Wisconsin Coalition for Advocacy.

Evidence-Based Practices: Integrating Evidence-Based Practices and the Recovery Model

Frederick J. Frese, III, Jonathan Stanley, Ken Kress, and Suzanne Vogel-Scibilia

At the time of original publication, author affiliations were listed as follows: Frederick Frese, III, PhD, is assistant professor of psychology in clinical psychiatry at the Northeastern Ohio Universities College of Medicine and former first vice-president of the National Alliance for the Mentally Ill (NAMI); Jonathan Stanley, JD, is assistant director of the Treatment Advocacy Center in Arlington, Virginia; Ken Kress, PhD, JD, is professor of law and director of the Mental Health Law Project at the University of Iowa College of Law in Iowa City; and Suzanne Vogel-Scibilia, MD, is a psychiatrist in private practice in Beaver, Pennsylvania, and a board member of NAMI. All of the authors are active consumer advocates.

This article was published previously in *Psychiatric Services,* 2001, 52, 1462–1468 and is reprinted with permission.

Abstract: Consumer advocacy has emerged as an important factor in mental health policy during the past few decades. Winning consumer support for evidence-based practices requires recognition that consumers' desires and needs for various types of treatments and services differ significantly. The authors suggest that the degree of support for evidence-based practices by consumer advocates depends largely on the degree of disability of the persons for whom they are advocating. Advocates such as members of the National Alliance for the Mentally Ill, who focus on the needs of the most seriously disabled consumers, are most likely to be highly supportive of research that is grounded in evidence-based practices. On the other hand, advocates who focus more on the needs of consumers who are further along their road to recovery are more likely to be attracted to the recovery model. Garnering the support of this latter group entails ensuring that consumers, as they recover, are given increasing autonomy and greater input about the types of treatments and services they receive. The authors suggest ways to integrate evidence-based practices with the recovery model and then suggest a hybrid theory that maximizes the virtues and minimizes the weaknesses of each model.

INTRODUCTION

Shortly after the National Institute of Mental Health was returned to the National Institutes of Health in 1989, President George H. W. Bush declared the "Decade of the Brain." Federal funding for research on the brain was greatly increased during that time, resulting in remarkable scientific progress (*NAMI Advocate,* 2000). The 1990s saw advances not only in our understanding of the working of the human brain but also in our approaches to the treatment of the mental illnesses that are caused by brain abnormalities.

During the past decade, confidence in scientific research, with its objective observations and measures, has increased considerably in the mental health arena.

EVIDENCE-BASED PRACTICES

In recent years, this increased confidence in scientific treatment methods for mental illnesses has given rise to a movement that calls for more widespread adoption of treatment approaches that are scientifically grounded. This movement has been developing under the rubric of "evidence-based practices" (Torrey, et al., 2001; Drake, Goldman et al., 2001; Bond, et al., 2001; Drake, Essock et al., 2001; Minkoff, 2001; Mellman et al., 2001). Under this concept, the call for greater reliance on scientific evidence is being extended to treatment approaches that are supported by psychological and sociological evidence as well as by the findings of biological research.

In an earlier article on evidence-based practices, Drake and associates (Drake, Goldman et al., 2001) provided an overview of the topic, outlining the research findings and philosophical underpinnings of the evidence-based practice movement. They spelled out specific reasons for the special focus by *Psychiatric Services* on evidence-based practice interventions. These reasons include the belief that routine mental health programs do not provide evidence-based practices, that implementation of services resembling evidence-based practices may lack fidelity to evidence-based procedures, and, especially, that in the context of limited resources consumers have a right to interventions that are known to be effective. So described, evidence-based practices appear to be unassailable. Who could object to promoting the use of treatments that work rather than those that do not?

Drake and colleagues (Drake, Goldman et al., 2001) also delineated a core set of interventions: prescription of medications within specific parameters, training in self-management of illness, assertive community treatment, family psychoeducation, supported employment, and integrated treatment for co-occurring substance use disorders. The authors stressed that "mental health services for persons with severe mental illness should reflect the goals of consumers."

Drake and colleagues further stated that "mental health services should not focus exclusively on traditional outcomes such as compliance with treatment and relapse or rehospitalization prevention, but should be broadened to include helping people to attain such consumer-oriented outcomes as: independence, employment, satisfying relationships, and good quality of life." Finally, they allowed that evidence-based practices "do not provide the answers for all persons with mental illness, all outcomes, or all settings" (Drake, Goldman et al., 2001).

In light of this characterization of evidence-based practices, particularly the openness to consumers' needs and aspirations, one might expect that the consumer advocacy community would be pleased that the views of consumers are emerging as a major matter of interest. This move beyond traditional, "provider-centric" factors seems to be a healthy, consumer-friendly development. In consumer advocacy circles, "Nothing about us without us" has increasingly been adopted as a slogan for expressing the desire for more dignity and autonomous control for the recipients of mental health services (Pelka, 1998). This reaching out for consumer input should be a welcome development.

THE RECOVERY MODEL

At the same time that the Decade of the Brain initiatives and evidence-based initiatives have been emerging in the mental health arena, a more personalized and subjective approach to caring for persons who have mental illness has also been emerging—the recovery model.

William Anthony, a major supporter of the recovery model (1993), describes recovery as "a deeply personal, unique process of changing one's attitudes, values, feelings, goals, skills, and/or roles. It is a way of living a satisfying, hopeful, and contributing life, even with limitations caused by the illness. Recovery involves the development of new meaning and purpose in one's life as one grows beyond the catastrophic effects of mental illness." Sullivan (1994) called for "a broad definition of recovery, one that not only focuses on the management of the illness, but also highlights the consumer's performance of instrumental role functions and notions of empowerment and self-directedness."

The recovery model emphasizes that responsibility for and control of the recovery process must be given in large part to the person who has the condition. Indeed, some advocates for the recovery model have stressed that overdependence on others prevents recovery. The locus of control thus becomes less external. Mental health interventions are designed to be empowering, enabling the persons themselves to take responsibility for decisions about their lives (Beale & Lambric, 1995; Jacobson & Greenley, 2001). Recently, some states—for example, Wisconsin and Ohio—have been redesigning their mental health systems to stress recovery-model values, such as hope, healing, empowerment, social connectedness, human rights, and recovery-oriented services (Jacobson & Greenley, 2001).

Although the recovery model has been garnering support among consumer advocates and mental health administrators, objections to this approach have recently been raised among mental health professionals. Pointing out that the recovery model is subjective, not data based or scientific, Peyser (2001) suggested that it may in fact interfere with treatment. He pointed out that psychotic illnesses and similar illnesses can subvert the thinking process to the point that the patient's self is taken over by the disease. He asked how we can speak about empowerment and collaboration in such cases and suggested that there are "dangers in going too far" toward fashioning a model that focuses primarily on hope, empowerment, and human rights.

Two apparently very different approaches to treatment of mentally ill persons are emerging. The scientific, objective, evidence-based approach emphasizes external scientific reality, whereas the recovery model stresses the importance of the phenomenological, subjective experiences and autonomous rights of persons who are in recovery. The two models will conflict under many circumstances. Obviously, when consumers make decisions about treatment, they will sometimes make choices that are not evidence based. Treatment decisions cannot be made entirely on factual, scientific grounds. Rather, treatment decisions involve both medical facts and choices based on values.

Science can identify alternative possible treatments and an outcome-probability distribution of efficacy and adverse effects for each treatment option. The decision as to which combination of anticipated improvement and anticipated adverse effects is preferable is a value judgment. Consumers' decisions about treatment will be more likely to reflect their values than will decisions by treating professionals, even when professionals attempt to determine consumers' preferences. Thus evidence-based treatments may differ from treatments that are based on the recovery model insofar as they reflect different judgments of the value of various treatment outcomes by service providers and consumers.

The recovery model has found significant support in the mental health field, particularly among consumer advocates. Thus the question arises as to whether these apparently opposed approaches to mental health care can coexist. And can efforts to expand the influence of evidence-based practices somehow accommodate the more subjective philosophical thrust of the recovery movement?

Increasing the use of externally derived interventions while maximizing individual empowerment that emanates from an internal locus of control will be a challenge. However, if we are to win consumer advocacy support for evidence-based practices, we should accommodate the insights of the recovery movement.

INTEGRATING THE RECOVERY MODEL AND EVIDENCE-BASED PRACTICES

One approach to reconciling scientific and subjective approaches to treatment was recently suggested by Munetz and Frese (2001). They suggested that the traditional evidence-based approach—the "medical model"—can be compatible with the recovery model. In their view, the evidence-based, medical model has been highly paternalistic, emphasizing illness, weakness, and limitations rather than the potential for growth. They claimed that the evidence-based medical model has been perceived as stamping out hope by implying that biology is destiny and emphasizing an external locus of control. They also mentioned that some consumer advocates view the physician as a powerful and oppressive figure who "at best is acting out of misguided beneficence" and at worst fosters "helplessness and chronicity."

Munetz and Frese also described extreme critics of the medical model who accept Szasz's position that mental illnesses do not really exist as biopsychosocial disorders (Szasz, 1961). However, they also pointed out that some consumer advocates, including the psychologists Deegan (1992, 1993) and Frese (1993), accept the existence of their illnesses and recognize that they have certain limitations because of their illness. Deegan (1992), however, also warned of the "cycle of disempowerment and despair" that is engendered by traditional, objectively based, paternalistic approaches to treatment of mentally ill persons.

Munetz and Frese (2001) have shown how this alleged conflict between objectivity and subjectivity can be largely resolved. For persons who are so seriously impaired in their decision-making capacity that they are incapable of determining what is in their best interest, a paternalistic, externally reasoned treatment approach seems not only appropriate but also necessary in most cases for the well-being of the impaired individual. However, as these impaired persons begin to benefit from externally initiated interventions, the locus of control should increasingly shift from the treatment provider to the person who is recovering. As individuals recover, they must gradually be afforded a larger role in the selection of treatments and services. Throughout the recovery process, persons should be given maximal opportunity to regain control over their lives. They should be given increasingly greater choice about evidence-based interventions and other available services.

To accommodate the precepts of the evidence-based medical model with those of the recovery model, Munetz and Frese suggested an approach consonant with the observations of Csernansky and Bardgett and others. After surveying recent research on the pathophysiology of the brain, Csernansky and Bardgett (1998) pointed out that the degree of impairment in serious mental illnesses falls somewhere on a continuum that ranges from severe, refractory psychosis to less serious, responsive psychosis and on toward normality.

Munetz and Frese (2001) pointed out that many individuals are so disabled with mental illness that they do not have the capacity to understand that they are ill. Giving such individuals the right to make decisions about their treatment is tantamount to abandonment. They noted that it is "inconsistent with the recovery paradigm to allow incapacitated individuals to remain victims of their serious mental illness." For these persons, measures must be taken so that they become well enough to be able to benefit from the recovery model. That is, one treatment goal whose significance should be accentuated by evidence-based practices is enhancement of the consumer's ability to make autonomous decisions about treatment as a means of gaining control of his or her treatment.

Thus persons who are very disabled by mental illness are those most likely to benefit from objective, evidence-based approaches to treatment. For these persons there is less of a need to focus on the person-centered principles of the recovery model. However, as such persons begin to benefit from treatments, they should be afforded opportunity for greater autonomy. As they progress along the road to recovery, their growing capacity for autonomy should be respected, eventually to the point at which treatment personnel assume the role of consultants and virtually all decisions about treatment are in the hands of the persons who are making the journey of recovery.

Persons who have substantially recovered can be viewed as those likely to benefit the most from the autonomy-centered recovery model. Alternatively, such persons could be viewed as having sufficient capacity for autonomy to have the same right to make their own decisions about treatment—even if those decisions are not evidence based or maximally therapeutic—as is routinely accorded to persons who are viewed as having no decision-making impairments.

CONSUMER'S VIEWS

An important and logical step in increasing consumer empowerment is to identify the concerns of the consumer. Attempts to determine how psychiatrically disabled persons perceive their needs is a relatively new concept in mental health. Until the latter part of the 20th century, persons with schizophrenia and other serious mental illnesses were generally viewed as being so delusional or otherwise cognitively impaired that they were incapable of providing substantive input about their care. Although many such persons did recover, the opprobrium they faced was so ingrained that few of them, or even their family members, would openly acknowledge their experiences with these conditions. As is the case today, there were significant disincentives to make such disclosures for those who were, or had been, considered "insane." A similar stigma discouraged openness by persons who had "insanity in the family."

However, beginning in the 1960s, some persons who had been subjected to treatment for serious mental illnesses began to identify themselves openly. In addition, some of these recovering persons took steps to organize themselves and started to give voice to their views. The advocacy efforts of consumers and family members have mushroomed and today represent a valuable and formidable force that affects all aspects of mental health policy (1998).

NATIONAL ALLIANCE FOR THE MENTALLY ILL (NAMI)

Of the consumer advocacy entities that were formed during the past quarter century, the National Alliance for the Mentally Ill (NAMI) is by far the largest. NAMI was founded as recently as 1979. As of the summer of 2001, NAMI had a membership of more than 210,000—with more than 1,200 affiliates—located in all 50 states. NAMI currently supports a full-time staff of more than 60.

NAMI initially functioned as a group that advocated primarily for the families of persons with serious mental illnesses. However, the influence of the consumers in NAMI has become increasingly important. The organization has a large consumer council. During the past several years at least one quarter of the members of NAMI's board of directors have been consumers. However, despite this growing influence, the tens of thousands of consumer members of NAMI do not speak as an independent organization but blend their concerns with those of the majority of the NAMI members—for the most part, family members.

NAMI has a long and complex policy agenda but recently has given special prominence to what the organization sees as eight particularly important policy issues. These priorities are characterized by NAMI as being "based on the most effective standards and programs demonstrated to empower individuals on the road to recovery." Published and widely distributed as the "Omnibus Mental Illness Recovery Act: A Blueprint for Recovery—OMIRA" (1999), these eight NAMI priorities are participation by consumers and their family members in planning of mental illness services; equitable health care coverage, or parity, in health insurance; access to newer medications; assertive community treatment; work incentives for persons who have severe mental illness; reduction in life-threatening and harmful actions and restraints; reduction in the criminalization of persons who have severe mental illness; and access to permanent, safe, and affordable housing with appropriate community-based services.

There is noticeable overlap between NAMI's policy priorities and the six core interventions outlined by Drake and colleagues. One area—assertive community treatment—is clearly prioritized, under the same term, by both NAMI and proponents of evidence-based practices. The call for prescription of medications within specific parameters is somewhat addressed by NAMI's prioritizing access to newer medications. Moreover, NAMI was an active participant in the public launch of the findings of the Schizophrenia Patient Outcomes Research Team (PORT), which gave wide distribution to the specific recommended parameters for prescribed antipsychotic medications (1998). NAMI also produced and distributed more than 500,000 brochures highlighting these recommendations.

These efforts, which support the PORT results, also highlighted the recommended evidence-based interventions for assertive community treatment and for family psychoeducation. Indeed, although neither is explicitly designated as an evidence-based practice, NAMI has two major training initiatives related to psychoeducation: the Family-to-Family program, which focuses on education of family members, and the Living With Schizophrenia program, which teaches consumers to better live with their disorders. This latter effort primarily involves self-management of illness and thus is also related to another of the designated core interventions of Drake and colleagues.

The fifth core initiative under the evidence-based practice model—supported employment—is encompassed in OMIRA under work incentives for persons with severe mental illness, even though the two are not identical. Finally, although NAMI has yet to develop an explicit policy initiative that calls for integrated mental health and substance abuse treatment, the national NAMI board has been actively weighing the pros and cons of taking a position that supports this initiative.

In a broader yet specific demonstration of support by NAMI for the six evidence-based practice initiatives, the president of the NAMI board recently sent a letter to all 16 national board members that highlighted the importance of the evidence-based practices movement.

NAMI, of course, was started by family members of persons who were very disabled with mental illnesses. The needs of the most disabled persons continues to be the organization's priority. Many of the consumers for whom NAMI lobbies tend to be too disabled to effectively speak for themselves. Many of them are not ready to benefit from the recovery model. NAMI can be expected to provide strong support for evidence-based practice initiatives but will not necessarily be uncritical. On the other hand, agenda statements have been made by organized groups of consumer advocates during the past decade that have presented the collective voices of persons who are further along in their recovery—persons who are better able to speak for themselves.

THE NATIONAL MENTAL HEALTH CONSUMERS' ASSOCIATION

One of the more successful attempts to characterize the spectrum of concerns of recovering persons is embodied in the mission statement and the national agenda of the National Mental Health Consumers' Association (NMHCA). Although the organization has not been active during the past few years, from the mid-1980s through the mid-1990s it was widely viewed as the most organized and largest independent, non-disease-specific organization for persons who had been treated for serious mental illness.

Consumer advocates all over the country regularly participated in the election of members of the NMHCA board. Meeting monthly via conference call, the board had some claim to reflecting the collective voice of consumers' concerns nationally because of NMHCA's organizational structure. In the early 1990s and after lengthy deliberations, NMHCA produced a mission statement and a national agenda. The wording of their documents was approved overwhelmingly by both the board and the NMHCA membership in attendance at their meeting held December 12, 1992, in Philadelphia during the annual national Alternatives Conference. Although the NMHCA mission statement was widely distributed in consumer advocacy circles, to our knowledge it has not previously been published.

Examination of NMHCA's mission and national agenda statements (see Table 1) reveals that NMHCA's priorities are, by and large, dissimilar from the evidence-based practice initiatives. Although the latter focus heavily on the use of medications and on other services, NMHCA's priorities primarily stress factors that should better enable recovering persons to more easily integrate into society. Indeed, the six items on NMHCA's national agenda overlap very little with stated targets of the evidence-based practice core interventions. The NMHCA agenda item on benefits calls for entitlement to comprehensive health care. This may or may not include various types of mental health care; such care is explicitly mentioned only in the items on mental health systems and self-help. In addition, the major focus of these latter items is on more consumer-oriented priorities in the overall structure of the mental health system, not on increased availability of psychiatric services.

The statement of NMHCA's priorities is, in essence, a call for a reexamination of the philosophy and focus of the mental health establishment. It endorses the primary purpose of the development and implementation of mental health services to be for "recovery and healing," not for "social control." The individuals constructing and supporting NMHCA's statement of its national priorities are apparently reasonably far along in their own recovery. Indeed, they appear to be sufficiently recovered to focus primarily on how they can reduce environmental barriers to recovery rather than on examining which treatments they should be receiving. NMHCA advocates who are mostly recovered clearly argue for a more internal locus of control.

This heavy stress on increased autonomy and other recovery priorities by consumer advocates who are mostly recovered fits well with an approach that increases the consumer's autonomy as recovery progresses. However, a serious question remains about the degree to which the views of NMHCA activists reflect the concerns of nonactivist consumers who are less recovered and perhaps less articulate. Similarly, some advocates of the recovery model may not reflect the concerns or needs of this latter group of consumers.

To our knowledge, no national attempt has been made to systematically capture the sentiment of consumers who are more seriously disabled. Attempts have been made in several states to survey such consumers about their views on services. One of the more active of these efforts has been under way in Ohio for the past 5 years or so.

Table 1. NMHCA Mission Statement and Agenda

Mission Statement

Guided by the principles of choice, empowerment, and self-determination, the National Mental Health Consumers' Association is a human rights organization that advocates for employment, housing, benefits, service choice, and the end of discrimination and abuse in the lives of persons who use, have used, or have been used by the mental health systems.

National Agenda

Employment

We support the full implementation of the Americans with Disabilities Act and the Rehabilitation Services Act. We must be given every opportunity to be gainfully employed in occupations where we, with reasonable accommodation, can contribute. We call upon the mental health system to practice affirmative action in training and employing mental health consumers in professional careers in the mental health system.

Housing

All persons, particularly those identified as being mentally ill, are entitled to adequate, permanent homes of their choice.

Benefits

All psychiatrically disabled persons must be entitled to sufficient income, social supports, and comprehensive health care to enjoy an adequate quality of life.

Mental Health Systems

Recovery and healing, not social control, must be the goal and outcome of the mental health system; therefore, the mental health system must be client driven.

Self-help

We support the full and sustained funding and development of user-run alternatives and additions to the traditional mental health system, self-determined and governed by and for members, in every community.

Discrimination

Discrimination, abuse, ostracism, stigmatization, and other forms of social prejudice must be identified and vigorously opposed at every opportunity.

OHIO CONSUMER QUALITY REVIEW TEAMS

Beginning in 1996, consumer quality review teams were established by the Ohio Department of Mental Health to determine consumers' views of the mental health delivery system in 22 of Ohio's 88 counties. Although a few family members and professionals participated as employees in the teams' projects, the overwhelming majority of employees were persons in recovery from serious mental illness. The primary method for collecting data about consumers' perceived needs in this team effort was through consumer-conducted, structured individual interviews, each of which lasted for up to two hours.

From July 1996 to March 1999 some 890 adult consumers of Ohio's public services for the seriously mentally ill were individually interviewed about their views of mental health services. Consumers volunteered for participation in the project. Their names were drawn in a quasi-randomized, stratified manner from both rural and urban areas of the state.

An analysis of the data gathered from these Ohio consumers indicated three general areas of concern (1999). One was services that consumers believed were needed but either were not available or were seriously undersupplied: crisis stabilization, longer-term secure residential programs, clubhouse services, housing, meaningful retraining and job placement opportunities, and consumer-run services, which were reported to be "highly valued" by consumers.

These consumers, as a group, also indicated that they viewed some services as being both available and particularly helpful. These were emotional support, education and information, social support, treatment, stabilization, and financial support. A third area of consumer interest related to aspects of care that were seen as needing the greatest improvement: access to services, adequate numbers of staff, greater consumer influence, and more considerate behavior from mental health staff. One final finding of note was that a significant proportion of consumers was unsure or unaware of which services were in fact being provided in their areas.

The consumers who were interviewed by the consumer quality review teams were all clients of the public mental health system in Ohio. Attempts were made to ensure a maximally random selection of subjects, so one could conclude that this sample of opinions was more representative of the "typical" person who has serious mental illness than those who structured the NMHCA priorities.

Nevertheless, the consumers stressed several of NMHCA's priorities. These include housing, consumer-run activities, increased consumer influence, benefits such as financial and social support, and access to treatment and health care services. However, unlike the NMHCA advocates who are further recovered, these consumers expressed a desire for services that resembled evidence-based practice interventions. These include the explicit mention of medication, presumably in appropriate dosages; education and information, similar to training in illness self-management and family psychoeducation; retraining and job placement opportunities, which could include supported employment; and more staff as well as staff who are more understanding, both of which are, or should be, components of assertive community treatment.

Thus the findings of the consumer quality review teams suggest that consumers who are probably not as far into their recovery may be more receptive to the types of services that make up the core interventions of the evidence-based practice model. More detailed and current information about the Ohio consumer quality review teams can be found on the Web sites www.qsan.org and www.qrsinc.org.

DISCUSSION AND CONCLUSIONS

Over the past three decades, increasingly influential consumer voices have emerged and have advocated for improvements in the treatment of persons who have mental illness. Two recently developing philosophical forces are competing for the support of these newly enfranchised consumers. One of them is based on science, premised on the identification and implementation of modalities that have been demonstrated by scientific evidence to be effective. The other is the recovery model, which emphasizes the personal nature of the recovery journeys and insists that the final arbiter of how one should recover should be the person who is recovering.

This article has reviewed the viewpoints of three groups of consumers. Although there are numerous similarities, such as a unanimous call for adequate housing, the positions of the various consumer advocates largely reflect the degree of disability of those for whom they are advocating. Those who represent the most disabled, such as family members who believe that they are advocating for those who are not capable of speaking rationally for themselves, tend to be very supportive of evidence-based practice initiatives. Consumers who themselves have recovered fairly well tend to stress the importance of taking control of their own lives. Such persons value their own ability to make choices and even their ability to risk failure. For them, the improvements in treatment that accompany evidence-based practices may be important, but not as important as the rights of consumers to make their own decisions about what services are best for them. As they see it, they themselves—and not more detached scientific researchers—must be the final arbiters of how they will go about their recovery.

Examining the views of consumers who tend to be sufficiently recovered to be able to rationally discuss their opinions, but not so recovered as to have become "advocates," we find the desire for a little of both worlds. These consumers want better treatments, but they also desire more influence and autonomy.

These observations have several implications for those who are interested in garnering maximal support for evidence-based practice initiatives. NAMI members and other advocates who sometimes speak for "those who cannot speak for themselves" are likely to be very receptive to evidence-based practice initiatives. Indeed, the NAMI leadership already has indicated a willingness to help support and implement evidence-based practice interventions. Those who are interested in encouraging consumer advocacy support for evidence-based practices are likely to find significant assistance here.

On the other hand, advocates who speak for consumers who are further along the recovery process often belong to this group of consumers themselves. They tend to be more focused on regaining personal control, placing a higher priority on rights and opportunities to improve quality of life. They also desire more interaction and influence with the groups that make mental health decisions that affect their lives.

To better gain support from these consumer advocates, a number of actions might be considered. First, more consumers can be invited to participate in groups that are responsible for conducting, overseeing, and implementing evidence-based practice activities. As changes to treatments are being considered, having consumers "at the table" goes a long way toward letting them feel that their contributions are valued and that the decision-making process is fair.

Second, because participation in discussions of scientific matters usually requires familiarity with scientific methods and principles, better efforts should be made to encourage graduate and professional schools that train and accredit mental health providers to recruit consumers in recovery. Such efforts could help increase the number of consumers who are able to contribute to the development and implementation of evidence-based practice interventions. Some academic entities, such as the Nova Southeastern University Center for Psychological Studies and the Program in Psychiatric Rehabilitation of the University of Medicine and Dentistry of New Jersey, have made good starts in this direction, but the number of such efforts is woefully small.

Third, a small but growing number of psychiatrists, psychologists, social workers, and other mental health professionals who are in recovery from mental illness have decided to openly identify themselves as such. Psychiatrists Carol North (1987), Dan Fisher (1994), and Suzanne Vogel-

Scibilia (2001) have all publicly declared that they have experienced serious mental illness. Psychologists Ronald Bassman (2000), Al Siebert (2000), Kay Jamison (1995), and Wendy Walker Davis (1997) and social workers Donna Orrin (1997) and David Granger (1994) have made similar disclosures. In all probability, many other such professionals are also in recovery. If these professionals could begin to be more open about their experiences and those of their family members, consumer advocates could better realize that mental health policy and research decisions are not being made as much in isolation from consumer influence as it may appear.

Most consumers fall somewhere between the two ends of the cognitive impairment spectrum. These individuals, when asked, appear to desire more control and influence but also seem to realize that they need more and better treatment. In that this is the group that probably constitutes the majority of those served by public facilities, advocates for evidence-based practices would probably be well advised to meet often and frequently with public-sector mental health professionals and administrators. In this regard, it would probably also be judicious to include recovering persons in such discussions. Although we all should embrace maximization of choice and the rights of consumers to make mistakes, we also need to ensure that enthusiasm for the recovery model does not become so sweeping as to deny the benefits of scientific progress to persons who need treatment.

In summary, the main thesis of this article is that consumers who are more severely disabled, particularly in their decision-making capacity, can best be treated with evidence-based approaches and perhaps with less attention to recovery-model considerations. However, for those whose mental illnesses become less disabling, the principles of the recovery model become increasingly applicable.

REFERENCES

Anthony, W. (1993). Recovery from mental illness: the guiding vision of the mental health service system in the 1990s. *Psychosocial Rehabilitation Journal* 16(4), 11–23.

Bassman, R. (2000). Consumers/survivors/ex-patients as change facilitators. *New Directions for Mental Health Services, 88,* 93–102.

Beale, V., Lambric, T. (1995, August). *The Recovery Concept: Implementation in the mental health system: A report by the Community Support Program Advisory Committee,* 1–20. Columbus, Ohio: Ohio Department of Mental Health.

Bond, G. R., Becker, D. R., Drake, R. E., Rapp, C. A., Meisler, N., Lehman, A.F., Bell, M., & Blyler, C. R. (2001). Implementing supported employment as an evidence-based practice. *Psychiatric Services, 52,* 313–322.

Csernansky, J. G., & Bardgett, M. E. (1998). Limbic-cortical neuronal damage and the pathophysiology of schizophrenia. *Schizophrenia Bulletin, 24,* 231–247.

Deegan. P. E. (1992). The independent living movement and people with psychiatric disabilities: Taking back control of our won lives. *Psychosocial
Rehabilitation Journal, 15*(3), 3–19.

Deegan. P. E. (1993). Recovering our sense of value after being labeled mentally ill.
Journal of Psychosocial Nursing, 31(4), 7–11.

Drake, R. E., Essock, S. M., Shaner, A., Carey, K. B., Minkoff, K., Kole, L., Lynde, D.,
Osher, F. C., Clark, R. E., & Rickards, L. (2001). Implementing dual diagnosis
services for clients with severe mental illness. *Psychiatric Services, 52,*
469–476.

Drake, R. E., Goldman, H. H., Leff, H. S., Lehman, A. F., Dixon, L., Mueser, K. T., &
Torrey, M. (2201). Implementing evidence-based practices in routine mental
health service settings. *Psychiatric Services, 52,* 179–182.

Fisher, D. B. (1994). Hope, humanity, and voice in recovery from psychiatric disability. *Journal of the California Alliance for the Mentally Ill, 5*(3),7–11.

Frese, F. J. (1993). Cruising the cosmos: Part three: Psychosis and hospitalization: A
consumer's recollection. In A. B. Hatfield & H. Lefley (Eds.), *Surviving mental
illness: Stress, coping, and adaptation.* New York: Guilford.

Frese, F. J. (1994). A calling. *Second Opinion, 19*(3), 11–25.

Frese, F. J. (1998). Advocacy, recovery, and the challenges for consumerism for
schizophrenia. *Psychiatric Clinics of North America, 21,* 233–249.

Frese, F. J., & Davis, W. W. (1997). The consumer-survivor movement, recovery,
and consumer professionals. *Professional Psychology: Research and Practice 28,*
243–245, 1997.

Granger, D. A. (1994, November). Recovery from mental illness: A first person perspective of an emerging paradigm. *In Recovery: The new force in mental health.*
Columbus, Ohio: Ohio Department of Mental Health.

Jacobson N., & Greenley, D. (2001). What is recovery? A conceptual model and
explication. *Psychiatric Services, 52,* 482–485.

Jamison, K.R. (1995). *An unquiet mind: A memoir of moods and madness.* New York:
Knopf.

Lehman, A. F., & Steinwachs, D. M. (1998). Survey coinvestigators of the PORT
project: Translating research into practice: The Schizophrenia Patient
Outcomes Research Team (PORT) treatment recommendations. *Schizophrenia
Bulletin, 24,* 1–10.

Mellman, T. A., Miller, A. L., Weissman, E. M., Crismon, M. L., Essock, S. M. &
Marder, S. (2001). Evidence-based pharmacologic treatment for people with
severe mental illness: A focus on guidelines and algorithms. *Psychiatric
Services 52,* 619–625.

Minkoff, K. (2001). Developing standards of care for individuals with co-occurring
psychiatric and substance use disorders. *Psychiatric Services, 52,* 597–599.

Munetz, M. R., Frese, F. J. (2001). Getting ready for recovery: Reconciling mandatory treatment with the recovery vision. *Psychiatric Rehabilitation Journal 25*(1),
35–42.

NAMI Advocate. (2000, May/June). The decade of the brain in its final year—And what a year it was! *NAMI Advocate., 21*(4), 1,3.

North, C. S. (1987). *Welcome silence: My triumph over schizophrenia.* New York: Simon & Schuster.

Orrin, D, (1997). How I earned my MSW despite my mental illness. *Journal of the California Alliance for the Mentally Ill, 8*(2), 61–63.

Pedon, S. (1999, December). *Learning from our past: Building toward our future.* Columbus, Ohio: NAMI Ohio.

Pelka, F. (1998). Shrink resistant. *Mainstream: Magazine of the Able-Disabled 22*(9), 22–27.

Peyser, H. (2001). What is recovery? A commentary. *Psychiatric Services, 52,* 486–487.

Ross, E.C. (1999). NAMI campaign, policy team launch Omnibus Mental Illness Recovery Act. *NAMI Advocate, 20*(4), 1–5.

Siebert, A. (2000). My transforming peak experience was diagnosed as schizophrenia. *New Directions for Mental Health Services, 88,* 103–111.

Sullivan, P. (1994). Recovery from schizophrenia: what we can learn from the developing nations. *Innovations and Research in Clinical Services, Community Support, and Rehabilitation 3*(2), 7–15.

Szasz, T. (1961). *The myth of mental illness.* New York: Harper and Row.

Torrey, W. C., Drake R. E., Dixon L., Burns, B. J., Flynn, L., Rush, A. J., Clark, R. E., & Klatzker, D. (2001). Implementing evidence-based practices for persons with severe mental illnesses. *Psychiatric Services, 52,* 45–50.

Vogel-Scibilia, S. (2001, Winter). Reflections on recovery. *NAMI Advocate, 5,* 6.

The Challenge of Implementing and Sustaining Integrated Dual Disorders Treatment Programs

William C. Torrey, Robert E. Drake, Michael Cohen, Lindy B. Fox, David Lynde, Paul Gorman, and Philip Wyzik

At the time or original publication, the author affiliations were listed as follows: William C. Torrey, MD, Associate Professor of Psychiatry, Dartmouth Medical School; Robert E. Drake, MD, PhD, Professor of Psychiatry, Dartmouth Medical School; Michael Cohen, MA, CAGS, Executive Director of NAMI New Hampshire; Lindy B. Fox, MA, LADC, Research Associate at the New Hampshire-Dartmouth Psychiatric Research Center; David Lynde, MSW, West Institute at the New Hampshire-Dartmouth Psychiatric Research Center; Paul Gorman, EdD, Director, West Institute at the New Hampshire-Dartmouth Psychiatric Research Center; Philip Wyzik, MA, Vice President of Operations, West Central Behavioral Health, Lebanon, NH.

This article was published previously in the *Community Mental Health Journal,* December 2002, 38(6), and is reprinted with permission. © 2002, *Community Mental Health Journal*

Abstract: Integrated dual disorders treatment programs for people with severe mental illness and co-occurring substance use disorder have been implemented in a variety of community mental health center sites across the U.S. and in several other countries over the past 15 years. Consumers who receive services from programs that offer integrated dual diagnosis treatments that are faithful to evidence-based principles achieve significant improvements in their outcomes. Unfortunately, not all programs that attempt implementation are successful, and the quality of high-fidelity programs sometimes erodes over time. This article outlines implementation strategies that have been used by successful programs. As a general rule, success is achieved by involving all major participants (consumers, family members, clinicians, program leaders, and state or county mental health authorities) in the process and attending to the three phases of change: motivating, enacting, and sustaining implementation.

INTRODUCTION

Integrated dual disorders treatments involve combining and blending the delivery of mental health and substance abuse interventions for persons with co-occurring disorders. These interventions are now widely accepted as a critically important evidence-based practice in community mental health (Drake et al., 2001). The rationale is simple. First, substance abuse has a high prevalence of 50% or more among persons with severe mental illness (Cuffel, 1996; Mueser, Bennett, & Kushner, 1995; Regier et al., 1990). Second, co-occurring substance abuse is responsible for a range of negative client outcomes, including rehospitalization, incarceration, homelessness, victimization, and hepatitis C (Drake & Brunette, 1998; Rosenberg et al., 2001a; Rosenberg et al., 2001b). Comorbidity also produces high costs in the family system (Dixon et al., 1990), the mental health system (Bartels et al., 1993; Dickey & Azeni, 1996), and the criminal justice system (Abram & Teplin, 1991). Finally, integrated dual disorders treatments are demonstrably more effective than parallel mental health and substance abuse treatments delivered in separate settings or by separate programs (Drake et al., 1998). Nevertheless, integrated dual disorders treatments, like other evidence-based practices, are generally not available in routine mental health settings.

Over the past 15 years, staff at the New Hampshire-Dartmouth Psychiatric Research Center have assisted with multi-site demonstrations of integrated treatment in more than a dozen states and with single-site projects in numerous other states. Success has been less than universal; only half to two thirds of the programs that attempt to implement integrated treatments are able to establish and maintain a high-fidelity program. On the positive side, consumers who receive services in programs that do attain high-fidelity implementation have excellent outcomes, with much higher rates of stable remission than those achieved by consumers in low-fidelity programs (e.g., Carmichael, Tackett-Gibson, & Dell, 1998; McHugo et al., 1999; Ohio SAMI Conference, 2001).

These findings parallel those from implementation studies of other evidence-based practices. For assertive community treatment (Phillips et al., 2001), supported employment (Bond et al., 2001), and multi-system treatment of children (Schoenwald & Hoagwood, 2001) implementations that are faithful representations of the researched program, i.e., high-fidelity, are difficult to achieve and sustain but are associated with excellent outcomes. Given that faithful implementation is so critical to outcomes, the fact that we have little evidence regarding the effectiveness of techniques for implementing high-fidelity evidence-based practices is an unacceptable gap in knowledge (Goldman et al., 2001).

Our current understanding regarding the implementation of complex programs can be summarized in three main points (Torrey et al., 2001). First, promoting practice change involves focusing efforts on all stages of the change process from inspiring people to change, to helping them make the change, to reinforcing the change (Green et al., 1980, Green & Kreuter, 1991). *Motivating* efforts educate and engage stakeholders so that they want to work for the change. *Enacting* the practice involves putting the change in place by learning new behaviors and restructuring the flow of the daily work so that clinicians routinely give care in the new way. *Sustaining* efforts focus on reinforcing the new practice to ensure that it will persist over time. Second, in a complex system, all stakeholders can play helpful roles in promoting implementation (Batalden & Mohr, 1997). And third, the more elements of the system of care that can be marshaled to support change (and reduce resistance), the more likely the practice implementation will occur. In other words, intensity of effort appears directly related to success in studies of practice change (Davis et al., 1992; Schulberg et al., 1998).

The purpose of this paper is to present strategies for implementing integrated dual disorders treatment programs. The implementation approach outlined below has been synthesized from interviews with stakeholders who have participated in successful implementations over the last 10 years. Upcoming field trials of the Implementing Evidence-Based Practice Project will test the components of this approach more fully. This paper is intended to help people who are currently attempting to improve consumer outcomes by implementing integrated dual disorders treatment programs.

STAKEHOLDER PARTICIPATION

The core purpose of mental health services is to support consumers in their life goals (Rapp, 1998) and consumers consistently report that they want services to promote recovery (Torrey & Wyzik, 2000). Consumer definitions of recovery stress the importance of hope, personal responsibility, illness management, healthy adult roles, and quality of life (Deegan, 1988; Mead & Copeland, 2000; Ralph, 2000). The recovery paradigm can help focus and align the efforts of stakeholders, such as consumers, families, clinicians, program directors, and policy makers, who influence the provision of services. All these stakeholders can make important contributions to the high-fidelity implementation of evidenced-based practices, such as integrated dual disorders treatment, that have been proven to be effective in promoting outcomes that are critical to consumers. Reviewed below are some of the ways that stakeholders can contribute to the implementation of integrated dual disorders treatment programs (Table 1).

CONSUMERS

For consumers with co-occurring disorders, recovery necessarily involves learning to overcome or manage two intertwined illnesses. Fortunately, many dually diagnosed individuals are in recovery, willing to share their stories, and interested in helping others receive state-of-the-art services (Caswell, 2001; Fox, 1998; Green, 1996). Recovering consumers can play vital roles in promoting integrated dual disorders programs through advocating, teaching, providing clinical care, and participating in the governance of provider organizations.

Consumers who appreciate the importance of integrated dual disorders treatment can be effective advocates at the state and local level for the initiation or expansion of these services. Their real-life testimonies can be powerfully convincing, bringing color and life to the research findings that back up their argument for services. Unlike service providers, consumers can advocate for the resources for integrated dual disorders treatment without the appearance of financial self-interest.

Once a provider organization has decided to implement the practice, consumers can help the program leader to motivate change by speaking to relevant clinicians and administrators. Consumers' personal stories and experiences can infuse hope and flesh out the vision of recovery. Recovery is a process, a journey, that involves not just rejecting drugs of abuse and learning to use medicines effectively, but developing the confidence, skills, supports, and resources to live a satisfying life. The mental health care system can promote recovery by helping in all of these areas (Anthony, 1993; Mueser et al., 2004; Torrey & Wyzik, 2000). Almost inevitably, consumers' stories describe the frustrations of searching for and the positive experience of finding a clinician who could understand and provide help with intertwined illnesses (Fox, 1998; Green, 1996). Thus, they convey the need for integrated treatment.

While integrated dual disorders treatments are being enacted, consumers in recovery can help to train clinicians to recognize, understand, and respond to substance abuse. One message that consumers consistently deliver to new clinicians, for example, is the importance of persistence. People with dual disorders often feel demoralized and hopeless, and they may initially deny problems and reject attempts to help. Over time, however, persistent caring, outreach, and optimism will help most to take responsibility for their health and get on with creating life beyond illness.

Some consumers in recovery will have clinical training or experience, and will be able to serve as effective independent members of the clinical team immediately. Others will be able to help with the outreach process, by co-leading groups, or in the process of linking others to the self-help system. As programs evolve, more and more recovering consumers will be prepared to step into clinical roles. Helping others is often part of the journey of recovery (Rapp, 1998).

Sustaining programs over time is the most difficult part of implementation. It requires maintaining the vision, the structures, the procedures, and the expertise in the face of multiple exigencies, personnel changes, financial challenges, and new priorities. Who is better able to stay focused on the importance of these services than consumers with firsthand experience? Consumers can contribute to the ongoing life of a program through continued advocacy, teaching, and active clinical involvement. Some provider organizations seek consumer perspectives on their quality improvement teams and to help evaluate programs. In addition, many provider organizations now have consumers who serve on their governance boards. Consumer board members are in an excellent position to monitor the effectiveness of and reinforce the importance of ongoing dual disorders programming.

Table 1. Some Possible Roles for Stakeholders in Implementing Integrated Dual Disorders Treatment Services

Consumer Roles

- Educate and motivate professionals by writing and speaking from first hand experience
- Advocate for effective services
- Provide training to clinicians
- Become clinicians and provide service
- Monitor and support services through involvement on boards and planning committees

Family Roles

- Educate and motivate professionals by writing and speaking from first hand experience
- Advocate for effective services
- Provide training to clinicians
- Help family members with dual disorders
- Help others families
- Monitor and support services through involvement on boards and planning committees

Clinician Roles

- Focus the attention of other clinicians on integrated dual disorders treatment
- Advocate for effective services
- Help the program leader plan service changes
- Form a study group to learn about dual disorders
- Master new skills
- Help consumers to achieve dual recovery
- Train new clinicians

Program Leader Roles

- Expand personal knowledge and skill in creating and sustaining change
- Devise an implementation plan that attends to the three phases of implementation
- Demonstrate active leadership
- Involve all stakeholders in building consensus
- Engage the help of key clinical leaders early in the process
- Organize training and ongoing clinical supervision
- Communicate program goals
- Create administrative structures to support integrated dual disorders treatment
- Overcome management, personnel, and financial barriers
- Improve quality continuously by optimizing processes to support high-fidelity practice
- Create an ongoing training program
- Measure client outcomes and practice fidelity
- Publicly celebrate success

Policy Maker Roles

- Articulate the vision of integrated treatment and dual recovery
- Create a system-wide plan
- Establish expectations
- Provide training funds
- Create resources, regulations, requirements, supports, and oversight
- Measure practice fidelity
- Provide structures to maintain a focus on integrated dual disorders treatment

FAMILY AND OTHER SUPPORTERS

Families and other close friends are caught in the middle of the dual disorders problem, trying to be helpful but often lacking good information and supports (Mueser & Fox, 1998; 2002). They can play an important role in their own relative's (or friend's) recovery and also in creating local and system-wide solutions. In this section we refer to "family," but our remarks may apply to other close supporters of the consumer as well.

When motivating change, families can describe first hand to other stakeholders why it is so critical to implement integrated dual diagnosis treatments that have demonstrated effectiveness. They can relate their experiences with the painful realities of co-occurring substance abuse, which sometimes include interpersonal discord, violence, financial problems, involvement with the criminal justice system, and serious medical problems (Clark, 2001). Their personal stories, including stories of help and recovery, can inspire change at all levels of the system.

During the enacting stage, families can help train clinicians and provide political support for the general overall change. They can also advocate specifically for the inclusion of family interventions, which are an effective component of integrated dual disorders treatments (Barraclough et al., 2001; Mueser & Fox, 1998). Families can also help other families, by providing outreach, information and support, and advocacy for good services at all levels.

Families have an ongoing role in sustaining good programs. As mental health staff turn over and political contingencies change, even highly effective programs are at risk. Families can serve as enduring advocates, continuously pressing for the availability of evidence-based practices (Frese et al., 2001). Moreover, as they increasingly take on quality assurance roles within programs and systems by joining boards, councils, and review bodies, they can use the available information on evidence-based practice to effectively fulfill these important functions (U.S. Department of Health and Human Services, 1999).

CLINICIANS AND CLINICAL SUPERVISORS

The heart of implementation lies in the interaction between consumers and those who directly provide professional mental health care. To offer a new service, clinicians must learn new skills and apply those skills appropriately. Clinicians are strongly motivated to help their clients recover. In focus groups, they report that they are particularly motivated to learn a new practice if they believe it will help them in a clinical area where they currently feel ineffective (Torrey et al., 2001). For this reason, many clinicians are eager to learn dual diagnosis treatment skills.

To enhance motivation, clinicians who understand the importance of providing integrated dual disorders treatment services can bring others along. Informal peer-to-peer communication can powerfully affect clinician behavior, as studies of academic detailing have shown (Soumerai, 1998; Soumerai & Avorn, 1990). Clinicians who would like to participate in organizing the change can offer their help in discussing new programs, choosing to move ahead, identifying barriers and needs, and planning the details of change. Study groups on integrated treatment assure that some clinicians will be prepared to bring others along when the program is implemented.

To enact the implementation, clinicians can work together to gain competency in the integrated treatment approach. Clinicians learn best through a longitudinal process of acquiring skills, practicing skills, getting feedback, and refining skills. Working in a team structure promotes the natural exchange of knowledge and skills. For mental health clinicians who do not have training in integrated dual disorders treatment, treating substance abuse requires mastery in four areas:

1. basic knowledge about drugs of abuse and how they affect mental disorders;

2. assessment of substance abuse;

3. motivational counseling for clients who are in early stages of recovery and are not yet ready to pursue abstinence, and

4. active substance abuse counseling for clients who are trying to become abstinent (Mueser, Drake, & Noordsy 1998).

Particular clinicians will require additional skills depending on their roles in the larger integrated treatment program. For example, clinicians that work in residential treatment, in supported employment, in group therapy, or in other specialized programs will need to learn the appropriate techniques that fit those settings.

Clinicians learn in different ways. For example, some like to read and discuss case vignettes, some prefer video demonstrations, and some enjoy practicing role-plays with peers. Different resources therefore need to be available to fit their diverse learning styles. One constant is that all clinicians learn best when they have an opportunity to discuss their work with other clinicians or supervisors over time.

In most mental health settings, a relatively small group of clinical supervisors, team leaders, and doctors oversee the work of other clinicians. To function effectively in their roles, these individuals should achieve mastery of integrated dual disorders treatments first because they will be responsible for training front-line clinicians, reinforcing their work, and ensuring continuity over time.

Clinicians and their supervisors also need to be involved in developing mechanisms for sustaining new skills. Given the high rates of turnover in many community mental health programs, experienced clinicians can consolidate and reinforce their own skills by participating in the constant process of absorbing and training new clinicians. A leader of the integrated dual disorders treatment program and a cadre of committed clinical supervisors, particularly when supported by family members, can ensure the continuity of the program and its fidelity to evidence-based principles.

PROGRAM LEADERS

In establishing high-quality programs, especially in new areas, there is no substitute for leadership (Batalden & Stoltz, 1993; Corrigan et al., 2000; Liberman & Eckman, 1989). A designated integrated treatment program leader implements the program by ensuring that administrative mechanisms support clinical operations. Program leaders must attend to both the processes involved in providing care and all the related supporting processes (e.g., records, billing, staff training, and information systems).

Before taking direct action, many program leaders benefit from reading about the phenomena of change as it applies to clinical or business organizations and devising a detailed implementation plan for their organization. The literature on leading organizational process improvement can help program leaders to anticipate the array of administrative challenges that they will face and offers concrete techniques for dealing with resistance (e.g., Addiction Technology Transfer Center, 2001; Joint Commission on Accreditation of Healthcare Organizations, 1995; Langley et al., 1996; Nelson, Batalden, & Ryer, 1998; Prochaska, Prochaska, & Levesque, 2001; Spaniol, Zipple, & Cohen, 1991). With this background, program leaders can design a careful plan that considers the major objectives and action steps to be taken to bring about each of the three phases of change.

The implementation plan must address motivation. Effective leaders typically articulate the goal of providing optimal care to consumers with dual disorders and actively engage all stakeholders in creating the envisioned services. Motivational, consensus-building activities typically involve outside speakers, internal task forces to develop training and other procedures, and discussions with consumers and families about realistic expectations. These preparations need to engage key staff in the process of taking ownership so that active support for the change broadens.

During the enacting stage, leaders must specify clear program goals, timelines, and roles. Though committees can fill in details, the leader must make sure that recruitment, training, supervision, records, billing, quality improvement, case reviews, liaison with outside agencies, and outcomes are attended to and integrated into a system of care. The organization must have management structures, personnel, and financing strategies in place. The program leader needs to work toward integrating the program horizontally and vertically into the service delivery system.

Over time, practices are sustained because they become part of organizational culture. They cannot depend on outside supervision, exhortations of charismatic leaders, or popular trends. Instead, all the routine operating procedures of an agency should make it easy to maintain fidelity and difficult to drift. In other words, all the arrows must line up in one direction to ensure long-term maintenance. A sustaining plan can encompass the use of ongoing fidelity measurement data, collected regularly and graphically reported to staff and stakeholders. Periodic booster training sessions can help train new staff and help others develop their clinical skills. Supervision, financing, records, and feedback must all be organized to reinforce good practice. Celebrating success, rewarding providers for doing good work, and involving consumers who are in recovery also support continuity.

POLICY MAKERS

Policy solutions to clinical problems are necessary though not sufficient (Goldman et al., 2001). Administrators of the public mental health system, such as state and county authorities, recognize that they ultimately have responsibility to promote all aspects of recovery, including recovery from substance abuse, among persons with severe mental illness. Referral to a separate agency or another system of care is inadequate, demonstrably ineffective, and far from optimal. Therefore, the mental health system must develop the motivation, capacity, and competence to address co-occurring substance abuse.

Policy makers can motivate this development in several ways, most importantly by articulating the vision of dual recovery for clients with dual disorders and elevating its importance by expressing it as a requirement. Part of articulating the vision involves establishing expectations, goals, funding, and oversight. If the substance abuse authority is administratively separate from the mental health authority, collaboration and regular communication to establish the vision is essential.

To enable local providers to enact the vision, the mental health authority establishes its support through contracts, regulations, payments, training programs, and other mechanisms. Depending on the amount of resources that can be assembled, implementation may begin as several demonstration programs or as a state-wide initiative. One important point is that while policy makers can establish priorities through various mechanisms, local programs need the freedom to establish their own implementation plans. An inspiring vision linked with minimal financial incentives can lead to creative responses, whereas rigid guidelines may engender resistance.

Sustaining new programs over time involves infrastructure and problem-solving at many levels, including by the state health authority (Ohio SAMI Conference, 2001). Programs will not be able to sustain themselves if they are not reimbursed, if they do not have incentives to maintain appropriate personnel, and if they do not have clear outcomes as goals. The health care authority must provide each of these over time. Typical structural components include establishment of an office at the state mental health authority level responsible for ongoing consultation and fidelity, development of a state-wide training program, integrated dual diagnosis program certification standards, and a financial plan that includes Medicaid and state funds.

DISCUSSION

Several assumptions and values underlie effective approaches to implementing integrated dual disorders treatment programs. First, the approach is holistic. We assume that the individual with dual disorders needs treatment that addresses multiple interlocking problems and that these problems cannot be separated into components. Second, we assume that consumers are at the center of the treatment system, which exists to help them reach their goals. Third, we assume that the mental health system should include integrated dual disorders treatments for persons with severe mental illness as a core service and that its leaders and other stakeholders must work together to overcome barriers to implementation.

Policy makers and program leaders can use specific guidelines, consultants, and existing models for moving in the directions that we have outlined. Fortunately, a number of state mental health systems, e.g., Ohio, Texas, Illinois, and New Hampshire, have already done a credible job in this area, and others, e.g., Vermont, Rhode Island, Kansas, New York, and Oregon, are engaged in the process of developing state-wide training programs. In addition, the Robert Wood Johnson Foundation and the Center for Mental Health Services of the Substance Abuse and Mental Health Services Administration have funded the development of training and implementation materials that will be field tested in 2002. This effort provides specific guidelines, training materials, educational information, service forms, clinician workbooks, videos, consultants, fidelity measures, outcome measures, and sites to visit.

CONCLUSIONS

Implementing effective integrated dual disorders treatment services on a system-wide basis requires the active participation of many stakeholders. Consumers and families are involved in creating demand and providing motivation, training, advocacy, and services. Clinicians must acquire and maintain new skills. Program leaders and policy makers develop the infrastructure and reinforcements to support a dually trained workforce and a system of integrated dual disorders services. High quality implementation results in higher rates of recovery, quality of life, and satisfaction for many consumers.

REFERENCE

Abram, K., & Teplin, L. (1991). Co-occurring disorders among mentally ill jail detainees: Implications for public policy. *American Psychologist, 46,* 1036–1044.

Addiction Technology Transfer Center (2001). *The change book: A blueprint for technology transfer.* Kansas City, Missouri: Addiction Technology Transfer Center National Office.

Anthony, W. A. (1993). Recovery from mental illness: The guiding vision of the mental health service system in the 1990s. *Psychosocial Rehabilitation Journal, 16*(4), 11–23.

Barrowclough, C., Haddock, G., Tarrier, N., Lewis, S. W., Moring, J., O'Brien, R., Schofield, N., & McGovern, J. (2001). Randomized controlled trial of motivational interviewing, cognitive behavior therapy, and family intervention for patients with comorbid schizophrenia and substance use disorders. *American Journal of Psychiatry, 158*(10), 1706–1713.

Bartels, S. J., Teague, G. B., Drake, R. E., Clark, R. E., Bush, P. W., & Noordsy, D. L. (1993). Substance abuse in schizophrenia: Service utilization and costs. *Journal of Nervous and Mental Disease, 181,* 227–232.

Batalden, P. B., & Mohr, J. J. (1997). Building knowledge of health care as a system. *Quality Management in Health Care, 5*(3), 1–12.

Batalden, P. B., & Stoltz, P. K. (1993). A framework for the continual improvement of healthcare: Building and applying professional and improvement knowledge to test changes in daily work. *The Joint Commission Journal on Quality Improvement, 19*(10), 424–445.

Bond, G. R., Vogler, K. M., Resnick, S. G., Evans, L. A., Drake, R. E., & Becker, D. R. (2001). Dimensions of supported employment: Factor structure of the IPS Fidelity Scale. *Journal of Mental Health, 10*(4), 383–393.

Carmichael, D., Tackett-Gibson, M., & Dell, 0. (1998). *Texas Dual Diagnosis Project Evaluation Report 1997–1998.* College Station, Texas: Texas A&M University, Public Policy Research Institute.

Caswell, J. S. (2001). Employment: A consumer's perspective. In D. R. Becker & M. Barcus (Eds.), *Connections-State Partnership Initiative.* (Spring/Summer, pp. 5). Fairfax, VA: Virginia Commonwealth University.

Clark, R. E. (2001). Family support and substance use outcomes for persons with mental illness and substance use disorders. *Schizophrenia Bulletin, 27*(1), 93–101.

Corrigan, P. W., Lickey, S. E., Campion, J., & Rashid, F. (2000). Mental health team leadership and consumers' satisfaction and quality of life. *Psychiatric Services 51*, 781–785.

Cuffel, B. J. (1996). Comorbid substance use disorder. Prevalence. patterns of use, and course. In R. E. Drake and K. T. Mueser (Eds.), *Dual diagnosis of Major Mental Illness and Substance Disorder: II. Research and clinical implications* (pp. 93–105). San Francisco, CA: Josssey-Bass.

Davis, D. A., Thomson, M. A., Oxman, A. D., & Haynes, B. (1992). Evidence for the effectiveness of CME: A review of 50 randomized controlled trials. *Journal of the American Medical Association, 268*(9), 1111–1117.

Deegan, P. E. (1988). Recovery: The lived experience of rehabilitation. *Psychosocial Rehabilitation Journal. 11*, 11–19.

Dickey, B., & Azeni, H. (1996). Persons with dual diagnosis of substance abuse and major mental illness: Their excess costs of psychiatric care. *American Journal of Public Health, 86*, 973–977.

Dixon, L., Haas, G., Weiden, P., Sweeney, J., & Frances, A. (1990). Acute effects of drug abuse in schizophrenic patients: Clinical observations and patients' self-reports. *Schizophrenia Bulletin, 16*(1), 69–79.

Drake, R. E., & Brunette, M. F. (1998). Complications of severe mental illness related to alcohol and other drug use disorders. In M. Galanter (Ed.), *Recent developments in alcoholism. Volume XIV, Consequences of alcoholism* (pp. 285–299). New York: Plenum Publishing Company.

Drake, R. E., Goldman, H. H., Leff, H. S., Lehman, A. F., Dixon, L., Mueser, K. T., & Torrey, W.C. (2001). Implementing evidence-based practices in routine mental health settings. *Psychiatric Services, 52*, 197–182.

Drake, R. E., Mercer-McFadden, C., Mueser, K. T., McHugo, G. J., & Bond, G. R. (1998). Review of integrated mental health and substance abuse treatment for patients with dual disorders. *Schizophrenia Bulletin, 24*(4), 589–608.

Fox, L. (1998). Surviving and thriving with a dual diagnosis. *Understanding Stress Anxiety and Depression, 2*, 5–7.

Frese, F. J., Stanley, J. D., Kress, K., & Vogel-Scibilia, S. (2001). Integrating evidence-based practices and the recovery model. *Psychiatric Services, 52*(11), 1462–1468.

Goldman, H. H., Ganju, V., Drake, R. E., Gorman, P. G., Hogan, M., Hyde, P. S., & Morgan, 0. (2001). Policy implications for implementing evidence-based practices. *Psychiatric Services, 52*(12), 1591–1597.

Green, L., Krueter, M. (1991). *Application of Precede/Proceed in community settings: Health promotion planning: An educational and environmental approach.* Mountain View, CA: Mayfield Publishing Co.

Green, L., Kreuter, M., Deeds S., & Partridge K. (1980). *Health education planning: A diagnostic approach.* Palo Alto, CA: Mayfield Press.

Green, V. L. (1996). The resurrection and the life. *American Journal of Orthopsychiatry, 66*, 12–16.

Joint Commission on Accreditation of Healthcare Organizations. (1995). *Cycle for improving performance: A pocket guide.* OakBrook Terrace, Il: Joint Commission on Accreditation of Healthcare Organizations

Langley, G. J., Nolan, K. M., Nolan, T. W., Norman, C. L., & Provost, L. P. (1996). *The improvement guide: A practical approach to enhancing organizational performance.* San Francisco: Jossey Bass Publishers.

Liberman, R.P., & Eckman, T. A. (1989). Dissemination of skills training modules to psychiatric facilities: Overcoming obstacles to the utilization of a rehabilitation innovation. *British Journal of Psychiatry, 155 (suppl. 5),* 117–122.

McHugo, G. J., Drake, R. E., Teague, G. B., & Xie, H. (1999). Fidelity to assertive community treatment and client outcomes in the New Hampshire Dual Disorders Study. *Psychiatric Services, 50*(6), 818–824.

Mead, S., & Copeland, M. E. (2000). What recovery means to us: Consumers' perspectives. *Community Mental Health Journal 36*(3), 315–328.

Mueser, K. T., Bennett, M., & Kushner, M. G. (1995). Epidemiology of substance abuse among persons with chronic mental disorders. In A.F. Lehman & L. Dixon (Eds.), *Double jeopardy: Chronic mental illness and substance abuse* (pp. 9–25). New York: Harwood Academic Publishers.

Mueser, K. T., Corrigan, P. W., Hilton, D. W., Tanzman, B., Schaub, A., Gingerich, S., Essock, S. M., Tarrier, N., Morey, B., Vogel-Scibilia, S., & Herz, M.I. (2004). Illness management and recovery: A review of the research. *Focus, 2,* 34–47.

Mueser, K. T., Drake, R. E., & Noordsy, D. L. (1998). Integrated mental health and substance abuse treatment for severe psychiatric disorders. *Journal of Practical Psychiatry and Behavioral Health, 4*(3), 129–139.

Mueser, K. T., & Fox, L. (1998). Dual Diagnosis: How families can help. *Journal of the California Alliance for the Mentally Ill, 9,* 53–55.

Mueser, K. T., & Fox, L. (2002). A family intervention program for dual disorders. *Community Mental Health Journal, 38,* 253–270.

Nelson, E. C., Batalden, P. B., & Ryer, J. C. (Eds.). (1998). *Joint Commission clinical improvement action guide.* Oakbrook Terrace, Illinois: Joint Commission on Accreditation of Healthcare Organizations.

Ohio SAMI Conference (June 7–8, 2001). *Integrated services for the treatment of co-occurring disorders: Making it work in Ohio.* Der Dutchman Restaurant & Conference Center, Bellville, OH.

Phillips, S. D., Burns, B. J., Edgar, E. R., Mueser, K. T., Linkins, K. W., Rosenheck, R. A., Drake, R. E., & McDonell Herr, E. C. (2001). Moving assertive community treatment into standard practice. *Psychiatric Services, 52,* 771–779.

Prochaska, J. M., Prochaska, J. O., & Levesque, D. A. (2001). Transtheoretical Approach to Changing Organizations. *Administration and Policy in Mental Health, 28*(4, 247–261.

Ralph, R. O. (2000). *Review of recovery literature: A synthesis of a sample of recovery literature 2000.* Alexandria, VA: NASMHPD/National Technical Assistance Center for State Mental Health Planning.

Rapp, C. A. (1998). *The Strengths Model.* New York, NY: Oxford University Press, Inc.

Regier, D. A., Farmer, M. E., Rae, D. S., Locke, B. Z., Keith, S. J., Judd, L. L., & Goodwin, F. K. (1990). Comorbidity of mental disorders with alcohol and other drug abuse. *Journal of the American Medical Association, 264,* 2511–2518.

Rosenberg, S.D., Goodman, L.A., Osher, F.C., Swartz, M., Essock, S.M., Butterfield, M.I., Constantine, N., Wolford, G.L., & Salyers, M. (2001a). Prevalence of HIV, Hepatitis B, and Hepatitis C in people with severe mental illness. *American Journal of Public Health, 91,* 31–37.

Rosenberg, S. D., Mueser, K. T., Friedman, M. S., Gorman, P. G., Drake, R. E., Vidaver, R., Torrey, W. C., & Jankowski, M. K. (2001b). Developing effective treatments for post-traumatic disorders among people with severe mental illness. *Psychiatric Services, 52,* 1453–1461.

Schoenwald, S. K., & Hoagwood, K. (2001). Effectiveness, transportability, and dissemination of interventions: What matters when? *Psychiatric Services, 52,* 1190–1197.

Schulberg, H. C., Katon, W., Simon, G. E., & Rush, A. J. (1998). Treating major depression in primary care practice: An update of the agency for health care policy and research practice guidelines. *Archives of General Psychiatry, 55*(12), 1121–1127.

Soumerai, S. B. (1998). Principles and uses of academic detailing to improve the management of psychiatric disorders. *International Journal of Psychiatry in Medicine, 28*(1), 81–96.

Soumerai, S. B., & Avorn, J. (1990). Principles of educational outreach (academic detailing) to improve clinical decision making. *Journal of the American Medical Association, 263*(4), 549–556.

Spaniol, L, Zipple, A., & Cohen, B. (1991). Managing innovation and change in psychosocial rehabilitation: Key principles and guidelines. *Psychosocial Rehabilitation Journal, 14*(3), 27–38.

Torrey, W. C., Drake, R. E., Dixon, L., Burns, B. J., Flynn, L., Rush, A. J., Clark, R. E., & Klatzker, D. (2001). Implementing evidence-based practices for persons with severe mental illnesses. *Psychiatric Services, 52,* 45–50.

Torrey, W. C., & Wyzik, P. Y. (2000). The recovery vision as a service improvement guide for community mental health center providers. *Community Mental Health Journal, 36*(2), 209–216.

U.S. Department of Health and Human Services (1999). *Mental health: A report of the Surgeon General.* Rockville, MD: U.S. Department of Health and Human Services, Substance Abuse and Mental Health Services Administration, Center for Mental Health Services, National Institutes of Health, National Institute of Mental Health.

Acknowledgements

Supported by grants from the West Foundation, the Robert Wood Johnson Foundation, and the Substance Abuse and Mental Health Services Administration.

Planning a Community-Based Mental Health System: Perspective of Service Recipients

Judi Chamberlin and Joseph A. Rogers

At the time of original publication, author affiliations were listed as follows: Judi Chamberlin, National Association of Psychiatric Survivors, Sioux Falls, SD; and Joseph A. Rogers, National Mental Health Consumer Self-Help Clearinghouse, Philadelphia, PA.

This article was published previously in the *American Psychologist*, 1990, 45(11), 1241–1244, and is reprinted with permission.

Abstract: Two former patients, long-term activists in the self-help/advocacy movement, combine to provide a consumer perspective on planning mental health systems. Separately, each author notes current system problems, the need for new services—including self-help—and the opportunities provided by Public Law (Pub.L.) 99-660 (1986), for meaningful change, based as it is on the fundamental principle of involving the recipients of services in any planning effort.

JUDI CHAMBERLIN

It is part of the conventional wisdom in this country that the mental health system is in trouble. For many years, people pointed to state hospitals—large, impersonal, underfunded, neglectful of the basic human rights of their inmates—as the main problem. More recently, it has become fashionable to blame deinstitutionalization (the process by which the state hospital population has been reduced to a fraction of those who were incarcerated a few decades ago) for all the faults of the mental health system. As with most things, the truth is far more complex.

Criticism of the mental health system comes from many directions and focuses on many different aspects. The media, which plays a large role in shaping public attitudes, tends to highlight stories of escaped or discharged patients who commit notorious acts of violence, despite the fact that "the mentally ill" as a group are no more violent (and probably are less violent) than the population at large. The public, therefore, tends to link mental illness with violence and tends to believe that people labeled *mentally ill* need to be incarcerated for society's protection. Meanwhile, most of the mental health disciplines have concluded that long-term incarceration is part of the problem, and not the solution, and that mental health services can best be delivered in community-based programs, which have proliferated in recent years.

Average citizens seldom consider mental health issues at all, unless they directly affect their own lives. Therefore, public debate on mental health tends to be framed in a highly simplistic, media-influenced manner ("Ex-mental patient kills two"; "Homeless mental patients clog downtown"). Meanwhile, almost unseen by the media and by the major decision makers in mental health policy, such as psychiatrists and government bureaucrats, a new group has begun debating these issues and devising solutions and programs that challenge the conventional wisdom.

Former mental patients have been organizing in the United States since the early 1970s. Small, locally based, and virtually unfunded, these groups have become increasingly vocal and active. Often highly critical of the existing mental health system, they have proposed major changes in the way the system is run and on where its focus should be.

The prime motivation of people who join ex-patient organizations is a desire to counteract the feelings of powerlessness they experienced as patients in the system. Traditionally, mental patients have been viewed as incapable of defining their own needs, and others (family members, mental health professionals, the state) have controlled their lives and made decisions on their behalf. These interventions, always justified as being in the best interest of the patient, have been responsible for much human suffering, including long-term incarceration, forced drugging, massive use of electroshock and lobotomy, and the denial of basic legal rights and human dignity. It is not surprising that patients themselves have begun to define themselves as an oppressed group, to call for their own liberation, and to redefine problems and solutions.

Among the many goals of the ex-patients' movement (which includes diverse local, regional, and national organizations) is to play a part in devising mental health policy, rather than to be merely the passive objects of policies designed by others. Public Law (Pub.L.) 99-660, which requires states to develop plans for implementing a community-based system of mental health care and requires the participation of diverse constituencies in the planning process, is one possible vehicle for the ex-patients' movement to promote its visions of how help should (and should not) be made available to people who are troubled or dysfunctional.

It is not surprising that the various constituencies have highly differing visions of what the mental health system should do and how it should be organized: Like the blind men and the elephant, each group sees the problem from its own perspective and each tends to think its view is the whole picture. Thus, psychiatrists call for more psychiatrists and psychiatric control of the system. Other mental health practitioners (psychologists, social workers, nurses, occupational therapists, and so forth) call for more money and prestige for their respective disciplines. Legislators want to see that costs are kept low and the public is protected. State hospital administrators believe state hospitals are essential. Community providers think that too much money goes to the state hospitals and not enough to their programs. Family members focus on the urgent needs of their relatives.

Now here comes a new group—patients and ex-patients, the actual recipients of services—presenting a whole new viewpoint. If Pub.L. 99-660 is implemented as intended, it will provide an opportunity for these diverse groups to interact, exchange ideas, and, perhaps, to begin to understand their often dramatically different viewpoints.

In addition to providing for planning by the diverse mental health constituencies, Pub.L. 99-660 requires that state mental health systems be community based. This is highly significant, because although state hospitals may possibly still play a part in such a system, they will no longer be its focus, and it is quite possible that states may devise systems that eliminate them entirely. Vermont is currently implementing a carefully crafted plan (which included the participation of diverse constituencies, including, very prominently, ex-patients) for virtually closing down its state hospital, without abandoning people to the streets or to shelters (Carling, Miller, Daniels, & Randolph, 1987). It is exciting to look forward to a variety of approaches in different states to making mental health programs truly serve the needs of those who receive services, by including their representatives in the processes of change.

I have worked in the ex-patients' movement for more than 15 years, and have seen the movement grow from a few scattered local groups to a profusion of organizations and projects. Ex-patient self-help groups, which I first wrote about in 1978, are now a reality in dozens of locations around the country (Chamberlin, 1978; Zinman, Harp, & Budd, 1985). Self-help will surely be included as a component of many state plans: One of the goals of the ex-patients' movement is to ensure that each state includes provisions for adequate funding of self-help programs and whatever technical assistance is necessary to aid groups to develop such programs.

It has become fashionable in recent years to refer to recipients of mental health services as consumers, a term that I and many other ex-patients find objectionable because it implies that we have choices and power. In fact, we are seldom consulted about whether we want services at all or what form such services should take, or asked whether we are satisfied with the services we have received. Whereas corporations spend millions of dollars to try to find out what their customers or potential customers want, mental health systems often work with a captive population that cannot take its business elsewhere. The term consumer in itself is not empowering, in fact, it is often used to obscure the true power relationship in which the service recipient has no leverage at all.

Perhaps the planning process required by Pub.L. 99-660 will help us to become true consumers, who "shop" for services we want and reject those that do not meet our self-defined needs. Then we will see real, fundamental change—not just new names for old institutions and programs, but a true revolution challenging the very basis of paternalism and control.

JOSEPH A. ROGERS

I know, from personal experience, what a mental health system should *not* be. I have sat, strapped in restraints, in an isolation room in a community hospital for 3 days, while people came and went, not to talk to me but to drug me into a stupor. I know that's not the way to help people.

I also know that state hospitals are not the way. Almost all of the state hospitals that I've had experience with are huge, antiquated, wasteful places in which precious little help can be found (Rogers & Centifanti, 1988). They seem to exist mostly to provide jobs for staff.

So how can you improve a system such as this? How do you build a mental health system that comes as close to the ideal as possible? Very simply, you start by considering clients' needs and how those needs can be met. Second, you involve clients as equal partners in the system in planning, implementing, and providing services.

Building a System Based on the Needs of the Individuals It Serves

First, what do we need? We need what everyone else needs: a place to live, a job, and friends.

Work is vital to people's sense of self-worth, not to mention their ability to be independent. Although adequate public benefits should be available for people who need them, it is damaging to a person's self-esteem to have to depend upon them. Unfortunately, many people with psychiatric histories don't think there is any other option, because their involvement in the mental health system has drained whatever self-esteem they had. A lot of people are scared: Finding a job and risking losing it and not being able to get back on Social Security can feel like tightrope walking without a net. And the public benefits system, with all its disincentives to work, needs to be overhauled with an eye to helping people get on their feet so they won't need public benefits.

The recent passage of the Americans with Disabilities Act (Pub. L. 101-336) not only establishes work as an obviously vital part of rehabilitation, but mandates that all people with disabilities, including mental disabilities, have a right to work.

An ideal mental health system would include job training. I'm talking about a program that would help people achieve their highest potential, not just a menial job. Helping people become independent through work should be a key element in all rehabilitation programs. Work need not be the traditional nine-to-five job—it can also be volunteer work or an education program—but people need to do *something*.

A lot of what passes for job training (e.g., vocational screenings and "sheltered workshop" programs) is actually disabling. It makes people more dependent on the system because it gives people the impression that the world of work is a "big deal," some kind of secret society that they can never break into. In some cases, if we just gave people the want ads and said, "Here are some subway tokens; I know you can do it, good luck," people would go out and get jobs. They may get fired from the first job, or the second or the third. Or they may not like a job and quit. But who has not had these experiences? They're part of life.

Jobs also provide social supports—a network of people you can socialize with, at least casually around the water cooler once or twice a day. People need contact with other people. If you're living on Social Security, there's almost no money left for any kind of luxuries, including social activities. Even if you're working, it's usually at a menial job with a low salary. People end up sitting in a room by themselves watching TV, if they're lucky enough to have a room. The poverty, anxiety, and loneliness contribute to a huge sense of social isolation. A good community-based system would address that need.

Self-help programs are an indispensable part of any community-based mental health system and should be a high priority to receive funding. Such user-run programs as drop-in centers and peer case management provide people with a feeling that they can give as well as receive help, which builds self-esteem. At drop-in centers people can find friends and a sense of belonging, maybe for the first time in their lives. They also meet role models—other consumers who are making it in the community. Self-help groups and other user-run programs answer the question, Is there life after psychiatric hospitalization? With a resounding Yes! (Artison-Koenning & S. Rogers, 1988; Centifanti, 1988a, 1988b; Lovejoy, 1988; Meek, 1988; National Mental Health Consumer Self-Help Clearinghouse, 1988a, 1988b; J. A. Rogers, 1988a; J. A. Rogers & Centifanti, 1988; S. Rogers, 1988).

Housing is another great need. Being on Social Security brands you as an undesirable tenant in the eyes of any landlords. The housing that the mental health system offers is usually short-term, congregate living.

Although congregate living may actually alleviate some of the isolation people feel by providing an instant support network, it is important that it not be so transitional in nature (e.g., the "two years and out" policy in Pennsylvania). With short-term housing, just as you are beginning to stabilize your life you are under pressure to leave the residence.

If the system took a portion of the money spent on residential programs and put it into rent subsidies, it would help people grow to independence. Apartments that are almost impossible to rent on a few dollars, especially on Social Security, are attainable with some help, such as money toward the first and last months' rent and maybe some help with furnishings, supplies, and utilities. That may be all some people need. Others may need a continued rent subsidy, such as is available under Section 8 housing. But there must some kind of subsidization so that people can live independently and with dignity.

Consumer Advocacy

Self-help programs empower people so that they can participate not only as clients of the mental health system but as vocal advocates for whatever is positive in the system and, more important, for systems reform. Empowered consumers can testify to the importance of funding mental health programs. Self-help programs are also a formalized way of getting people who have overcome their problems to continue to be involved and provide role models for those coming after them.

Peer support may be best, but other volunteers of the community, such as members of church groups, can also be caring friends and excellent role models. An ideal system would recruit volunteers from the community.

In self-help groups people can organize for change, not only in the system but in the community, against the stigma and discrimination that plague people with psychiatric histories.

Mandate for Consumer Involvement in System Planning

I am extremely excited about the possibilities that the Mental Health Planning Act (Pub.L. 99-660) presents. This is one of the first pieces of national legislation to mandate consumer involvement. I believe that any planning process that fails to significantly involve consumers from the ground up is not living up to this mandate. By significant involvement, I mean a cross-section of individuals, not just one or two token consumers; I mean people representing geographic, racial, political, and experiential diversity.

Part of the organizing that the National Mental Health Consumer Self-Help Clearinghouse has done is to consider how to have an impact on services. We are organizing consumers who are involved in the mental health system. They are interested in what the services look like, how to fund them, and how to improve them. This is taking place all around the country. In fact, the National Mental Health Consumer Self-Help Clearinghouse has done consulting in some 30 states and Puerto Rico.

If any plan for systems change is going to be realistic and work, it must involve us, because as we become more organized we are demanding systems change (J. A. Rogers, 1988b). In essence, unless planning groups and councils are made up of at least one-third mental health consumers, they are failing to live up to what we consider the mandate of the plan.

Consumer involvement is an essential part of putting together a good plan. Who except the actual users of services can give you the straight dope on the impact of services? Until you've actually lived in an inpatient program, you really can't get a sense of what the program does for you or to you. Until you've been dependent on a case manager for basic essentials, such as income, food stamps, and so on, you don't really have a sense of how vital those services can be and how great the frustrations that you may have to face can be in dealing with the bureaucracy that doles them out.

We have found that individuals in our movement have a commitment (no pun intended) to seeing changes made that often surpasses the commitment of people who never expect to have to live with the results of their planning.

Beyond experience and commitment, consumers also generally have untapped amounts of time and resources in many cases. Unfortunately, many consumers are unemployed. This is a resource that should be tapped, both on a volunteer basis and, I hope, on a paid basis.

Financing Mental Health Services

The final question is the bottom line: How should mental health services be paid for? I suggest that the most workable system is one of single-stream funding, which gives communities both the incentive and the funding to come up with a decent community mental health system.

Under single-stream funding, local governments would be responsible for determining the individual needs of persons with mental illnesses and for developing programs to meet those needs. The system allows funds to follow the patient, and places fiscal incentives on the least restrictive treatment consistent with excellent care.

Unfortunately, in many states the lion's share of the mental health budget is fed into the gaping maw of the state hospital system. This makes the local government a kind of toothless tiger, with neither the incentive to develop cost-effective community-based alternatives to costly inpatient treatment, nor the funds to do so (Rogers & Centifanti, 1988).

Single-stream funding is an eminently reasonable system, under which local authorities would be responsible for treatment decisions and control the funds to implement those decisions. They would thus have an incentive to implement programs to intervene before hospitalization becomes necessary, to develop more effective community alternatives to inpatient hospitalization, and to limit the length of any hospitalization to the necessary minimum.

How would this work? For example, local authorities would contract for the use of state hospital beds for their committed patients on the basis of where they are treated or the specific type of service they receive. The fewer patients they sent to state hospitals, the more money they would have for community programs. Meanwhile, those overusing their share of state hospital beds would pay for that privilege. What do you want to bet that fewer folks would be sent to state hospitals?

Under the ideal mental health system, there would be no need for involuntary commitment. The concept rests on the false notion that committing more people to mental hospitals will increase public security. In fact, for each person thus expensively committed, several more people with serious mental illness will remain in the community with no hope of receiving any help at all.

Take the state of Washington, which in 1979 changed its laws to make it easier to lock people up. According to University of Washington professor Mary L. Durham, who did a 5-year study of the effects:

> Broadening involuntary commitment laws did *not* protect the community from dangerous people, it did not solve problems of homelessness, it *wasted* precious resources and it created a dependency on the involuntary commitment system that brought people back again and again to that hospital system…Washington State now represents what I would consider the worst of both worlds (Joint State Government Commission Task Force, 1987).

We don't need more people committed to programs; we need more programs committed to people. Ultimately, an ideal mental health system would concentrate on the belief that success is possible—that people can overcome their problems and live independent, productive lives in the community.

REFERENCES

Artison-Koenning, R., & Rogers, S. (1988). *How to develop a consumer-run newsletter.* Philadelphia, PA: National Mental Health Consumer Self-Help Clearinghouse.

Carling, P. J., Miller, S., Daniels, L., & Randolph, F (1987). Operating a state mental health system without a state hospital: The Vermont feasibility study. *Hospital and Community Psychiatry, 38,* 617–623.

Centifanti, J. B. (I 988a). *Systems advocacy.* Philadelphia, PA: National Mental Health Consumer Self-Help Clearinghouse.

Centifanti, J. B. (I 988b). *Who's who in the mental health system.* Philadelphia, PA: National Mental Health Consumer Self-Help Clearinghouse.

Chamberlin, J. (1978). *On our own: Patient controlled alternatives to the mental health system.* New York: Hawthorn Books.

Joint State Government Commission Task Force on Mental Health Laws. (1987). *Transcript of public hearing: Vol. 1.* Wednesday, January 28, 1987. Harrisburg, PA: Author.

Lovejoy, M. (1988). *Organizing and operating a speakers' bureau.* Philadelphia, PA: National Mental Health Consumer Self-Help Clearinghouse.

Meek, C. M. (1988). *Consumer-run drop-in centers.* Philadelphia, PA: National Mental Health Consumer Self-Help Clearinghouse.

National Mental Health Consumer Self-Help Clearinghouse. (1988a). *Jobs, jobs, jobs!* Philadelphia, PA: Author.

National Mental Health Consumer Self-Help Clearinghouse. (1988b). *Making our voices heard—Consumer representation on decision-making committees: "No longer will we be silent."* Philadelphia, PA: Author.

Rogers, J. A. (I 988a). *How to start a self help/advocacy group.* Philadelphia, PA: National Mental Health Consumer Self-Help Clearinghouse.

Rogers, J. A. (1988b). We have to begin to create a movement that is basically a civil rights movement. *Your Choice, 1*(3), 2, 5, 7, 15.

Rogers, J. A., & Centifanti, J. B. (1988). Madness, myths, and reality: Response to Roberta Rose. *Schizophrenia Bulletin, 14,* 7–15.

Rogers, S. (1988). *Fighting stigma.* Philadelphia, PA: National Mental Health Consumer Self-Help Clearinghouse.

State Comprehensive Mental Health Plan Act of 1986, Public Law 99-660, Title V. (1986).

Zinman, S., Harp, H. T, & Budd, S. (Eds.). (1985). *Reaching across: Mental health clients helping each other.* Sacramento: California Network of Mental Health Clients.

Evidence-Based Practices: Setting the Context and Responding to Concerns

Susan M. Essock, Howard H. Goldman, Laura Van Tosh,
William A. Anthony, Charity R. Appell, Gary R. Bond, Lisa B. Dixon,
Linda K. Dunakin, Vijay Ganju, Paul G. Gorman, Ruth O. Ralph,
Charles A. Rapp, Gregory B. Teague, and Robert E. Drake

At the time of original publication, author affiliations were listed as follows: Susan M. Essock, PhD, Division of Health Services Research, Department of Psychiatry, Mount Sinai School of Medicine, New York, NY, and Mental Illness Research, Education, and Clinical Center, Veterans Affairs New York Healthcare System, Bronx, NY; Howard H. Goldman, MD, PhD, Department of Psychiatry, University of Maryland, School of Medicine, Baltimore, MD; Laura Van Tosh, Mental Health Policy and Services Research, Silver Spring, MD; William A. Anthony, PhD, Center for Psychiatric Rehabilitation, Boston University, Boston, MA; Charity R. Appell, New Hampshire-Dartmouth Psychiatric Research Center, Lebanon, NH; Gary R. Bond, PhD, Department of Psychology, Indiana University-Purdue University Indianapolis, Indianapolis, IN; Lisa B. Dixon, MD, MPH, Division of Health Services Research, Department of Psychiatry, Veterans Administration, Capitol Health Care Network MIRECC, Baltimore, MD; Linda K. Dunakin, MALS, Connecticut Department of Mental Health and Addiction Services, Hartford, CT, and Department of Psychology, University of Connecticut, Storrs, CT; Vijay Ganju, PhD, Center for Mental Health Quality and Accountability, NASMHPD Research Institute, Alexandria, VA; Paul G. Gorman, EdD, West Institute, CMH, New Hampshire-Dartmouth Psychiatric Research Center, Lebanon, NH; Ruth O. Ralph, PhD, Edmund S. Muskie School of Public Service, University of Southern Maine, Portland, ME; Charles A. Rapp, PhD, Office of Mental Health Research and Training, The University of Kansas, School of Social Welfare, Lawrence, KS; Gregory B. Teague, PhD, Department of Mental Health Law and Policy, Louis de la Parte Florida Mental Health Institute, University of South Florida, Tampa, FL; and Robert E. Drake, MD, PhD, New Hampshire-Dartmouth Psychiatric Research Center, Lebanon, NH

This article was published previously in *Psychiatric Clinics of North America,* 2003, 26, 919–938, and is reprinted with permission.

In its report, Crossing the Quality Chasm, the Institute of Medicine (IOM) (2001) states, "evidence-based practice is the integration of best research evidence with clinical expertise and patient values." This statement serves as a reminder that there is more to consider in practice than the scientific rigor of the evidence base for these services. Simultaneously, it is imperative to apply clinical judgment and to respect individuals' choices and preferences.

Two rights are central to the principles of evidence-based medicine. Consumers with serious mental disorders and their families have a right to accurate information regarding interventions and their outcomes, and they have a right to choose among effective services. Practitioners, administrators, and policy makers therefore have an obligation to make such services available and, in so doing, make sure that limited health care dollars are spent on effective services. The movement toward evidence-based practices (EBPs) in mental health care prescribes that research evidence regarding interventions and outcomes should be part of the basic educational materials provided to consumers and families, should be part of the discussion between practitioners and consumers leading to shared decision making, and should be part of the knowledge base of administrators and policy makers. As in the rest of health care, the notion is that, before submitting to a course of treatment, individuals have a right to know its success rate compared with alternatives, the likelihood of various adverse effects, and the likely consequences associated with forgoing the treatments offered.

Although the origins of the EBP movement are rooted in the values of self-determination, shared decision making, and consumer-centered services, some EBP initiatives also have been criticized for undermining each of these core values. The purpose of this article is to help understand this paradox by setting forth concerns about the adoption of EBPs as voiced by members of diverse stakeholder groups: consumers, family members, policy makers, administrators, and researchers. Most stakeholders in all groups likely endorse the basic aims of EBP: to improve services by paying attention to interventions that enhance outcomes that people value. The disagreements come largely in the details of how to do this. Each of the authors belongs to one or more of these stakeholder groups, and, while not presuming to be representative of all members of these groups, felt it important to gather together concerns being voiced about EPBs to facilitate addressing them in ways that encourage further planning and discussion across stakeholder groups.

Why now? Along with consumers' and family members' rights to accurate information and service choice, tax payers, legislators, insurers, and employers increasingly also are pressuring providers to demonstrate that the services being provided are likely to be dollars well spent. Concurrently, court cases question whether care provided meets minimally acceptable standards even though the research base is too scanty in most areas to speak to what would be minimally appropriate. And, for those areas where the research base is strong enough to define EBPs, people are unlikely to have access to such care because of the gulf between science and practice (Lehman & Steinwachs, 1998a, 1988b; National Advisory Mental Health Council's Clinical Treatment and Services Research Workgroup, 1999) and because of budget priorities for available funds. Each of these forces creates support for expanding the knowledge base about what services work best, for whom, under what circumstances, and how to make certain that such services are available, accessible, and acceptable. Nevertheless, change stimulates legitimate fears, questions, and concerns. These fears can be reinforced by providers who feel their traditional ways of doing things are being threatened, consumers who feel disenfranchised from the process of designating what constitutes evidence, consumers of services who are new to receiving mental health services and learning of the shortcomings of treatment systems, policy makers who want to avoid the political turmoil that can come with shifting funding from one set of services to another, and countless other sources. In the spirit of science being transparent and welcoming a public discussion of issues, the authors offer this collection of concerns raised by the EBP movement among various mental health stakeholder groups, noting differences and common themes. Although the authors cannot claim that these listings are representative or exhaustive, they have raised or heard them repeated frequently as they have worked to understand, research, or disseminate EBPs. The authors hope that these summaries will be useful to others. This article considers one stakeholder group at a time, fleshing out concerns raised by that group. Concerns across stakeholder groups overlap, and, once discussed, a particular concern is revisited only if the perspectives of the next stakeholder group to be considered are different from those previously considered. Table 1 summarizes the concerns.

CONSUMER CONCERNS ABOUT EVIDENCE-BASED PRACTICES

Because the different stakeholder groups echo, in various ways, consumer concerns, this section elaborates on them in some detail.

In the competition for funding, will only the most evidence-based practices survive?

Mental health systems are chronically underfunded, leading to competition among providers, including consumer-operated services, for scarce program dollars. A move to emphasize funding for what is evidence-based means that innovative services that have yet to acquire an evidence base, including many consumer-operated programs, could risk closing for lack of funding. Here the risk is that absence of evidence will be mistaken as evidence of absence of effectiveness and that an effective program could be closed for lack of evidence of its effectiveness. In the absence of such research evidence, consumers will continue to speak from their lived experiences and continue to lobby for consumer-run services emphasizing recovery, peer support, self-help, and empowerment.

The use of treatment algorithms based on evidence-based practices may prevent individualized treatment.

Consumers are concerned that the EBP movement may be used by policy makers to justify implementing treatment algorithms that narrowly define what treatments a person may have. Consider the area of pharmacotherapy, where treatment algorithms are relatively well-developed. By implementing such treatment algorithms, one goal of program administrators is to minimize the likelihood of suboptimal care, the notion being that following a road map for care helps assure that paths with the greatest likelihood of success are offered and that repeated deviations from these proved paths would prompt review. By examining the prescribing patterns of individual psychiatrists, those psychiatrists who deviate frequently from the algorithm can be identified and reviewed more closely.

For example, the Texas Medication Algorithm Project (TMAP) treatment algorithm calls for offering a trial with clozapine rather than coprescribing multiple antipsychotics when trials of two or more of the other newer antipsychotics have failed to have satisfactory results (Texas Medication Algorithm Project Management Team, 1997). Identifying and intervening with psychiatrists who deviate from this treatment algorithm can help ensure that people are offered medications that have been shown to be effective. For example, because clozapine is a relatively expensive medication and can be cumbersome for physicians to prescribe, identifying areas of apparent underuse serves to ensure that consumers are being offered access to medications that are most likely to be effective. The decision to begin a trial on clozapine should entail open conversations between the psychiatrist and the consumer about the risks and benefits associated with the medication compared with alternatives, along with offers of close contact during any medication change. The concern is that psychiatrists who rarely or never prescribe clozapine, but who move people on to multiple concurrent antipsychotics, are failing to offer participation in shared decision making with consumers who might benefit from the medication, by failing to offer them a trial on clozapine. Having the treatment algorithm and identifying where it is not being followed helps assure that consumers will be offered effective alternatives, thereby assuring a higher quality of care.

The treatment algorithm always contains a path labeled "consumer declines"; the goal of the EBP movement is to make sure that that path is taken with full information available to the consumer about what the evidence base indicates is most helpful to most people. By identifying the clinicians associated with those consumers who are most likely to opt out, one can identify clinicians who may need further help, including more education about the facts of the evidence base and enhancing skills in engaging people in a treatment partnership. Consumers should have the right to know the latest information so that they can make truly informed choices and the right to be in treatment with practitioners who keep up with the evidence base and can be a source of reliable information for consumers making these choices.

Table 1. Stakeholder Groups' Concerns About Evidence-Based Practices

Concern	Stakeholder Group					
	Consumers	Family Members	Practitioners	Administrators	Policy Makers	Researchers
Concerns Related to Change Process						
EBPs will disrupt the status quo			X	X	X	
Lack of time to learn new skills			X	X	X	
EBPs just another fad			X	X	X	
Concerns Related to Funding						
Funding priorities displaced	X	X	X	X	X	
Cost too much at start-up				X		
EBPs not compatible with funding streams			X	X	X	
Concerns Related to Scientific Method						
Skepticism about scientific method used (i.e., RCTs)	X	X	X	X	X	
Some valued practices cannot be studied readily by RCTs (e.g., self-help groups)	X		X			X
EBPs de-emphasize recovery	X					
EBPs focus on wrong outcomes	X	X	X			
EBPs will stifle innovation	X	X	X		X	X
Decision process for choosing EBPs is arbitrary or invalid	X	X	X	X	X	X

Table 1. Stakeholder Groups' Concerns About Evidence-Based Practices (continued)

Concern	Stakeholder Group					
	Consumers	Family Members	Practitioners	Administrators	Policy Makers	Researchers
Concerns about Prescribing *any* EBP in Routine Practice						
EBPs are antithetical to clinical judgment and consumer choice	X		X			
EBP rigid and mechanistic	X	X	X			
EBP emphasize technique, not relationship	X	X	X			
EBPs ignore individual differences	X	X	X			
Power and influence of group will diminish	X	X	X	X	X	
EBPs not relevant to real world	X	X	X			
Limits of EBPs						
Existing EBPs do not address all consumer needs (e.g., housing, trauma, not evidence-based)	X	X	X	X		X
EBPs do not generalize to all cultures	X	X	X	X	X	X
Power and Control						
Stakeholder group's influence will be diminished	X	X	X	X	X	
Valued practices (e.g., family-family, and consumer-run services) will be devalued and discarded	X	X				
EBPs challenge professional autonomy			X			

The influence of researchers and the professionals who implement the evidence-based practice will diminish the power of consumers.

Consumers have made initial strides in terms of influencing the direction of mental health systems, and mental health systems today commonly have vehicles by which service recipients provide input (Van Tosh & del Vecchio, 2000). Because that input has included calls for effective, accountable services, consumers have been participants in, and proponents of, movements promoting EBPs. Nevertheless, consumers also are concerned that an emphasis on EBPs may devalue their experiences simply because so much of what is known comes from sources other than randomized clinical trials. Many important treatment questions simply are not addressable by means of randomized clinical trials (Essock, Drake, Frank, & McGuire, 2003; Anthony, Rogers, & Farkas, 2003), hence a challenge for the EBP movement is to determine the criteria for what constitutes objective evidence. For example, given the open-access principles that are central to many forms of peer support (e.g., the open-door policy of drop-in centers), random assignment to receive or not receive peer support could be a highly artificial test of the impact of peer support. Given the emphasis of the EBP movement on data from randomized trials, services that are not amenable to assessment by means of randomized trials would appear to be at risk of being overlooked unless advocates and researchers are there to remind policy makers that absence of evidence is not evidence of absence and that solid evidence is obtainable from designs other than randomized trials.

Consumers and researchers emphasize different outcomes.

Important outcomes commonly mentioned by consumers include personal empowerment and self-efficacy, work, hope, attainment of individually set goals, enhanced quality of life, housing stability, self-esteem, and health. These outcomes have some overlap with the outcomes used in the studies that led up to the designation of some interventions as EBPs (such as the relatively easy-to-measure outcomes of symptom reduction and fewer days hospitalized) (Anthony, 2001). The risk here is that achieving a particular set of outcomes might be mistaken as synonymous with achieving recovery, because those more easily measured outcomes may be poor proxies for the rich fabric that constitutes recovery, with all of its individual variations. These outcomes are consistent with the goals voiced by many consumers, however, and, for some individuals, form a foundation on which to build a meaningful life (Torrey, Rapp, van Tosh, McNabb, Ralph, & Tracy, 2003). As studies are mounted to expand the evidence base, inclusion of additional outcomes important to consumers and other stakeholder groups will help ensure consumer endorsement of the research findings and a broadening of evidence-based services.

FAMILY MEMBERS' CONCERNS REGARDING EVIDENCE-BASED PRACTICE

Family members of persons who have serious mental disorders have voiced a range of concerns regarding the implementation and funding of EBPs. Some of these concerns overlap with those of consumers. Families, like consumers, have fought hard for a voice in the delivery of clinical care and are concerned that the implementation of EBPs could reduce or replace that voice.

Increased emphasis on evidence-based practice will shift funding away from family-to-family initiatives and diminish evaluation opportunities for such initiatives.

Family members worry that an emphasis on EBP could mean that funding for family-based initiatives would be reduced or eliminated. The source of this concern may be the designation of family psychoeducation, a clinical intervention that involves families but is focused on patient outcomes, as an EBP (Dixon, McFarlane, Lefley, Lucksted, Cohen, Falloon et al., 2001). Although family initiatives usually can be delivered with a minimum number of resources, family members are concerned that resources will not be available to offer both family psychoeducation and family initiatives. Families believe that family initiatives like the National Alliance for the Mentally Ill's (NAMI's) family education program (Dixon, Stewart, Burland, Delahanty, Lucksted, & Hoffman, 2001; Burland, 1998) have a place in the service array, because, unlike family psychoeducation, they serve families whose relatives are not in treatment or whose relatives will not give permission to clinicians to contact families. Family members are also concerned that, because family psychoeducation requires a long-term commitment to be effective, it will benefit only families who are able to make such a commitment. In the absence of other choices, many families could be left without services. The research base for family education programs is growing, but it has not yet reached the standard necessary to be considered an EBP. Family members emphasize that the implementation of EBPs should be considered within the universe of family needs, with families asking that other services be made available for those who are left out of family-oriented EBPs.

The methods of science that underpin evidence-based practice emphasize data from narrow clinical trials at the expense of reports of lived experience.

Family members may question whether some of the EBPs are well anchored in the real world of service delivery, that they are impractical for their participants (efficacious but not effective). In general, family members want services to reflect the best scientific evidence available and to be feasible to undertake.

Family members will lose hard won positions of agents of reform as data are emphasized over values and evidence-based practice may stifle innovation.

These issues are similar to the concerns of consumers discussed previously.

PRACTITIONER CONCERNS

Practitioner concerns about EBP are numerous and often overlap with concerns of other stakeholders, such as families and consumers, with respect to whose interests are controlling the mental health system.

Research findings have limited relevance to practice.

The research base is small enough, and consumer needs complex enough, that much of what clinicians do has no evidence to guide it and is based more on clinical wisdom gained through experience combined with consumer preferences. The challenge, therefore, is twofold: increase the amount of research relevant to clinical practice, and make sure what is known makes its way into practice (National Advisory Mental Health Council's Clinical Treatment and Services Research Workgroup, 1999). Relevance to routine practice is the crux of effectiveness research, and materials relating to EBPs must be produced in ways that are amenable to practitioners (Torrey, Drake, Dixon, Burns, Flynn, Rush et al., 2001). Continued evaluation and refinement of clinician-level material should lead to improved practitioner materials and a tested methodology for how one bridges science and practice.

Lack of time and support for learning new skills.

Most clinicians have sat through countless hours of required continuing education presentations with only limited relevance to their day-to-day practice. Hence, it is not surprising that many clinicians are skeptical about investing even more time in new approaches. On the other hand, clinicians are eager to acquire new skills in areas where they perceive a need to improve their skills (e.g., with respect to trauma, dual diagnosis). Given the severe limitations of the continuing medical education (talking-head) approach, the current approaches to implementing EBPs are much more extensive (Torrey, Drake, Dixon, Burns, Flynn, Rush et al., 2001). Implementing EBPs will require ongoing support for practitioners as they learn new practices. And, once learned, new practices will require time for clinical supervision to be enhanced and sustained. Ultimately, if practitioners are to incorporate EBPs into their practice, medical educators must modify their curriculums so as to incorporate, promote, and facilitate their use.

Today best practices may be discredited tomorrow.

Experienced practitioners have seen it before: a new idea that will revolutionize the field. Some of these ideas have staying power, such as intensive case management in its many variations. Other ideas (e.g., sensitivity training and assertiveness training) shine briefly before fading. Practitioners know that it is hard for systems to embed new initiatives and question the investment of energy in what just may be another fad. Yet, virtually no one is content with the quality and effectiveness of current services, recognizing that some services based on theory, ideology, or practice have tended to go on for many years with modifications that may suit practitioners or administrators but do not improve outcomes. The mental health field must change continuously to improve. Practices should change over time as more is learned about what works, the standard approach in the rest of health care. A focus on outcomes, quality improvement, and change is fundamental to EBPs.

Evidence-based practices challenge professional autonomy and replace clinical judgment.

Like all other stakeholders, practitioners want to have a significant say in how practice is done. Practitioners mistakenly may perceive EBPs as antithetical to clinical judgment. This is not the case. Although EBPs may be taught with a specific curriculum, their effective implementation relies on clinical judgment. In the case of EBP, as reflected in the IOM definition, clinical skills are integrated with the best research evidence and the preferences of the consumer. Clinical judgment is necessary to combine evidence, the consumer's individual circumstances, and the consumer's preferences. EBPs are highly individualized, and good outcomes depend critically upon practitioners' skill and judgment (Haynes, Devereaux, & Guyatt, 2002).

ADMINISTRATOR CONCERNS

For administrators charged with using scarce health care dollars wisely, EBPs are welcome ways to address issues of quality and accountability, and a means to bring about change. The rub comes in the efforts to implement them. As a means of emphasizing the importance of EBPs and to help garner implementation support, state mental health agency directors have adopted a 50-state consensus position to move the EBP agenda forward. They have established a Center for Mental Health Quality and Accountability at the National Association of Mental Health Program Directors Research Institute to support and buttress this effort (Center for Mental Health Quality and Accountability, 2003).

Although evidence-based practices may be cost-effective once implemented, the startup investment may be prohibitive.

The challenge to administrators is to implement systems committed to quality improvement and efficiency. The lack of resources is always an obstacle to making infrastructure changes, implementing training, or incorporating EBPs into the service array (which can require start-up or bridge funding). Existing funding sources and mechanisms are also often constraining. Many providers are funded through reimbursements, and in some cases, certain EBPs are not covered as part of the eligible benefit package, so that a separate payment source must be developed to fund the practice. Administrators need to assess the financial flexibility that may be available to them and the relative advantages of implementing EBPs, rather than services that might be less cost-effective. At the same time, especially when budgets are tight, administrators must work with other stakeholders to develop a consensus regarding implementation of EBPs and their benefits.

Implementing evidence-based practices necessitates rocking the boat by displacing services being provided by established, politically powerful provider groups who may have no incentive to change.

In most mental health systems, evidence-based services constitute a small sliver of the service array, in terms of number of services and service expenditures. Although EBPs and other services must coexist, the expectation is that the practices that have a high level of evidence would be the cornerstone of the service array. To expand EBPs in the service array, administrators must recognize that they need to make adjustments in their administrative, information, quality management, financial, and contracting systems. Often, especially in environments with fixed or diminishing budgets, the expectation is that the transition to EBPs will use resources previously allocated to other services. Sometimes this reallocation will involve different providers, requiring the development of new organizational relationships and infrastructure. Given the current state of knowledge, administrators cannot fund EBPs alone; they must judiciously balance evidence-based services with the other services. If research and experience in routine practice settings have shown that the outcomes associated with some sets of services are worse than the outcomes associated with other sets of services, then the entrenched services should be phased out and the resources invested in services supported by the evidence base.

Evidence-based services must be adapted to fit specific local and cultural contexts. Administrators have to use the limited knowledge and experience base in situations when existing research results are inadequate. For example, evidence-based service models for rural or frontier areas where sparse population and scarce mental health resources require evidence-based models to be fitted to their context, but the knowledge base in this area is, for the most part, deficient.

Training capacities are limited, and training needs are continuous because of turnover in the workforce.

The basic model for implementing new practices is to train clinicians and service providers to deliver the new service. Many providers are funded through reimbursements based on the provision of services, which do not explicitly finance training. Training initiatives for EBPs need to be ensconced in a larger system-level training context, and training must be ongoing because of staff turnover and the need for ongoing supervision and support. Because of financial and time constraints, however, large systems are often unable to provide ongoing training to sustain the new practice.

Substance Abuse and Mental Health Services Administration (SAMHSA) implementation resource kits, materials for the implementation of multisystemic therapy for children/adolescents, technical assistance, and resource centers are available to help support administrators with EBP implementation. A major aspect of these resources is the emphasis of consensus among stakeholders and the alignment of the policy, clinical, and administrative aspects of EBPs.

POLICY MAKER CONCERNS

Over many years, the mental health care field has experienced a series of system reforms related to the delivery of mental health services (Office of the Surgeon General, 2001). Each reform generally has been embraced, because it either reduces inefficiencies or sets the stage for innovation. Reforms also have been the product of efforts of an informed and influential constituency base of organizations and advocates. Mental health systems today are at another juncture: to embrace EBPs and either to add them to traditional services or replace those existing services. In a time of economic instability, policy makers are challenged by decisions about the delivery and acceptance of EBPs. They must find budget savings to provide scientifically proven services to support people with mental illnesses in the community and encourage change to service design and delivery of proven effectiveness.

What are the objections most often raised by policy makers about implementing evidence-based practices?

How can we pay for evidence-based practices that do not fall within typical benefit structures?

Medicaid regulations dominate how funds flow, and states have experienced a shift in expenditure patterns as Medicaid polity evolves. The biggest implementation challenge for state and local policy makers may be figuring out how to finance EBPs within existing payment mechanisms. Some EBPs do not fit easily into existing benefit packages. Even in Medicaid, where many of the EBPs can be reimbursed at least partly, working with the regulations can be complex, and developing the associated changes in regulations requires expending political capital.

Strong pressure to fund vested interests.

Policy makers may feel they will lose political capital if they move against current services and the constituents who support them. If stakeholders perceive the introduction of an EBP as a threat to other more standard mental health services, state policy makers must explain how and why EBP will improve outcomes. State-level policy makers must translate research findings into services in their communities by maintaining direct and sustained contact with state and local constituency organizations.

No money for new initiatives and hard to divest from old ways.

Retrenchment and current budget crises will necessitate cuts. Perhaps the budget crises represent an opportunity to cut services that have limited evidence and replace them with EBPs. These new EBPs do not need new money if the system already spends money on services that consumers do not like and that may not have good outcomes.

The reach of evidence-based practices is limited.

Policy makers have seen that many research studies are not relevant to their major concerns. Services for children are a current, critical concern, but EBPs for children are limited to a few practices (e.g., medications, therapeutic foster care, nurse home visiting, and multi-systemic therapy). These EBPs do not address many of the problems considered pressing by policy makers, nor do they cover all of the conditions that children and adolescents present to the mental health service system. Although more EBPs for adults have been identified, they also are limited. EBPs cover only some situations; they are neither cookbooks nor panaceas, and clinical judgment remains critical.

Policy makers operate under pressure to be conservative and avoid scandal, which dampens enthusiasm for the risks of new initiatives.

Almost as a condition of office, many policy makers are concerned with avoiding scandals, and they may find that there are few political rewards for increasing the quality of mental health services. Exposes and scandals dot the history of mental health services as prime motivators for change, however, because the typical state of affairs has been to continue to provide the same sets of services, in the same ways. Indeed, absent the impetus of scandal, it can be very difficult for policy makers to amass the political capital necessary to force change in the face of an entrenched and politically powerful provider community. This climate may be changing, however, as legislators are asking questions about value for money and seeking greater evidence of effectiveness and accountability.

Lawmakers are motivated by anecdote and data.

Policy makers, including lawmakers, welcome anecdotal testimony. The important role of constituency groups and an active and informed electorate help drive this phenomenon. The combination of reliable data and anecdotes can become a powerful tool to affect a change in policy.

RESEARCHER CONCERNS

Gaps in the research base.

The National Evidence-Based Practices Project (NEBPP) study groups identified six EBPs for community mental health treatment of persons with severe mental illness (Drake, Goldman, Leff, Lehman, Dixon, Mueser et al., 2001). These practices-assertive community treatment, integrated dual disorders treatment, family psychoeducation, supported employment, illness self-management, and medication practices—do not span the full range of services needed by people with severe mental illness. If systems of care were limited to those EBPs, important consumer needs would not be met. Although the six EBPs provide a strong foundation for defining minimal services for people with severe mental disorders, neither the mental health consumer in need of trauma treatment or housing support, nor the practitioner who would provide the service, can find help from these EBPs. The challenge to researchers is to increase the number of EBPs so that the all of the stakeholders will be able to make informed choices about treatment for the broad range of needs.

Evidence-based practices stifle innovation and new research.

Some researchers (O'Brien & Anthony, 2002) have expressed the concern that the identification of a small number of established EBPs will create an orthodoxy that chokes off new research. In one version of this concern, only research on EBPs will be funded, and practices that are untested will be ignored, thus not meeting the needs of all consumers. To determine whether there is an empirical basis for this concern, researchers will need to monitor patterns of research and patterns of research funding and address any inequities. Certainly, no philosophical conflict exists between accepting a set of practices as evidence based and seeking to establish new effective practices. Indeed, researchers who have contributed to establishing EBPs also have been instrumental in identifying new areas for research.

Evidence-based practices may be based on out-of-date research.

At least one critic (Seifert, 2002) has asserted that many of the studies that are counted among those showing the effectiveness of EBPs were done many years ago when services systems were significantly different. That Assertive Community Treatment (ACT) EBP includes studies from the 1980s is cited as an example. Research on ACT has continued, however, even in the last 5 years, evolving to answer more specific questions than the broader landmark studies or to target different populations or settings. Research for other EBPs has less of a history. All of the major studies of supported employment have been completed in the last decade, and the same is true for studies in integrated dual-disorder treatment. That said, as part of the EBP process, studies completed in different eras or under different service delivery systems must be scrutinized carefully.

Generalizability of the evidence.

Recently, some researchers have noted the limits of generalizability in EBPs (Anthony, Rogers, & Farkas, 2003; Dixon, McFarlane et al., 2001; Bond, Becker, Drake, Rapp, Meisler, Lehman et al., 2001; Drake, Essock, Shaner, Carey, Minkoff, Kola et al., 2001; Mellman, Miller, Weissman, Crismon, Essock, & Marder, 2001; Mueser, Corrigan, Hilton, Tanzman, Schaub, Gingerich, et al., 2002; Phillips, Burns, Edgar, Mueser, Linkins, Rosenheck et al., 2001). People in need of mental health services, particularly those accessing public mental health services, come from diverse settings and ethnic groups, and the evidence of the EBPs often is limited to specific settings and populations. This limitation speaks to the feasibility concerns of administrators and policy makers listed previously. The urban Latino or Asian mental health consumer seeking treatment does not have a large evidence base to make a truly informed choice about treatment options. Still, the research literature for each of the six EBPs has some delineated area of generalizability, and as researchers seek to broaden ethnic participation in their studies and to replicate studies in various settings, generalizability for EBPs should expand. In the meantime, as noted in the supplemental Surgeon General's mental health report on culture, race and ethnicity, members of ethnic minority groups are encouraged to use these EBP services while the research base develops (2001).

Ambiguities in establishing a hierarchy of evidence and disagreement on levels of evidence and methods.

Researchers have used various systems for identifying levels of evidence for EBPs, none of which is entirely satisfactory (Chambless & Ollendick, 2001). Some observers argue that too much weight has been given to randomized controlled trials or too little weight to qualitative approaches or experiential evidence. Some questions relevant to the effectiveness of services for people in the real world may not be addressable by means of randomized control trials (Essock, Drake, Frank, & McGuire, 2003), hence never may reach some group's criteria for being evidence-based. Researchers also can differ as to the importance of other criteria, including quality of the research (e.g., the impact of sample attrition, sample size, and length of follow-up) and the independence of the research teams. Decision rules have been devised for weighting different types of research designs (e.g., experimental quasi-experimental, and prepost design) in the consideration of levels of evidence. Systems differ not only in their weighting schemes but also in their leniency for identifying an EBP. Because the methodologies for designating something an EBP have some variation across groups, the selection process contains some degree of arbitrariness. Converging expert opinion from the Patient Outcome Research Team (PORT) panel, the Robert Wood Johnson panel, and systematic reviews of the literature on the core EBPs, gives some credence to the selection of EBPs, but this area requires more work.

COMMON THEMES

Four common themes emerge from the discussion of stakeholder concerns.

Skepticism about scientific methods.

The IOM definition of EBP emphasizes that EBP is a process of integrating the best research evidence with clinical expertise and patient values. The relevant domains in this definition—research evidence, clinical expertise, and patient values—are themselves ever changing. Recognizing that scientific methods evolve (randomized control trials, the gold standard for EBPs, came to prominence only in the 1960s) mean that practitioners must be alert to spot methodological biases. To consumers, for example, the lessons they may value from peer accounts of recovery are not yet apparent in the evidence base of EBPs, because these accounts have not been incorporated into the methods of the larger research community.

Limited fiscal and other resources.

Stakeholders are concerned about financial and nonfinancial costs associated with the implementation and maintenance of EBPs. Successful implementation will require not just the initial installation of a particular set of practices, but a reworking of the fabric of service systems to ensure initial and ongoing training and supervision, monitoring, quality improvement, reconfiguration of financing, and other incentives and accountability structures. What will be removed to make room for the new approaches? These systems, once established, must be supported to achieve a shift in the culture of practice: individual and organizational change that can be difficult and protracted. The prospect of large up-front investments for gains down the road (perhaps under someone else's administration) is rarely welcome in behavioral health care, and the current economic climate is particularly challenging for finding service-system resources to invest in change.

Power and control.

Stakeholder groups express concern over competition for limited resources. Given the scarcity of resources, if resources are allocated to a few identified EBPs, other favored services may lose resources. Because the specific practices identified as having a strong evidence base do not cover the full range of need, reallocating resources may mean a loss of support for programs favored by a particular group. Historically, nonprofessionals have played peripheral roles in the venues for setting policy and for establishing scientific evidence. Any increase in emphasis on using research findings to set policy may be seen as implicitly disempowering nonprofessionals and threatening the gains they have made in shaping system priorities. Consumers are not alone in this concern. EBPs also may seem to threaten the prerogatives of administrators and clinicians by constraining their opportunities to fund services not supported by the evidence base. Perhaps the good news is that ideally, unlike ineffective but entrenched services, EBPs are not beholden to any particular stakeholder group.

Waste as the enemy.

Concerns about control over scarce resources exist across stakeholder groups. These conflicts over scant and limited resources for new services, such as conflicts between advocates for EBPs and advocates for consumer-operated services or family support services, exist in the much larger shadow of the main body of resources. Most mental health services resources go toward inpatient care or to longstanding services that often are untested, rather than to EBPs or innovative services operated by consumers or families. Although requests for implementing new EBPs may squeeze out other initiatives, advocates of EBPs and other innovative services can form natural alliances. In the realpolitik of mental health advocacy, these groups could improve services by joining together to advocate for withdrawing service dollars from ineffective traditional services that lack an evidence base and that do not seem to meet consumer and family needs or preferences. Waste, rather than a different stakeholder group, is the common enemy, along with the inadequacy of current resources. Rather than fighting over limited dollars available for innovative services, practitioners should fight to use well whatever resources are available and end ineffective services.

DISCUSSION

Many of the concerns that have been raised by different stakeholders are shared, and many others can be inductively grouped together, because they represent similar themes and underlying issues. Table 1 illustrates the authors' attempt to create a categorization of concerns. Each of these categories now is discussed as a group.

The first group of concerns relates to fears and distress regarding change. Professionals and human service organizations are notoriously resistant to change, which is one stimulus for huge literatures on organizations, change processes, diffusion of innovations, implementation dilemmas, and others (Rogers, 1983). These types of concerns are inevitable, because professionals and human service organizations have to respond to changes in technology, demands for services, demographics, ideology, and other forces, but these concerns have little to do with EBPs. The underlying issue has to do with how to create self-renewing health care organizations that expect to change and embrace necessary and healthy changes.

The second category of concerns addresses funding and other limitations of resources. Successful implementation of EBPs will require not just the initial installation of a particular set of practices, but a reworking of the fabric of service systems to ensure initial and ongoing training and supervision, monitoring, quality improvement, reconfiguration of financing, and other incentive and accountability structures. These systems, once established, must be supported to achieve a shift in the culture of practice: individual and organizational change that can be difficult and protracted. Stakeholder groups are concerned about financial and nonfinancial costs and competition for resources. These concerns speak loudly to policy makers. The crux is that stakeholders and vested interest groups inevitably compete for limited resources in the policy arena. With the inexorable pressures of aging demographics, technology expansion, and increased expectations of the health care system, policy decisions regarding health care funding priorities must be made, even when the economy is healthy. Science is one tool that policy makers use in this situation. That is, a common strategy in making these decisions is on the basis of accountability for outcomes. Therefore, one consequence of the evidence-based medicine movement is to shift funds away from practices that do more harm than good to practices that do more good than harm (Muir Gray, 1996). For example, in mental health, practices that involve institutional, custodial, segregated care have little empirical support, and the influence of EBPs would be to replace them with practices that help people to succeed in preferred roles in the community, for which there is a great deal of empirical support. Practices of unknown efficacy generally are left out of this equation. Researchers can and should identify practices that are ineffective or harmful as well as practices that are effective. Of course, the difficulty is that ineffective practices often are supported by powerful lobby groups (e.g., unions protecting positions, hospitals' protecting revenue streams from inpatient services, pharmaceutical industry's proffering advise favoring their products, physicians tied to particular hierarchical models of clinical organization), which is how they survive beyond their usefulness to the health care system. This category, like the first category, has little to do with EBPs, except that many stakeholders and vested interest groups would not like science to be used as a criterion for policy decisions, because they have little research support for their own favorite activities.

In the third category, some people misunderstand research, and some simply reject the methods of science. Misconceptions regarding science may be overcome by education. For example, it may be helpful for people to understand that evidence-based medicine advocates use the best available evidence, conceived as a hierarchy that is open to public debate, rather than only randomized controlled trials (Essock, Drake, Frank, & McGuire, 2003). On the other hand, for people who reject scientific medicine for religious or other reasons of basic belief (e.g., past life therapists), further explication of the methods, fairness, and reliability of science probably will be unhelpful.

The fourth category of concerns perceives EBPs as rigid, orthodox, driven by fidelity scales, discounting clinical wisdom and experience, and diminishing consumer choice and individuality. Most of the authors of this paper have been involved in the evidence-based medicine movement and believe that these concerns are based on misconceptions and poor applications of some practices. As attested by the articles in this issue, if one looks in detail at the interventions that prove to be effective in almost any area of mental health care, they are characterized by sensitivity to individual differences, by attention to choices and preferences, by client centeredness, by empowerment, by diversity of methods, and by reliance on clinical skills and judgment. These common features undoubtedly are related to their effectiveness. The reliance on fidelity is to ensure that these types of elements, as opposed to a rigid, one-size-fits-all approach, are present.

The fifth set of concerns addresses issues that represent legitimate limitations of EBPs. EBPs are not a panacea; they do not address all problems. There are many legitimate weaknesses. These are concerns that need to be identified, defined carefully, and addressed fully.

Finally, the sixth set of concerns is related to issues of power and control. If resources are allocated to a few identified EBPs, other services may lose resources. Any increase in emphasis on using research findings to set policy may be seen as implicitly disempowering nonprofessionals and threatening the gains they have made in shaping system priorities. They also may seem to threaten the prerogatives of administrators and clinicians by constraining their opportunities to fund or provide services not supported by the evidence base. This is an expected part of the political process. Payers, policy makers, and legislators, along with all those who receive services and mental health service funding, are legitimate players in the political process. Respecting and valuing the emphases of all stakeholder groups may be quicker route to reforms that will improve services than setting the weakest players up to cannibalize each other. Consumers, families, and researchers are all relatively new to seats at the policy making table. Making room at the table should help ensure that practices within mental health systems integrate the best research evidence with clinical expertise and consumer values.

REFERENCES

Anthony, W. A. (2001, November 5). The need for recovery-compatible evidence-based practices. *Mental Health Weekly,* p. 5.

Anthony, W. A., Rogers, E., Farkas, M. (2003). Research on evidence-based practices: Future directions in an era of recovery. *Community Mental Health Journal, 39*(2), 101–14.

Bond, G. R., Becker, D. R., Drake, R. E., Rapp, C. A., Meisler, N., Lehman, A. F., et al. (2001). Implementing supported employment as an evidence-based practice. *Psychiatric Services, 52,* 313–324.

Burland J. (1998). Family-to-family: A trauma and recovery model of family education. *New Directions in Mental Health Services, 77,* 33–44.

Center for Mental Health Quality and Accountability. National Association of Mental Health Program Directors Research Institute. Retrieved March 26, 2003 from www.nri-inc.org.

Chambless, D. L., Ollendick, T. H. (2001). Empirically supported psychological interventions: Controversies and evidence. *Annual Review of Psychology, 52,* 685–716.

Dixon, L., McFarlane, W. R., Lefley, H., Lucksted, A., Cohen, M., Falloon, I., et al. (2001). Evidence-based practices for services to families of people with psychiatric disabilities. *Psychiatric Services, 52*(7), 903–910.

Dixon, L., Stewart, B., Burland, J., Delahanty, J., Lucksted, A., & Hoffman, M. (2001). Pilot study of the effectiveness of the family-to-family education program. *Psychiatric Services, 52*(7), 965–967.

Drake, R. E., Essock, S. M., Shaner, A., Carey, K. B., Minkoff, K., Kola, L., et al. (2001). Implementing dual diagnosis services for clients with severe mental illness. *Psychiatric Services, 52,* 469–476.

Drake, R. E., Goldman, H. H., Leff, H. S., Lehman, A. F., Dixon, L., Mueser, K.T., et al. (2001). Implementing evidence-based practices in routine mental health service settings. *Psychiatric Services, 52*(2), 179–182.

Essock, S. M., Drake, R. E., Frank, R.G., & McGuire, T. G. (2003). Randomized clinical trials in evidence-based mental health care: Getting the right answer to the right question. *Schizophrenia Bulletin, 29*(1), 115–123.

Haynes, R. B., Devereaux, P. J., Guyatt, G. H. (2002). Clinical expertise in the era of evidence-based medicine and patient choice. *American College of Physicians Journal Club, 36*(A), 11.

Institute of Medicine Committee on the Quality of Health Care in America. (2001). *Crossing the quality chasm: A new health system for the 21st century.* Washington, DC: National Academy Press.

Lehman A. F., Steinwachs, D., & the Schizophrenia Outcomes Research Team. (1998a). Patterns of usual care for schizophrenia: Initial results from the schizophrenia PORT client survey. American Psychiatric Association. *Schizophrenia Bulletin, 24,* 11–29.

Lehman, A. F., Steinwachs, D., & the coinvestigators of the PORT program. (1998b). At issue: Research into practice: The Schizophrenia Patient Outcomes Research Team (PORT) treatment recommendations. *Schizophrenia Bulletin, 24,* 1–10.

Mellman, T. A., Miller, A. L., Weissman, E. M., Crismon, M. L., Essock, S. M., Marder S. R. (2001). Evidence-based pharmacologic treatment for people with severe mental illness: A focus on guidelines and algorithms. *Psychiatric Services, 52,* 619–625.

Mueser, K. T., Corrigan, P. W., Hilton, D. W., Tanzman, B., Schaub, A., Gingerich, S, et al. (2002). Illness management and recovery: A review of the research. *Psychiatric Services, 53*(10), 1272–1284.

Muir Gray, J. A. (1996). *Evidence-based health care.* New York: Churchill Livingston.

National Advisory Mental Health Council's Clinical Treatment and Services Research Workgroup. (1999). *Bridging science and service,* NIH 99-4353. National Institute of Mental Health. Rockville, MD.

O'Brien, W. F., & Anthony, W. (2002). Avoiding the any models trap. *Psychiatric Rehabilitation Journal, 25,* 213–214.

Office of the Surgeon General. (2001). *Mental health: Culture, race, and ethnicity.* (A supplement to *Mental health: A report of the Surgeon General* [1999]), SMA-01-3613. Washington, DC: Department of Health and Human Services.

Phillips, S. D., Burns, B. J., Edgar, E. R., Mueser, K. T., Linkins, K. W., Rosenheck, R. A., et al. (2001). Moving assertive community treatment into standard practice. *Psychiatric Services, 52,* 771–779.

Rogers, E. M. (1983). *Diffusion of innovations, 4th edition.* New York: The Free Press.

Seifert, P. (2002). Statement of the International Association of Psychosocial Services (IAPSRS) to the President's New Freedom Commission on Mental Health. *PSR Connection, 2,* 6–7.

Texas Medication Algorithm Project Management Team. (1997). *Texas Medication Algorithm Project (TMAP): An evaluation of the clinical and economic impact of medication algorithms in public sector patients with severe and persistent mental illnesses.* An interim project report. Austin, Dallas, San Antonio, TX.

Torrey W., Rapp, C. A., Van Tosh L., McNabb, C., Ralph, R. O., & Tracy, B. (2003). *The recovery paradigm and evidence-based practice: Conflict or consonance.* Hanover, NH: Dartmouth Psychiatric Research Institute.

Torrey, W. C., Drake, R. E., Dixon, L., Burns, B. J., Flynn, L., Rush, A. J., et al. (2001). Implementing evidence-based practices for persons with severe mental illnesses. *Psychiatric Services, 52*(1), 45–50.

Van Tosh, L., & del Vecchio, P. (2000). *Consumer-operated self-help programs: A technical report.* Rockville, MD: US Center for Mental Health Services.

Coping with Mental Illness

Gwen Davis

This article was published previously in the *Psychiatric Rehabilitation Journal*, 2005, 28(3), and is reprinted with permission.

That schizophrenia!" my inpatient doctor exclaimed, "It's playing tricks on my friend Gwen! This person your mind created, Shalom, is not real!"

The memory of this conversation slowly crept back into my consciousness as I sat on the floor, locked in the seclusion room in the psychiatric unit of Children's Hospital. I was covering my eyes so I wouldn't see Shalom's frightful glares, and I was screaming, so I wouldn't be forced to listen to Shalom's torturous inside information. All of a sudden, nothing made sense anymore. What if in fact, Shalom wasn't real? What if I were only imagining him? What if I really did have schizophrenia?

It all started when I was in 9th grade, when Shalom first appeared in my life. "You have been chosen," he had said to me, "You have been chosen to be part of my secretive, privileged organization. With my help, and with the inside information I will give you, you will be able to accomplish great things for yourself and for all of humanity."

With that declaration, Shalom began to relay his secret messages to me. At first the information was about how special I was, how I stood out from everyone around me, and how important the things I did were, but slowly these messages began taking a darker turn. Soon, Shalom began to tell me that my teachers and acquaintances were thinking terrible things about me, that they hated me, that the whole world was out to get me. From the feelings of unworthiness that I then experienced, I began to cut myself on my legs with a knife or scissors, with anything sharp that I could find, in order to make myself feel that I was good enough to be redeemed. And finally, I began to know that people whom I loved would die. "Your mom along with all your friends will be burned alive!" Shalom said. This last message, of how people would come to a painful demise, scared me so much that I began warning the potential victims. "Someone will have to die. Someone will have to die!" I whispered. It was at this point that it became apparent to the people around me that I was ill, and that I needed to be hospitalized.

After the painful diagnosis of schizophrenia, after months of hospitalization, and after many lengthy medication trials, the psychotic reality that I had known, the reality of Shalom, slowly began to crumble. My doctors had steadily been telling me that Shalom was not a real person, but it wasn't until now that I began to wonder if this could be true.

But I was still fastened in a struggle of confusion. It was difficult to accept my doctor's words that I had been hallucinating. I held onto all kinds of rationalizations of why my doctors had thought Shalom wasn't real. One, I told myself, was that Shalom was very clandestine in his activities, and only revealed himself to me. He thereby kept everyone else completely oblivious to his existence. Since I was the only one who was a part of his secretive organization, only I was special enough to know him. This, I tried to believe, was why everyone else thought I was only imagining Shalom, and why everyone thought I was suffering from an illness.

But as I was given medicine, a combination of Abilify and Risperdal, I began to get more and more muddled, for now I wouldn't see Shalom as much anymore. And when he was there he was much quieter, and no longer would tell me of terrible things that would happen to me or to others.

"This is odd," I thought to myself. "It's too much of a coincidence that when I started taking antipsychotic medication, Shalom started to go away. Maybe the medicine really is fixing my brain, enabling me to experience the world as everyone else experiences it."

I also began to realize that none of Shalom's threats ever came true. No one had died a terrible painful death, and I began to comprehend that there was no reason to believe that I was less worthy a human being than others. That's when I decided my doctors must be right—that Shalom wasn't real, that schizophrenia was playing tricks on my brain.

Coming to terms with the fact that I had a severe, chronic mental illness was unspeakably difficult in a number of different ways. Firstly, I felt shocked in knowing that my brain could be so dead wrong in its perceptions. For years Shalom had been in my life, and it had been crystal clear to me that he was just a regular, normal person. He looked like other people, he had a regular voice, and he seemed just as real as anyone else. How could my mind do this to me? How could it have gone so haywire as to have me imagine someone who didn't really exist? And it wasn't that he just looked and sounded normal, but we interacted with each other like two typical friends.

Secondly, it was hard to accept the reality that I was an ordinary person, not someone who was part of a secretive and omnipotent organization. All throughout high school, I had known that I was one of the greatest, most important people on earth; that I, because of my camaraderie with Shalom, was practically omniscient, and exceptional. But now, all of a sudden, I realized that the way I thought of myself was not accurate. For if Shalom wasn't real, then I wasn't omniscient, I wasn't special—I was just me, Gwen, a regular person, who had regular abilities, and possessed ordinary skills.

In addition to all this, it was painful to come to terms with how much Shalom had controlled my life. He had made me cut myself, he made me terrified for other people's safety, and he had prevented me from going to certain places, from talking about various things, and engaging in different activities. He had greatly circumscribed my life, I now realized, and he could have made me do almost anything.

At the same time, however, the understanding that I had an illness, meant that I had to say goodbye to Shalom. It was a very strange feeling that overcame me. On the one hand, Shalom had created absolute hell for me, yet on the other, he always provided me with attention and company—he was always there to tell me what to do, how to act, and what to say. Without him, even though I would not miss his terror, I would be alone—alone by myself.

By all of this, I was disheartened. It disturbed me that Shalom wasn't real; it saddened me that I wasn't part of a major organization; it troubled me that Shalom made me do dangerous things; and it definitely depressed me that Shalom wasn't in my life anymore.

This new awareness, furthermore, radically shook the way I identified myself. If I wasn't a friend of an omnipotent person, than who was I? If I didn't have supernatural abilities to know what was going on in the world then what was I? And if I was just a simple, mundane individual, which I invariably now knew I was, than what was my place in the world?

I knew that I had to start engaging in activities that would again give meaning to my life. I had to find new things that would help me gain a grip on who I was; other things that would fill the loneliness that consumed my heart; other things which would excite, stimulate, and intrigue me. At first I was at a loss as to how to go about this—Shalom had been essentially my life for a long time, and it was he who provided all the purpose, friendship, and the excitement I needed.

Slowly, I was able to find daily tasks to fill me. First, I found the art of writing. I discovered that anything from journal to memoir to poetry writing was extremely therapeutic. I bought a pretty, hard-covered journal from Barnes and Noble, and began recording my days. I would write about the ordinary things that I did from grocery shopping, to taking walks, to having a nice lunch. But then I'd also record my moods, the different emotions I felt, and also thoughts I had about what was happening in my life or in the world—how I felt about my twin sister getting into college, how I felt about the war on Iraq, and what I thought about different cultures. Memoir writing gave me a chance to reflect back over the past few years, as I began to record some of my past experiences—my trials in school, my hospital visits, and my struggles with getting well. And poetry writing was pure fun—coming up with groups of rhyming words, counting syllables, and playing with metaphor. Through writing, I was given the chance to take a break from the present, to express my creativity, to reflect on what had been happening in my life, and most of all, to validate my experiences and feelings.

I also discovered art and music to fill the gap within my soul. I learned how to crochet, and was able to create colorful baby blankets and scarves. I also learned how to do origami. I'd buy scrapbook paper of beautiful hues, cut them into squares, and then delicately fold the squares into intricate cranes. Music was also a good distraction, and I would listen to anything from pop to classical to country. I'd allow myself to get lost in the beat, hidden within the melodies, and to become absorbed by the words. It created such peace for me.

Also, I realized that getting together with friends was a good tactic to alleviate some of the loneliness. I had had many friends from when I was in school, but had disconnected from them once I got sick and was hospitalized for so long. Now, I made an effort to get back together with them. On Saturdays, I'd invite them over to my house and we'd talk about teenage girl stuff, play games, and take walks. Hanging out with them, though not as intense an experience as hanging out with Shalom, made me feel that I wasn't so alone, and that there were people who were connected and dedicated to me.

Finally, having sessions with my psychiatrist was extremely helpful. We'd talk about my worries of being lonely, of my fears that certain things which happened in the past would occur again, and we would also converse about strategies such as deep breathing and visualizations that could relieve some of the tension that I felt at difficult moments. Talking with my doctor was very soothing, and in a comforting way he let me know that no matter what happened to me, nothing was too bad, nothing was too horrible, and that we'd simply deal with whatever came up.

With all of the activities and support which now filled my life, I didn't feel as depressed, as disturbed, or as disheartened as I had before. I now had meaningful distractions and methods to make me feel more at ease with myself. But now that I had successfully pulled myself out from an internal crisis, I knew I needed bigger things: I needed to have goals for the future. I needed some larger ideas for what I wanted to accomplish with my life.

First of all, I realized that I needed to finish high school. I had initially entered the hospital in the middle of my 10th grade year, and had been in and out of the hospital through what would have been my senior year, so I obviously missed quite a lot of school. Since I very much wanted a high school diploma, I looked into different ways I could possibly earn one. One program which was recommended to me by a school counselor was a home-schooling program offered by Brigham Young University. I took a psychology course through this program, but after I was through with it, I realized that

I missed being in the classroom, being able to interact and engage with other students and teachers.

So, I looked at what the community colleges offered. I found that there existed a program called Running Start through which I could take college classes, and earn both my high school and college credits at the same time. I would then end up not only with a high school diploma, but with an associate's degree as well. This sounded perfect. In the past, when I became really stressed, and especially stressed by academic work, Shalom would start reappearing and telling me to do harmful things to myself, so this time I made sure to start school slowly, and only take one class at a time. I took English 101, and found that it wasn't too stressful, and that I really enjoyed it. This gave me confidence, for now I knew that even if it would take a few years, I'd eventually be successful at getting my high school diploma.

And that is where I am today—I'm at the community college taking classes. But as I reflect on it, I understand that earning a high school degree or even an associate's degree, for me, isn't a big enough goal—I want to eventually go on to a 4-year college and get the education I need to be a mental health counselor. From all of my experiences in dealing with my illness and being in hospitals, I want more than anything else to be able to help people like myself. I want to be able to reach out to others who have schizophrenia or other mental diseases, and to be able to give back to them some of the help that I had received.

One last goal I now have is not only to help people like myself, but to try to help society understand mental illness better, and to come to appreciate what living with mental illness is like. I know that there is a tremendous amount of stigma, ambiguity, and fear which is associated with mental illness, and I want to help change this. I want everyone to see that mental illness does not turn humans into non-humans who may be ignored or ridiculed, but that mental illness is just as much a part of life as anything else. I desire for the world to know that people suffering and recovering from mental disorders deserve being treated with respect and dignity, and even more, should be cared for with empathy and compassion.

Even today, I still struggle with the arduous issues related to my illness. But while I understand that I'll forevermore live with a serious mental disorder, I now have ways to cope, and make myself feel better. By using my different forms of distraction, by keeping connected with my doctor and with friends, and by working towards my short-term as well as my long-term goals, my life is worth living each and every day.

Chapter 7   An Agenda for Recovery Research and Practice

Current Status and Future Directions for Research

Larry Davidson, Courtenay Harding, and LeRoy Spaniol

We ended our introduction to this two-volume collection of seminal articles of research on recovery and recovery-oriented practices by noting our need to move beyond the obvious, if continuously overlooked, point that people with severe mental illnesses remain people—both first and foremost and despite the severity or duration of their illnesses. What is true for everyone else—such as the importance of loving and of being loved, of having a sense of home, of the roles of friendship and family, of spirituality, of sex, and of ways to be productive citizens and included in the community—we therefore should assume will remain equally true of individuals with severe mental illnesses. How these activities and involvements are to be pursued may depend, in part, on the severity and duration of the person's condition; but that engagement in such relationships and roles is desired should now be assumed rather than needing to be established or proven through some other, likely artificial, means.

We hoped that by compiling a substantial portion of evidence that has established the reality of improvement and recovery in severe mental illness repeatedly, consistently, and unequivocally over the previous 50 years, that we would be in a position to embark on a new generation of research that moves the field beyond restating these obvious, if nonetheless important, findings. We view this body of research and innovation in practice to make it possible for the field to move into new, exciting directions. Our vision for this new research and practice is that it will be focused more specifically on the unique challenges presented by these illnesses, shedding more detailed and useful information on the various ways through which people figure out or learn how to live with, manage, and eventually overcome these challenges. For what also has changed in the interim, due to the public efforts and successes of consumer advocates as much as to the contributions contained in these volumes, is that people with severe mental illnesses have stepped into the foreground to reclaim the territory of recovery as their own. What does this mean and how does it shape our future research and practice?

Early in the days of bringing people out of the hospital and into the community, ex-patients founded the clubhouse model called Fountain House as a social club (Beard, Propst, & Malamud, 1982). In the mid 1950s, it began it began to provide a "work ordered day" and to provide a model of psychosocial rehabilitation. These activities led to the idea that rehabilitation is not something that one person can do to or for another person; rather, it is a process in which the person him or herself must be actively engaged

(Peterson, 1982). We would suggest that the same is true for recovery. Unfortunately, much of the previous half century of clinical research and evaluation has focused on what happens to, or what can be done to, people with severe mental illnesses, under what circumstances, and with what anticipated impact and outcomes. *The Vermont Story* (Chittick, Irons, Brooks, & Deane, 1961), described in detail in the first volume of this series, offers a significant exception, as it was conceived and implemented throughout as a collaborative enterprise. Most research, however, has yet to explore what people with severe mental illnesses can, and may need to, do for themselves. It has been as if the person with the mental illness had been relegated to a passive and receptive stance, relying—not unlike Blanch DuBois in *A Streetcar Named Desire* (Williams, 1986)—on the kindness (and competence) of strangers. Such a view, we suggest, has its origins in the assumption that once a person has a severe mental illness he or she becomes entirely and permanently lost to the illness; the core assumption which these volumes have sought to refute and overcome.

With the jettisoning of these assumptions, and acceptance of the fact that the person remains standing alongside of the illness with various competencies, strengths, abilities, and integrity intact, we have arrived at a point at which we can now reframe the research and practice enterprises from the perspective of this person. This requires reframing our questions from those that focus on what we need to do to treat and rehabilitate people with severe mental illnesses to what opportunities, tools, and supports people with severe mental illnesses need in order to manage, compensate for, and recover from these conditions. Our roles as investigators and practitioners remain very much intact, but the focus of our work shifts dramatically. Like other health care providers and clinical investigators, we enter into a collaborative relationship with members of our population of interest, working closely with them to determine what aspects of these illnesses get most in their way, what will be of most use to them in their battles with these illnesses, and in what ways services and supports can be best designed and delivered to promote their adaptation to illness, recovery, and wellness. Within the broader field of psychiatry, this represents a true and enticing paradigm shift.

As these volumes are coming to press, the field of psychiatry is just beginning to grapple with the far-reaching implications of the CATIE study, the $43 million NIMH-funded study involving almost 1,500 individuals with schizophrenia carried out over 5 years in 57 sites and 24 different states across the country (Lieberman, Stroup, McEvoy, Swartz, Rosenheck, Perkins, Keefe, Davis, Davis, Lebowitz, Severe, & Hsiao, 2005). In this landmark study, investigators not only found that the newer, so-called "atypical" anti-psychotic medications had no substantial advantage over the older, "typical" medications, but that overall effectiveness was significantly limited by the fact that almost three quarters of the individuals participating decided to stop taking the medications. In considering the possible reasons for what they considered to be this widespread and "premature" discontinuation of treatment, the authors conceded not only that the side effect profiles of these medications remained problematic but also that the medications themselves demonstrated only partial efficacy in addressing the symptoms of the illness.

In addition to concluding, as did the study's authors, that our current psychopharmacologic treatments are limited in their effectiveness to combat schizophrenia, we suggest that this study offers important object lessons for psychiatric research more broadly. Of what value is it to develop and test a treatment for a medical condition, when very few people who have that condition will willingly use the treatment? Regardless of the reasons given for the major findings of the CATIE study, we are left to conclude that clinical psychiatry has made very little progress in developing new and more effective somatic treatments for schizophrenia over the preceding half century. We are left to wonder if perhaps some, if not many, of the millions of dollars that have gone into researching and developing, not to mention marketing, new medications would have been better spent had people with schizophrenia been involved as partners in, rather than viewed as objects of, the scientific enterprise (Davidson, 1997). An analogy to a more traditionally-defined physical condition may be useful here in suggesting how the work might get carried out differently once the person with a severe mental illness is accepted as a partner in, if not frankly the customer of, our clinical research and practice.

In other publications (e.g., Davidson & Roe, in press; Davidson, Tondora, O'Connell, Lawless, & Rowe, in press), we have suggested that our current mental health system may be at a point in its development similar to the point at which the field of orthopedics stood prior to the design and broad-scale use of the wheelchair. Prior to the development and acceptance of assistive technology, orthopedic specialists had a very limited range of options with which to treat people with spinal cord injuries. As a result, people who had lost the use of their legs through accident or illness were either left to languish in hospital or nursing home beds or left largely up to their own devices to craft prostheses, and a life, outside of and with little help from the health care system. One imagines perhaps Dickensian images of former soldiers hobbling about on make-shift crutches or frail orphans pushing themselves through the London streets on wooden carts. We suggest that our misguided assumptions have led the current mental health system to maintain a similar relationship to the needs and desires of people with severe mental illnesses, offering little more than crutches or wooden carts to facilitate their recovery and inclusion in community activities. We suggest further that it is perhaps for this reason that so many people choose not to follow through with prescribed treatments. Instead, they cobble together what supports they need and can find inside and outside of the mental health system. They fashion as best a life they can, often recovering despite, rather than as a result of, the treatments and supports offered to them (Deegan, 1993).

Readers who do not feel that such a criticism of the current system is warranted are encouraged to consider the fact that tens of thousands of people with severe mental illnesses are still living out their lives confined to the locked wards of mental hospitals around the country. Tens of thousands of others are restricted both psychologically and socially—if not literally held behind locked doors—to the similarly stark, dreary, and empty community-based ghettos of segregated psychiatric program settings. How else are we to understand that caring professionals continue to insist that these people receive the same treatments and participate in the same rehabilitation programs they have already tried for many years, while nonetheless expecting different results? In addition to stigma, discrimination, and societal indifference, these tragedies continue to occur due to the fact that we, as a field, continue to focus on ridding people of their illnesses—securing a cure instead of helping to heal by focusing on how people can be assisted in recovering and having a life. Unfortunately, as the CATIE study clearly showed, we do not yet possess such a cure and are very limited in our ability to contain and/or minimize the effects of the illness.

While biomedically-oriented research continues to search for the causes and cures of severe mental illnesses (hopefully becoming more informed by the perspective of those suffering from these illnesses themselves), we suggest that clinical research and program innovation and evaluation might shift to new approaches, including focused investigations of how these illnesses get in the way of people's day-to-day lives; what will be of most use to them in doing battle with these illnesses; and in what ways services and supports can be best designed and delivered to enhance their ability to live safe, dignified, and productive lives in the face of enduring symptoms and/or disability. Such a stance by no means represents capitulation in the face of the illness, but is driven instead by a recovery-oriented vision that insists that these are illnesses that most people can learn to live with and manage most of the time until significant improvement and full recovery occurs.

Indeed, the preponderance of research that we have available today suggests that this is a more effective route to recovering from the illness over time than putting one's life on hold while waiting passively for medications or other treatments to take effect. That is, rehabilitative and recovery-oriented practice has shown that focusing on clients' efforts to reclaim their lives—

by working together to identify each person's strengths and desires and then by helping the person to acquire decent, safe, and affordable housing; helping him or her to find a satisfying job-person match or to return to school; helping him or her to have mutually caring and gratifying relationships; to express or exercise his or her spirituality; to play and have fun, etc.—all reduce symptoms and enhance social functioning. As such, it makes no sense to conceptualize these pursuits as ancillary to, supportive of, or following after treatment per se.

Similarly, in Chapter 5 we provided information on the role that families can play in the recovery process. Future research should help us to better understand the experience of family members from their own perspective. What is their response to the illness? How does it affect them? How can we best help them deal with the onset of the illness and the stresses of care giving many continue to provide? How can we help individual family members with their own recovery and how can we help them to be more supportive of their family member's own efforts? In addition, family education has been found to be a very effective intervention, especially when the person with the psychiatric disability is integrally involved. Research must be applied to developing even more beneficial models of family intervention, addressing the differential concerns of parents, siblings, and children of adults with mental illnesses.

Perhaps it is surprising to some readers that we choose to end a two-volume series on recovery from severe mental illnesses by arguing for a shift away from cure to a focus on how people can learn to live with, manage, and eventually overcome these conditions. Perhaps some readers will even view this as a basic contradiction in terms. There appear, however, to be many such contradictions inherent to the nature of severe mental illnesses. Deegan (1993), for example, has described the "paradox of recovery," in which, she argues, it is by "accepting what we cannot do or be [that] we begin to discover who we can be and what we can do." In a similar vein, we suggest that it is only when we stop trying to rid people of these illnesses (cure or "fix" them) and begin to focus instead on how we can support them in their own struggles with the illness that we will become truly helpful, either in our research or in our practice. This is the vision we hope to see established for, and guiding, the next 50 years of research and practice in promoting the recovery, community inclusion, and self-determination of people with severe mental illnesses, regardless of the degree of severity, duration, or disability associated with their condition.

REFERENCES

Beard, J. H., Propst, R. N., & Malamud, T. J. (1982). The Fountain House model of psychiatric rehabilitation. *Psychosocial Rehabilitation Journal, 5*(1), 47–53.

Chittick, R. A., Irons, F. S., Brooks, G. W., & Deane, W. N. (1961). *The Vermont story: Rehabilitation of chronic schizophrenic patients.* Burlington, VT: Free Press.

Davidson, L. (1997). Vulnérabilité et destin dans la schizophrénie: Prêter l'oreille á la voix de la personne. (Vulnerability and destiny in schizophrenia: Hearkening to the voice of the person). *L'Evolution Psychiatrique, 62,* 263–284.

Davidson, L. & Roe, D. (in press). Recovery from versus recovery in serious mental illness: One strategy for lessening the confusion plaguing recovery. *Journal of Mental Health.*

Davidson, L., Tondora, J., O'Connell, M.J., Lawless, M. S., & Rowe, M. (in press). A *practical guide to recovery-oriented practice: Tools for transforming mental health care.* New York: Oxford University Press.

Deegan, P. E. (1993). Recovering our sense of value after being labeled mentally ill. *Journal of Psychosocial Nursing, 31*(4), 7–11.

Lieberman, J. A., Stroup, T. S., McEvoy, J. P., Swartz, M. S., Rosenheck, R. A., Perkins, D. O., Keefe, R. S. E., Davis, S. M., Davis, C. E., Lebowitz, B. D., Severe, J., Hsiao, J. K. (2005). Effectiveness of antipsychotic drugs in patients with chronic schizophrenia. *New England Journal of Medicine, 353,* 1209–1223.

Peterson, R. (1982). What are the needs of chronic mental patients? *Schizophrenia Bulletin, 8*(4), 610–616.

Williams, T. (1986). *A streetcar named desire.* New York: Signet.